THE NATION LOOKS
AT ITS RESOURCES

THE NATION

LOOKS AT ITS

Resources

REPORT OF THE
MID - CENTURY
CONFERENCE ON
RESOURCES FOR
THE   FUTURE

Washington, D. C.
December 2, 3, 4, 1953

Conference Officers

Chairman

LEWIS W. DOUGLAS
Chairman of the Board, Mutual Life Insurance Company of New York

Vice-Chairmen

HERMAN W. STEINKRAUS
President, Bridgeport Brass Co.

KARL T. COMPTON†
Chairman of the Corporation
Massachusetts Institute of
Technology

LEWIS WEBSTER JONES
President, Rutgers University

Director
NORVELL W. PAGE

Counsel
SAMUEL H. ORDWAY, JR.
Executive Vice-President
The Conservation Foundation

Conference Steering Committee

HARRISON BROWN
California Institute of Technology

IRA N. GABRIELSON
Wildlife Management Institute

MARGARET HICKEY
National Federation of Business and
Professional Women's Clubs and
Ladies' Home Journal

JAMES R. KILLIAN, JR.
Massachusetts Institute of Technology

ALLAN B. KLINE
American Farm Bureau Federation

ROBERT KOENIG
Cerro de Pasco Corporation

JAMES L. MADDEN
Hollingsworth and Whitney Company

WILLIAM R. MATHEWS
Arizona Daily Star

ALBERT MITCHELL
T. E. Mitchell and Son Cattle Ranch

LLOYD E. PARTAIN
The Curtis Publishing Company

BORIS SHISHKIN
American Federation of Labor

ANTHONY W. SMITH
Congress of Industrial Organizations

H. DEWITT SMITH
Newmont Mining Corporation

H. CHRISTIAN SONNE
National Planning Association and
Amsinck, Sonne and Company

A. C. SPURR
Monongahela Power Company

JOHN R. SUMAN
American Petroleum Institute and
Standard Oil Company (New Jersey)

ABEL WOLMAN
Johns Hopkins University

EX-OFFICIO MEMBERS
HORACE M. ALBRIGHT
Chairman of the Board
Resources for the Future, Inc.

R. G. GUSTAVSON
President and Executive Director
Resources for the Future, Inc.

† Died June 22, 1954.

Council of Sponsors

ARTHUR S. ADAMS
American Council on Education

JOHN H. BAKER
National Audubon Society

HARRY BARTELL
National Association of County Officials

DETLEV BRONK
National Academy of Sciences

MRS. E. E. BYERRUM
General Federation of Women's Clubs

WILLIAM G. CARR
National Education Association

EDWIN R. COTTON
American Watershed Council, Inc.

WATERS DAVIS
National Association of Soil
Conservation Districts

PAUL H. DURRIE
Adult Education Association

MRS. MALCOLM J. EDGERTON
Garden Club of America

JONATHAN FORMAN
Friends of the Land

IRA N. GABRIELSON
Wildlife Management Institute

U. S. GRANT, III
American Planning and Civic Association

WILLIAM B. HARTSFIELD
American Municipal Association

ARTHUR A. HAUCK
Association of Land-Grant
Colleges and Universities

FRANK HUSSEY
National Council of Farmer Cooperatives

MISS HELEN G. IRWIN
National Federation of Business and
Professional Women's Clubs

DON P. JOHNSTON
American Forestry Association

CLAUDE D. KELLEY
National Wildlife Federation

MEYER KESTNBAUM
Committee for Economic Development

ALLAN B. KLINE
American Farm Bureau Federation

MRS. JOHN G. LEE
League of Women Voters

GEORGE LEIGHTY
Railway Labor Executives Association

OTTO T. MALLERY
National Recreation Association

OLAUS MURIE
Wilderness Society

HERSCHEL NEWSOM
National Grange

FAIRFIELD OSBORN
The Conservation Foundation

R. J. S. PIGOTT
Engineers Joint Council

FRANK M. PORTER
American Petroleum Institute

WALTER P. REUTHER
Congress of Industrial Organizations

BORIS SHISHKIN
American Federation of Labor

H. CHRISTIAN SONNE
National Planning Association

WILLIAM VOIGT
Natural Resources Council

C. I. WEAVER
Ohio Fuel and Natural Gas Company

CLYDE WILLIAMS
Battelle Memorial Institute

CONFERENCE REPORT STAFF

Editor: HENRY JARRETT
Associate Editor: VERA W. DODDS, *Assistant Editor:* NORA E. ROOTS
Assistant Editors (part time): SAMUEL BOTSFORD, FRANCIS T. CHRISTY, JR., MARTHA GIBBON
Chief Clerical Assistants: ELLEN H. RYAN, MARIETTA SCHIRF

CONTENTS

Appendix

Introduction

MID-CENTURY
CONFERENCE

THIS REPORT PRESENTS HIGH POINTS of the discussion of the Mid-Century Conference on Resources for the Future, held in Washington, December 2, 3, and 4, 1953. It expresses the thinking of many of our citizens, reflecting many viewpoints, in regard to long-range problems of natural resources.

The 1,600 men and women who made up the Mid-Century Conference shared a deep concern over the outlook for resources. They explored and sought to relate issues that will be before the people of the United States during the next 25 years and beyond.

These issues are large. Our population is growing; our economy is expanding. The peacetime demands are great and, much as we may dislike the prospect, we probably shall for a number of years need more materials for military preparation and civilian defense. What the exact rates of increase in demand may be, whether we believe our civilization already is too materialistic, whether we think the 20th Century has proved Malthus was right or wrong, are beside the point. The underlying problem is the mounting pressure on our natural resources.

As agreed from the beginning, the Mid-Century Conference did not develop any kind of proposed program for resources, or recommend or endorse anything. It had no shred of legislative authority; its members were there as individuals, not as official spokesmen for constituencies. But this group did something that a more compact action group could not have done. It laid the basis for better understanding of thorny issues on which contending groups still have much to learn about each other's hopes and fears.

Different people look at the major resource problems in different ways. Some are convinced that continued and rapid growth of world population is the chief issue—relieve this pressure and many resource problems become easier. Others are sure that technology holds the key—realize the potentialities of science and we need fear no lack of the things we really need. Still others see no unified pattern, but a series of separate situations that we must meet as best we can. There also are differences of more immediate interest. Resources like ores and oil, timber and crops, mean jobs and profits both now and in the future to millions of people. On the other hand, many of these same resources are seen by organizations and individuals primarily as a national heritage to be shared with future generations. These differences

1

are deeply rooted and keenly felt. It is difficult to see how some can be entirely reconciled even over long periods. But they must be taken account of if we are to make the most of our resources. Its very diversity is what gave the Conference its strength and made its work worth while.

The Mid-Century Conference took the broad view. This was its unique contribution. Its range encompassed soil, water, and mineral resources from the viewpoint of producers, consumers, and the public at large, and with a special eye to problems of world relationships, research policy, and patterns of cooperation. Although it was concerned primarily with domestic resources, it often looked far beyond our own borders. No one forgot that this country is part of a larger world! The Conference stopped just short of going directly into human resources, which would have been too vast a subject for such a group to attempt. But all natural resource problems were looked at in terms of what they mean to people, and in the background was recognition that the country's greatest resource is people. Even the history-making Roosevelt-Pinchot conference of 1908, to which the cause of conserving and developing resources owes so much, did not have comparable representation from nearly so many fields. To a large extent, though, the Mid-Century Conference was conceived as the successor to the conference of 1908, and I only hope that its influence will be as great and as long-continued.

The Conference record is a vast mine of experience, learning, and creative thinking brought to bear upon resource problems. It contains opinions, interpretations, and suggestions that I hope will be useful to the persons who make, administer, or study resource policies.

For all the diversity of views, three significant themes recur frequently in all of the section discussions: (1) The need to enlarge our knowledge through research; (2) the need to disseminate new knowledge more widely through education; and (3) the need to apply knowledge more effectively through cooperation. As for the many differences and the unresolved questions, do they not in themselves carry a positive message: that the problems of resources are so deep and so tangled that we should always be wary of the simple answer, the one easy way out?

A big job of resource conservation and development lies ahead. The fact that we still know so little is not entirely a disadvantage; it means that gains can be made. In looking ahead, the Conference dealt mainly with already-won knowledge, though there were glimpses of new gains on, or just below, the horizon. We can learn much more about the care of the soil, the production of renewables, and the location and extraction of nonrenewables and we can then put the new knowledge to work. We can learn much more about the utilization of resources—finding new uses and improving old methods. We can learn more also, about the complex interrelationships among the different resources—what the long-range effects may be if a piece of land, or a particular material, or a unit of trained manpower is used for one purpose rather than another. And we can learn much more about improving the human organizations that bear on the production and use of resources—such things as the training and assignment of physical scientists and the devising of better means by which groups with various interests may work together. The work of the Mid-Century Conference helps to point the way. I hope that for a long time to come it will stimulate advance in knowledge and in putting those gains into use.

The Breadth of the Conference

The Mid-Century Conference was broadly based, in planning as well as in attendance. A few of the facts on how the Conference was developed will show why this was so. At the same time they will indicate some of the obstacles to completely representative scope and participation.

The original impetus and the necessary funds for the Conference came from The Ford Foundation. Resources for the Future, Inc., was the sponsoring organization. Dozens of people from industry, universities, government agencies, and private organizations contributed to the detailed planning and preparation.

From the time of its organization, The Ford Foundation has taken the strengthening of the American economy through economic development and administration as one of its major fields; and it has recognized the importance of natural resources within that area. In March, 1952, officers of the Foundation met with a group concerned with development and conservation of resources to consider what more might be done along those lines. A program development committee that was established soon afterward recommended a national conference to explore and draw public attention to major, long-range resource problems and to the establishment of an organization to conduct continuing research and education programs in the resources field. In October, 1952, Resources for the Future, Inc., was organized as a nonprofit corporation. Its first substantive assignment was to develop and hold a national resources conference.

Active preparations were begun by a small staff in the late fall of 1952. With the help of experts from industry, universities, federal departments, and private organizations, a detailed set of proposals was drawn up for review by a Council of Sponsors consisting of about 40 representatives of business, farm, and labor organizations, conservation groups and other citizens' associations, and representatives of federal, state, and local government. (See page vii for full list.)

From then on preparations were under the direction of the Conference chairman, Lewis W. Douglas, along the general policy lines laid down by the Council of Sponsors. (See page v for list of officers and Conference Steering Committee.)

Section chairmen and co-chairmen were chosen by the Conference chairman and general steering committee, with special regard to nominations made by the Council of Sponsors. Steering committees of from six to nine members were appointed for each section by the conference chairman and an executive committee of the general steering committee. An effort was made to obtain a broad range of the major interests and viewpoints bearing on the subject matter of each section. Subsection chairmen and section and subsection rapporteurs were selected by section officers and steering committees. The names of section officials are listed at the beginning of each section report.

The Conference officials tried to make participation as inclusive as possible. More than 3,000 invitations were mailed to a list based on nominations of the Council of Sponsors, the Conference Steering Committee, government, industry, and private organizations interested in resources, and the steering committees of the eight sections. Invitations also were sent to all persons who requested them. No one who wanted to come was turned down.

On the whole, I believe that the effort to put on a representative, free, and meaningful discussion of long-range resource problems succeeded remarkably well. Of course, there were limitations: the eight sections could not cover all the major areas of the resources field. Sections on marine resources, and on food as such, for example, had been suggested at the Council of Sponsors' meeting. Administrative difficulties and lack of time were the main reasons they were not organized. In the sections that were organized, not all the important problems could be canvassed during a three-day conference.

The record of the Conference should not be read as if it were a public opinion poll. The section steering committees and the full attendance at each section were not scientifically arrived-at statistical samples. The resources field is vast; it would have been quite possible to have had a different section line-up, different people, different questions for discussion. Although the door to participation was open wide, the membership of each section and subsection was not automatically a true cross section of national interests and opinion. Some groups quite clearly were not: in some, for instance, attendance was largely from industry; in others, it was mainly from universities and government.

Many of those who took part in the discussions were experts, including some of the most distinguished in their respective fields. Others were laymen with deep interest in resource problems and something worth while to say about them, who would quite cheerfully acknowledge their lack of technical background. Not all of the record, therefore, can be termed a handbook of current scientific opinion. Some statements probably would not stand up under expert analysis.

In the hasty preparation of the chairmen's summaries for the last day of the Conference, it was sometimes difficult to give the gist of the section discussions without in some degree implying that such-and-such was the consensus of preponderant view of a section or subsection. This was true even though the general Conference rule against putting issues to vote or offering recommendations was observed scrupulously.

Apprehension that some viewpoints were not represented adequately and that some passages of the section chairmen's summaries might be misinterpreted was expressed by Stanley Ruttenberg, Director of Research and Education for the CIO and a director of Resources for the Future.[1] The record of the Mid-Century

---

[1] MR. RUTTENBERG (at the final session of the full Conference, December 4): As I listened to all of the summaries of section chairmen, there ran through the various papers these words: "There was a consensus"; "There was general concurrence"; "There was no opposition"; "There was little support for some of the views."

There are represented in this Conference many points of view. There are some points of view represented better than others. There are other points of view which are represented by only a relatively few people, but it doesn't necessarily mean that because a relatively few people are present that that point of view is necessarily in the minority and necessarily, therefore, has to be referred to as stated by only a few in the group.

It is well to attempt to get to areas of agreement if we can point out areas of agreement. In many instances the use of the words "concurrence" and "consensus" was justified. In other instances it certainly was not.

Do organizations and individuals in attendance, or not in attendance at particular sessions, have the right to present a point of view which is not actually or adequately represented in the papers to be included in the final report which emanates from the Conference?

Conference of necessity has been held to what was said there, plus the normal revisions and directly pertinent comments received later from people who took part. But it is important to note that Mr. Ruttenberg's reservations are part of that record.

[Some further details of how the Conference was organized are given in the Editor's note, page 377.]

Acknowledgements

The Conference owes much to President Eisenhower for his continuing interest and for the support from federal agencies without which the whole undertaking would have had to be on a very different scale. We are also indebted to former President Truman, whose administration gave invaluable assistance in the earlier stages. Gabriel Hauge, Assistant to the President, and Stephen Benedict, of the White House staff, gave constructive advice and unfailing assistance.

I must make special mention of the wise, skillful, and patient leadership of Horace M. Albright, Chairman of the Board of Directors of Resources for the Future, at all stages of the long process, and the chairmanship of Lewis W. Douglas, which was both solid and brilliant.

Norvell W. Page, as Conference director, ably coordinated a complex and comprehensive enterprise and directed an exacting staff operation. He handled both tasks in an outstanding manner and did more than any other one person to make the Conference a success. In this he was greatly aided by Henry Jarrett, assistant director of the Conference, and a competent staff which worked hard, long, and well.

Chester C. Davis, a former Associate Director of The Ford Foundation, had a leading part in the original idea of the Conference and in the formation of Resources for the Future. Charles W. Eliot, staff consultant to Mr. Davis, was Conference director during the early stages.

To acknowledge our full indebtedness would be to call over the entire role of those who shared in planning and preparing for the Conference and those who participated in it. Everyone who took part either as a listener or a speaker helped make the Conference a success.

Finally, I have been helped greatly by nine men of broad and varied interests in resources who have, at my request, gone over the entire manuscript of this report as a supplement to the individual review of the section officers. These advisers are: Lewis W. Douglas, Chairman of the Board, Mutual Life Insurance Company of New York, and Chairman of the Conference; Harrison Brown, Professor of Geochemistry, California Institute of Technology; Samuel T. Dana, Dean Emeritus, School of Natural Resources, University of Michigan; Ira N. Gabrielson, President, Wildlife Management Institute; Evan Just, Vice-President, Cyprus Mines Corporation; Edward S. Mason, Dean, Graduate School of Public Administration, Harvard University; William R. Mathews, Editor and Publisher, *Arizona Daily Star*; Stanley Ruttenberg, Director, Department of Education and Research, Congress of Industrial Organizations; H. Christian Sonne, Chairman of the Board, Amsinck, Sonne and Company. Theirs has been a hard task, over and above their earlier large contributions to the Conference. Their constructive suggestions have been most helpful.

Looking to the Future

One major aim of the Mid-Century Conference was to enlist wider interest in significant resource issues that the people of this country will be coping with in the years ahead. Another was to help bring about greater mutual understanding among the diverse groups that have the most direct stake in resource problems and that will have much to do with how they are met. On both of these scores the Conference succeeded even beyond our expectations and many of the impulses generated there will be active for a long time.

The Conference had still another important purpose—to serve as a source of suggestions for the continuing work of Resources for the Future. In this respect, too, the results were rewarding. Also, the Conference record suggests many other promising fields for future work simply by showing that there are large gaps in existing knowledge which need to be filled.

In June, 1954, The Ford Foundation made a grant to Resources for the Future that will enable it to carry out over the next five years a program of research and education. The program, and the separate projects which make it up, will aim to provide a basis for better understanding of major and critical resource problems upon the solutions to which the material and, in important ways, the spiritual future of the American people depends.

The program will be as imaginative as we can make it in fundamental and applied research and in education. In comparison with all that needs doing, the work of Resources for the Future will be on a modest scale. That would be true of any single organization. But by working in cooperation, rather than in competition, with the private and public agencies already active in different corners of the resources field much can be accomplished.

In this creative age, with so much of the promise of science, technology, and the social sciences still before us, Resources for the Future has an unusual opportunity to make a significant contribution to a better future. Through a direct research and education program and through grants to other organizations, we shall try to move forward from the good beginning made in the Mid-Century Conference.

R. G. Gustavson

President and Executive Director
Resources for the Future, Inc.

INTRODUCING
THE CONFERENCE

The Conference Begins

TWO KEY
ADDRESSES

AT A GENERAL LUNCHEON SESSION on the opening day, two major addresses prefigured the importance and scope of the Mid-Century Conference. The President of the United States personally greeted participants. At the close of President Eisenhower's welcoming remarks, the chairman of the Conference, Lewis W. Douglas, outlined the reasons for holding the Conference, the breadth of the problems to be considered, and the free-discussion method by which they were to be approached.

President Eisenhower ——

From time to time I have the privilege of welcoming different types of bodies of American citizens to the nation's capital. Normally, each of these bodies is engaged, or committed, or dedicated, to some kind of public service. Consequently, the duty of extending this welcome is always a pleasant one.

In this case I must assure you that my satisfaction, my gratification, that you are here and engaged in the work you are doing, could not possibly be exceeded.

Something on the order of 25 or 30 years ago, as a junior officer in the War Department, I attended a lecture in which a man happened to state that if the United States could be assured of all the supplies it needed in rubber, tin, and manganese, it would never have to fear exhaustion of resources in any war. In other words, for emergencies, it would be well fixed. And as of that time this was, of course, very largely true, because other necessary imports were either easily available, like nickel in the Sudbury mines, or they were of such small quantities that it was not any very great task to get them.

Now, I had a younger and far wiser brother who was more interested in conservation on a wider scale. And when I repeated this statement to him, he said, "Well, how about the spot on which you are standing? Do you mean to save that, if you are going to fight a war in the future?" And so, in the resulting conversations, I got interested in conservation on a broad scale. I should like to make clear— and I think that this opinion is shared by everybody here—that when we are talking conservation, we are not talking about locking up and putting resources beyond the possibility of wastage or use. We are talking about the intelligent use of all the resources we have, for the welfare and the benefit of all the American people.

I was delighted to see that this great body is dividing itself up into parts, each of which is taking a particular great portion of this conservation problem. You are not going to waste your time taking votes and forming a lot of conclusions. In other words, this looks to me like a body that is really going to work on the subject.

One of the things in which I have become very interested is water. I have heard so much argument about multiple-purpose dams, and the headwaters, and saving the different resources of the water that we have; I have been so plagued by droughts this year—not nearly as much, of course, as the farmers that had to suffer them, in many cases. But every time you turn around in this conservation problem you run into the question of water.

Now, I noticed in a piece of literature sent to me by the leaders of this group that you are going to approach water from the standpoint of what is the best use that can be made of every drop of water that falls on the United States. And if we start on the tip of the Continental Divide, or the Ridge, and follow those drops of water all the way to the oceans and to the Gulf, maybe we can find an answer. Maybe there is more froth and fury than there is good sense in all this argument as to whether we should have a great dam down in front of Kansas City, or a little dam up in the Blue River in what they call Tuttle Creek Dam in Kansas—if you don't know about that, it's a very good one to look up.

We have got to be intelligent all over the United States, and not let pressure groups or any extremists lead us into erroneous directions. I think this applies to iron as it does to soil. It applies to every kind of metal, as it does to the water that drops upon our continent. It is a very complicated and interrelated problem.

Certainly we have got sense enough to know, when we talk about our so-called irreplaceable resources, that some day, projected into the future as it were, some day the world will run out of manganese, tungsten, tin, oil—anything that you want to use up. Finally, humans use it all up.

Well, of course we blithely say that before that time occurs, science will have produced methods for the production of plastics that will take the place of all kinds of steel, and every other thing, and I hope and I sincerely trust they will. But then, how many years are going to have to be devoted to the production of the kind of things from which those plastics will be made?

In other words, what I am trying to say is, when I personally get to speculating about this problem of conservation, and let my mind run on into the future, I get into such an intricate problem that I am forced back, willy-nilly, to the immediate problem of the day, and that is: What do we do now in order that we may get to the next step?

But I do believe this dreaming, this looking ahead, is well to do, because it encourages the broad surveys, as I understand it, that you are preparing to make, so that the things we do today will not be antagonistic to, but, on the contrary, will be in furtherance of the achievement of these broad aims. In other words, we think in terms of decades, not merely in terms of months, or the next election, or anything else that is temporary and passing.

So not only do I take the greatest gratification in welcoming here this particular body, but I felicitate and congratulate you on the methods chosen for the division of your work, its coordination, and the very broad scope in which it is conceived. I believe this must be done. This job must challenge the brains of everybody, be he preacher or teacher, or college man, or farmer, or businessman—everybody. Everybody is in this, and can't escape it. So you truly must be a representative congress of the interests of all the United States.

Again I say, it is a great honor to welcome you here. I hope you have the most successful meeting that any one of you has ever enjoyed. I am sure it will redound to the great benefit of the government, and of the people—which is so far more important.

Lewis W. Douglas ——

This meeting has not been convened for the purpose of preparing a program for the ultilization or preservation of our resources. Its purpose is not to state any categorical conclusions. Its object is not to draft any pious and awesome encyclical about the treasures of nature on which we depend. We meet rather in a collective attempt to define some of the issues which are implicit in the subject of raw materials—the raw materials of the atmosphere, the raw materials of the seas and of the waters, and the raw materials of the land. These issues also are relevant to the economic and businesslike employment of resources, to a wise and appropriate conservation of them, and to the replenishment of them by new discoveries of new sources, new substitutes, and new discoveries of new methods for making new discoveries.

I would not be stating the proposition with complete accuracy if I were not to say that our national concern also is with the resources for that portion of the world community of which we are a part, for in almost every sense the community of nations with which we are associated can no more exist happily and in peace without us, than we can live within the context of a society based upon traditional American economic, political, and moral views without them. But after having stated what seems now to be a generally accepted conclusion, the criteria which we apply to the definition of issues, to the examination of facts, and even to the suggested reviews of interpretation of facts should be solely the criteria of our own national interests.

I would express the hope that the Conference would consider the wide variety of questions which here will be raised without undue emphasis upon the military and defense presumptions of this particular moment in history. I am not suggesting that the defense of the land and of our community is not important to our future survival, but I do intimate that if an undue emphasis be placed upon the military and defense aspects of the various problems with which we are associated, and that if this emphasis should too darkly color our views and too firmly mold our national action, a society which was conceived in liberty and dedicated to the proposition that all men are created equal may find itself in desperate straits to preserve itself. The questions with which we deal should primarily, though not exclusively, be considered in a social and political context which is not crushingly burdened by an overwhelming threat of armed conflict or a call to arms itself. Let us not presuppose that the war drums will not throb once more, but let us not assume that the battleflags will be inevitably unfurled.

All societies, from the most primitive to the most complicated, are largely shaped by the resources which their members in one form or another employ directly or indirectly to satisfy the desires and the tastes of mankind. One of the presumptions about which there is considerable difference of opinion is that a community which is dynamic, vigorous, expanding, and in which the population is ever growing, will consume more materials of the air, of the earth, and of the waters upon the earth, than these three media are capable of supplying over a protracted period of time. In a more limited sense, this view of the matter was powerfully stated by Malthus toward the end of the eighteenth century, when he announced his theory that the tendency of population was to increase more rapidly than the subsistence which could be supplied for it.

The broader statement of this hypothesis, which underlies so much of the thinking of today, requires re-examination and needs reassessment. Scarcity and abundance, generally caused by wars, have plagued the world since the dawn of history, and if the pessimism of Malthus forecast inadequate supplies as the population continued to grow, he could not have foreseen the scientific contributions that were packed into the nineteenth century and the first half of the twentieth, and was unable to appraise the way in which they could make available within much of the western world a vast wealth of resources which in the eighteenth century lay hidden in the darkness of ignorance. It was only some 20 years ago that men here at home were worried lest the world could produce too much. There was too much cotton, there was too much wheat, there was too much copper, there was an oversupply of lead and zinc, indeed there was hardly a commodity to which one can now refer of which it was not said there was an overproduction.

Just as it is probably true that the preoccupation of man a fifth of a century ago with overproduction was based upon a fallacy, so it may be true that our concern today with scarcities is derived from a too narrow view of all of the factors—scientific and economic—that play their roles in creating what, from moment to moment or even year to year or decade to decade, appears to be a real but transient condition of affairs. It may be that the marketplace, preserved as a free institution, and a flourishing inventive science will be unable to reconcile scarcity and abundance in accordance with their historic role, but a careful view down the corridors of time suggests the question: Does burden of proof fall heavily upon those who hold the view that man's ingenuity combined with the price mechanism, individual initiative, private enterprise, generally, and research are incapable of resolving the problems which, unmolested and undisturbed and unmagnified by wars and threats of wars, they have historically been capable of resolving, without a too abrupt distortion of the social fabric?

In a sense, whether this hypothesis, which I have suggested needs re-examination, be generally accepted or widely rejected, there still remains a fruitful field for the definition of issues and the interpretation of facts with which the question of natural resources is associated. Our own history has demonstrated that it is easy for a people to plunder that which nature has made available to them. Moreover, even if it were not easy to plunder there are many different uses to which materials and resources may be put and many ways in which they may be prudently conserved. There are, therefore, a host of contradictory interests in and claimants for a wide order of our resources.

If this Conference serves no other purpose than to acquaint each one of us with the variety of these different claims and the justification upon which each claim rests, it will not have been held in vain. We are all disposed to live in our own personal prison houses which chain our minds and confine our intellectual horizon. Often the prison house blocks out the light that other people's activities and minds shed upon our mental landscape and we become in fact the captives of our own interests. This has both its merits and its demerits. But no one can successfully deny the proposition that it is helpful for all of us to become acutely aware of our own limited understanding and of the parochial nature of our own tastes and predilections, to understand more fully the preoccupations of others and the reasons for these preoccupations; for that marks the progress of mankind toward freedom. This is what provides the guideposts for advancement and illuminates the way.

There is hardly a section of this Conference that will not be concerned with issues about which there may be several opinions. For some sections the variety of views will cover a broader domain than in others. In some there will be more emphatic contradictions of opinion than in others. This Conference on a miniature scale is a test of the reasonableness of our society. More and more I have been impressed with the disposition of men to question the motives, impugn the character, and deliberately cast suspicion on, if not in fact to indict, the integrity of those with whom they disagree. It is not so much that men disagree which corrodes the fabric of civilized society, as it is the manner of the disagreement. It would be a sorry state of affairs if all men held identical views. It is an even sorrier state of affairs when men cannot hold contradictory views without plundering and making raids upon the reputations of those who hold opposing opinions.

This Conference, in a sense then, is measure of our ability to try to define the issues, to suggest re-examination of facts, and to propose a review of their meaning within this broad and important sphere of natural resources, and to do this with respect for each other and the consciousness of the deep concern that every person attending this Conference entertains for the public welfare. It was Acton who said, "We cannot make men agree but we can make men disagree reasonably." This is an indispensable characteristic and quality for the men and women who deserve to enjoy the fruits of a free society.

A MID-CENTURY LOOK
AT RESOURCES

BEFORE THE CONFERENCE split into its eight working sections, a basic background paper, which had been prepared by Wilfred Owen of The Brookings Institution and distributed earlier to all participants, was introduced in general session for round-table discussion. Robert D. Calkins, President of The Brookings Institution, chaired this discussion; speakers were James Boyd, Exploration Manager of Kennecott Copper Corporation; Theodore W. Schultz, Chairman of the Department of Economics, University of Chicago; and Earl P. Stevenson, President of Arthur D. Little, Inc.

Summaries of the paper, A Mid-Century Look at Resources, and of the four statements it elicited, are presented here.[1]

SUMMARY

The United States still has an enormous wealth of natural resources. But recent rates of drain and the prospect of further increases in demand are causing concern over future supplies and costs. What is the general outlook for the nation's natural resources?

What will our country be like in the years to come; what population and national output can we expect; and how will changes in the nation's economy be reflected in the type and volume of resource use?

Can current trends of mounting resource demand and difficulties of supply be expected to continue to a point where resource limitations will hamper the national growth we anticipate?

Do we know enough about our needs and resources, and those of other nations, to make it possible to anticipate critical shortages? Will science and engineering meet the challenge by developing new materials, new methods of obtaining them and better ways of using them?

To what extent will the second half of the century see the material aspirations of less fortunate nations fulfilled; and how might an improvement in the economic conditions of the rest of the globe affect the resource and economic position of the United States?

---

[1] Reprints of the full-length paper are available from The Brookings Institution, Washington, D.C. Single copies free; two or more copies 20 cents each.

The First Half-Century

The task of looking into the future requires first of all a glance backward at past trends and experience as a means of gaining perspective. Half a century ago the United States was a relatively new nation in terms of economic development. With 76 million people, and a high proportion on farms, only the beginnings of an industrialized economy were evident. Today there are 160 million people in the United States, and energy from hydropower or fossil fuels does 95 percent of their work. At current rates of consumption these 84 million extra people consume a billion and a half tons of materials annually. We account for nearly half the industrial production of the world.

The greatest changes have taken place in the short period of the past decade or two. The array of new developments affecting the resources picture includes electronics, atomic energy, synthetic fibers, high octane gasoline, the jet engine, and a host of others.

On the economic front the revolutionary impacts of less than a decade and a half have been no less spectacular. In 1953 there were 15 million more people at work than in 1940. Demand for materials has multiplied with population growth, full employment, and expanding national income, and with changes in the distribution of income. In addition, global war and, in its wake, cold war, Korea, and defense build-up, have increased the pressures on our total resources.

In the period 1900 to 1950, we have used up 40 billion barrels of petroleum, 26 billion tons of coal, 3 billion tons of iron ore, 33 million tons of copper, 26 million tons of zinc, and 22 million tons of lead. The amount of copper, lead, zinc, and oil taken from the ground during the past 50 years is considerably greater than present known reserves. Since 1900 our total consumption of agricultural products increased 2¼ times, and our consumption of minerals, including fuels, 6

times 1900 totals. By 1950, as compared with 1900, we were taking from the earth 2½ times more bituminous coal, 3 to 4 times more copper, iron ore, and zinc, 26 times more natural gas, and 30 times more crude oil.[2]

To meet timber requirements, millions of acres of forest land have been cut without enough attention to regeneration. Agricultural lands have been mined of fertility and often seriously impoverished in the effort to produce cash crops or to meet the expanded needs for products of United States farms during the war and immediately thereafter. In many parts of the country the thirst of modern industry and the demands of irrigation and urban living have put heavy pressure on supplies of fresh water.

U.S. PRODUCTION AND CONSUMPTION OF SELECTED COMMODITIES, 1939 AND 1950

Percent of Free World

Commodity	Production		Consumption	
	1939	1950	1939	1950
Aluminum.........	27	51	22	63
Cobalt............	—	4	27	63
Copper...........	31	38	30	61
Iron ore..........	31	51	32	54
Lead.............	24	29	25	64
Manganese ore.....	1	4	31	56
Newsprint.........	12	11	43	65
Nickel............	—	—	51	68
Petroleum.........	70	57	62	62
Rubber...........	—	20	59	53
Sugar.............	17	16	28	27
Tin..............	—	—	45	65
Tungsten..........	13	23	23	65
Wood pulp........	33	43	40	52
Wool	11	6	20	32
Zinc.............	34	33	38	55

SOURCE: Based on Council of Economic Advisers, *The Midyear Economic Report of the President* (July 1951), p. 74.

Among the ferro-alloys, only molybdenum is available domestically in abundant quantities. We are highly dependent on foreign sources of nickel, cobalt, tungsten, chromite,

[2] The President's Materials Policy Commission, *Resources for Freedom*, June 1952, Vol. I, pp. 5 and 25.

and columbite. The United States has practically no domestic tin, natural rubber, cordage fibers, or chromite of certain grades, and practically no nickel or cobalt. Other minerals found at home but in insufficient amount at economic costs include copper, lead, and zinc. Sixty percent of bauxite supplies come from abroad, and of the 13 pounds of manganese required per ton of steel, the United States produces half a pound.

The list of imported vegetable and animal products in critical short supply currently comprises 75 items. The United States obtains coconut oil from Indonesia for lubricants and incendiaries; palm oil from the Belgian Congo for the manufacture of tin plate and cold rolled steel; silk from Japan and Iran for powder bags for large guns; special cotton from Sudan and Persia for airplane fabric; and castor oil from Brazil for brake fluids and nylon. The United States is the world's largest importer of timber products. Many items that we produce at home, which showed a substantial surplus of production over consumption as recently as 1939, now indicate a deficit that has to be made up through imports from other nations.

This trend raises important questions. Can world development of resources keep pace over the long run with the growing needs of the American economy? To what extent will the aspirations and mounting requirements of people in other countries permit United States industry to attract as large a share of total production of raw materials as is now the case? What are the security implications of dependence on distant supplies and vulnerable supply routes?

Future Demand of Resources

A diversity of factors will govern the future demands on our resources. These factors include population growth, national output, composition of the national product, distribution of income, standards of living in the broad

sense of what people will be doing with their time and money, and the kinds of products that will derive from future scientific and engineering advance. There remains the question of war or peace, and the effect of political and economic conditions throughout the world. We can only guess, but an informed guess is essential in anticipating problems and acting to avert difficulties.

In looking to the future the most practicable assumption is that international tensions will continue for some years, but that there will be no major war. But even under the assumption of no world conflagration, military demands for materials continue to grow steadily. Federal outlays for national security in 1952 were approximately $49 billion, or 90 percent of total federal purchases. An indication of the heavy consumption of resources for new weapons is the fact that a medium bomber requires 50 percent more aluminum than the heavy bomber of the Second World War. A submarine requires 1,600 tons of steel and 195 tons of copper, and one-tenth of its weight is rubber. There is enough steel in one medium tank to produce 30 automobiles.[3]

In addition to current requirements, stockpiling goals have greatly expanded materials acquisition. The focus of government research on even more costly instruments of defense will probably mean that for many years the net result of scientific investigation in the area of materials will be in the direction of larger requirements rather than the alleviation of supply problems.

Revival of war-disrupted economies, and Western European rearmament have further multiplied materials needs in the postwar period, while at the same time many Communist-controlled areas have been closed to the Free World as a source of raw materials supply. Since the war an unprecedented peace-

[3] Karl R. Bendetsen, Assistant Secretary of the Army, "The Defense Program—Its Dependence on Raw Materials," address before the American Mining Congress, October 22, 1951.

time volume of materials has been exported from the United States, largely in connection with military and economic aid. In the period 1946 through 1952, the United States exported $122 billion of goods and services, and exports exceeded imports by $45 billion.

To meet these extraordinary requirements has called for heavy expansion of American plant in recent years, involving approximately $25 billion of capital expenditure annually, or five times the plant expansion of 1939. In the postwar defense program the United States increased its economic base by about 16 percent.

The record of past efforts to predict the economic future and to anticipate technological change provides ample indication of the pitfalls of projection. But over a period of years marked improvement has been made in techniques of projection and the statistical basis on which estimates may be based. Industry has come to depend on market forecasts; even weather predictions have advanced to the point where they play an important part in agriculture and many other affected activities. Even more important may be the fact that today we are consciously directing our efforts, private as well as public, toward predetermined future goals. The predictability of certain events may be greater, for example, if maintenance of full employment continues as a basic national policy, if the present efforts devoted to scientific and industrial research are maintained and carefully observed, and if the standards of living to which we aspire sharpen our perception of the invention that necessity will stimulate. Many goals toward which we are working—the achievement of better communities, the perfection of industrial products, the development of new consumer goods—give clues to the possible future uses of resources.

What can we anticipate with respect to future population growth and its impacts on the problem of resources? Recent Census Bureau estimates based on detailed study of the population outlook indicate a range of 198 to 221 million by 1975.[4] Although it is undoubtedly true that "no projection of our population to 1975, 1980, or 2000 can be trusted," we can probably agree on the assumption that a marked increase in population will occur, that 200 million should be a minimum figure, and that this growth factor together with the changing composition and distribution of the population will be of great significance to the American economy.[5]

WORLD AND UNITED STATES POPULATION

In millions

Year	World	United States
1800........	836	5.3
1850........	1,098	23.3
1900........	1,551	76.1
1920........	1,800	106.5
1930........	1,901	123.1
1940........	2,170	132.1
1950........	2,400	151.7
1953........	—	160.0

SOURCES: National Industrial Conference Board, *The Economic Almanac, 1951–52; Encyclopedia of the Social Sciences*, Vol. 12.

On the assumption that resources will be sufficiently plentiful to provide for continuing increases in production, it has been assumed by some that the year 1975 will see the total gross national product double that of the 1950 figure; and the President's Materials Policy Commission, which made this assumption as the basis for its estimates of requirements for materials, concluded that this growth of economic activity would involve 50 to 60 percent more resource use than in 1950.

But it is quite probable that the rate at which revolutionary products and improved methods of production are introduced in the next several decades may increase the annual growth of the national product substantially above the

[4] U.S. Bureau of the Census, *Current Population Reports*, Series P-25, No. 78, August 21, 1953.

[5] Joseph S. Davis, "The Population Upsurge and the American Economy, 1945–80," *The Journal of Political Economy*, October 1953, pp. 369-88.

2.5 percent average of the recent past. As early as 10 years from now we could be producing some $500 billion of goods and services, measured in today's prices, with only an average increase of 3 percent a year.[6] On this basis, our economy by 1975-80 could be producing at least three-quarters of a trillion dollars of goods and services.

What relationship will hold between rising national product and the use of materials is difficult to judge, however, because of the increasing relative importance of services in the total goods-and-services output, and because our concepts of higher standards of living may in the future attach greater significance to objectives of a well-rounded life rather than to a mere increase in materials consumption. The extent to which American standards of living will continue to be measured in material terms rather than in cultural activities is one of the areas of study to which the efforts of the social scientists need to be directed.

However, until the one-fifth of our population that now has only the minimum requirements for subsistence can improve its position, the potential national requirements for materials will be great regardless of increases in population. If recent trends toward a broader distribution of personal income continue, millions of people who now have vast unsatisfied wants should be able to afford higher levels of living, and at the outset this would mean a sharp increase in the demand for material-consuming durable goods.

To the extent that the peoples of the rest of the world also succeed in achieving higher consumption levels the mounting world demand for resources will accelerate. The recently won political independence of underdeveloped areas can be expected to provide the setting for new efforts toward material betterment through industrialization and the development of native resources.

It seems clear, on the demand side, that the

combination of population growth, rising economic activity, further innovation, and increasing equality of living levels among individuals and nations will exert pressure on world resources far in excess of today's demands. How much greater these demands will be depends not simply on anticipated economic growth but on political decisions, the climate for capital investment in foreign countries, economic policies with respect to distribution of income, and future relations among the nations of the world.

Future Supply of Resources

Determining the outlook for supply is in many respects a more difficult task than estimating potential demand. It depends on what we already have here at home, how we use it, how we manage it, what new sources we find, what improvements we make in discovery and extraction, what we get from abroad, the efficiency of management and economic organization, and finally on invention, technology, the engineer, and the scientist. It depends also on the availability of goods at the lowest possible cost in labor and materials so that increasing productivity will allow a continuing rise in standards of living.

We see on the one hand the evidences of overuse and misuse of resources, diminishing reserves, resort to less economical sources, and global efforts to discover and develop materials than can no longer be provided at home. But if we can assume that the rate of technological development will continue if not increase with advancing scientific knowledge, our supply position, despite widespread depletion of many of the kinds of materials we use today, may be better than is at first apparent. At least it may be kept from serious deterioration as growing shortages cause us to turn to sources and methods that we are capable of developing and using, but which have not been used in the past because of the absence of economic incentive or compulsion.

---

[6] President of the U.S., *Economic Report of the President,* January 1953, p. 24.

Attempts to weigh the major factors governing the future of resource supply and demand have led to a variety of conclusions, some sharply conflicting. One important interpretation of the available facts is the belief that population growth will continue to the point where food requirements will ultimately outstrip supply.

We are told, for example, that the appearance of 70,000 additional mouths at the breakfast table each morning "will reduce the world to poverty and destroy mankind." Medical science and improved sanitation will mean more millions living in greater misery.[7] Growth of the world's population today is "startling to comprehend," and the rate of population growth in the United States is higher than the world growth rate—higher even than that of India. The present trend shows little tendency to stop "while new processes are being invented or perfected to provide food and other needs."[8]

It is maintained further that widespread evidence substantiates the belief that in the long run "the avalanche of births will outweigh all possible scientific advance unless factors enter the situation that cannot now be foreseen, factors on which we dare not count."[9]

Plans to meet the problem of balancing populations with resources are said to be grossly inadequate to meet the mounting crises. The logic of the theory that food supply has fixed a ceiling on population has not been disproved, we are told, but only postponed by the economic gains of recent years.

According to another interpretation, the answer to much of our resources problem will be found in the potentialities of science, especially chemistry. The chemical revolution now under way, it is said, will through industrial synthesis free mankind from agricultural pursuits as a means of sustenance and release millions of farmers, as well as the surface of the earth, from dedication to food production.

With respect to population growth, the view has been expressed that a slowing down and leveling off of population is under way in many parts of the world, and that total world population will stabilize in the next century and a half "at a level the earth can well support." Many countries have already reached the stage of "incipient decline," whereas other nations are in an earlier stage of demographic evolution or just entering it. The past population surge of recent history, according to this view, is a "unique, unprecedented, and unrepeatable phenomenon of limited duration."[10]

Regardless of rapid population growth and past depletion of resources, many believe that innovation is today providing us with a far broader and stronger usable resource base than ever before. What we use today is limited by prevailing physical, technological, and economic conditions. As conditions change, the availability of usable resources will change. As the President's Materials Policy Commission has pointed out, we have depended on supplies of the highest grade materials occurring on the surface, yet the earth holds tremendous stores that improved methods of subsurface exploration will reveal and improved methods of extraction and recovery will make worth mining. In many respects major materials research, including the development of synthetics, has yet to begin.

To many observers either of these interpretations will appear extreme, and a large number of persons therefore prefer a broad middle ground. In any event the possible positions that may be taken do not necessarily stand in the way of agreement on what to do now about many specific resource problems.

[7] Robert Gesell, *University of Michigan News Service*, May 12, 1953.

[8] Population Reference Bureau, Inc., *Population Bulletin*, Vol. 9, July 1953, p. 50.

[9] Bruce Bliven, *Preview for Tomorrow*, 1953, p. 14.

[10] W. S. and E. S. Woytinsky, *World Population and Production*, 1953.

The conclusion seems inescapable that now at mid-century the time has come to examine forthrightly the resources future of our nation and to arrive cooperatively at an acceptable basis for action to assure the continuing adequacy of our natural resources.

That domestic and world requirements will increase during the half century ahead, regardless of the absence of quantitative precision, seems clear and this certainty is matched by the uncertainty that is found in the whole complex picture of world supply. But the conflict of views about how both the supply and demand picture can or cannot be altered in the years ahead poses the basic question for the Mid-Century Conference: *Having as our goal the long-range economic health and security of the nation, what set of basic premises should guide industry, government, and citizens in the policies and actions that determine resource supply and demand?*

To arrive at such a set of premises will require answers to many questions and a concensus on many vital issues that will determine whether or not we can meet the demand for resources that rising population and the upward trend in living standards entail.

DISCUSSION

• ROBERT D. CALKINS: If we are to act with appropriate consideration for the long-range economic health and security of this nation, and of the other free nations, we must examine now our resource supplies and needs. If, a generation or more hence, we are destined to encounter serious shortages, this should be discovered as soon as possible so that appropriate measures may be developed in time to relieve or avoid these dangers. Even short-run commitments cannot wisely be made without some premise or implication as to the seriousness of our resource problems for the future.

The paper which forms the basis for this discussion, A Mid-Century Look at Resources, sets forth some of the facts, the speculations, and the influences that affect our views of problems concerned with the nation's renewable and nonrenewable resources over the next 25 years.

Whether the trends outlined will continue, and if so what their consequences will be, are basic issues. If population and gross national product continue to rise at the pace that is apparently indicated, it seems inevitable to some that we are destined for serious resource trouble a generation hence or a little later. The notion that we can rely on foreign supplies is rendered uncertain by the combined growth of population and rise of living standards abroad.

What then, of our resource supply situation? Some people believe that population growth will so outrun our powers to expand resources that scientific effort is doomed to be outstripped by hungry mouths. Others see in the minds and hands of this population our greatest resource. To these optimists science, technology, and skill will supply the way out for those intelligent enough to use them. Such projections are difficult to appraise. Even a middle-ground view, using projections within our range of vision, is a broad enough field for controversy. At this conference we are not seeking predictions for the 21st Century or later, we are only asking what expectations are reasonable for the 20th Century and what constitutes prudent action in light of these expectations.

• JAMES BOYD: It is often assumed that the greatness of this nation and its successful economic development have been possible largely because of the abundance of our natural resources; yet we can observe that some nations with the highest standards of living are the poorest in physical resources, while others with the lowest living standards are perhaps the richest, resource-wise, in the world. Clearly, the most important resource in any country is the ability and initiative of its people. Given the courage, intelligence, and ingenuity of a virile people, virtually any country's physical resources, no matter how limited, may provide a base for development which can reach presently unimagined heights. Factors of statistics and economics, while extremely important as projections upon which policies may be founded, rarely evaluate the outcome of human ingenuity.

Again, some have assumed that the dependence of this country upon others for certain raw materials is a serious weakness. Is it not possible that the growing interdependence between nations of the Free World may be a point of strength rather than weakness? As long as there is any semblance of free trade, consumers will naturally purchase raw material at the most favorable price irrespective of its source. While it is true that we have skimmed the cream from our easily discovered high-grade resources and our domestic industries thus come into competition with the higher grade resources of foreign countries, this change in flow pattern does not mean that we have exhausted our own mineral deposits.

Let us take the mining industry as an example of the most acute problem—that of apparent shortages in the face of sudden increases in demand. Experience has shown that shortages may be temporarily brought about by insufficient flexibility of supply, and that many of the current problems, in the mineral industry at least, are brought about by overcorrection of these temporary shortages. This condition is symptomatic of one of the really critical problems of mineral supply—the impossibility of bringing new mines into production in a short time or of quickly suspending operations when the supply is in balance.

It is time that we strip away the legends and superstitions surrounding resource questions. For instance, in the basic paper for this discussion, it is said that a medium bomber now requires 50 percent more aluminum than the

heavy bomber of the Second World War, but the paper does not say how many more or how many less bombers are required. It says, "enough steel in one medium tank to produce 30 automobiles." Such statistics are meaningless and confusing. Resource consumption is a function of total manpower availability and efficiency—not the material in each bomber. It also took double the manpower to manufacture such a machine.

It is quite obvious that the studies produced by the President's Materials Policy Commission, and those presented before this Conference, cannot possibly predict in detail or even in principle what the resource requirements will be 5 to 6 years from now, let alone 25 to 30. The one fact we are certain of is that there will be a continuing increase in requirements and a varying mixture as technological developments advance. Consequently, these problems will be with us constantly. It appears to me that the most important contribution that this Conference can make to the whole resource question is that of pointing the way towards the creation of an atmosphere in which many individuals dealing with an infinite variety of problems can, as they always do in the end, exercise judgment in the right direction.

• THEODORE W. SCHULTZ: Suppose, to make a very drastic assumption, that 50 years from now the United States should have 320 million people—double the present population. What conditions would we have to meet to produce enough food for that population and, in addition, enough to further upgrade our diets and food intake per capita, maintain net exports at the level of a few years ago, and still have sizable surpluses—all this at a unit price of farm product less than today?

I speculate in this way because these are precisely the conditions we have satisfied during the past 50 years. How did we manage to do it? Where along the way did we do badly?

Has our achievement been the fruit of more toil and more work and longer hours to get more out of our acres? I should emphatically say no. Has it been the result of a lot of luck

—good weather, no insects, no diseases? No, we have had our quota of all of these. Has it come about through exploiting a lot of virgin land? Surely not during the last 30 years. Has it been due to the stimulus of two world wars? A study of how these wars affected our agriculture indicates a negative answer.

Yet somehow during the last 50 years we have achieved fundamental advances in the supply of food. Our agriculture today responds more readily than it did earlier to our efforts to achieve specific production results. At the same relative prices, we find it easier today than in 1920 to expand farm food production by 1, 2, or 5 percent. Moreover, a higher relative price—a 10, 15, or 20 percent increase in a given period of say two or three years— will today bring about a substantially greater response in output than was formerly the case. One need only compare our difficulties in increasing the output of food in World War I with those encountered during World War II, to see some evidence that is relevant here.

Going beyond these fundamental economic changes, from 1910 to 1950 (data prior to 1910 are unsatisfactory) with only 14 percent more input, we increased our output of farm products by about 75 percent.

These are basic figures representing much progress in the productive arts in farming. We have developed and applied many new techniques which have saved labor, saved capital and, to a marked extent, saved land. During this period there have been substitutions among factors, and this you would have expected because the unit price of human effort has risen sharply compared with other factors. It has risen relative, certainly, to capital forms, whereas land (the rent it earns) has not risen relatively, comparing 1910 and 1950.

Yet I would hazard a guess that our technological advance has not favored any one factor. It appears to have saved labor on the one hand about as much as it has saved land, or saved other forms of capital. What then have we done that accounts for this outstanding outcome?

What exactly have been the contributions of the land-grant colleges and universities?

And what about the 48 agricultural experiment stations that are a part of that system; the several state extension services which take the ideas from the experiment stations and from elsewhere, to farmers? What about the U.S. Department of Agriculture and its researches? What about the fundamental research that is done elsewhere as it comes to bear upon farming? What have been the contributions of developments in our general education?

While I was at Ames, trying to determine the impact of the AAA on the Corn Belt, Professor Brownlee and I discovered that during the late thirties, when the United States reduced its corn acreage from 100 million to 85 million acres, the aggregate impact was to increase the total feed supply. Our interpretation was that the reduction in corn acreage produced a shock that caused a lot of new techniques, hitherto on the experiment station shelf, to move into agriculture. It is one of the effects of the AAA that had been completely overlooked, but is relevant to our inquiry, here.

Despite our over-all achievements we have made some mistakes, and I want to emphasize the areas in which we have in part failed.

There is, until very recently, the by-passing of the South in this whole advance. This mistake is being corrected.

There is the neglect of the intermountain area. It is not an accident that the intermountain area lags so far behind the rest of the country in terms of ratio of output to input. It may well be that this is because our really powerful research and experiment stations are to be found in Iowa, Minnesota, Wisconsin, Illinois, Indiana, Michigan, Ohio, New York, California, and in a few other strong states. They are very expensive stations and the weaker states such as those in the intermountain area cannot afford them. Take the genetics of grass to get higher yields from grasses suitable to the open ranges: I don't think we will get results until we are willing to invest, as we did with hybrid corn across the Corn Belt, large resources and talents.

Another mistake is the misuse of our land that is directly attributable to our primitive landlord-tenant relationships. Here we can learn wisely and well from Western Europe. We are, indeed, a backward people when one looks at the legislative framework used to handle these various complex property relationships.

Underinvestment in experiment in extension work is another error we have made. Another is failure to provide for fundamental research. As a people we are still not prepared to understand what is required of science. We all want applied results, forthcoming in two or three years.

Finally, despite our encouraging successes, we have at many points an unsatisfactory combination of private and public decision-taking and administration bearing upon our food-producing resources.

It is high time we took stock of what tools, among the many we have been using, account for our record of achievement. Perhaps then we can determine their suitability for future use and the need for better or different approaches.

• EARL P. STEVENSON: In the field of industrial research, with which I am concerned, our motivation is to increase the consumption of the very things that this Conference group in large part would like to conserve. I am in favor of increasing the tempo of our industrial research so that our people in consuming more, can earn more.

According to the Conference working paper, the hope of continuing technological progress alone appears to balance the increasing drain upon our resources as population expands and wasteful habits of utilization continue. It is recognized that the results of scientific research may be applied to modify habits of utilization and consumption as well as broaden the base of resources supply.

Is this hope justified? A glance backwards recalls that 100 years ago, all materials used by man were derived directly from natural sources. Today, dye-stuffs are 99 percent synthetic; drugs and medicinals, 75 percent; rubber, 50 percent; textiles, over 20 percent; detergents replace soap. With the advent of titanium—an abundant element—there will

be industrial repercussions and adjustments. Technology is prepared to take up any shortage in liquid hydrocarbons as long as coal and oil shale are available. Here the known resources are reckoned in hundreds of years. Plastics are in their infancy.

Two years ago we heard the lament that the new developments in nuclear energy would not be as significant for us as for others, since we lacked uranium. But incentive has produced scientific prospecting tools and, as a consequence of the Atomic Energy Commission's research program, the picture has been radically changed. We now know more about uranium and its distribution in the earth's crust than we do about any other metal. Basic knowledge of the geochemistry of heavy metals, how they are distributed and how they build up to form ore bodies, should disclose hidden resources.

The most contentious item in the field of nonrenewable resources appears to be petroleum, both oil and gas. The industry is certainly of the cornucopian faith, while the conservationists warn of the dangers of continued disregard of our dependence upon limited resources. Big numbers in themselves can induce false conclusions. Those who live and work day by day in the presence of the reality for which they stand are apt to see them in different perspective. One side of the petroleum-reserve controversy may express the quantity of oil so far extracted from the earth in barrels, if not in gallons; the other group quotes the figure, in a different reference frame, of $1\frac{1}{16}$ cubic miles.

But these issues appear to be of secondary importance as we greet 70,000 additional mouths at the breakfast table each morning. We are told by some that the contributions of research to agriculture have provided only a temporary stopgap to the needs of a constantly increasing population. Dr. Schultz's remarks on this point were to me very reassuring. Others seem to believe that the total world population will stabilize in the next century-and-a-half at a level the earth can well support.

On these questions, I am not going to take the position that we shall shortly be living on synthetic food, but I do take courage from the assurance given me by Dr. Edwin Cohn, that pioneer in the field of blood chemistry and protein structure who passed away about seven months ago, that we now have the key to the structure of the protein molecule. As you know, this has been done in the laboratory on a small scale. We have here a very simple building block, amino acids, the raw materials for which are extremely plentiful—the air about us, water, coal.

Surveying the prospects for resources as a whole, it seems a predictable conclusion that man's insatiable curiosity concerning the physical world, both inanimate and animate, is the greatest resource of all. Research viewed as a resource immediately focuses attention on man

as an individual. Our great concern should therefore be to insure that the gifted few are identified and confirmed in the secondary schools, committed to careers in science as a result of their college experience, and given the opportunity for graduate study as the final step in their dedication. This educational process now appears to be breaking down at the first stage. There are those who advocate that the teaching of physics and chemistry be abolished in the great majority of high schools in the absence of a sufficient number of competent teachers. We are in danger of not developing and conserving the renewable resource that is unique in affording the only hope for a long-term solution of the major problems before this Conference.

THE WORK OF
THE CONFERENCE

Chairman

CHARLES C. COLBY
Professor Emeritus of Geography
University of Chicago

Co-Chairman

HARRY R. WELLMAN
Vice-President of the
University of California
at Berkeley

Steering Committee and Advisers

Steering Committee: ROBERT F. CHANDLER, JR., President of the University of New Hampshire · RAYMOND B. HOLBROOK, Attorney with U.S. Smelting, Refining and Mining Company · WILLIAM R. MATHEWS, Editor and Publisher, *Arizona Daily Star* · JULIAN F. McGOWIN, Secretary, W. T. Smith Lumber Company · WILLIS H. MILLER, Director of Planning, San Diego County, California · JOSEPH PRENDERGAST, Executive Director, National Recreation Association · A. W. SAMPSON, Professor Emeritus of Forestry, University of California at Berkeley · ANTHONY W. SMITH, Assistant General Counsel and Secretary of the Conservation Committee, Congress of Industrial Organizations · *Section Rapporteur and Assistant to the Section Chairman:* JAMES G. RETTIE, Forest Service, U.S. Department of Agriculture

Subsections

A. URBAN LAND

Chairman: WILLIS H. MILLER

Rapporteurs: VICTOR ROTERUS, Chief, Area Development Division, U.S. Department of Commerce; MARCUS ROSENBLUM, Staff Associate, Office of Chief Sanitary Engineering Officer, U.S. Public Health Service

B. RURAL LAND

Chairman: ROBERT F. CHANDLER, JR.

Rapporteurs: WAYNE DEXTER, Secretary of Outlook and Situation Board, Agricultural Marketing Service, U.S. Department of Agriculture; EDWIN VAN HORN LARSON, Editor, Northeastern Forest Experiment Station; H. H. WOOTEN, Production Economics Research Branch, Agricultural Research Service, U.S. Department of Agriculture

About 150 persons took part in the work of Section I. The 139 who registered formally are listed on pages 381-83. The full section met briefly during the early part of the afternoon of December 2 to consider the whole problem of competing demand. The two subsections met in the latter part of the afternoon and held morning and afternoon sessions the following day. The work of the subsections was reviewed the morning of December 4 by the whole section. Inevitably, the discussions of the Rural Land subsection often led to general areas that were discussed (from a different viewpoint) by Section II. Close ties of this kind are indicated by cross references.

COMPETING DEMANDS
FOR THE USE OF LAND

THE POPULATION OF THE UNITED STATES keeps growing—210 million by 1975 is the middle-range estimate of the Census Bureau. The national economy keeps expanding at a rate well ahead of the increase in population. But the total land surface within our continental limits remains relatively fixed. Thus more people will be looking to the same land base for more things—materials such as food, fiber, and timber; space for industrial and transportation development, as well as for housing and recreation.

Interest in this section was centered on how best to meet increasing demands on the nation's fixed land base. Up to now, really sharp competition for the use of land has been localized rather than general. Will this hold good in the future? Even if it should, are we as a nation prepared to deal with mounting and intensified local competition? Do we have enough information of the kind needed for sound decisions?

Although use of land for towns and cities represents only a small fraction of the country's total surface, it is a use that will grow rapidly. This growth will sharpen the competition, since any additional acreage will have to come from farm and forest lands, which at the same time may be called upon for greater production.

A diversity of viewpoints and a variety of suggestions came out of the discussions of both rural and urban aspects of competition among land uses. But in both areas, and in the particularly troublesome zones where the two converge, it was apparent that more basic facts and analysis are needed, and that more should be done toward applying the knowledge that already is available.

Subsection A

URBAN LAND

The transformation of the United States from a predominantly rural to a highly urbanized nation during the past 50 years has created conflicts both within and outside the limits of incorporated cities. Urban and industrial uses now occupy 25 million acres. If expansion continues at the rate of about a third of a million acres per year, the total 1975 demand will be about 35 million acres.

Much of this addition to urban land, as well as increases in highway and airport uses, undoubtedly will come from land now used for agriculture. Conflicts between urban and rural uses will be accentuated. The use of space by industrial and commercial establishments brings in its wake the use of space for housing, transportation, and urban facilities. Competition between these urban uses will also arise. Security, through dispersion, is another factor. How can future demands be determined and satisfied?

In the pages that follow, excerpts from the record of discussion are grouped under four major headings:

1. Centralization vs. decentralization.
2. Major forms of competition for space (especially urban vs. rural uses).
3. Competing demands for land within cities.
4. Can urban development be made more orderly?

Centralization vs. Decentralization

Does decentralization have net advantages? If large-scale decentralization is desirable, is it attainable? In considering these basic questions, the group also examined present trends. There was a wide range of opinion on whether the type of growth now being experienced by many large cities is a trend toward decentralization or simply a sprawling expansion, and on whether the forces behind the growth stem from a natural desire for more space or population pressures from the central core of the city.

The proponents of decentralization took the view that a carefully planned and organized decentralization would retain the advantages of present concentrations and add new advantages by providing for more leisurely and wholesome living. Others felt that large cities have certain commercial, economic, and social advantages that would be destroyed by decentralization; that at a certain point the transportation, production, and general economic disadvantages of decentralization would outweigh the advantages. The group was in general agreement that a high degree of decentralization would make the United States less vulnerable to enemy attack, but there were differences over how quickly any significant results could be achieved.

Lack of public information on urban vulnerability to attack and lack of penetrating research into urban problems were noted as serious handicaps to profitable discussion.

FROM THE RECORD

Is There a Clear Trend?

American cities are still growing, pushing out into the surrounding countryside, but some participants questioned whether this in itself is evidence of a general move toward decentralization.

WILLIS H. MILLER (Director of Planning, San Diego County, California): In many cities the central core is decreasingly the focal point of all the so-called downtown activities of a mercantile and office and industrial type; there is an expansion of the service centers into fringe areas. This development often is referred to as decentralization. Centralization has been rather traditional in our urban pattern and has certain values. Are these values changing or being lost in this newer approach of decentralization?

HAROLD M. MAYER (University of Chicago): There is a middle ground between the urban core and the urban periphery which has received far from adequate attention throughout the years. In Chicago, for example, over half of the population lives in an intermediate area between the urban core and the so-called blighted area surrounding it on the one hand, and the fringe area on the other. I would like to see some attention directed, not specifically to centralization versus decentralization, but to the middle-aged areas within cities where these two forces are meeting head on.

The pressures from the center of the city, particularly the pressures that are added by redevelopment of the more centralized residential areas, force the people who can't move into the new redeveloped areas into the next best thing—generally these middle-aged areas. This is part of the process of decentralization. The population pressures bring about conversions, often illegal, often inadequate, with shared bathrooms and community kitchens, and contribute to the deterioration of the area. This process of moving out toward the periphery of the city is having a serious effect on the area which contributes most in terms of population and human resources.

FRANCIS L. HAUSER (American Institute of Planners): Project East River and other figures do not bear out the assumption that there was a definite unchecked trend toward decentralization in the early forties. Cities are merely getting industry and gaining population at a slower rate than their own periphery sections and their satellites.

T. LEDYARD BLAKEMAN (Detroit Metropolitan Area Regional Planning Commission): Residential construction has been practically stopped since 1929, except for the last two or three years. For this reason I don't think we can look to the mobility studies or the internal migration studies that were made

during that period—the pressure was there, but you can't move unless you have a place to move to.

MAX S. WEHRLY (Urban Land Institute): What we have been experiencing and, I think, will continue to experience is growth and not decentralization. Urban and industrial decentralization will occur only as rapidly as the economics of production and distribution will permit.

Where Does the Net Advantage Lie?

TRACY B. AUGUR (Office of Defense Mobilization): The issue before us today is not whether a centralized or decentralized form of urban life is the more pleasant or healthful or economical; the issue is whether a nation with its population and industrial production highly centralized, highly massed, in small areas can survive the onslaught of world Communism. Space is one of the most potent weapons of defense. Properly spread, urban development makes a much less attractive target. It is entirely possible to retain the advantages of the big city without cleaving to its concentrated form.

CLARENCE S. STEIN (Regional Development Council of America): Regardless of the argument for defense, we have come to the point where we have to consider a different pattern—a pattern of moderate-sized cities, separated by much wider areas of open land and connected by superhighways, each a center for some business activity or art form.

JOHN W. DYCKMAN (University of Pennsylvania): I do not think we are ready to arrange all our values in a scale which would place survival that far above other considerations. We will either have a great many much larger cities in 1975 or we will have to establish an enormous number of new communities before that time, which will mean an order of investment well beyond what we are now able to invest. In fact, it might well be beyond the sum we now invest in defense.

HAROLD S. BUTTENHEIM (*The American City*): Since the end of World War II, large numbers of city dwellers have fled to the suburbs or the country in search of light and air and grass and trees and better conditions for bringing up children.

If it is desirable to check this flight, three essentials for municipal government will be: (a) redevelopment of areas of urban blight and slum; (b) amendment of outmoded zoning ordinances to require larger lots and less land-overcrowding; and (c) provision of more ample areas for parks, playgrounds, school sites, and parking lots.

PHILIP H. CORNICK (Yonkers, N.Y.): To decentralize immediately would take so much in the way of labor and materials that we would not have any manpower and materials left to use for defense purposes. In addition, you cannot decentralize beyond a certain point. You have to have a big plant to do certain things. And you have to have people to run the big plants. You cannot very well decentralize Oak Ridge.

CHARLES C. COLBY (Professor Emeritus of Geography, University of Chicago): I doubt if you could decentralize the essential transportational, commercial, and financial elements of New York and Chicago without killing those great centers, and that would be a tremendous handicap in our economy. It may be possible to decentralize such industrial centers as Detroit and Philadelphia. But what can be done with our major commercial centers other than to accept the risk?

MR. BLAKEMAN: It would take a minor revolution to get any substantial decentralization within the next 20 to 50 years. Although we should go ahead and decentralize new construction for defensive purposes we had better continue to be concerned primarily with the social and economic effects of decentralization.

CHAUNCY D. HARRIS (University of Chicago): We say we must decentralize for defense purposes and for better living, and yet people continue to live in the big cities in increased numbers. I wonder if we don't need better understanding of the causative factors. There are obvious advantages in these great urban concentrations. I think, for example, that the Soviet Union's decentralization has

increased costs of transportation and of operating the economy; the net loss in efficiency may equalize the greater defensive potentialities.

OLIVER BEIMFOHR (Southern Illinois University): In southern Illinois there is a concentration of some 250,000 or more people within a radius of some 50 miles— what you might call a dispersed city. The difficulties of dispersal relate to jobs, transportation, amenities, housing, taxation, and government financing. You have some highly undesirable conditions when you separate our population into little cities.

MR. STEIN: I think our mistake has been to decentralize on the basis of small communities with no provision for the things people moved out for. Anything of this kind must be planned on a regional basis.

MR. COLBY: The situation in southern Illinois illustrates the principal point that in a country as diverse as the United States no plan, no law can possibly be applied equally satisfactorily in all sections of the country.

Unanswered Questions and Other Obstacles

Whether or not true decentralization is taking place on a large scale—whether or not it is better than centralization—people are on the move, generally into urban areas but away from the center of town. What can be done to make this trend as orderly and useful as possible? Do we yet know enough about major aspects of the problem to make sound decisions and plan practicable action?

LLOYD RODWIN (Massachusetts Institute of Technology): It seems to me that either way you stand on the issue of decentralization, the need for research is important. There is practically no research on any aspect of this —on where things should be in the cities, on what the costs are when shifts occur, on the type of economic and administrative mechanisms required. We will be forced in the future to do a lot of things before we know what the answers are; but we should be investigating at the same time.

MR. COLBY: Has anybody ever investigated why people want to live in the suburbs? Quite evidently some people do, but there are probably a lot who don't. The only way to get the latter group out in the suburbs is to move jobs to that area. The vital question is whether industry and other forms of business can best be served by moving out.

E. DANA CAULKINS (Westchester County Recreation Commission, N.Y.): One thing that is slowing down decentralization from New York City into Westchester County is the lack of low-cost housing. Industries have great plans to come out, but some have postponed moving because they don't have living accommodations for their employees.

MR. BUTTENHEIM: I hope that special thought will be given to a possible method of property taxation that would help to encourage more rational land uses, both urban and rural.

Major Forms of Competition for Space

The simple fact that cities are expanding is the root of many problems of conflicting use, and is by far the largest factor in terms of acreage. Generally speaking, how rational a process is this constant spread of urbanization? Are the potentialities of rural land being needlessly sacrificed through unwise choices of the areas taken over, or preemption of too much land too soon? Does the present course of expansion best meet the needs of the city-dwellers? What economic and political stresses accompany the shift of land from country to town, and how many might be prevented or reduced?

FROM THE RECORD

Urban Uses vs. Rural Uses

Should excellent farm land be subdivided? Should urban expansion be by "jumps," or progressively in areas where facilities can be provided at reasonable cost?

ERLING SOLBERG (Agricultural Research Service, USDA): Shall our better soils grow crops or houses? In the early years, incorporated communities depended upon the countryside for sustenance. Now the urban populace looks to the countryside for living and working space as well.

Expansion on the urban fringe usually does not proceed outward uniformly from city boundaries. Generally it radiates out along the highways. Sometimes urban development tends to leapfrog over suitable lands near the city to create residential islands or pockets in farm communities further out. Into this agricultural hinterland urban-oriented people have penetrated for many miles to establish country homes and part-time farms.

What does this transformation mean in terms of competing uses for rural land? Fertile acres are lost to agriculture annually through use as nonfarm living and working space.

In the last decade, an average of 650,000 new families, urban and rural, were formed each year. Living, transportation, and working space for urban people and for farmers requires an average of 1.4 acres per family. The average for farmers includes farmsteads only, but not the farm. On this basis approximately 924,000 additional acres are needed annually for these purposes. Land must be found to accommodate this urban and suburban expansion. Are we wise when we continue to build houses and factories on our better farm lands and ultimately push our farmers up on the less productive hill slopes? We may not miss these good farm lands for a few years, but what about agricultural needs 25 or 50 years hence?

Motor transportation, which has made this

expansion possible, can help remedy the situation, for it allows the community a large area of choice in allocating more fertile soils for farming and less fertile lands for development.

HAROLD TAUBIN (Planning Division, Montgomery County, Md.): In the upper portion of Montgomery County, some 350 square miles of rural land are under pressure for residential development. We can, through farsighted planning, accommodate 350,000 people in this rural area and still maintain a major portion of our farm economy. The proper laying of water and sewer lines, and the proper location of schools, libraries, fire stations, police stations, and other public facilities will help bring about such a land settlement pattern. A great many other considerations, however, will affect the pattern of development; and the local community has no control over many of these. To encourage rational development the local community requires the assistance of banks, investment houses, the Federal Housing Authority, and the Veterans Administration. Our county may decide, for example, to zone its most fertile areas for agricultural use. A land development plan of this sort requires the assistance of the federal government, through the underwriting activities of the FHA and the VA, if it is to be effectively carried out.

MR. MILLER: You mean that the FHA should not underwrite loans for residential developments on first-class agricultural lands?

MR. TAUBIN: Yes, if that is the policy that has been duly adopted in a local area.

MR. SOLBERG: In some states and some areas, urbanization is becoming quite a problem. In California, for example, some counties have lost vast areas of their best farm lands, which means the loss not only of farm income but also of processing industries.

We should classify our lands, designating the lands that are most suitable for farming on a statewide basis, and then take measures to protect that land, to reserve it for future farm uses. There are millions of acres that are less desirable for farming that can be used for residential and industrial purposes. But because the farm land is usually level and has roads and utilities, it is more easily developed and goes first.

MR. BLAKEMAN: Position is important. Some good agricultural land may be in a position that makes it highly desirable for urban uses. The use of good agricultural land for urban purposes may hurt the agricultural economy of a given county, but what does it amount to in the total agricultural picture of the nation, or even of a state?

MR. HARRIS: I doubt that it is economically feasible as a general rule to reserve to agriculture the first use of land. There are two questions involved: One is whether good farm land should be used for urban purposes; this is a debatable issue. The other is whether there should be a better pattern by which some degree of urbanization can proceed into agricultural lands. On this I think there would be general agreement that the hazards of sprinkling urban residences among farm lands may cause undesirable characteristics for both. The main question here is one of policy improvement.

MR. COLBY: I think it is a major mistake for a citrus area to be put out of existence by the development of industry and urbanism. You can't grow citrus fruits just anywhere. But you could take a dozen farms in southern Illinois and not hurt the total crop production. It all depends upon the part of the country.

MR. SOLBERG: The tax impact should also be mentioned. The influx of suburban population usually brings with it an increased demand for schools and roads. In states where the primary tax load for schools and roads is on the towns or townships, this increases the tax load on the farmer, and it becomes exceedingly difficult for him to operate. Now, in states where a large proportion of the cost of schools and roads is borne by the state as a whole, the situation wouldn't be as critical from the point of view of the farming economy. But in Connecticut, Massachusetts, and New Jersey, the farmers are really concerned about the impact of the suburbanization movement. Frequently an industry will be located in one township and the larger proportion of the workers will be in another township. One gets the tax income from the new industry; the other carries the load.

Airports vs. Other Urban Uses

Airports, especially those serving jets, are a disturbing feature of our urban pattern. Unless airports are relatively close in they are not really functional. If they are close in, they dominate scores and even hundreds of acres of land which otherwise could be used for a variety of urban purposes.

MR. BLAKEMAN: Zoning will carry you only so far. Phobias and superstitions about air travel are widespread. Property owners and school authorities are sure airplanes will be falling in their laps.

MR. MILLER: Within a radius of 12,000 feet from the center of the runways the noise of jet planes is so great that any ordinary use of the land within that circle is badly inhibited. That takes in a lot of territory.

MR. BLAKEMAN: We worked on the zoning for one of our major airports, and came to the conclusion that the airport did definitely inhibit residential development. It also inhibits smoke- or dust-producing heavy industry. You have to control an enormous amount of land outside the airport. And you should consider as part of the cost of the airport some rapid means of ground transportation from the airport into town.

MR. MAYER: The commercial field should be as close to the urban area as is possible, consistent with safety and other requirements of urban growth. The military field should be farther out. The jet fields, the intercontinental and long-haul passenger fields, are tending to go farther out at the same time that the short-haul fields are coming closer in. A continuation of this trend holds the solution to the problem. The development of helicopter air taxi service will reduce the necessity for having large major airports so close to the urban centers. However, I think we can all agree that airports should be as close as possible to the urban centers compatible with such matters as land values and the effects upon the surrounding areas.

Competing Demands for Land Within Cities

Within cities, there are strong demands for the use of land for a number of different purposes. Open space is needed for recreation, for streets and highways, for schools and other public buildings; building sites are needed for residential, industrial, and commercial purposes. Many of these uses are not limited to any one district and are in direct competition for space with all other urban functions. The resulting pressures have created many problems. Central traffic congestion, spreading of depreciated areas, blight uses, inadequate reservation of land for industry, and haphazard development in the outskirts were singled out for particular attention.

FROM THE RECORD

Open Space vs. Buildings

How can open space be provided for recreation areas, for schools and other public buildings, for streets and highways, for airports, and so on? The problem is not only how to provide open space as such, but how to allocate it among these uses, for they compete with one another as well as with other urban uses. The need for adequate planning of recreational space in metropolitan and rural areas was discussed also in Section II, pages 103-6.

MR. RODWIN: Open space has been neglected in urban areas; the distribution, the pattern, and the quantity of open space need further consideration.

MR. TAUBIN: The competition for land between new highway construction and existing park facilities is a very real problem. Parks and other recreation areas acquired in anticipation of population growth should not be sacrificed because it may be cheaper to turn land already in public ownership over to the highway engineer. In built-up areas it is especially foolish for communities to resolve the problem along lines of least resistance.

MR. CAULKINS: Studies have been made showing great increases in land values and tax income in areas within the vicinity of developed recreational facilities, open parks, and so on. We might try using these findings to check the tendency to say, "Here is some free park land; let's use it for a freeway or something else." Maybe in so doing we are going to cause depreciation of the land nearby and so lose more than we gain.

MR. STEIN: We should remember that the pattern of open spaces is quite as important as the quantity. It is important to have recreation space close to houses, small towns with open spaces around them, safe areas for children. Our experience in building towns where there are larger blocks and where the different functions of roads are separate, is that we have less highway, less cost, and more space for green areas.

JOSEPH PRENDERGAST (National Recreation Association): We have a rule of thumb that one acre for recreation per 100 people is a good round figure to try for. Some communities have more; some have less. This would include not only playgrounds, swimming pools, and community centers, but parks and reserves outside the city limits.

MR. CAULKINS: Considered nationally we are going to have to take care of the young people. They are not served very well by our great beautiful parkways and our tot lots; they need ball fields, places where they can get out and run. I would like to charge off two acres per 100 population for open space, tot lots, playgrounds, parks. We have to think mainly in terms of the areas within the urban center and immediately adjacent. For week-end use, large park reservations within a 25-mile radius are needed. In some cases our state or federal parks may serve.

PAUL M. REID (Regional Planning Commission, Detroit): I would like to suggest a geographic approach to meet the needs of different groups: (1) small parks and play areas to serve community needs within a large city or a small unit of government; (2) intermediate open space for the zoo and golf courses, for example, available to people in crowded areas but outside the core city; and (3) larger open spaces with lakes and camping grounds, available to the metropolitan population as a whole and lying between the central city and a satellite city.

MR. BLAKEMAN: Water frontage is of enormous recreational value; and wherever possible—after giving due consideration to water-using industries—you should get as much of it as you can for the active or passive use of the public.

C. W. DEEG (Philadelphia Electric Company): I am disturbed at the emphasis placed on recreation at this Conference, and the lack of consideration given to the future development of industry. Even now, it is almost impossible to locate heavy industry in New York, Philadelphia, and Baltimore, owing to the lack of waterfront land. We must remember that the ability to vacation is the result of gainful occupation. If the limited amount of land bordering our navigable waterfronts is utilized for recreation to the exclusion of industry, which requires such waterfront lands, I fear our economic structure may be affected to the degree that would-be vacationers will not have the means to utilize such facilities.

MR. MILLER: The freeway development in urban areas is an important element of competition for land. When you take 300 feet or so and go across an urban area, you make substantial changes in the use of land and frequently in the pattern of development and occupancy. With good community planning, the total net area devoted to street purposes can and should be reduced and used for something better.

MR. BLAKEMAN: How can we get hold of land to create a satellite plan for a large metropolitan area? What is the possibility of getting open space for green belts to cut off the satellite community from the central urban mass? Is there any way we can do that without radical changes in our laws?

Mr. Buttenheim: Spaciousness in zoning is coming more and more to be recognized as a legal possibility. The alternatives are low density provisions under the zoning ordinance or public acquisition of the land.

Mr. Blakeman: If you had to buy the amount of land I am talking about, you would go broke. I wish somebody would get his teeth into the whole problem of preserving open land.

Mr. Reid: Adequate open spaces in metropolitan areas cannot be guaranteed by an unrelated series of units of government but only by a metropolitan approach and agency. In the Detroit area, one of the cities that has very little industry is contemplating selling some very valuable park and recreation land to one of the big chain stores to set up a big shopping center. They do not have enough taxpayers and need money to run the city.

Mr. Buttenheim: One of the big problems of the metropolitan form of government is that the satellite cities, particularly the suburban communities around bigger cities, often have higher standards than the bulk of that particular region. And they want to maintain them. Therefore, if you adopt a metropolitan charter and give control to some central group, it should not be assumed that such control will improve, for certain communities at any rate, the standards already locally in force.

Depreciated Areas vs. Urban Redevelopment

Mr. Miller: I think that we recognize the trend toward depreciated areas. What can we do about it? We have urban redevelopment programs. Are they effective? How could they be made better?

Bryn J. Hovde (Pittsburgh Housing Association): The trend toward depreciation can be halted by the adoption and enforcement of building, safety, and sanitary codes governing all structures; by the adoption and enforcement of adequate zoning regulations; by the progressive and continuous planning of urban areas by the municipal authorities in constant consultation with private civic organizations; by the systematic planning of financing, if necessary guaranteed by the public; and by the orchestration of all instruments, public and private.

I would say that the present urban redevelopment program is not as effective as it could be. How can it be improved? By appropriations, both national and local, sufficient to reduce land costs to the whole range of use values for the uses planned for each redevelopment area; by reducing to an absolute minimum the procedural red tape and the continuing obligations that private redevelopers must assume.

And, as to the roles of private initiative and government in this field, I would say that private enterprise should be favored but both private and public initiative should be welcomed.

Mr. Miller: Are present urban redevelopment programs too much directed toward housing, with not enough provision for business or industry?

Mr. Mayer: Other types of development could be greatly facilitated if Title I of the National Housing Act were administered by some agency other than a housing agency. Many nonresidential areas in our cities should be developed for other types of nonresidential use; but there is no adequate provision for such redevelopment.

Mr. Hauser: A city may want to develop a fringe area for industry so as to decrease density either as a defense or good-planning measure. But it cannot have federal aid under Title I for this purpose. Federal assistance in the form of loans and grants-in-aid is available only for clearance and redevelopment; for building up slum sections for any purpose, industrial or commercial; and for development of vacant land or premature or retarded subdivisions for residential areas.

35

MR. DYCKMAN: The problem is really one of the relative magnitude of your sunk capital investment to the total capital resources of the community. It may not be so unwise on a purely economic basis sometimes to abandon central areas of cities.

Any redevelopment or rehabilitation is more expensive than building outlying areas. This is often true socially as well as economically. The people we are moving out of the redevelopment areas are going to have to pay more for housing than they did before, and this will have repercussions on other consumer expenditures in the community. This same kind of upgrading of commodity is not true of commercial or industrial redevelopment. There, the client is often granted a subsidy—presumably for locating where social costs will be less.

MR. REID: I would like to suggest two reasons why we have decadent areas in our cities: First, the functional purpose of these areas may have changed. Second, governmental regulations, such as 30-foot lots and mixed zoning of industrial and residential use and things of that type, may have contributed to depreciation.

MR. MAYER: The projects now being carried out under Title I of the National Housing Act generally replace existing communities; some of the people forced out go into the middle-aged areas and add to pressures there. This creates another problem.

Redevelopment isn't the answer for the middle-aged areas. These areas are too good for complete demolition; they are existing communities. Many of them house institutions of regional or national importance. Now, we have heard a good deal about conservation measures, many of which are stressing enforcement of minimum standards that have to do with occupancy and so forth. That isn't enough because the pressures are inevitable as the city expands.

An understanding of the underlying forces which affect the growth and development of our cities is a prerequisite to an understanding of these areas which constitute the greater portion of our urban areas.

Industrial Districts

As a general rule, heavy industry seeks the periphery of cities for its original location. Before long, however, the city usually grows around the industrial plant and pushes on beyond. Many heavy-industry plants are now deeply imbedded in cities. Problems of smoke, dust, bad odors, and noise grow more serious as the surrounding land use is intensified. Should homes be permitted in industrial districts? Should industries be permitted in residential districts? Can industrial districts be compatible neighbors with good residential areas?

MR. MILLER: One of the objectives of many areas is to have sufficient territory for industrial development. Often the problem is to prevent good industrial land from being so built up with residences that it is difficult or impossible to reassemble it for industrial use.

MR. BLAKEMAN: Under the older method of planning you first picked out your residential areas, and maybe your commercial and park areas. Then what was left was zoned industrial, although a lot of it was simply not usable. Now, if you make a careful analysis and decide that an area is well suited for industry you should zone it for that and keep residences out, for two reasons: first, because the requirements for industrial property are much more strict than for almost any other type of urban use; and, second, because the same health factors that you use to keep industry out of residential areas would apply to keeping residences out of industrial areas.

DOROTHY A. MUNCY (Washington, D.C.): We should start thinking of city planning in terms of where people are going to work. Then we can find the other amenities for them within that area. The prejudice against industry is carried over into zoning in our lack of performance standards. We just assume that all industry is going to be dusty, dirty, noisy. We haven't evaluated the changes in industrial processing that are making many industries very good neighbors.

We have had very little research in the past on the land area requirements for specific types of industries. There have been two or three broad studies, but we need more specific data on area requirements, and some of that is going to have to come from industry itself.

MR. MAYER: Performance standards for industry should be incorporated in zoning ordinances, and industry should not be arbitrarily excluded from any community.

RITA D. KAUNITZ (New York): Although industry can be compatible, I think we tend to get idealistic about having industry in satellite towns in order that workers can walk to work, and the like. Workers don't always like to walk to work, and there may be more than one breadwinner in a family. We ought to think as well about giving people in outlying districts alternative employment opportunities.

MR. REID: In the Detroit region, we have areas with industry but no homes for the workers. We have residential areas with no industry. If you are going to run sewer and water out to a plant on the periphery, residential areas can be developed nearby. Instead of running one set of sewer and water lines 6, 8, or 10 miles from our metropolitan areas for industry, and another set of lines for residential areas, they could be built together in a functional relationship that would give much better community character and a much better tax basis.

"Blight" Uses vs. Other Uses

What provision should be made for dumps, auto wrecking yards, junk yards, sewage plants, and similar obnoxious land uses necessary to the operation of an urban area?

MR. BLAKEMAN: A properly operated sewage plant can be a very good neighbor. I know of several that are perfectly clean, and have no odor.

MR. CAULKINS: One of the best dumps I ever saw was developed right through the middle of Scarsdale, N.Y. A stretch of lowland was segregated for public use rather than turned loose for low-grade housing. Trash was dumped for years and years, but so promptly covered that you would hardly know what was going on. Recently, the new library was built on that filled land. To me that is a shining example of "dump and cover."

MR. DYCKMAN: I would like to have a good definition of substandard industry or industrial use. When I was working for the Chicago Housing Authority, we did redevelopment of areas which seemed to us to qualify as "blighted uses." They were largely auto wrecking yards, junk yards, dilapidated-looking little shops. But when we went to acquire these things a lot of planners got the shock of their lives. Many of these shops, which were physically blighted according to all the land-use surveys ever made, were turning out fancy machined parts, and some were providing incomes of $100,000 a year. We found also that the highest and best use of some of this land was in terms of the earning power of auto junk yards. The same situation obtains to a very high degree in New York. So I wonder on what basis city planners are going to develop criteria that can guide them in questions of redevelopment. In one city we had a modern-looking building housing a drop forge which resounded for about a mile and a half around a proposed residential area. And no planner would claim that that was fit for redevelopment. Planners coming at this from an architectural standpoint have a very strong bias which I think is treacherous in the matter of classification.

MISS MUNCY: Often these somewhat blighted areas and loft buildings, and even the single-story areas, are incubators for industries. The ones that can't afford much rent start there. Eventually, if the business is profitable, it is put on a mechanized basis and moved farther out. That is something we have to think about in redevelopment.

"Ribbon" Business vs. Normal Highway Frontage Use

Should all frontage on all major streets and highways in an urban area be expected to support business establishments? Or should such frontage be considered appropriate for any normal urban use, including residential?

HOMER HOYT (Washington, D.C.): Most of our shopping centers grew up before the automobile was so widely used, and were located on narrow strips of land along streetcar lines, at streetcar intersections, and at subway or suburban railroad stations. No provision was made for parking. The stores were often built solid right up to the lot line. And the early zoners paid no attention to any economic calculations as to how much land you could use for business. In Chicago they zoned enough of it as "business" for 10 million people. And the land became tax delinquent.

Now, a revolutionary trend has become evident since the end of World War II—the opening up of new shopping centers in rectangular tracts. Some of the larger department stores occupy as many as 100 acres and have space for as many as 5,000 to 10,000 cars. Even the smaller centers with the stores set back from the road and parking areas in front require a depth of 500 or 600 feet and an area of 5 to 25 acres. So there is less demand than ever for the strip areas zoned for business in the past.

MR. BLAKEMAN: As the new centers take the business, the old ribbon development becomes even less economical. By proper design and by turning the houses to face the side streets, you can give a little land to the highway and keep it from blighting the residential development. But in the older sections of our cities the design is more or less fixed.

MR. MILLER: If the street frontage isn't any good for business, is it usable for other purposes?

MR. CORNICK: It might be used as recreational land.

MR. HOYT: And you might make a shopping center out of some of these strips, if the surrounding land was deteriorated, by getting more land and creating an area for supermarkets or neighborhood shopping centers.

MR. CAULKINS: On Westchester County's Central Avenue, which primarily has been thought of as a business street, with trucks driving by and heavy traffic, we have in recent years had successful garden apartment developments, shielded from the noise somewhat by rows of garages.

MR. REID: I would like to suggest an economic attitude toward these strips. Let them deteriorate to the point where they are worth so little that the city can use them for some other development. They were put in there as risk capital; they made profit for a while.

MR. MAYER: I disagree emphatically. These strips are one of the leading causes contributing to the decline of the middle-aged good residential areas. The quality of the development which is now obsolete in these ribbons is below the quality of development in the residential areas they were originally intended to serve.

MR. REID: That is right. I am thinking about the peripheral area, not the stuff in the city.

Rapid Transit vs. Private Cars

Because location is all-important to some businesses, and because land is high in price, the buildings in the central business district are higher than elsewhere. This tends to increase traffic congestion. What is the best way of overcoming this situation? Should downtown centers be provided with multiple freeways and extensive off-street facilities, or should rapid transit carry the bulk of people to and from the downtown centers? Can freeways and rapid transit be combined effectively? Some of the problems of urban transportation also were discussed in Section V from the standpoint of energy conservation (see pages 240-43).

HARLEY L. SWIFT (Harrisburg Railways Company): I have been rather startled by so much talk here of spreading business all over the place; the success of any business city depends on concentration of people. To survive, a city must have a central business section. Who is going to pay for fire protection, water protection, police protection, if all these businesses move out of town? One of the first things that stores and other businesses look for in locating is availability of public transportation. Downtown centers should be provided with both kinds of transportation—automobile and rapid transit. And it can be done. In Dallas and San Antonio, for example, freeways and rapid transit have been combined effectively. But downtown centers should be supplied with multiple freeways only if the necessary off-street parking facilities are provided.

Our downtown life depends on the movement of people and materials; not of vehicles. You talk about providing free parking space. Did it ever occur to you that there is as much reason to think that your office space ought to be subsidized, that a hotel room should be supplied for transient customers?

Some cities are making provision for a rapid transit system by rail. You can move more people more rapidly by rail on private right-of-way than any other way.

Rapid transit is feasible economically and from a private capital standpoint provided politicians and other people realize that transit companies are private enterprises, competitive enterprises, that transit companies are not monopolies. You won't have any trouble with transit if it is permitted to compete.

B. M. STANTON (Park and Shop, Norfolk, Va): Much of the downtown congestion and parking problem can be solved by greater use of public transit. We believe there will be more efficient use of existing transit and off-street parking facilities if public transit is used to a greater degree.

Rapid transit should carry the majority of people to and from downtown centers. But the minority must be provided for by off-street parking facilities and freeways. If you have freeways, you must have off-street parking to accommodate the vehicles when they come in.

We need an education program to open up the real solution to our problems. If more workers and shoppers used public transit, or pooled their rides, there would be less congestion and more efficient use of the space a car occupies once it is in the downtown area.

More space would be available for the short-term visitors to banks and business offices who, because of the timing, find it difficult to use public transit or pool their rides.

With the right kind of cooperation from the city officials, merchants, civic clubs, and businessmen in the downtown area, it should not be a difficult job to make people realize that it just doesn't make sense for one person to bring a car downtown and leave it all day in a congested area; that the space could be used four or five times.

The real problem is the congestion on the streets rather than actual lack of off-street parking facilities. A parking problem has nothing to do with whether it is free or not. Too many people refer to a parking problem when they mean they cannot find a free space or a meter space to park in.

There has been an increasing pressure for the municipalities to do something about off-street parking. The automobile population increase has been unprecedented and unexpected, but parking facilities are increasing rapidly. We feel that the threat of municipal intervention should be relegated to the background and private enterprise should be given an open opportunity to do the job.

MR. SWIFT: Public transportation is still carrying from 60 to 80 percent of the people. It is carrying 24 percent more passengers than it did before the war. So don't write public transportation off your books when you are making your plans.

EARL R. FELDMAN (Association of American Railroads): The railroad industry has no policy on this matter, but my personal opinion is that in the long run we are going to have to inject the dollars and cents item to discourage motorists from coming into town. We must make the motorist think twice before he gives up the use of rapid transit. Don't keep him out of town; but don't facilitate his use of a freeway if it causes greater congestion when he gets downtown. I think we will have to come to the use of tollways.

MR. BUTTENHEIM: Mr. Swift, what is your opinion of having a circumferential freeway around the central business district with ample parking spaces wherever an express highway comes toward the central district, and making the central district almost wholly dependent on mass transportation.

Mr. Swift: As long as you say "almost wholly" and not "wholly" I would go along with you. That is one solution. But it is difficult to find fringe parking areas that will attract motorists. The experience was unsuccessful in Baltimore and some other cities because you couldn't get a big enough volume of parking to support the frequency of public transportation that is necessary to make the fringe parking lot attractive and convenient. However, in Philadelphia and New York fringe parking has been successful in certain areas. The problem is to get people to want to park somewhere along public transit and ride downtown.

Can Urban Development Be Made More Orderly?

Could many of the competing demands for urban land be resolved by a competent planning program? How can such a program operate successfully in a metropolitan area? Is regional government a prerequisite for orderly regional development?

No one seemed disposed to question that really comprehensive, intelligent, planning *could* prevent or smooth out many of the conflicts over land use that accompany the disorganized growth of cities. The main issues here concerned practicability. What degree of broad, effective planning is attainable against the economic and political background of modern urban communities? And even if the obstacles are overlooked, would the drawbacks of centralized planning outweigh its advantages? Here, as elsewhere in the group's discussion, the need for research was emphasized. We still lack many of the basic facts, and don't fully understand those we do have.

FROM THE RECORD

Mr. Blakeman: A competent planning program could resolve many of the competing demands for urban land. But actual solution demands a lot of other things such as new legislation and financing—things that we find hard to get.

Is regional government a prerequisite for orderly regional development? I hope not; because most of our efforts in the Detroit area have been concentrated on accomplishing our ends, or at least a major proportion of them, without a regional government. We do not expect one very soon.

The leaders in the area are working toward a form of regional government. This does not mean that we think local government should be handled at the regional level. I don't like the connotation of regional government unless it is some kind of a federation whereby the local units agree to let certain functions be handled on a regional level but maintain their local autonomy and keep direct control of much of the local service.

Whether such a program can operate successfully in a metropolitan area without regional government has yet to be proved. But the keystone to our operation, which we think is going to work, is participation in the planning process on the part of at least the local government officials: If it were not for the fact that we have 3 million people and 129 governments to serve and 2,000 square miles to plan, I would try to get it down to actual citizen participation.

We have no legal powers whatsoever; so what we did was to get each government to appoint a delegate and alternate to a central council for a subsection of the region. They meet about once a month, and we go to them with anything that affects their area. We are now going to them with our master land-use plan, which is as much their plan as ours. Also we have over 200 people on various special advisory committees working with us.

The problem is to get the people that have to make the decisions working with you in the process of preparing a plan. I think we are doing it.

Mr. HOVDE: In Allegheny County (Pennsylvania) we have 130 municipal subdivisions and a little over a million and a half people. Efforts to organize a metropolitan form of government have always failed. Now a different approach is being taken. By an act of the legislature, a metropolitan study committee was set up. One of our large foundations has provided the money for research. The Pennsylvania Economy League is doing the research and organizing the studies. A good many people are helping, and the work is under the auspices of the Allegheny Conference on Community Development, a voluntary outfit which includes most of the public and private powers in the community. We are hoping that out of those studies will come a recommendation not necessarily for a consolidation of all the governments in Allegheny County, but at least for federation on some problems—a recommendation that a central government, probably the county, would take over basic functions like planning, installation, and operation of certain utilities and highway systems.

Mr. REID: In the concept of the metropolitan area there must also be a comprehensive idea of the complex of forces that make, move, and cause the growth of a metropolitan area. These economic and social forces know no governmental lines. Control, direction, or molding of these forces needs to be viewed in the light of the total complex, not by a piecemeal approach.

Mr. MAYER: I have been tremendously impressed by our vast areas of ignorance on subjects of urban and metropolitan development. We need support for basic research on these problems.

Mr. BLAKEMAN: I would like to back that statement a hundred percent. A public planning agency supported by tax funds never can do the basic research that ought to be done.

We have just been turned down by our local group directing an origin and destination traffic study. We have been turned down by the Bureau of the Census, and to a certain extent by the Bureau of Public Roads, in an attempt to get tacked onto that survey for a minor part of their total sample, a study of population mobility, a study of what people want in the way of living conditions. We can't afford to do it ourselves.

There is need for this kind of study. I question very much if standards built up on the basis of studies in England or on the East Coast apply in certain areas of Detroit or in Chicago.

Mr. RODWIN: Many people—economists and planners and sociologists—have become interested and concerned with urban problems, and research centers have sprung up at several universities in recent years. They could do a very useful job but they are financially undernourished and need assistance.

Mr. BLAKEMAN: We have restricted this discussion to land uses, but there is much urban social and economic research that is as basic, if not more so, than anything that has been mentioned here today.

Another aspect of comprehensive planning came up at the final session of the whole section when a pattern for future consideration was proposed—and questioned.

Mr. STEIN: I propose a practical pattern for future urban use: (1) dispersal of population in moderate-sized communities, according to a broad, regional plan; (2) homes of workers located closer to varied working places, and to open country; (3) green areas of open country separating towns to be used for recreation, farms, and forests; (4) a group of such towns will be planned, developed, and operated as a regional entity; (5) this constellation of towns will be large enough to support all the day-to-day activities and small enough to foster a sense of unity as well as closeness to countryside; (6) the total population of a regional group of towns and farms would be adequate to support and utilize central facilities equivalent to those of the present-day metropolis, including the best of universities, hospitals, museums, central libraries, wholesale markets, business centers, auditoriums, symphony halls, and something similar to the 42nd Street area of New York; (7) these varied centers will be in different towns so as to balance traffic loads and do away with the deadening congestion of our old central areas; (8) the towns, though widely separated by open areas, will be closely connected to each other by throughways or parkways, so that the time-distance from one part of the federated group to the others will be less than from the present congested metropolitan center to its periphery; (9) industrial plants will be dispersed so as to give adequate and varied opportunity of employment close to all communities in time-distance.

Our discussion of the conflicting demands in urban or metropolitan areas has emphasized the urgent need of research. We should view the thing as a whole, as a base for such research, so as to lessen congestion of highways, the wide separation of time-distance of houses and open spaces, the destruction of our fertile and beautiful lands around our cities, and the congestion which endangers life and property in time of war as well as in peace.

MR. CAULKINS: The hazards and handicaps of congestion and bogged-down travel conditions, threats of bombs, et cetera, make apparent the need for radical alterations in our planning of communities. Therefore, I urge that this proposal presented by Mr. Stein be made the subject of an early and thorough research and that the report be widely publicized.

WILLIAM R. MATHEWS (*Arizona Daily Star*): I want to enter an objection to that. That proposal calls for the exercise of governmental power that would be possible only in a regimented society. I would rather be free and enjoy some of the penalties of freedom than live in a dollhouse community like that.

MR. AUGUR: I object to the implication that Mr. Stein's proposal has anything to do with regimentation or government control. This sort of development can be carried out through existing means, through planned zoning and all the powers normally used in controlling urban development.

MR. MATHEWS: I am actively at work in a booming community, and I have found if you are going to organize it right, you have to exercise complete dictatorial power. We haven't been able to do that at home at all. We have missed the boat on a lot of things, but I would say this: such a community as Mr. Stein proposed would call for practically directed labor. It couldn't be made otherwise. And it would call for the exercise of political power that would have to be able to go through with its project in spite of public opposition that would develop.

Subsection B

RURAL LAND

More than 1.7 billion of the nation's total 1.9 billion acres of surface are used primarily for farming, forestry, or grazing. Upon this land we depend for food, cotton and other fibers, and industrial farm products, and lumber, pulpwood, and other forest products. At the same time, we depend on it for many other services such as watershed protection; recreation, including scenic and historic values; and support of wildlife. The same acres often do double, and sometimes triple, duty; as a result, specific conflicts in use already have arisen, and more can be expected in the future.

Can our rural lands continue to meet the growing and varied demands upon them? Are there things we should be doing now to make sure that all legitimate requirements will be satisfied during the next generation and beyond? These were the main questions before the subsection. In exploring them, the emphasis was on whether the increasing demands would call for shifts in ownership or use. This necessarily entailed some consideration of long-range productivity of farm and forest land, and in some respects discussion overlapped that of Section II, which dealt specifically with ways and means of meeting demands through more efficient use (pages 62-125).

Acquisition of additional land was not emphasized as a major issue for either agriculture or commercial forestry. Discussion centered on questions of ownership and basic purpose. For example, will shifts in ownership and use be needed to assure the nation of enough food and fiber in the future? Should industry be encouraged to acquire a larger proportion of commercial forest land? There was widespread belief that most problems would be settled as they arose by the traditional play of market forces, and that emphasis should be on education rather than regulation at the present time.

The fact that a larger proportion of a growing population will be living in cities was seen as a strong force that will intensify needs for outdoor recreation, fostering of wildlife, and protection of water supplies. Many participants felt that the answer will lie more in the direction of devising ways of multiple use and making better use generally of existing acreage for recreation, than in the large-scale addition of new tracts.

Some of the most clearly defined zones of conflict concerned the special uses of rural land—notably, whether land should be drained for farm production or left wet for wildlife; and what kind of land and how much it might be best to flood for reservoir purposes. Among the possible ways of adjusting such conflicts as have reached the active stage, rural zoning alone was given serious consideration. From the longer range viewpoint of heading off or reducing conflicts, it was recognized that much more research was needed, including better appraisals of coming requirements and fuller basic information on the characteristics of the nation's land base and on how it is being used.

High points from the record of the subsection's discussion are presented here under four major heads.
1. Agricultural land.
2. Commercial forest land.
3. Special uses: recreation, wildlife, water projects.
4. Methods of adjusting or reducing conflicts.

Agricultural Land

In general, members of the subsection felt that larger demand for farm products would call for some additions to crop acreage, even with chief reliance on greater productivity per acre: perhaps between 25 and 50 million acres by 1975.

Although such an increase would be small on a percentage basis it would, as the section steering committee pointed out, intensify competition for the use of rural land.

Two sets of problems emerged as centers of major interest. One concerned demand for farm products. Are current surpluses temporary, chronic, or a recurring phenomenon? Or, as some participants asked, can it be said that there are true surpluses even now, considering worldwide undernourishment? The second concerned low-producing farms as a factor in land use and competition related to it.

FROM THE RECORD

Possible Patterns of Future Demand

At present, production of several important commodities is running far ahead of domestic consumption or commercial export. Does this cast doubt on the widely accepted belief that in the long run the great problem in United States agriculture will be to produce more? Does it imply that a certain amount of cropland should be shifted to other uses? If so, how can we encourage genuine shifts in use and avoid the more common abandonment?

JOHN D. BLACK (Harvard University): This surplus situation is more or less temporary. We always have a surplus of some crop or product. That is inevitable. What we have now is a bunching of surpluses of a considerable group of farm products. We expanded our production during and after the war and now we don't need all of it. We have a readjustment on our hands.

The most efficient and effective way to dispose of our surpluses is to shift to smaller acreages of corn and other cultivated crops and to grow more hay and forage. Accompanying that would be a larger production of livestock products and a relatively smaller production of foods for direct human consumption.

How long will these surpluses last? If you go at it by an old-fashioned process and just let prices fall, the farmers will reduce their acreage and the surpluses will disappear. It can be done that way, but it might take seven or eight years. Or, we could keep on with what we are doing now—hold the prices too high by price supports of various kinds and attempt to control production by means of quotas. That would prolong the period of adjustment, for the farmers would just intensify their production. There is another possibility: If you could keep prices at a reasonable level, at an equilibrium level, and then put on a vigorous program of helping farmers and ranchers make the adjustments—education and that sort of thing—the adjustment could be made more quickly. That is a rational program we ought to try to work out.

J. RUSSELL SMITH (Professor Emeritus of Geography, Columbia University): We are essentially in a pegged society, with every group pegged except the farmer. The banker has his rate of interest. The manufacturer, with set prices, works on orders or does no work. Labor has union wages or no work and goes on relief. The farmer is about the only really competitive group, and about the only cure the individual farmer can see is to produce more and make the surplus worse.

TED F. SILVEY (Congress of Industrial Organizations): If the majority of the families of this country had a more adequate annual income than $3,000, wouldn't they use up this surplus mighty fast? Food would go through the human alimentary tract instead of lying in warehouses.

HARRY R. WELLMAN (University of California, Berkeley): By 1960 our surplus situation may disappear—I use "surplus" only in the sense that there is a larger supply of products than people are able or willing to buy. Present trends indicate that in 1960 there will be 16 percent more people in the United States than in 1950, and it is not unreasonable to believe that our total agricultural output will be about 10 percent higher than in 1950. Exports will probably be lower. But even if they drop from around 7 to 8 percent of total agricultural output in 1950 to 4 percent in 1960, the supply available per capita might still be less in 1960 than in 1950.

K. C. McMurry (University of Michigan): We have succeeded in producing these surpluses through our increased ability to produce and not through expansion of our agricultural area. In the future we should probably play down improvements in agricultural technology and put more effort into the problem of balancing production and demand.

Robert F. Chandler, Jr. (University of New Hampshire): Actually, there has been a great stimulation in marketing research, which tends in that direction.

Discussion of price and acreage programs aimed at surpluses led to examination of responses by different kinds of farmers. These comments appear with those bearing on problems of low-production farmers (see below). Returning to the surplus problem itself, some members suggested that it called for a really long-range look.

Theodore W. Schultz (University of Chicago): We should take the long-run view and shoot at generating some surpluses. We should ask the question: How can we use our resources—land, labor, and capital—so that we will continue to have an abundance of agricultural products?

Samuel Van Valkenburg (Clark University): Something seems substantially wrong. Here, we have to try to eliminate our surpluses while in great parts of the world there are deficits. I don't think we should continue giving food away, but I hope some way can be found for the surpluses to take care of the deficits.

Mr. Black: If you were to ship 100 million bags of wheat to India, it would cut its imports from the United States and other countries. That wouldn't help. It isn't a simple

problem. The Food and Agriculture Organization of the United Nations has worked on the problem, and the Foreign Operations Administration people are working on it just as hard as they can.

H. W. Voorhees (N.J. Farm Bureau): If we will use abroad the techniques that have made this country great in the distribution of products domestically, I think we can develop a program whereby we need not reduce production. Reduction of production is basically immoral, in my opinion, especially as it refers to food.

Mr. Black: Getting production back into equilibrium is not immoral. That is what we are trying to do now. I agree that one way is to increase consumption. I would take advantage of an occasion of this kind myself to develop a stamp plan to get people to consume more milk.

Mr. Silvey: Our marvelous agricultural technology allows nearly 90 percent of the food and fiber to be produced by about 40 percent of the farm population. Technology has already outstripped the capacity of the market to buy the things that the farms can produce. We'll face the problem in industry five or eight years from now when machines will turn out goods without manual labor at all. The machines will be able to do everything except buy what they make. There has to be money in people's pockets to buy the products of both the technological farm and the technological factory.

The Ownership Problem: Low-Production Farmer

About 59 percent of the total farm population lives on residential, part-time, and low-production commercial farms that occupy about 31 percent of the total land in farms and that in 1949 contributed less than 12 percent of the total value of farm products sold. Does this distribution of land, people, and output give reason for concern? It was recognized that the day may come when we cannot permit low-level production, when we need more food. But for the present, most participants felt, what we need is not regulation of owner-ship and land use—but efforts to help the low-production commercial farmer to make a better living.

MR. SCHULTZ: Today, most of agriculture is in an excellent position in terms of combina-tion of resources—probably the best in our history. This remarkable balance has come about in the last decade and a half on all but perhaps 1.5 million farms—mostly in the South, but also in widely scattered pockets elsewhere. On these low-production farms there is a disequilibrium in the use of resources —largely too little capital and too much labor and the wrong combination as it affects land. A better combination of the family's labor, capital, and land would achieve either a larger output or the same output with resources left over for other things.

Such balance is important. For instance, Elizabethton, in Carter County, Tennessee, has large rayon mills that employ hundreds of people. Here the part-time farmer works full time in the mill and still sells more farm products than the full-time farmers. I think this is entirely a capital phenomenon. The part-time farmer can go to the bank and get money for cattle or chickens, feed, fertilizer, and so on. The full-time farmer is so poor that the credit capital market serves him either not at all, or not so well.

In other areas of the South, the production of poultry for the broiler market has become a flourishing enterprise. Here, capital has moved not through banks or government agencies but through the feed dealers. Since the capital mar-ket started to work, production per person has risen by leaps and bounds.

Earlier discussion of surpluses had led to mention of programs to combat them. How do low-production farms and farmers respond to price and acreage programs and, indeed, to market forces in general?

GLENN D. STOCKWELL (Blue Valley Study Group, Kansas): Trying to solve the surplus problem by letting prices and production seek

their balance will more than likely tend to de-plete our resource base. Farmers will intensify the immediate use of the land in a dropping price market.

MR. BLACK: Some farmers increase produc-tion when prices are low, but more don't. The net effect is not an increase but a decrease in production.

MR. STOCKWELL: The solution is related to ownership and land-tenure policies. Our present adjustment policies tend to give us a straight-line reduction in acreage and don't consider land usage at all. Would the com-mercial or the low-production commercial farmer be more responsive to supply and de-mand factors?

ELCO L. GREENSHIELDS (Agricultural Re-search Service, USDA): I expect the com-mercial farmer would be more responsive. The low-production farmer has so little land, espe-cially Class 1 land, that it is really difficult for him to make a reduction in cash crops. How can you shift inefficient land to no production, to grass, to the other things the soil scientists say it should be in, when that land is occupied by small farmers who are dependent upon it for a living?

MARVEL L. BAKER (University of Ne-braska): Any farm or land-use program should be pointed toward good land use. Any land policy should be positive instead of negative. We should use government policy to get the land that should not be in crop production into some other productive use. This is not as easy as it sounds, because it means upsetting present capitalized values of land.

MR. McMURRY: At one time during the New Deal period a specific program was undertaken for the reduction of submarginal farmers and farm land. It was an effort to re-duce surpluses, and it soon became clear that any program to reduce submarginal farm land would have no effect whatsoever upon the sur-plus problem, because this group of people pro-duced so little anyway.

How much can be done to help farmers at the lower end of the scale?

Mr. Chandler: I presume that the 30 percent of the farm population that produces about 9 percent of the value of farm products sold are in general on poorer lands, where farms are small and the market situation may be bad. We shouldn't attempt to do anything about this from the standpoint of regulation. If a man has a small farm, the way to work with him is through education and advice to help him raise his income.

Mr. Baker: We should separate low-production commercial farms in our thinking from other commercial farms and from residential and part-time farms, and we should have a positive program to deal with that group. We should help shift to more efficient production, so that living standards for families on these farms can be raised.

Farm woodlands were also suggested as an important source of income for low-production farms.

Julian F. McGowin (W. T. Smith Lumber Company): Forest products can be produced successfully in small units, on small farms, and will provide a useful and productive use for that land.

Edmund O. Ehrhart (Armstrong Forest Company): More attention might be given to the farm wood lot, which is a storehouse for labor as well as the product. For example, 80 or 90 percent of the price of a product like pulpwood goes into labor. When some of the farmer's intensive crops don't need labor, wood products can be produced.

Several speakers touched on the social values that support part-time and residential uses, and it was brought out that much of the land being used for these purposes is not high-production agricultural land.

J. Elmer Brock (Wyoming National Resource Board): There is a place for a small farm for factory workers and people living close to towns. But many people spend their whole time on farms that are not large enough to give them a living.

Henry M. Kendall (Miami University, Ohio): I doubt that the part-time use of many small units is of any general significance in the over-all farm picture. The difficulty probably arises because of the definition of "farm." I spend some time in Vermont primarily for recreation. I do grow some produce in the summers, but I certainly know nothing about farming. Yet from the census point of view, this is a part-time farm.

Robert M. Howes (Tennessee Valley Authority): The part-time and residential farms seem important in the light of increasing leisure, particularly the earlier retirement age.

Mr. Stockwell: The small farm may not be a bad usage. It gives a man contact with the soil and may substitute for using a like amount of land for recreation.

Commercial Forest Land

In recent years the pattern of timber consumption has been changing fast. Consumption of lumber was smaller in 1950 than in 1906, and there have been declines in use of other timber products such as fuelwood and railroad ties. On the other hand consumption of pulpwood and plywood has greatly increased.

The section steering committee had noted this mixture of trends, and had put forward only a very general suggestion that in the future timber should be grown in this country at a rate considerably above recent levels of harvesting. The committee had also noted that there is little likelihood that any large amounts of good timber-producing land now in other uses will be shifted to commercial forest.

Since practices that can raise sustained production to higher levels were the concern of Section II (see pages 76-93), attention here centered largely on general patterns of ownership and operation as they might affect long-range production.

FROM THE RECORD

*Should Industry Own and
Manage More Forest Land?*

About 75 percent of the private commercial forest land is in small holdings. Timber-processing industries own a comparatively small share. What are the factors that limit industrial demand? Should industry be encouraged to acquire and manage a larger area of nonfarm commercial forest land?

CURTIS M. HUTCHINS (Bangor and Aroostook Railroad Company, Maine): The prime interest of industry is an even flow of raw material for its plants. It must control enough land or forest products to protect its investment and provide a continuity of labor both in the woods and the mills. The industrial demand for forest land to back up mills varies with areas, conditions, and opinions. I do not feel that the industrial demand has been dampened. The deterring factors are primarily the large capital investment required, and the lack of suitable land in some areas.

What we should encourage is not industrial acquisition but better forest management by small wood-lot owners. It is healthy to have plenty of small owners. It makes for better competition between companies and between landowners, and you have a less captive market. One of the deterrents to better forestry on the part of the small landowner is the lack of market. Another big deterrent in New England, and I suspect in other areas, is high local taxes.

CHESTER S. WILSON (Minnesota Department of Conservation): Our large timber-using companies in Minnesota are making quite substantial progress in acquiring timberland holdings. But now some of them can't find enough land in the areas where they operate. I have heard industry people say that control

of 25 percent or a third of their requirements would give them the necessary shock absorber; they would be willing to depend for the balance of their supply upon what they can get from other private owners, and from the state and national forests. The disease problem may not deter industrial acquisition, but it would probably limit large-scale private investment. Our average fire losses are reasonably constant, but you never know when disease will appear.

MR. McGOWIN: The area of timberland owned or controlled by the pulp and paper mills in the South varies considerably. Some mills have a very small acreage. Others have attempted to get enough to support almost their entire requirements. As far as timber production on farms is concerned, part-time farmers are in the best position. Sixty percent of the employees of one paper mill in the South live on farms in the area in which they work. Those farms are important, and they can produce cheaply.

MR. BLACK: There is a tremendous amount of land that industry doesn't want to buy because a harvest is too far off. That is the real crux of the problem in a good many parts of the country. One of the things that is needed is a market for inferior woods, stuff that won't make pulpwood. There is an awful lot of that on our farms.

You commercial folks may not buy the land and put it into good management as fast as we need it. You may be too conservative. We may have rising prices of timber products and find ourselves substituting other things for timber. We may go through a period of super-high prices for timber, which will induce a stepping-up of improvement in timber and buying land; we will find ourselves overexpanded and we will have low prices again. We should do everything we can to head off that kind of a cycle.

BERNARD L. ORELL (Weyerhaeuser Sales Company): I can't agree that the forest industries are buying only land with a good timber crop. In the pine belt of northern Minnesota, the Northwest Paper Company has purchased and planted thousands of acres of land on which nothing was growing. In the Pacific Northwest the forest industries are purchasing all the land that they can get their hands on and, again, they are planting it or encouraging natural regeneration where that is possible. This includes land covered by undesirable growth difficult to remove to make way for a new crop.

SHIRLEY W. ALLEN (Michigan Conservation Commission): In Michigan, jackpine timber is being cut for pulp in the Huron and Manistee National Forests. A farmer's cooperative bids on national forest timber, supplies pulpwood to one of the large paper companies, and also markets house logs and cedar posts. This may be an idea for other parts of the country—a cooperative of not fully-occupied farmers organized for the purpose of buying, cutting, and marketing federal timber.

Competition with Grazing

About two-fifths of the private commercial forest land is in farms. The section steering committee had pointed out that the bulk of this area is being grazed by farm livestock, often to the serious detriment of growing timber, and that burning of farm woodland to improve forage conditions is also a common practice in some localities. Is this a serious conflict in land use?

MR. ORELL: The effect of grazing depends on the timber species involved. In the pine regions in eastern Washington and Oregon grazing is compatible with timber growth. But in the Douglas fir area a decision has to be made between grazing and timber.

Now, a great deal of burning has been done all over the country on the mistaken assumption that burning produces good grass crops. Actually, what happens is that continued burning and reburning reduces the perennials and brings in the annuals, which have less forage

value. By this, I do not mean to imply that burning is not a forestry tool. Certain burnings are needed to obtain regeneration of a particular species.

MR. McGOWIN: Burning has been one of our principal problems in the South, but control is in sight in most states, primarily because the attitude of the people has changed. Fires just don't occur as they used to.

JACOB H. BEUSCHER (Madison, Wis.): In Wisconsin, we tried to control grazing in wood lots by granting tax exemptions. Wood lots that were not grazed would not be assessed for local real estate tax purposes. Our experience was a sad one. Recently, however, the wood-lot exemption law was amended. The farmer now pays only a 20-cent tax per acre on his wood lot if he complies with directions of the state conservation commission. Now, whether that will work is a serious question.

For and Against Federal Ownership

Eighty-three million acres—about 18 percent of the nation's commercial forest land—is federally owned. In the western states the proportion is much higher. Is this pattern of ownership an important factor in the way forest land is used?

MR. BROCK: In Wyoming almost one-seventh of the area is in national forests. It is not being taken care of properly for timber. It is not being given the maximum watershed use.

Grazing is one of the protections against forest fires. It should be and is a part of forest management. But there is a strong difference of opinion as to how much grazing should be allowed. Since the national forests were set up, grazing on the forests has been gradually reduced, while the forests have extended their area some 15 or 20 million acres. Now, drastic cuts have been ordered again—we think without justification. We finally reached an agreement that we would conduct some experiments through the University and the Forest Service cooperating, over a 5-year period. So far, I think that the operations have shown that the Forest Service was very much in error.

WILLIAM R. MATHEWS (*Arizona Daily Star*): The federal government owns 74 percent of the State of Arizona. It has been my observation that the Forest Service has done a magnificent job—not only in the regulation of the forests to provide timber, grazing, recreation of all kinds, and hunting, but in every way. If I am going to criticize the federal government, I would say it is the Department of the Interior that is hamstrung by some ancient legislation on mining claims, and by the Taylor Grazing Act.

Now, the next thing is that Arizona has 11 million acres of state-owned lands; 8 million are leased to livestock growers and 3 million are leased for agricultural purposes. The revenue from these lands has been rather insignificant.

But, from the Forest Service lands, we get steady revenue which represents pure net profit. That, I would say, is pretty good compensation in lieu of taxes. In addition, the revenue has been used to provide access roads and recreation sites. We ought to avoid this thinking in terms of absolutes. There is a middle way. The federal government and people and local communities and private industry can cooperate and work together.

CHESTER J. OLSEN (U. S. Forest Service): In the Intermountain Region, we have a lot of timberland. We have disease and insect problems, and we have overmature and mature timber. We want to get timber onto the market as rapidly as we can. But we can't do it without more funds with which to prepare for sale and to sell the timber as it should be sold.

We need more roads into these areas to do a good job of forestry management. The federal government should do more in the way of roadbuilding; the operators can and will do more where we can make larger sales. But we have to see that the small operator, as well as the large one, gets a chance at the timber.

Roads built by the operator come out of the stumpage, so the government pays for the roads either by direct appropriation or through stumpage deduction.

MR. ORELL: The tendency in the national forests has been to maintain the selling units in small areas. This is due partly to public pressure and partly to pressure from the small operators. Consideration should be given to this fact. There has to be a sufficient timber volume in the sale area to justify the expenditure for an access road. In many areas in the West, industry has built roads that cost upwards of $40,000 a mile, where the timber sale area was big enough to allow them to come out with enough to amortize that road.

MR. BROCK: In the West, we have many millions of acres of overripe timber—timber that the pulp mills seem to like. It would grow into a big industry if we had some roads in the forest. I would say there is enough demand and enough timber there to justify some extensions for that purpose. In addition, our research people tell us that with extensive supervised cutting they could quadruple the annual yield of timber and greatly increase the runoff of that forest for watershed use. We have a dying forest and we should have a growing forest. Why can't the government market its product?

MR. EHRHART: Part of this goes back to the fact that the Forest Service is predicated on protecting what it has, rather than using it. There have been no facilities in the past for developing the land. We have heard a lot of criticism about the small woodlot owner, his poor forest management. Yet, that class of ownership has done more in the way of producing forest products than any other class.

W. R. SCHOFIELD (California Forest Protective Association): The Forest Service policy of road construction within national forests is centered around a multiple use. I am not decrying that fact, but it may be a deterrent to access roads. If your sole concern is harvesting forest crops, then you can build access roads much cheaper.

The federal government has a policy (which, fortunately, is gradually being modified) of demanding exclusive title to private roads leading into the national forest areas where the access roads are to be constructed.

Industrial Competition

MR. EHRHART: In rights of way for power lines and pipe lines, a tremendous area is being taken out of productiveness in forest areas. In the rural area it doesn't make so much difference because the farmer can till his land under the power line or over a pipe line. But in some places in Pennsylvania the clearing and maintenance of the line has actually taken as much as 10 percent of the forest land out of production.

Special Uses: Recreation, Wildlife, Water Projects

Rural land has many uses other than farm and forest production. Three among them received special consideration here: use of land for (1) recreation, including preservation of scenic and historic values; (2) habitat for wildlife; and (3) reservoirs and other water projects that tie up acreage. Each of these three uses presents a variety of problems, but for all of them market forces are often ineffective in resolving conflicts. Dollar values are hard to compare and sometimes hard to find. Subsections C and D of Section II (pages 93-123) deal with other aspects of these land uses, and Section III (pages 126-75) with the problems relating to water.

FROM THE RECORD

Recreation

Between 30 and 35 million acres of rural land in public ownership have been set aside for recreational use or to preserve scenic, historical, or scientific values. Demands for recreational facilities are expected to rise even faster than population. Will present facilities meet the need? If not, does the chief answer lie in more land for recreation, or better use of existing land? What about conflict with other important uses? Some persons feel that too much of our timber, minerals, water power, and other natural resources has already been withdrawn from commercial use. Discussion brought out that the problem is not one of national parks and forests alone, but also of state and local areas.

MICHAEL FROME (American Automobile Association): Today travel is a big thing in terms of the individual, and also in terms of the economy. Development of recreation and vacation areas has not kept pace with the requirements of the American people. Government at the state and local levels must place increasing emphasis on new recreational resources throughout the country. As for our national parks, funds are needed for maintenance and for provision of facilities for the growing army of visitors.

The recreational aspect of the national forests also should be recognized. Their primary objectives, it is true, are watershed protection and timber protection. At the same time, however, the forests are now visited by 31 million persons annually in quest of outdoor recreation. Their accommodations and other facilities are being taxed far beyond capacity. Several areas had to be closed last year because they constituted a menace to health.

The development of adequate facilities in the national forests would also have a beneficial effect on nearby communities.

BERNARD DeVoTo (Cambridge, Mass.): It is desirable to add a few areas to the National Park System, but only a few—so far as

I am concerned, none in the West. A primitive beach area is desirable and should be added at once. It will be desirable, also, to add to Great Smoky National Park and that sort of thing. But what we have to do in the National Park Service is protect what we have.

Most of the additional recreational facilities that we will need as time goes on must be taken care of at the state and community levels. The state park system has to be enormously expanded, and I think most states realize that. Some state parks are already in splendid shape.

MR. ALLEN: The American people seem to believe in recreation if it doesn't cost anything. We have been trying to raise money to maintain our state parks. We have talked of several ways of raising it: charging an admission fee, raising the state automobile gas tax a little and taking some of that money. We have to find some way to convince those who handle the purse strings that the housekeeping of the outdoors is not automatic. Things just go to pieces if you don't have the money.

MR. DeVOTO: The best development for the most crowded parks is to have the amusement facilities, overnight accommodations, and all that, outside the park, where it is possible. But in parks difficult of access there have to be accommodations, and those accommodations have to be considerably better than what we have now in most places. Up in Glacier National Park this summer, they were afraid the water lines would give out any moment. The entire sewage system threatened to go out. Those things have to be taken care of. There is no place to get the money, except from Congress.

MR. SILVEY: Lands, forests, and water don't have to be destroyed in order to make a profit. We have destroyed our timber; we have polluted our water; we have worn out farm land; we have upset the topsoil to get minerals out. But now we have the opportunity for multipurpose use of land which can embrace the holiday and vacation aspect, for which I, among others, am pleading. The multipurpose use of land through TVA creates a whole new frontier.

MRS. CYRIL G. FOX (Pennsylvania Roadside Council): I should like to call attention to a practical demonstration of how some of the sins in the strip-mining business can be remedied. I know of an operator in western Pennsylvania who is taking his discarded land and, while the bulldozers are still there, grading it to a degree that nature will support. He is reforesting with a balanced planting. He is putting in dams and building lakes for fishing. He is turning the whole area into a beautiful recreational area for the time being, and later his grandchildren will be in the lumber business! He is a sound businessman, not a philanthropist.

MR. HOWES: One possibility is that government, in recreation activities, will end up in a service classification, and increasingly we will turn to private enterprise to handle the facilities that can be operated at a profit.

We need to examine the question whether the primary beneficiary should not pay the bulk of the cost. A national forest or reservoir may draw occasional visitors from all over the country, but the recreation facilities are used largely by local people and it seems to me that the taxpayer in the locality should pay for those facilities. We need some research in this field. I don't know of any instance where economists have truly assessed the meaning of this travel dollar.

Our section steering committee has asked whether commercial values should be locked up for the benefit of recreation. Are they in truth locked up? Take a look at the Great Smoky Mountains National Park. Its 500,000 acres are "locked up" against commercial development. But people go to the hotels in Gatlinburg primarily because they are next door to the Smokies. The economic effect of the park on the surrounding area is truly tremendous. On TVA lakes, we have done enough work to know that for every recreation dollar that visitors spend along our shorelines, they spend about $10 in the region. We need more research of this kind.

Above all, we need a positive approach. Just to decry the lack of funds is not enough. Any park man who enters the field with ideals and ends up as a janitor for a picnic area knows this.

There should be a comprehensive national study of the recreation resources, opportunities, and responsibilities of the United States, embodying the best efforts of recreation and resource development agencies at each level of government, federal, state, and local, citizen organizations interested in recreation, and lay leaders.

WESLEY C. CALEF (University of Chicago): In Chicago, we have done some research on recreational land. This research has been on private land, but the problems that develop on big acreages of public lands seem to be about the same. Most of these problems are not what we normally think of as conservation problems, at all. They are urban problems. You get blighted areas; you start, for example, with fairly well-spaced cottages around the lake on private land; the cottages begin to deteriorate; the lots are split; more cottages come in; and so on.

CHARLES C. COLBY (Professor Emeritus of Geography, University of Chicago): Most of the patrons of recreational facilities are in our big cities, and we need to get the facilities near them. The critical need here is for a well-planned national survey participated in by people from the county level, from the state level, and from the national level. Such a survey should go thoroughly into the whole question, should survey the problem, should analyze the findings, should create a great national design, and then tell us how to get it effectuated.

Wildlife Habitat

As other demands upon the land surface grow, interest in wildlife also increases on the part of hunters, and others who just like to watch birds and animals thrive in natural surroundings.

The major center of interest here was conflicting government policy on wetlands. The federal government and the states are spending millions of dollars annually to protect and restore waterfowl habitat; at the same time they are encouraging drainage operations that reduce the amount of land for waterfowl use. What is the answer?

IRA N. GABRIELSON (President, Wildlife Management Institute; statement given by Clinton R. Gutermuth): Despite efforts of the federal government and the states to develop and improve waterfowl refuge land, the acreage of suitable waterfowl habitat developed has not kept pace with the shrinking of such habitat elsewhere. This has been due in large part to the subsidies paid by the Department of Agriculture to encourage the draining and clearing of land to increase agricultural production. Not only are the Interior and Agriculture Departments working at cross purposes but the Department of Agriculture is paying subsidies to farmers to develop more land to produce more crops, some of which it has to buy to keep from breaking the market. In addition to encouraging the clearing of land, often submarginal, for additional farm acreage, the subsidy program has operated to keep people on land that should not be farmed.

Wetlands should be classified both as to their wildlife and potential agricultural values. If such a program had been in effect early in this century, much of the past drainage would never have been undertaken. Perhaps the surveys now being undertaken by the Fish and Wildlife Service will furnish a basis for reserving the more valuable wildlife lands.

No subsidies should be paid for drainage or land clearing until more land is needed, and then such activities should be encouraged only on soils that are suitable for farming. I have seen land being cleared, under the agricultural subsidy program, so steep that the first rain would cause excessive erosion as soon as the vegetative cover was removed. I have seen many drainage programs that have resulted in loss to everyone involved except the promoters and contractors who did the work.

MR. WILSON: Drainage is being encouraged by the agricultural production program payments. Those incentive payments are wholly unnecessary; with present surpluses, there is no need to bring more land into production. The farmers have been running their farms with potholes and getting along pretty well for many years. Neither is there any excuse for providing technical service through the Soil Conservation Service beyond an analysis to determine how the soil should be managed and whether the soil or the area is suitable for drainage. The proposition that drainage promotes soil conservation does not hold up under analysis. It is easy to argue that if a farmer can get some good rich bottom land under cultivation, he can take the pressure off his higher land. But he can increase his production by using better soil conservation and land management practices on the land he is already working. The scale tips heavily against a program for supporting the drainage of wetlands from the standpoint of the public interest. And the benefits to private owners are not enough to warrant these great inroads on our important waterfowl areas.

What constructive measures can be taken? Persuasion and education of the land owners have their values, but our experience in Minnesota has demonstrated that you can't get far with that method. We have tried to persuade the farmer that in the long run he will be better off if he maintains these wetlands, but the profit motive is too strong and the opportunity to get good land under cultivation is too powerful an incentive. Zoning doesn't offer much hope, because the areas are so small and dispersed—little dots of water surrounded by private land. Government purchase may be the answer, but there are heavy demands on the funds now available. If we are going to get anywhere with this problem we must provide additional revenue, for example, by increasing the Duck Stamp fee.

MR. WELLMAN: We are not actually talking about a situation in 1953, but about the prospective situation in 1975, when instead of surpluses we may have shortages. Looking forward to the population needs in 1975, should we devote land capable of yielding 100 to 150 bushels of corn to a habitat for wildlife?

MR. WILSON: There is no immediate need for that land, and as long as it stays under water it will be in good shape. With modern drainage machinery, it can be converted to production on very short notice.

MR. VAN VALKENBURG: I am from Holland. At home we had to decide whether our country was to be for waterfowl or Dutchmen; we selected the Dutchmen.

MR. GREENSHIELDS: Many of the payments are made to farmers who are trying to improve fields already used for crops. They have low spots that are poorly drained. The total program is not draining areas that really benefit wildlife; many fields being drained have no benefit whatsoever to wildlife.

MR. ALLEN: Much of this land that is planned for drainage has some economic value, not just the sports value of shooting waterfowl and so on. We have a 2.5 million dollar fur crop coming off the marshes in Michigan. That isn't very much money any more, but it pays taxes on a lot of farms. Then, too, the matter of changing water levels is important.

After the Conference the following comment was added:

MR. BLACK: It should be made clearer that there should be no one general rule as to development of wetlands. On farms with too little cropland, drainage will be desirable at once; and this will be true, but with a longer time span, for potentially good crop and grass land needing drainage within the present boundaries of farms generally. It will be the swamps not now in farms that had best be held in wet storage for the time being.

Reservoir and Other Water-Project Land

Reservoirs and land in surrounding reservations occupy 9 to 10 million acres in the United States. New proposals, some already authorized, would take a substantial added acreage. Conflicts between farming areas where land would be inundated and downstream areas that want flood protection, though localized, are often serious. Do present survey methods adequately weigh the whole range of social and economic gains and losses?

MR. GREENSHIELDS: Compared with cropland, pasture land, forests, and urban uses, reservoirs do not loom large in the land-use picture. However, the controversies over this use are probably the severest, primarily because we are not convinced that the values from some of the reservoirs are worth the cost, and we do not have full confidence in the findings of the agencies proposing them.

We must be certain that reservoirs take a minimum of the land capable of producing food and fiber. But at the same time, we must recognize their place in enhancing the beneficial use of our water resources and in reducing floods. I should like to suggest three major steps to accomplish this goal.

First, the reservoir site selected should be the one that will best serve the multiple purposes of the land and the water involved. Whether it is a single-purpose or multiple-purpose reservoir, we must make a full analysis of all the costly adverse effects as well as the expected benefits. We must go beyond the land acquisition cost in measuring the cost to the nation.

Second, once the selection is made, we must attempt to minimize the impacts on the whole economy. Better land-acquisition procedures and greater local participation are steps in this direction.

Third, once the reservoir is constructed, we must adopt sound land and forestry management plans for the land within the reservoir. We have done too little in making the most of the resources now in our reservoirs, particularly the so-called dry flood-control reservoirs. In New Hampshire, for example, it would appear that maximum use is not being made of Franklin Falls and Blackwater reservoir lands. The lands within the higher elevations of these reservoirs are not flooded very much and could be used more intensively. We need some program for the proper management of these reservoir lands.

The solution to this whole problem seems to be better assembling and understanding of the facts. Geographers and members of other sciences and professions besides engineers and economists have contributions to make.

MR. STOCKWELL: There is something rather final in reservoir inundation. The question should be viewed objectively without any preconceived idea that reservoirs are sacrosanct.

On the one hand, our increasing population insures a continuance of the pressure for food-producing land. On the other hand, as long as the federal government pays the entire cost of reservoirs, the downstream areas will attempt to transfer the costs of their flood-plain occupancy to other segments of our society. Since we can do very little to increase the supply of food-producing land, the question is one of reducing the demand for reservoirs. As in balancing any supply and demand, care must be taken that the price represents all of the public costs and that the demand is real, not based upon false assumptions as to results.

Many projects and even entire river basin programs have been presented to the people in formalized form with no more explanation than that they are "unquestionably justified." The lack of open discussion in early survey stages tends to crystallize public opinion and leads to the formation of countervailing forces instead of consideration of facts.

With reservoir sites, the usual custom is to consider only land acquisition in determining the public cost, under the specious assumption that the capital, labor, and skills now employed upon pre-project lands can be as efficiently employed on other lands of like capabilities. The entire agricultural production loss resulting from a reservoir is a public loss and should be calculated in the same way as the benefits.

Possible social losses from reservoirs are most pronounced in the prairie plowlands of the Middle West, where the agricultural economy is based upon an integrated use of upland forage and valley feed crops in livestock production. The region faces the following losses from changed land usage: loss of production by inundation of the reservoirs; loss of integration between valley crop production and upland grazing, which will force a more intensive use of the erodable uplands as the region seeks a new balance between crop and pasture land; loss upstream from the reservoirs by aggradation and swamping—this loss might easily exceed the loss from inundation; loss of the valleys as corridors of transportation; depletion of downstream flood plains; and loss of trade by perimeter towns.

The present federal policy disassociates the purchaser and the demand. A change of policy whereby the areas directly benefited must assume an equitable share of the costs and adjustments would lessen the demand for upstream reservoirs located hundreds of miles from the area seeking protection. People occupy flood plains by choice, and they should recognize that they have a dominant landlord, Old Man River. If they encroach indiscriminately upon his domain they must be prepared to pay for the advantages.

The remedy lies partly in basic policy and legislation and partly in agency procedures. We need a clarification of the term "flood control" and a de-emphasizing of the glamour of huge engineering works. Alternate methods of avoiding flood loss can then be more fully explored. Often they can represent a decided saving to the people as a whole and eliminate taking great acreages from productive use.

MR. CHANDLER: We should also keep in mind the benefit to downstream residents. In spite of the criticisms Mr. Greenshields made of our New Hampshire project, we have found that the Merrimack River has given us much less inundation at times of flood in the spring since that dam came in. It has helped a great deal.

Methods of Adjusting or Reducing Conflicts

Sometimes a workable plan for multiple use can be devised for an area wanted for two or more uses at the same time. Sometimes the land in dispute is apportioned among different uses. Sometimes there is a flat decision in favor of one use. Sometimes no agreement is reached; the situation just stays tangled with the land serving none of the purposes for which it is best suited.

By what methods can we head off, mitigate, or cure such situations? Among the several possible mechanisms for adjusting conflicts that have developed, rural zoning was the center of interest. The subject of wider public ownership of multiple-use lands had been pretty well covered in the Conference-wide program of the preceding night (see pages 361-67). Obtaining more of the basic information and better analysis of the data that are available were seen as essential to heading off land-use conflicts as well as adjusting them. Needs for research and education in the characteristics and potential of the country's total land base were emphasized.

FROM THE RECORD

Rural Zoning

Where has rural land zoning been useful and effective? Should this method be more widely applied? If so, what should be done to encourage it? What are its basic difficulties and limitations?

ERLING D. SOLBERG (Agricultural Research Service, USDA): Thirty-eight states have passed enabling laws authorizing local units of rural government to adopt zoning ordinances. Slightly more than a third of the country's 3,000 counties are empowered to zone. By 1949, rural zoning ordinances had been adopted by 173 counties in 23 states and also by many townships.

Zoning has been successfully used to attain a variety of ends: to promote the rehabilitation of cutover counties in Wisconsin and other states; to protect highways from economic suffocation, particularly in Florida; to guide community growth on urban fringes; to preserve the amenities of residential districts; to protect farm communities in many states from disrupting activities; and, more recently in California and a few other states, to preserve the better agricultural lands for farming.

Considering the range of accomplishments, why hasn't zoning been used by more rural governments? One reason, I think, is lack of understanding.

Zoning regulations may benefit a locality, a community, a state, or a region, depending on the scope and character of the regulations. Some regulations have mainly local benefits. Others confer state or wider benefits and may or may not benefit the community or its land-owners. For example, benefits from roadside zoning accrue primarily to the traveling public. The local community also benefits, but the interest of those who own land adjoining the road may often conflict with the interest of the traveling public.

Now, zoning authority is permissive, the community may choose the tools it wants to use; but this fact is not fully recognized by many people. The pattern of benefits from the various types of zoning regulations may promote conflicting interests and pressures. Also, local governments are primarily the ones authorized to zone; their number and size have precluded the use of zoning tools in achieving wider public ends. Some of the other reasons are the pressure of local property taxes and the general inability to equate such taxes with desirable zoning district patterns, the position of nonconforming properties in zoning law, and frequent failure to take appropriate action in time.

MRS. FOX: We in Pennsylvania have fought for state highway zoning protection for the past 10 years. We have been unsuccessful just as every other state has been, and in the meantime highway values continue to be adversely affected. A fine new four-lane highway, for example, is built to carry 50-mile an hour traffic. Soon the speed must be reduced to 25 miles an hour because of the commercial development which has moved in. Have we not

reached the point where we must advocate as a proviso for federal aid to state highways that the states be required to take adequate measures to protect the public's investment in highways? Local government has failed to protect the highways within its boundaries, and too often state highway departments hesitate to designate a new highway as limited-access, which is now their only means of providing partial protection for it.

MR. SOLBERG: Where the benefits from zoning cut across local boundary lines where the benefit goes to the traveling public, it seems to me there is a place for re-examining the level at which that type of zoning should be considered. If zoning is performed at a higher level of government, that does not mean that that zoning agency should engage in all the zoning powers that are usually granted local governments. The power that might be granted to the agency that cuts across local boundary lines should be only that required to the particular job.

MR. OLSEN: We live in one of the 38 states that has state zoning legislation. The state law gives the county commissioners authority to set up zoning districts. This law was brought about by public pressure. Back of that was a lot of education. I believe that is one place where the local people should function in getting their state to pass legislation and then getting their counties to establish zoning ordinances and zoning districts to take care of these problems.

MRS. FOX: We have had zoning-enabling legislation in Pennsylvania for about 15 years, but local pressures have prevented its being put to adequate use.

Basic Knowledge About the Land Resources

Where are the serious gaps in our technical information on our land resource? Do we need to speed up and intensify the basic surveys such as (a) cadastral, geologic, and hydrographic; (b) soil surveys; (c) forest and range surveys; (d) land capability surveys; (e) comprehensive land classification?

How can these scientific investigations be better integrated?

STEPHEN N. WYCKOFF (California Forest and Range Experiment Station): We have less knowledge on how to handle uncultivated lands than we have on the cultivated lands. An effort comparable to that of the agricultural sciences would undoubtedly step up production on the wild lands—the forests, range lands, and watersheds.

The land surveys—topographic, hydrographic, and cadastral—are facilitating surveys that provide the basis for resource inventories and surveys of productivity potentials. When the latter undertakings are integrated they give the information needed for resource management.

Both types of surveys should be speeded up. It has been estimated—on the assumption that the surveys of the type we are discussing will be made primarily by the federal government—that at the rate of progress being made in 1949 it would take 158 years to complete the geologic mapping of the nation, and 90 years to complete the soil mapping. Various other types of mapping are not so far behind, but even they would take many years. We cannot afford to wait this long for the completion of the surveys necessary to the orderly development of the wild land resources.

If survey intensification means a greatly increased degree of detail, I consider it unnecessary. Surveys should classify, locate, describe, and measure areas of specified degrees of homogeneity. They should not attempt to provide the detailed analyses of conditions requisite either for intensive research on the resources or more intensive use of land. The more detail you add to a survey, the more you increase the cost and retard the rate of progress.

Surveys can be integrated in two ways. One way is to bring together the results of several separate surveys. This involves a correlation of survey data, often including the use of overlay maps and, in some cases, the preparation of new maps depicting an integration of several forms of data. For such undertakings uniform base maps are necessary. The second type of integration is achieved by combining two or more types of survey in one field operation.

I would like to give you an example of this kind of survey. In California we have large areas of foothill land between the areas of intensive cultivation and the commercial timber belt. To learn more about this type of land, a Soils-Vegetation Survey is being conducted by the State Division of Forestry on state and private lands and by the U.S. Forest Service on national forest lands. Based on photogrammetric methods, the survey delimits vegetation types and conditions and soil series and depths in one operation. Soil mappers have long recognized the value of natural vegetation types as indicators of soil types, but, so far as is known, this survey is the first formalization of this knowledge in a single survey method.

Other instances of this kind of integration could be cited, for example, in geologic and soil surveys. I suggest that a careful study of the possibilities for such integraton of other surveys might lead to valuable results.

JOHN F. LOUNSBURY (Antioch College): Any land survey, to be meaningful, should be a total land survey. Geology, climate, soil, slope, erosion, and drainage must be considered and mapped along with the present land use in existing cultural patterns. This can be done by a group of trained investigators at one time. All the mapping can be done at one run through the country.

Now there is a place for both general and detailed surveys. But general surveys and the resulting generalizations can be dangerous and often misleading. To be useful for detailed planning in densely populated areas, surveys must be detailed—a scale of 1:5,000 or 1:10,000. Otherwise, the money and effort are wasted. On a detailed scale, the optimum use for a particular type of land can be determined. When we talk about general physical and economic conditions, competing uses are greatly maximized and consequently cause conflicts. But if we talk about a small individual plot of land, it will often be found that that one plot can be best used for one particular use under the existing physical and economic conditions.

Surveys take time and effort; I believe that problem areas should have preference over others.

MR. VAN VALKENBURG: I have been trying to get an inventory of what the earth's surface is used for. Such a survey in Britain became the basis for planning the food supply during the war.

Now that kind of survey can be done in the United States without much money. At Clark University, in Worcester, my graduate students have practically completed the mapping of the State of Massachusetts. We have trained geographers all over the United States who can be called upon. In Britain they trained high school students to help. That is something that can be done in a fairly short time—not in 150 years, but in 10 or 20 years. It is factual mapping. It is something upon which all those other maps can be based.

JACOB E. SHILLINGER (National Catholic Rural Life Conference): If there is any one thing lacking in our whole land use and wildlife promotion it is intensive, well-organized research. I have been on waterfowl refuges where you could walk for a mile or more, stepping from one dead duck to another. It seems to me that a lot of errors might have been avoided by preliminary research.

MR. MCMURRY: There is no general answer to what type of survey should be made, nor how it should be carried on.

We know how to do the over-all, small-scale survey, such as our topographic surveys and geological surveys; we know what the results are, and their usefulness is recognized. Those are basic and certainly should be continued and accelerated. I don't think there is much need for detailed surveys on scales of 1:5,000 and 1:10,000. What's the use of spending that amount of money per acre when the land itself is probably not worth the price of the survey?

We should be spending vastly more money now on our systematic surveys, our geological and soil survey work.

MR. WYCKOFF: Modern photogrammetric methods give a great deal of flexibility in the amount of intensification. In our forest survey in California the minimum homogeneous area we recognize is 40 acres. In the soils and vegetation survey the minimum area is 10 acres.

Landowners often buy the maps and also prints of the aerial photographs. Many of them are becoming skillful in the use of these prints. If they want more intensive information on a small area, they can study the prints and the maps and then divide it down just as finely as they wish, without the added cost of that high degree of detail on the whole area.

MR. CHANDLER: In New York State the soil surveyors feel that on intensively used agricultural land we should map everything we see, because some day it might have significance. I agree that forest crops do not call for the detailed survey required in the case of agricultural land.

The question of gaps in research came up again at the final meeting of the whole section December 4.

J. WILLCOX BROWN (University of Michigan): We lack adequate methods at the present time for measuring the values of the service uses of land. We need to develop better techniques of expressing such values. This is true of recreation, wildlife production, and watershed protection; and the problem is especially acute where service uses compete with commercial ones. Also, in the case of the family farm unit on the marginal farm, we have social values to which we cannot give adequate expression strictly through market-place measure.

JOEL D. WOLFSOHN (Chapman and Wolfsohn, Washington, D.C.): There are serious gaps in the available technical information on our land resources, particularly on federal lands. We not only need to speed up our survey work, but also to program it better and to establish mechanisms by which citizens working in these areas, at all levels, will have reliable and current data.

I suggest a 10-year program to complete the cadastral survey (or resurvey where needed) of the public domain. This is a first essential to management and disposal.

It is time that the U.S. Government, as the country's largest landowner, establish and maintain a current central real estate record. I believe this should be the responsibility of the Bureau of Land Management, Department of the Interior. Land records are now the responsibility of the administering agency or bureau, and not even, in all instances, of the departments. Thus, needs of agencies which frequently might be met by lands already in federal ownership, are not so met.

Unless we learn more about our land resources we shall fall into errors of administration in planning for the national economy or the national security. From the point of view of the whole nation and the states, a continuing, comprehensive land classification program should be carried out.

All of these surveys, classifications, and studies can best be integrated through an over-all land agency, which could then work out cooperative relationships with states and their subdivisions as regards their lands.

CHAIRMAN'S SUMMARY

As our population grows and our economy expands, under our competitive system of free enterprise, it is perfectly natural that competing demands for the use of land will also increase. There is and will continue to be competition between city uses and rural uses; and within the city and rural area the competition for use of land grows sharper.

Urban Land

Urban lands are important not only in their extent, but also in the high value they acquire because of the concentration of business activity on them, the investment in them, and the intense use to which they are put by the people who use them. Under the pressure of growth in industrial activity and population, and goaded by their sense of vulnerability to atomic attack, most of our large cities are undergoing some degree of decentralization. This inevitably brings about conflicting demands for use of land.

One conflict is between building sites and open spaces. Open space is needed for a variety of necessary uses such as recreation, public buildings, freeways, airports, flood channels, and residences. Urban areas, for example, do not have enough open space for recrea-

tion, and it is apparent that as growth continues this use in many cases will conflict with other demands upon the space. It is important to recognize that public recreation areas can add more to property values than they cost. There also seems to be a special need to reserve sections of waterfront space for public access and recreational use.

Urban development programs should be improved to give better balance to housing, business, and industrial uses.

In fringe areas between city and rural land serious conflicts can be expected. One of the most important issues concerns the removal of excellent farm land from production by subdivision into building lots—sometimes premature subdivision. How serious this loss of farm land will be to over-all crop production is still open to question.

On the question of traffic congestion in the central zones of our large cities there was general agreement in the subsection that rapid transit does now, and should in the future, carry most of the people going to and from the downtown center; and that freeways and ample parking space are needed to handle motor vehicles that properly must come downtown. People need to be educated in the best uses of private vehicles for trips to city centers.

The subsection agreed that the day of free parking in downtown areas is a thing of the past, and that parking meters encourage congestion more than they discourage it. The parking business represents a highly competitive use of land. In a large measure it should be developed by private enterprise, and with those serviced paying the cost.

It was generally agreed that commercial airports should be fairly close to population centers, and that rapid transit between the airport and the city it serves is essential. Obviously, the open space needed cannot be used for other purposes; both land purchase and zoning are needed to control land in the vicinity of a major airport. Military airports—in this era of jets—should not be located near major urban areas.

Rural Land

The most important use of our rural land is in producing the food and fiber we need to sustain us. One source of competition in the use of farm land is between the large high-production farm and the many low-production farms. As a whole, our farm economy is felt to be in excellent condition, operating with a good balance of land, labor, and capital. But some $1\frac{1}{2}$ million low-production commercial farmers struggle along spending too much labor on too little and often unproductive land, and with too little capital to provide for machinery and fertilizer. Some examples show that a proper use of capital can improve production from the resources of land and human energy on these farms.

In the use of forest lands, the competing demands differ from region to region. Those in the South are not the same as those in the North and West. No single pattern of ownership and control is suitable for all regions. There is a definite trend toward expansion of the area held by timber-processing industry, but it seems improbable that industry will find it economically or politically wise to own more than a part of the timber-producing land. The situation now and in the foreseeable future calls for increasing cooperation between timber-using industry and other forest land-owners—both private and public. The need for a more adequate access road system in the national forests of the West received considerable attention from the subsection. It appears that this problem is basically a matter of adjusting the conflicting interests of large and small operators and the general public.

Participants sensed a conflict in the use of wetlands. Many wetland areas formerly used as waterfowl habitat are being drained to permit their use for agricultural crops, even in the face of present surpluses. There was strong feeling that it is against the public interest to drain much of this land.

Construction of water reservoirs brings about other conflicts in demand for land. Works of this sort often seem to take some of the best farm land out of crop production. It was advocated that before such a project be undertaken, a thorough analysis of the net cost should be made, and of all other factors, especially those that would have impact on the local economy.

These are only some of the more important conflicts that we foresee in the demands on our land resources. Some of them will require considerable study before we can approach practical solutions. We suggest four areas for nationwide investigation. One is the complicated problem of decentralizing our large urban areas. Another is the congestion in urban centers, and the competing demands for land for transportation purposes. The third is the need for bringing our knowledge of wild lands more nearly into line with the scientific information we have about cultivated land. And, finally, it seems to us that we need a new nationwide appraisal of our land resource in the light of prospective needs during the next generation or two.

CHARLES C. COLBY
December 4, 1953

Chairman

LLOYD E. PARTAIN
Sales Manager and Farm Market Director
Country Gentleman Magazine
The Curtis Publishing Company

Co-Chairman

SAMUEL T. DANA, Dean Emeritus
School of Natural Resources
University of Michigan

Steering Committee and Advisers

Steering Committee: MURRAY R. BENEDICT, Professor of Agricultural Economics, University of California · BENTON R. CANCELL, Vice-President in Charge of Operations, Rhinelander Paper Company · WATERS S. DAVIS, JR., President, National Association of Soil Conservation Districts · GEORGE W. DEAN, Virginia State Forester and President, Association of State Foresters · PAUL A. HERBERT, Director, Division of Conservation, Michigan State College · R. C. JACOBSON, Secretary-Treasurer, Minnesota State CIO Council · HAROLD WILM, Associate Dean, College of Forestry, State University of New York · *Assistant to the Section Chairman:* JOHN B. BENNETT, Assistant Director, Technical Review Staff, U. S. Department of the Interior · *Section Rapporteur:* RICHARD L. KENYON, Managing Editor, *Journal of Agricultural and Food Chemistry*

Subsections

A. FOOD AND NONWOOD FIBERS

Chairman: MURRAY R. BENEDICT

Rapporteurs: WALTER B. GARVER, Manager, Agricultural Department, Chamber of Commerce of the United States; RAYMOND P. CHRISTENSEN, Agricultural Research Service, U. S. Department of Agriculture

B. TIMBER AND WOOD PRODUCTS

Chairman: BENTON R. CANCELL

Rapporteurs: LOWELL BESLEY, Executive Director-Forester, American Forestry Association; JAMES B. CRAIG, Editor, *American Forests*

C. WILDLIFE, SCENIC, WILDERNESS, AND OTHER RECREATIONAL AREAS

Chairman: PAUL A. HERBERT

Rapporteurs: EDWARD H. GRAHAM, Director, Plant Technology Division, Soil Conservation Service, U.S. Department of Agriculture; SIDNEY S. KENNEDY, Chief, State Cooperation Branch, National Park Service, U.S. Department of the Interior

D. WATERSHED VALUES

Chairman: HAROLD WILM

Rapporteurs: GORDON K. ZIMMERMAN, Research Director, National Agricultural Research, Inc.; D. HARPER SIMMS, Director, Division of Information, Soil Conservation Service, U.S. Department of Agriculture

About 340 persons participated in the work of Section II. The 295 who registered formally are listed on pages 383-89.

UTILIZATION AND DEVELOPMENT OF LAND RESOURCES

HOW CAN WE GET THE MOST out of our rural lands in the next 25 to 50 years? The problem is managerial, with the focus of discussion on the broad policies and general methods that will help us make better use of our different kinds of land.

That we will need to get more out of rural lands is not in question here. It was assumed from the start. Pressures on our land base are mounting. World-wide trends toward larger populations and higher standards of living will influence the ways we choose to develop our resources and the use we make of them. We shall need more farm products, both foods and fibers; more timber and other products of the forest. A larger total population, with a higher proportion living in cities, will have larger needs of scenic, wilderness, and wildlife values. At the same time, probably, those resources will feel the impact of pressures to increase their use for more grazing and timber production and more power and irrigation projects. Care of watersheds will become more and more important, no matter to what other uses their lands are put. In tackling these problems, how can we get all we need now from our land resources, and yet give decent thought to the needs of coming generations?

Possible trends in future demand and competition for specific uses are considered separately in Section I (pages 26-61), but some overlap is unavoidable, especially when discussion touches on problems of land ownership. A similar relationship is to be found when watershed issues linked with the management of farm, range, and forest land cross with the broader aspects of water resource management dealt with in Section III (pages 126-75).

It was impossible in a three-day conference to examine techniques of forestry and agriculture, or motives and mechanisms of broad farm policy, in any comprehensive detail; but many details inevitably were considered, often at some length, as they bore on major issues discussed. In the pages that follow, those issues are grouped under four main heads corresponding to areas surveyed by the subsections: Food and Nonwood Fibers; Timber and Wood Products: Wildlife, Scenic, Wilderness, and Other Recreational Areas; and Watershed Values.

Except as the pieces fit together into a larger pattern, the discussion in each area stands on its own feet. The section attempted no formal synthesis. But the whole record suggests that few people are inclined to doubt that we *can* get much more out of our land resources—that the major concern is whether we *will*, by picking policies and methods good for the long pull, get maximum use out of our resources without impairing their vigor. Three major requirements were stressed repeatedly: We need more basic research of the kind that developed hybrid corn; we need to step up the methods by which knowledge is brought into general application; and we need a greater degree of integration among agencies, particularly on federal and state levels.

Subsection A

FOOD AND NONWOOD FIBERS

How can we insure necessary increases in production? In seeking answers to this question, Subsection A surveyed (1) the farm and ranch lands for both extensive and intensive crop production; (2) the open range lands for both livestock production and multiple use; and (3) the water-surfaced lands for the intensive culture of fish, domestic waterfowl, and fur-bearing animals.

Farm and Ranch Lands

There can be little doubt of the nation's fundamental ability to produce enough food and fiber to satisfy our increasing needs during the next quarter-century. The acceleration of agricultural production over the past 15 years can be sustained and bettered, if need be. Working from these broad areas of agreement, the subsection concentrated on the range of methods that may be used to meet our future requirements efficiently and at low cost. A series of questions guided its discussions.

Will it be necessary to convert more land into more intensive production? While more land can be added to the present cropland area, it was generally agreed that most of the necessary increases in production will come from greater per-acre yields and per-animal production.

What methods of increasing production per acre are most important and efficient? The subsection looked first at programs of research and education. Are they on an adequate scale? What changes in emphasis are required? There was no disagreement with the view, dominant throughout all the discussions, that much more emphasis should be given to basic research and that much greater effort should be made to reduce the time lag between the development of a technique and its general adoption. But the suggestion that our reserves of knowledge from basic research are in danger of depletion aroused some strong contrary opinion in letters received immediately after the close of the Conference.

The subsection examined the range of soil and water conservation measures to improve land productivity. Are we providing enough engineering and technical aids? Are we providing them in the right ways? Considerable attention here was given to the continuing losses of the soil's organic content, and to the need for more work on trace elements.

On the question: "To what extent is continuation of the soil conservation payment program needed or desirable?" many and varied views were held. The rapporteur's digest said on this point:

> Several speakers expressed the opinion that the payment programs have stimulated land-operator interest in conservation and have induced farmers to make improvements they would not otherwise have made. Some members of the subsection stated that such payments are not needed or desirable in their areas. The more general attitude was apparently that some financial aid as well as technical assistance is needed in some areas and for some types of farmers. However, several participants expressed the view that there is need for more selective and discriminating use of soil conservation payments than in the past, in order that public funds may be used with maximum effectiveness.

As to the costs of conservation, it was suggested that public contributions would increase if there were a more realistic appraisal of the current value of the onsite and offsite benefits. The dual and sometimes differing approach of the two agencies concerned with good farming practice was criticized. What is needed is a meshing of the economic aspects of farming with broad soil conservation objectives.

Further research and further education were again emphasized in considering the question: Is commercial fertilizer being used to the extent needed and socially desirable? In general, it was considered that greater quantities of commercial fertilizer can and should be applied, but its use should be related to the requirements of the soil.

FROM THE RECORD

The Situation

SHERMAN E. JOHNSON (Agricultural Research Service, USDA): If we take 1950 as a base year and project our 1975 needs in terms of population increase, per capita consumption, and gradual growth in level of exports and imports, those needs seem likely to come within a range of 40 to 50 percent increase from 1950. I am optimistic about the physical possibilities of achieving an increase well within that range, but it will not come automatically. Projecting such increases with confidence assumes adequate attention to research, education, conservation, and other programs undertaken on a balanced basis. More land is available if we need the land, but most of this increase is likely to come from higher production per acre and per animal.

Factors favorable to expansion of production are: increased use of lime and fertilizers; the possibility of a major technological advancement; drainage, irrigation, and flood protection; waste prevention in production and marketing; animal breeding, feeding, and disease prevention; and basic and vocational education. Unfavorable factors are: the possibility of drought; needless exploitation of soil and water resources; the uneven flow of technological improvement; the greater difficulty of maintaining production at high levels; and the dependence upon adequate supplies of non-farm resources such as motor fuel, fertilizer, and pesticides.

On balance, assuming no unpredictable great catastrophe, the question does not seem to be "Shall we have enough food by 1975?" but rather, "How shall we produce the needed food and fiber efficiently; how produce it at low cost?" We can produce more at increasing cost as needed, but, unless we offset that in-

65

crease in cost with lower costs in other sectors of the economy, that implies a lower level of living. Therefore, we are extremely interested in producing the needed food at low cost. There is also the need to provide a contingency reserve of research against unforeseen needs to thinking beyond 1975.

WALTER W. WILCOX (Library of Congress): If anything, I am more optimistic than Dr. Johnson. The recent rate of technological increase looks as though it can be maintained. Consequently, barring drought and international emergencies, we are likely to have supplies pressing on available markets. It is my judgment that our "tremendous surpluses" are within a range of about 3 to 5 percent of our continual output. So we are very close to a balance and are likely to continue that way.

The whole set-up of our democratic procedures is such that it is likely to encourage this rate of increase in relation to market demand. I have in mind among other factors the tendency to try to solve current economic problems in terms of more cost-reduction research, which tends in the final analysis to be output-increasing research. So the very attempt to deal with current problems gives us the background for more output.

How Can Research and Education Help Increase Our Productivity?

BYRON T. SHAW (Agricultural Research Service, USDA): A couple of years ago the Agricultural Research Administration tried to estimate the size of this job, using the Census Bureau population projections of the time— 190 million people by 1975. In 1950 we were using for the production of food 462 million acres of cropland equivalent. We calculated that the requirement for the expected increased population would be 115 million acres more than was used in 1950, of which about 45 million acres would come from actual increases in cropland (15 million from the release of land now required to produce feed for horses and mules, and about 30 million through irrigation, drainage, land clearing, and various methods of that type). That left us with a deficit of 70 million acres. As against that

figure we should recognize that all of the improvements we have made in agriculture between 1935 and 1950 were equivalent to the production from 64 million acres.

On the basis of the latest Census Bureau population estimates for 1975, which range between a low of 190 million and a high of 221 million people, we can calculate therefore that the deficit in cropland availability will vary between a low of 98 million acres and a high of 165 million acres.

I have examined a number of situations in our agricultural production picture, and I find essentially the same story in each one of them: We are using up research information at a faster rate than we are producing it. As you get to higher levels of production, the hazards that go along with them give you quite a battle. It takes a large part of the research that we are now performing to hold even, and it will take more, too, to get ahead.

It is apparent that in the case of corn one innovation—hybrid corn—accounts for most of the production improvement between 1870 and 1950. Now, how do we get the innovations? We get them from fundamental research. Currently in the nation about 12 percent of our funds are going into basic research and 88 percent into applied. We have got to get a higher percentage of basic research to get the new innovations that are needed to raise the ceilings.

On the education side—we have a lag of 15 to 20 years between the potentially possible, as shown by research results, and average production. I think we can do a lot better educational job in getting results into use. When you sell a farmer a tractor, you sell him an assembled job; you don't try to sell him an improvement on the carburetor. There is a job for both research and education in integrating innovations into a package the farmer can use.

HERBERT C. HANSON (Grassland Research Foundation): Many people at state experiment stations and in the Department of Agriculture realize the problems that can only be answered by long-term research. But when the officers of an experiment station go to Congress every year to get funds, they must point to definite accomplishments during the past year. We need some education here in order to get funds for long-term research. A useful study could be made, analyzing the reasons why we cannot get funds for long-term research and recommending what is needed.

After the Conference, several participants questioned the extent of the land that might be converted to crop production. The governing factor, it would appear, will be cost of conversion. With regard to land now used for feeding draft animals, Mr. Fred A. Wirt questioned whether 15 million acres now used for this purpose can be released to cropland, in view of the upward trend in recreational use of horses. The degree to which our research reserves have been depleted also gave rise to comment.

JOHN D. BLACK (Harvard University): While it probably will be cheaper to get our 45 percent increase in output from cropland now in use, we do have 285 million more acres of potential cropland in this country, according to the Soil Conservation Service classification of land-use capabilities.

With regard to the need for research, there can be no proof of the statement that we are putting our technology into use faster than we are developing new technology. In the war years and in 1946 a backlog of unused technology of the depression 1930's was very rapidly applied, but since then the two processes have been in pretty even balance. I agree that research needs to be stepped up somewhat to get a 45 percent increase by 1975, but the research most needing increase is that required for extension. It is extension that needs to be stepped up.

RUSSELL G. HILL (Michigan State College): In addition to the need for basic research dealing with increasing the unit output of each acre or animal, there is a similar need for research on educational techniques to speed up application by farmers. We are on the threshold of information which will influence production to at least as great an extent as

that which helped produce recent production advancements. The use of antibiotics and hormones is but an example. Similarly, it is evident that land production can be greatly increased by land treatments with which we are already familiar and which have not as yet been universally applied.

Illustrations of the foregoing view had been offered during the Conference.

K. STARR CHESTER (Battelle Memorial Institute): A very interesting laboratory near Essen, Germany, is doing some revolutionary and yet sound things. A few years ago they settled a family of five on a little patch of land of $1\frac{2}{3}$ acres; the object was to see whether this family, using all the benefits of modern agricultural research, could get a moderate living. They passed the 4,000 calorie mark some time ago and the latest report which, I think, is a year old, is that they have now exceeded 5,000 calories per person. That shows what intensification can do.

J. RUSSELL SMITH (Professor Emeritus, Columbia University): The greatest natural producers of food are trees. Consider the acorn. It has fed the wild hog, the farmer's hog in the South, the bear, the raccoon, and the deer for centuries; also many generations of men. This acorn, high in nutrition, is produced by a dozen species adapted to nearly all parts of the United States. And there is the widely distributed honey locust; some of the bean pods carry more than 30 percent sugar.

The point is that we are now ready to apply plant breeding not merely to the annuals, but to the long-range job of tree breeding. It is a slow job, so slow that it has not yet received much attention from our agricultural experiment stations. We need a search of our country and of foreign lands to get promising wild mother trees. Then breed from these.

OVID BUTLER (American Forestry Association): Most of you know that a tree-breeding foundation is now being set up at Berkeley, Calif.; I think that research into the food possibilities of certain species of trees is well worth being included in their program.

Soil and Water Conservation Measures

FRED A. WIRT (J. I. Case Company): We have known for years the importance of organic matter content, but is it sufficiently emphasized to the farmers of this country? Because of the decrease in organic matter content, the water-holding capacity of the soil is declining. That is one of the reasons why farmers want larger tractors. Lack of organic matter in our soils, I believe, is due in some measure to lack of engineering and technical assistance.

Concerning trace elements, how does it happen that the farmers of this country cannot go to the United States Department of Agriculture or to the state agricultural colleges, or somewhere else, and obtain information as to what the soil requires in the way of trace elements?

CHARLES E. KELLOGG (U.S. Soil Survey): Actually, the Department of Agriculture and the various experiment stations have recently been doing a lot of work in the field of minor nutrients. Minor nutrients become limiting factors after we have begun to build up our soils in calcium, nitrogen, phosphorus, and potassium. The methods are fairly good now on cobalt and also on boron which, with magnesium, is going into a great many of our mixed fertilizers.

Greater coordination of conservation programs was urged to benefit both the individual farmer and, beyond him, the entire watershed.

MR. KELLOGG: Millions of farm families in this country have no money in the bank. If those people are going to continue farming, certainly they must have technical assistance, because the biggest limiting factor is skill. But if we give them the skill and they don't have some financial help to invest in lime and fertilizer and fencing and livestock, their skill will come to nothing. We have got to consider the balance between technical assistance and financial help.

O. C. STINE (Twentieth Century Fund): On the individual farm you need coordinated activity of the several government agencies to take into account not only what the farm should do in relation to the community, but also what the farmer can do in developing the long-run potentialities of the farm beyond the point that will pay him immediately or next year; and to some extent there should be public compensation for deferring income.

J. T. SANDERS (National Grange): Public support of soil conservation has rested too often on vague claims of its benefits to future generations and other indefinite national welfare claims. We need a more down-to-earth appraisal of the current value of onsite and offsite benefits of conservation, and its future values soundly discounted into present values.

Conservation work does not yield all its benefits to the farm, to the local conservation district, or to the county or the state in which the farm is situated. Its benefits stretch to the lowest parts of the largest watershed on which the farm is located. A sound program will not ignore or impair the function of any of these interests.

I do not believe the regional offices of the Soil Conservation Service furnished the missing link in a sound appraisal of all conservation benefits, because they did not cover an area co-terminous with most of the watershed. Neither does an independent federal bureau of the TVA type meet the need. The problem, it seems to me, resolves itself into setting up a watershed board for watershed policy determination purposes only, with authority to employ the necessary administrative staff only, but without power to employ its own technical and professional staff for planning, developing, and operating the watershed functions. All technical and professional staff members should be assigned to the watershed administration from national conservation and resources agencies and from such state agencies, with payments made to these agencies for these services by reimbursable vouchers from the watershed board. The watershed board would thus receive federal appropriations for watershed development, but these funds could not be used to employ directly the needed technical and professional men.

I would in no sense continue to tie conservation payments to price support programs.

PETE E. COOLEY (Decatur Farm Management, Inc.): I would like to see the soil conserved. On the other hand, I am radically opposed to soil conservation payments, because conservation pays for itself. But in a lot of soil conservation thinking we have left out our tenure system. We have farms owned by widows with big families to support, and somehow they must extract money from the soil.

Insofar as the technical assistance from the Soil Conservation Service is concerned, they do too much planning on paper with an eye on Congressional appropriations. Let's unshackle them and let them go to work on the farms, and let the congressman come out in his district and see what is on the landscape.

My final objective would be watershed control, but this land is owned by individuals, and unless they accept your program you are stymied. So let's teach them to crawl, then to walk, then to run, and eventually we will get our watershed control.

WALTER HOWE (Natural Resources Council of Connecticut): From the point of view of the individual farmer, and then eventually from that of the community, it is essential to bring out that soil conservation practices on the individual farm are not something specialized, but are a part of good farming, just as proper methods of tillage, use of fertilizer, animal breeding, sanitation, whatever you will, are parts of good farming. The more the agencies specializing in certain broad soil conservation practices can be brought together with those dealing with all aspects—educational, economic, marketing—of the farmer's problems, the more the routine use of sound soil conservation practices is going to increase on the individual farm.

MR. KELLOGG: When we started the Soil Conservation Program in the Department it was for a while primarily an anti-erosion control program. But those days are long past, and I think we have made a lot of progress among most of the agricultural people along this line of the inseparability of conservation and production. But when it comes to working out with the farmer a unique pattern for his condition, it's simply got to be done farm by farm. And you could have two men, identical in points of view, one with educational responsibility for things that can be generalized, and one with the responsibility of helping individual farms, and they would use individual techniques.

Many participants said that greater quantities of commercial fertilizer could and should be used to maintain or increase the fertility of the soil. There was wide recognition of the need for sustained research and for much greater effort to educate farmers in the intelligent use and economic advantages of commercial fertilizers.

PAUL T. TRUITT (American Plant Food Council): The fact that 25 percent of our food supply comes directly from fertilizer usage is evidence enough to prove its importance. Agricultural scientists predict that, for the future, much more than 25 percent, perhaps as much as 50 percent, of our food supply may be dependent upon the use of chemical fertilizers.

MR. KELLOGG: I should like to point out that we should put the emphasis not on what the plants take out, but what the soils need. If we had to be content with the nutrient level originally in the soils of the eastern part of the United States, there would be no farms in the coastal plain all the way from Long Island to Florida. In such cases we must increase the fertility far beyond what it was under natural conditions. Other soils have abundant supplies of phosphorus. We have to relate the use of commercial fertilizer to the soil type.

EVERETT H. BIXBY (Oregon Soil Clinic): Soil, in reality, doesn't wear out. It does get out of balance, too high in some elements, too low in others, so the reactions don't work as they should to make necessary food assimilable to our plants. Actually, we are putting on too much fertilizer with the knowledge we have about it. The important thing is to get the right things in the right amounts in the right places.

MR. CHESTER: In the case of mineral fertilization, let's not lose sight of the trace minerals, as well as major NPK fertilizer. There are showing throughout the United States increased possibilities of small additions of iron, copper, zinc, and boron for increasing per-acre production in a way we had not suspected.

The possibilities of using city sewage and industrial waste were briefly explored. The same subject came up from another angle in Section III's discussion of water resources (pages 138-43).

MR. CHESTER: At every harvest time long trains of empty cars go from the cities to the country and come back loaded with wheat. Why do they go out empty? Why can't they be carrying the city's organic wastes to the land that needs it?

MR. HOWE: I wonder if the scientific and economic possibilities of using city sewage and industrial waste are being explored sufficiently in areas with large urban populations at some distance from sources of normal commercial fertilizer. It is a field that would seem to require cooperation between a number of different types of research organizations.

MR. TRUITT: There is quite a bit of interest in that in some cities. The Hyperion Works of Los Angeles is an example. First, there is not enough plant food in city waste sludge to be really significant; second, it is a little expensive. You have to have a large appropriation from a municipality to set up the work. I believe it cost $45 million to set up the Hyperion Works.

Open Range Lands

By and large, prospects are favorable for the continuing healthy productivity of our open range lands. The subsection noted substantial improvement over the past 25 years and saw reason for both private owners and government administrators to look with some optimism to the future. Attention was drawn, however, to many remaining gaps in research programs and weaknesses in management practices.

Examination of policies and methods of management covered both lands where livestock production is of first importance, and lands considered primarily for multiple use. The merits of private or public ownership had already been rather fully covered during a panel discussion of the Conference as a whole (pages 361-67). Although some exceptions were noted, there was no broad dissent from the view that most of the range lands now in public ownership would fare best by staying there.

Continuing needs for large-scale reseeding programs and for better classification of lands from a soil standpoint were seen by many as a reason for maintaining some form of federal supervision. At the same time, greater flexibility was advocated in programs that provide technical assistance and financial aid to private range owners.

Differences between federal agency theories, as practiced by the Forest Service in managing the national forests and by the Bureau of Land Management in managing the public domain, were noted. The suggestion that federal activities relating to federal lands not in specialized use should be placed in a single agency was debated pro and con.

FROM THE RECORD

Public Ownership and Management

While no issue arose over continued federal control of range lands now in public ownership, some forms of management were criticized. It was urged in particular that more emphasis be placed on land classification to establish the best uses of the soil, and on research and testing of methods in grass reseeding and water conservation.

Leslie A. Miller (Cheyenne, Wyo.) Maximum yields of timber products and of water must be the first objectives of management practices in the western forested lands. Grazing in such areas must be a secondary consideration. Not all grazing is by domestic livestock—much is by wildlife. Therefore, we have multiple use of these lands, and in such circumstances it is imperative that we have one over-all ownership and management.

In certain cases there are heavily timbered areas on the fringes of the national reservations and outside the primary areas of water supply where perhaps some further disposition to private ownership could be arranged, but these would be relatively small in acreage.

In the main, then, I would say federal ownership of grazing lands should continue except in such cases where there are isolated tracts contiguous to base lands which could be gotten into private ownership to good advantage and to lessen costs of administration to the federal government.

Clarence L. Forsling (Albuquerque, N.Mex.): Disposal of scattered public domain lands is going on at entirely too slow a rate. But before they are disposed of, these areas should be examined in respect to their highest use, whether for turning over to a state for fishing, wildlife, or such other purposes.

Evan L. Flory (Bureau of Indian Affairs): We haven't looked at our range lands and our wild lands for their proper use. It behooves us to classify these lands from a soil standpoint and then manage them on the basis of what we find to be the best use.

The invasion of a relatively new weed,

halogeton, on the ranges of the West points to the need for accelerated research and action programs. The weed comes in where ranges have been misused. From western Oregon, we have had inquiries about tansy ragwort and goatweed. Many beet growers have complained about the leaf hopper, which comes from weeds on range lands. In these and other portions of the country, government agencies who administer range lands have been criticized because the condition of their ranges permits the growth of these weeds, which are a threat to private land. Whether such criticisms are justified is beside the point; we do have that growing problem.

Mr. Forsling: One need in the national forests is to step up research and action programs to rehabilitate the underproductive lands, including reseeding the depleted range lands. That will go further in increasing a supply of food and fiber than any amount of legislation that would change or freeze policy and favor one interest over another.

Varying reactions to federal range practice in different parts of the country led to discussion of the dissimilar methods of the two agencies principally concerned.

Mr. Black: In Section I this morning Elmer Brock of Wyoming talked about the forest grazing lands of that state as being very badly managed. William R. Mathews, on the other hand, says that in Arizona the Forest Service is doing a magnificent job, and that management of the range lands suffers by comparison.

Albert Mitchell (T. E. Mitchell and Son Cattle Ranch): Improvement in the management of the New Mexico public domain has been very constructive. They have definitely improved the quality of the grass, and the administration has been to the satisfaction of the ranchers. Altogether, it is one of the best programs that has been put into effect under federal management.

Frederic G. Renner (Soil Conservation Service): Take any body of land of 180 million acres and you are going to get variations in the management.

MR. FORSLING: There is no need for any violent or major changes of policies on the national forest ranges. Rather, there is a need to continue the provision for gradual changes from time to time as need and experience show them to be necessary.

One of the issues today—and there is a bill before Congress on the subject—is whether or not the law under which the public domain grazing lands are administered should not be changed so as to more nearly resemble national forest administration, by permitting more discretion to the Secretary of the Interior.

Whether or not these changes come about, there is need for certain strengthening in administration and management of these lands under present legislation. A primary defect with regard to grazing districts is that the cost of administration and improvement is geared to the amount of money collected for grazing fees in such a manner that by keeping the grazing fees low, range management is wholly inadequate, and range rehabilitation, particularly work to restore denuded or damaged watershed lands, is proceeding at a very unsatisfactory rate.

In New Mexico, livestock users pay about 1.4 cents per acre and in Arizona 0.7 cent per acre for year-long grazing. In contrast, for certain railroad lands in those two states, the charge is 15 cents plus an ad valorem tax of 3 to 8 cents per acre. I doubt if these land grants are 10 to 20 times better than the public domain lands.

MR. MITCHELL: In my own experience, the relationship between the man who uses the range and the range operator has worked more smoothly under the Taylor Grazing Act than under the Forest Service. It is just a matter of adjusting the regulations and differences there.

MR. MILLER: In Wyoming many a rancher grazes his livestock on both forested and nonforested lands. He will have a permit from the Forest Service to graze a certain number of animals during a specified part of a year on a forest preserve. He will also have a lease from the Bureau of Land Management to graze a less restricted number of animals in a grazing district for a longer period. Each agency has a different set of grazing regulations and a different approach to its fee system.

The greater part of Wyoming's national forests is in the regional jurisdiction of an office at Ogden, Utah. The regional headquarters for the Bureau of Land Management is at Billings, Mont. Thus, it may happen that a man must deal with offices hundreds of miles apart.

As a consequence of this type of administrational defect and others, the first Hoover Commission came up with a recommendation that the Forest Service and the Bureau of Land Management be merged into one forest and range service.

The suggestion that many of the conflicts could be eased by placing the two agencies in one administration received considerable support.

MR. MITCHELL: The establishment of one bureau that will handle the grazing problems of both the public domain and the national forests is highly desirable. It is the intention of the legislation that Congressman D'Ewart referred to last evening[1] and, frankly, I feel that that is the only way the lands can be administered to the best interests of the livestock industry and at the same time be satisfactorily maintained.

MR. BUTLER: The eventual need of having some machinery to determine whether we shall, say, graze or raise timber on fringe range and forest land is a compelling argument for administering all of those lands under one agency.

S. V. CIRIACY WANTRUP (University of California): Was it suggested that the Forest Service should take over the management of the Taylor grazing districts?

MR. MILLER: The Hoover Commission recommended that the suggested forest and

---

[1] See page 364.

range service be placed in the Department of Agriculture. There was a dissent in the Commission which urged the creation of a department of natural resources, in which this merger would be made. I was chairman of the Hoover Commission's task force on natural resources, and that was the recommendation we made—that a new department of natural resources be set up, because we felt that to take a bureau out of one department and put it in another would meet with such antagonism that it probably couldn't be accomplished. Others in the Commission recommended that the merged service be in the Interior Department. But I still think that a department of natural resources is a logical conclusion.

MR. BLACK: There is one slight difficulty connected with that—the peculiar position of the farm woodlands. I suppose they would still be in the Department of Agriculture, whereas, the nonfarm small wood holdings—165,000 of them in New England alone—would be in the department of natural resources, and they are side by side on the same roads scattered all over the country.

MR. MILLER: In our discussions of this proposed development, we took the attitude that the Department of Agriculture is a service governmental organization, whereas the Interior Department is more or less a management organization. Private farm wood lots need service; they provide their own management. The publicly owned timber lands and the grazing lands need management.

MR. WANTRUP: But the Department of Agriculture is not only a service department; to a large extent it is a research department. Moreover, the Forest Service, which is primarily not a service but an administrative agency, has operated within the Department of Agriculture quite successfully for many years. I would question the logic of insisting upon a sharp separation between research, service, and administration.

MR. BLACK: One managing unit for the publicly owned forests and the publicly owned grazing lands has a lot to recommend it. But it would tend to raise the question about

where research would be carried on. The department of natural resources could not do it all because research problems relating to public and private forests are reasonably different.

Improvement of Private Range Lands

Discussion here centered on federal assistance and on programs applying to private range land.

MR. RENNER: The most important factor contributing to the substantially improved condition of the range over the past 25 years has been a change of attitude, stemming perhaps from the depression-born efforts of the government in the thirties. More and more ranchers have come to believe that conservation practices are not only a good thing for posterity, but are sound business for themselves and the present generation.

There is still a long way to go. Some estimates indicate that there are approximately 760 million acres of range in the 17 western states that can be improved 150 to 300 percent. That is considered physically possible. The rapidity with which we attain it is, of course, another problem. We still have some 80 million acres to be reseeded; some ranges still need fencing; some are poorly watered. We certainly need more and better research. An unanswered problem is our need for more cost-of-production studies to help operators reduce their costs. We need concentrated study of conservation methods themselves to speed up their use. We need to concentrate on developing grass that offers promise of maximum nutritious forage. We need to study the adaptability of fertilizers in different areas.

With regard to technical and financial assistance, we need a great deal more flexibility in our programs. The fact that a program was appropriated $500 million or $400 million 10 years ago doesn't at all mean that we need that amount today. We may need much less; we may in some cases need more.

MR. MITCHELL: I want to commend the ACP payments, which have enabled ranchers to apply improvements at a time when they were financially not able to do it themselves.

When they saw the benefits that accrued to their ranges, it was the turning point in the proper utilization of the range.

MR. MILLER: Incentives for range improvements are receiving attention in the form of bills before the Congress. These incentives are economically good business in that they tend to the stabilization of the livestock industry. However, it is to be hoped that the incentive program will not be carried to extremes; some of the proposals to extend federal financial aid to livestock growers for purposes of construction and maintenance of more or less permanent watering and other improvements, could be so liberal as to downgrade the individual initiative of our western ranchers.

Multiple Use

Questions of multiple use came up repeatedly during the range-land discussions. Many political and economic factors figured in consideration of how to determine the soundest combinations.

MR. BUTLER: The question is complex. From what standpoint are we to judge the best combination of uses to which land may be put? Local welfare? Regional welfare? National welfare? While a great deal of information with respect to the productive capacity or potential of the land has been collected over the past 25 years, I think that the multiple-use principle is being applied mainly by the local administrators on the basis of needs of a local community. That is all right and proper, I would say, unless a large regional area is being affected or it is contrary to the best interests of the national welfare. And that brings us to the long-range view: Who is going to determine the regional or national need for the handling of particular areas on an extensive scale?

MR. FORSLING: The differences between the national forest lands and the grazing district lands bear on the problems of multiple use, particularly from the watershed protection standpoint. In the forest there is less conflict between practices that promote production and those that maintain conditions that will promote desirable runoff and control erosion so that sediment will not be carried downstream. The grazing districts are very susceptible to erosion; those lands comprise parts of such stream bases as the Colorado River, the Rio Grande, Arkansas, the Missouri, and the Columbia, and it is from these public domain lands that most of the silt load in the streams is carried. Not all of it is caused by bad grazing management, but a great deal is, and much of it can be controlled by proper measures.

MR. RENNER: Most of us will agree that multiple use is a sound theory, but I think we have made some pretty sad mistakes in its practice. We have used the theory to try to satisfy a great number of people with different intentions as to the land. We need more facts; we need the kind of land classification Mr. Flory mentioned [page 71]. After we have determined the primary use of an area, we should manage the land accordingly, recognizing the necessity of sacrificing some of the value of subordinate uses.

MURRAY R. BENEDICT (University of California): It is difficult sometimes to find out what is the primary use and, secondly, how much weight to give to supplementary uses. I think there is a field of research there that has been almost untouched.

Water-surfaced Lands

As a source of food and furs the ponds, lakes, streams, and marshes of the nation have limited significance today; but they offer virtually untapped opportunities for supplementing the production of food from farm and range. Looking to future population growth, we can develop now programs that will enable us to draw upon their fish and fowl resources when total demand for food increases. Many people feel, however, that the unique continuing contribution of these lands is to our social well-being and that, if only from the recreational point of view, conditions under which they can be made to produce and thrive should be encouraged. This aspect was discussed by Subsection C (pages 94-97) and also by Section I (pages 53-54). Subsection A, therefore, limited its attention to a survey of the food- and fur-producing potentialities of our inland waters and wetlands prepared by Albert M. Day of the Fish and Wildlife Service.

FROM THE RECORD

As a Source of Food

Today, inland waters contribute only 3 percent of the total food production. Reasons for this comparatively low level were considered by Mr. Day to be (1) the limited areas covered by our inland fisheries; (2) the small, individualistic character of the businesses engaged in the catch; (3) the psychological barrier which excludes from the American diet many edible and even choice species; and (4) the dominance of sport fishermen—some 30 million strong—in the administrative machinery of our public fisheries. "It is a common occurrence for a well-planned rough fish or surplus game fish utilization program to run aground on the shoals of sportsmen's indignation." But, with good management, he believed the inland waters of the United States to be capable of increasing their yield several times over.

MR. DAY: There is little doubt that one day, when our population overtakes our food-producing ability, we will be forced to develop the resources of our ever-increasing inland waters, but, as we undertake this development, the paramount interests of recreational fishing should be kept in the forefront.

We need, meantime, to emphasize our research in the field of fish population dynamics. Fundamental studies in the fields of electricity and electronics, and in developing other ways of leading, attracting, or concentrating fish are of high priority. And we must learn how to store, ship, and process the products of the fishery at economical rates. In time, it is possible that we may see our inland waters producing as much as a billion and a half pounds of fish and by-products.

A. J. CHRISTIANSEN: (Illinois Coal Strippers Association): Strip mining, as you know, creates ponds. In Illinois we have 2,500 acres of lakes that have been created by the final cuts. They have all been stocked with fish and have been used quite extensively by sportsmen's groups. About a year and a half ago one of the coal companies hired a full-time biologist to conduct research on developing some of the ponds for commercial fish raising.

DON B. GOODLOE (Maryland Beekeepers): I would like to ask Mr. Day if he can tell anything about fish ponds and crop rotation. If you have a farm pond and you drain it, can it be used for anything else?

MR. DAY: We have never developed that system here, although it is widely used in some low countries of Europe, and maybe 50 years from now we shall be doing it here. In Europe, they have their areas dyked similar to the rice paddy in California. Vegetable crops are grown for two years. When the crops are harvested, the areas are flooded and planted to fish. In a year they can produce 600 to 1,000 pounds of fish per acre. The areas are then drained, plowed, and put back in cultivation for agricultural use for another two years.

As a Source of Fur

The value of raw furs from the wetlands amounted in 1952 to about $50 million, but, with the exception of beaver, the harvest has been declining for the past several years.

MR. DAY: Fur animals can be an important by-product of management for waterfowl and fishing. By continuing research, we may develop new uses for raw furs and encourage the utilization of the carcasses. For example, the Horicon Marsh, a wildlife paradise in central Wisconsin, was drained years ago for agricultural purposes. This destroyed the wildlife habitat and attempts to farm the reclaimed marsh ended in costly failures. Subsequently, the Wisconsin Conservation Department and the Fish and Wildlife Service purchased and restored the area for wildlife purposes. Muskrats returned along with the ducks and geese. Last winter, almost two years after the major restoration was completed, the harvest on the state's 9,000-acre part of the marsh was nearly 37,000 muskrats, and on the Service's 12,000-acre portion it amounted to 48,000. At last year's average price of $1.50, the fur returns amounted to $127,500, or a per-acre yield of $6.07.

Reclamation and flood-control projects are exposing wildlife habitats to increasing hazards. Mr. Day emphasized the need for greater appreciation of good land use or multiple land use.

MR. DAY: In many instances, the dollar value of furs alone cannot offset the potential agricultural returns, particularly when the government shares the cost of reclaiming wetlands, and then provides price supports for resulting agricultural crops. However, there are several indirect values to the public that must be considered. As yet, we do not know the exact relationships of marshes and groundwater supplies, but we can readily visualize the importance of these lowlands as upstream storage basins which alleviate flood conditions. Recognizing these public benefits, we might offer wetland owners some form of tax relief.

MR. FORSLING: Isn't it true, too, that government subsidized drainage and flood control often destroy important wildlife habitat by converting to other use overflow land which, were it not for the subsidy, would have remained as good wildlife habitat—as in the Mississippi bottomlands, for example?

MR. DAY: Yes, in many areas, there is the threat of complete loss of wildlife habitat by inundation due to the building of flood-control storage areas. We are faced constantly with these threats toward wildlife values by these construction programs. In the six years 1947 through 1952, 1,122,000 acres of water storage reservoirs were added to the nation's total.

Subsection B

TIMBER AND FOREST PRODUCTS

What steps in forest management will help in satisfying future requirements? Timber growth is rising—so much so that total growth is now about equal to total drain. While the poor quality of much of the new growth raises problems of utilization, prospects for meeting future demands are encouraging, the subsection thought, if all groups concerned with the protection and management of the forests are fully aware of their interdependence. Teamwork—in research; in education; in protection from fire, insects, and disease; in reforestation—is the force that must pull together the efforts of federal and state governments, of industry, and of private forest owners.

How can the responsibility of each group be defined? And how can cooperative relationships be strengthened to encourage full utilization of public and privately owned forest lands on a sustained-yield basis?

The subsection examined these broad questions step by step, looking first at the whole series of assistance and service measures already established: *Educational and service activities*—are they provided in a manner that will encourage the small forest owner to practice sound forestry? *Grants-in-aid*—do they need adjusting to changing conditions in the states? *Legislation*—should it be employed to induce operators to use at least minimum forest practices? *Insects and diseases*—how can we obtain more effective control? *Timber Resource Review*—is its present form a suitable basis for the formulation of forestry policy?

In addition, the subsection considered the following two general areas: *Forest ownership*—is the time ripe for considering adjustments in the pattern of land ownership? *The national forests and other public ownerships*—what measures will improve forest productivity while safeguarding these lands for their best possible uses?

Throughout most of the discussions, the position of the small forest owner vis-à-vis state government, federal government, and industry was considered repeatedly. His marketing problems, for example, were seen to be affected by the educational services of the state and of industry, and by federal and state regulation and financial assistance. The willingness of industry to assume responsibility for part of his forestry education and some of his technical service was emphasized.

There were some differences of viewpoint on grants-in-aid and legislation. The varying needs for research—particularly basic research—were recognized widely, as was also the need for further education.

Education and Service

The general trend is toward greater state responsibility in varying degrees for activities beyond the research and financial and technical assistance provided by the federal government.

In forest management the need for greater coordination between state and federal governments was seen as especially acute. Good forest practice pays off, but still there are not enough public foresters to go around. Some form of harvesting and marketing assistance similar to that extended to farmers may be needed to assure sound cutting methods on wood lots and other small forest holdings. But, if only because a continuing timber supply is to its own interest, industry is likely to assume more and more responsibility in education and assistance, up to the point where the services of the consulting forester can be used to advantage.

FROM THE RECORD

To what extent can educational and service activities assure the use of reasonably adequate forestry practices on the farm wood lot and other small ownerships? What should be the division of responsibility between public agencies, industry, and consulting foresters?

CHARLES H. FLORY (South Carolina State Forester): It is impossible to determine with any precision the extent to which adequate practices may be achieved by education, demonstration, and service. It is clear to me that creating a desire on the part of the landowner and operator to bring about more adequate and acceptable practices through education and service shows more promise than will be achieved through regulatory legislation.

Federal participation in fire protection on private lands will undoubtedly continue in much the same pattern as in the past, under mutually acceptable programs with the states. The states will continue to take major responsibility for over-all activities up to the point of providing *basic* protection. A ceiling for the expenditure of public funds should be established, beyond which any greater intensification of fire protection desired would be borne by the landowner. Industry will continue to intensify its contributions in fire protection, both on its own holdings and on nonindustry lands; its cooperation in supporting the work of state and federal agencies is increasingly important.

In insect and disease control, the responsibilities of each group are quite similar to their responsibilities with regard to fire control, and require as great a degree of cooperation. Coordination of state service and research activities with those of the federal government is especially desirable.

Management assistance to private landowners is a rapidly growing field requiring full coordination between all agencies. Federal responsibility should be limited largely to financial and technical assistance to the states. States should take over-all responsibility in education, demonstration, and limited on-the-ground service to the small landowners and operators.

The number of private consulting foresters is increasing rapidly; many offer services beyond the scope of public foresters; they are contributing substantially to better forestry practices; public agencies should strongly encourage this expansion. Industry is contributing substantially in education, examinations, demonstrations, timber marking, harvesting, reforestation, and research. These efforts are supplementing the work of public and consulting foresters and are coordinated with the prevailing programs in the several states.

The job of initial and sustained contacts with landowners and operators is so huge that combined efforts are of great importance.

On the production and distribution of forest tree seedlings, there should be continued study at the regional level to improve production, distribution, and planting methods. The designated state agency should have primary responsibility for the production and distribution of forest tree seedlings.

FRANK HEYWARD, JR. (Gaylord Container Corporation): As recently as 1939 practically all of the pulpwood producers in the South were completely ignorant as to correct pulpwood harvesting methods. Today, practically all of these men use in everyday conversation such terms as "thinning," "partial cutting," "seedlings," "marking," "hardwood control," "salvage operation," and others.

A big step forward is the fact that banking groups are now including forestry in their periodic field trips.

Some of the most effective educational work of both public and private agencies is done through the 4-H and FFA groups. In this field the work of the pulp and paper industry through its Southern Pulpwood Conservation Association has been outstanding. The greatly increased interest in forestry on the farm may be accounted for by the educational work of the past decade.

Some participants believed that a service charge for management plans encouraged improved forest practice. The same attitude was also voiced in relation to the distribution of tree seedlings (see page 84).

MELVIN N. TAYLOR (Trees for Tomorrow, Inc.): Since 1946 my organization has prepared management plans for 120,000 acres of privately owned woodland. Seven years ago there was not too much demand for this service, which was free. This year, for the first time, we are charging a fee of 10 cents an acre for an over-all forest management plan and $1.50 an hour for estimating volume or marking for harvest. We have since received an unusually large number of requests for management plan service. People seem to feel more confident because they are paying, and I think we will get a higher degree of compliance. The ultimate step, of course, is a switch over to the consulting foresters' services where the marketing problems will be taken care of.

CHARLES H. FLORY: In South Carolina no charge is made by public foresters for woodland examinations, recommendations, and demonstrations. Where timber is to be harvested, we make a charge for marking and tallying services. Demand for such assistance is usually greater than we can service. Landowners and most operators are in accord with this practice.

Marketing problems were regarded by many to be a compelling reason for much poor forestry practice. Disagreement as to their solution recurred when the subsection discussed the question relating to legislation.

W. B. GREELEY (West Coast Lumbermen's Association): All agencies are needed and all combined cannot do too much, but I believe, in the last analysis, the man who provides the market for wood-lot timber will have the most to say about that situation. We have many examples all over the country of effective aid being extended to the wood-lot owner by his logical market.

I should like to see our forest industry adopt a primary responsibility for service to the small wood-lot owner, particularly with reference to the harvesting and marketing of his crop.

E. R. MARTELL (Purdue University): Unfortunately, in the hardwood industry we have two groups: we have what I call the reasonable operators, and then we have those who look down their noses at the small producer. But under our free enterprise system, I think both groups could be induced to do an excellent job along the lines suggested by Colonel Greeley.

In Indiana we have five Extension Foresters to cover 200,000 farms. The job can't be done by the state agencies or the private foresters; industry should assume responsibility.

RICHARD M. BRETT (Yale University Conservation Program): I am a small wood-lot owner. Our great problem is to market the wood we produce. I speak of those of us who produce small amounts of wood each year. If industry could find a way to make regular purchases from small wood-lot owners, it would mean, in the aggregate, a steady supply, and it might make the owner more interested in planting trees and growing timber.

CHARLES H. STODDARD (Independent Timber Farmers of America): One of the important needs of the small operator is a short-term production credit program. In the matter of long-term credit, we still haven't achieved any real program, although some success has been gained lately. Help is needed to take off some of the economic pressure when the small owner is liquidating his holdings or marketing his product. Along with that is a lack of general knowledge of market prices. The price reporting services and other farm programs that have been available to the farmer over the last 20 years should be available to the forest operator.

L. J. WILHOITE (Electric Power Board of Chattanooga): Down in the TVA area, I own 300 acres of forest land, which I just completed cutting over the last two years.

Clarification of the duties of the different governmental agencies concerned with wood-lot forestry is badly needed. In my own community I found six agencies, either local, state, or federal, concerned with providing me, as the owner of a wood lot, with technical advice and assistance. I got service from two sources, the TVA and the Soil Conservation Service. The rest were of no use to me. The sooner this is all concentrated in the county agent, the better off we are all going to be.

I hired two professional foresters and sold the timber on a stumpage basis; good experts say I received about two-thirds of what it was worth. In my community, most of the timber is cut by grasshopper sawmill operators. I

79

didn't sell to them, but people tell me I would have done just as well or better.

What the forest owner needs is market facilities. The problem won't be worked out except on the basis of a cooperative scheme, such as the farmers now have.

HENRY D. PALEY (United Paperworkers of America): Where contract cutters are limited, as far as the market is concerned, to one mill, their prices very often change at the whim of the mill and, as a result, the labor they employ becomes submarginal labor. Their aim is to get every ounce of wood out of an area. These operators should have other places to market their lumber so they could take advantage of some sort of competition. The present system is detrimental to good forestry practices.

LARRY COOK (Ohio Reclamation Association): State, federal, and consulting foresters are all important, but I believe the work of organizations like the Ohio Forestry Association is important to what we are talking about

here. It is educating the timber grower, and helping the small wood-lot owner to harvest and market his timber. Much of the financial support for this program has come from industries that are not interested in growing timber themselves. The result is that the Association has been able to carry on research, such as the program on the Dutch Elm disease, in which it works with federal and state agencies toward a solution of the problem. It has organized the timber cutters and is placing them on an ethical basis. It has also organized the small wood-lot owners and is giving them an opportunity to know what good forestry is.

The mills and manufacturers who depend upon timber cannot afford to jeopardize their supply for the future by condoning improper growing and harvesting practices. State and federal agencies alone can never solve the forestry problem. We must have as well the cooperation of industries that will suffer from improper forestry practices, and organizations like the Ohio Forestry Association can secure the cooperation and support of private industry.

Legislation and Grants-in-Aid

On the whole, legislation was regarded as a tool to be used sparingly, since education can often get better results. Difficulties of adjustment to a second-growth economy were cited as the main possible reason for regulation. When it appears necessary, operation at the state level, to implement the recommendations of local working committees, was suggested as the most promising method.

Opinion as to the need for further grants-in-aid differed with varying regional conditions. In the South and Northwest, industry's increasing contributions and the growing trend toward greater use of the consulting forester's services might lessen the need for federal assistance; but in the Northeast and in states where forestry is a secondary industry, further federal financial aid may be essential to state programs of education and service.

Similarly, while participants from some areas believed that state nursery programs are now able to stand on their own feet, others, from less well-organized areas, were convinced that federal grants should be continued at least until all state nurseries are actually self-supporting.

Cooperation among public agencies, industry, and private forest owners in fire prevention and control has worked with considerable success. Because forest lands are also multiple-use lands, and because some areas must consider measures to combat fire in case of war, increasing grants-in-aid may sometimes be justified. But the trend of the past five or six years has been toward proportionately greater state and private expenditures.

The same pattern was suggested for control of insects and diseases. There was little doubt in the subsection that the kind of pest control legislation being worked out by the Council of State Governments in cooperation with forestry associations, will enable regional committees to grapple more effectively with this problem.

FROM THE RECORD

Is the present gradual increase in timber growth likely to equal or exceed the drain without some type of legislation requiring the use of minimum forest practices?

DeWitt Nelson (California Department of Natural Resources): Possibly the best answer I can give is to cite California's Forest Practice Law, under which a committee for each of four Forest Practice Districts develops minimum forest practice rules applicable to its district. Rules that are agreed upon in public hearings of forest owners and operators and, after that, approved by the State Board of Forestry, have the full effect of law. It is estimated that 84 percent of California's production is harvested in compliance with the minimum forest practice rules, and much of that under practices in excess of the rules.

We have an unanswered problem in the field of forest taxation. Achievement of balance between drain and growth is not a true measure of forestry in all cases. In California, and the West generally, our extensive old growth areas reflect little net growth. More important here is the need to harvest those stands and put them in a productive state. There are problems of ownership. More than half of California's 7.5 million acres of privately owned timber cropland is held by small owners, many of them absentee. From these lands we cannot now assume a full and adequate level of production. Possibly part of the answer will come from very intensive management of choice timberlands in large private and public ownership. Better management, developments in genetics, and new methods of utilization will make more usable raw material available. If and when the three problems of management, protection, and taxation can be solved for all sizes of forest ownership, we should readily balance growth with drain.

H. R. Josephson (U.S. Forest Service): Much evidence indicates that timber growth is building up as a result of various forestry programs and there are very real prospects of continued increases in timber growth. But in many regions we have a lot of growth coming on in low-grade undesirable species of hardwoods of small sizes. These are not good replacements for the higher quality timber cut. Many industries will face difficult problems in shifting to hardwoods or low-grade material.

With respect to lumber, in particular, poor material at best means higher costs and higher prices. Also markets for high-grade lumber may be lost temporarily, and perhaps permanently, if only low-grade material is available.

So until the situation regarding future timber supply and demand becomes clearer, it seems the better part of wisdom to accelerate forest production by continuing or expanding those forestry programs which experience shows to be effective.

R. C. Jacobson (Minnesota State CIO Council): If we are going to make progress, the price of timber will rise to an unduly high point and science will figure out all sorts of ways to make a much fuller use of the whole tree, and you will find yourselves with a crop of timber on your hands greater than the need. So it is important that you don't get it too high.

Joseph F. Kaylor (Maryland State Department of Forests and Parks): I am very much in favor of some form of regulation in the state because, in Maryland, regulation has enabled us to do an effective educational job.

MR. BRETT: Legislative enactments, as applied to the small landowner, are not necessarily a solution to the problem. The place to start with the small landowner is to educate him that it is to his self-interest to use proper forestry practices. The small landowner frequently does not follow good forestry practices merely because he does not understand their value.

MR. GREELEY: The growing trend in dealing with forests is very definitely toward the Scandinavian system of local committees. These local committees have varying degrees of authority. In some states they have regulatory power, as in California. Or they may use educational means. Sometimes they use both regulation and education. The chief point is that the means they use should be flexible and adjustable to changing conditions.

Considerable discussion turned upon the purchaser's responsibility in influencing the practice of the small landowner.

JOHN W. O'BOYLE (Nebo Oil Company): Most of the Texas pulp people are very good about managing their own properties and they are very helpful to the small owners who have tracts to cut. But I am wondering if, by purchasing wood from the independent contractors who are guilty of violating all good practices, the large pulpwood purchasers aren't really acting as a "fence."

LOWELL BESLEY (American Forestry Association): Regulation within the industry has been a trend, and I think it has been a success, in some places. But such a program requires one purchaser only, or it must be a combination of all the purchasers who will agree to it, and that is something that is extremely difficult to work out.

EARL PORTER (International Paper Company): There are facts that make it impossible to do just what Mr. O'Boyle says, but what is being done is exactly what you are all advocating. Because industry has to provide for its raw material supply, it is taking care of its

timber supply through education, and through its contacts with small landowners. The industry needs the timber from small farms having 4 to 10 acres in woods; that supply can be doubled or tripled to meet the demands of the next 25 or 50 years, under the educational system now being followed by the industry.

ELWOOD L. DEMMON (Southeastern Forest Experiment Station): Certainly, southern industry has contributed a great deal and is still doing so, but pulpwood accounts for only about 25 percent of total drain in the South. Sawlogs account for more than half the drain, and most of this timber is cut by small sawmills.

ANTHONY W. SMITH (CIO Conservation Committee): We are still cutting our timber at the rate of three trees for every two trees grown. As a union, we favor the Gifford Pinchot policy of direct federal regulation of cutting on private lands; we would apply that policy to the holdings of the large privately owned monopolistic interests. If these groups really intend to do the magnificent work they talk about in forestry, then they have nothing to fear from regulation.

With regard to farmers and small holders, we favor a long-term contract system. We would have local public agencies with perpetual life enter by purely voluntary agreements into long-term contracts whereby small owners would undertake to manage their timberlands on a scientific basis, and whereby the federal government, acting through the local agencies, would provide financial and technical assistance. We propose that small holders be encouraged to form cooperatives for mutual aid in production and marketing.

EDWARD P. STAMM (Industrial Forestry Association): In the Pacific Northwest, we are not unaware of the fact that there are a lot of poor practices on the part of small woodland owners. Education is the answer and the large wood companies are participating in that, at the risk sometimes of being called paternalistic, domineering, arrogant, and sometimes downright nasty. But I think if we were in the position of a lot of woodland owners, and had their problems, we might be guilty of poor practice too. The fact remains, we are at least making progress.

HENRY J. MALSBERGER (Southern Pulpwood Conservation Association): Industry itself is using approximately 200 foresters today to carry the story of good forest practice to the small landowners. It will take us a long time to get it down to all of them, but industry is prepared to do it. I think it would be appropriate for the public agencies to refer such cases as we have heard about today to somebody in our industry.

LEON F. KNEIPP (Washington, D.C.): In Austria in 1935 I saw beautiful big logs allowed to tumble end-over-end down steep hillsides. The inspector almost wept when he saw it. And these were people brought up for generations with a full appreciation of what good forestry means. Can we depend entirely on education and persuasion?

Should federal responsibility for forest fire and pest control, forest management, and tree seedling production, through grants-in-aid, be greater or less than at present?

MR. MALSBERGER: There are some 58 million acres of forested land in the United States still needing fire control. The general public benefits from the forests in many ways but also causes more forest fires than do the owners. This justifies increased use of public funds until we reach a point of complete protection.

In 1948 appropriations for fire control amounted to some $8,605,000 from federal funds and nearly $15,000,000 from state and private funds. By 1952 the federal government had raised this by 4 percent, but the increase in appropriations from state and private sources was in the order of 78 to 79 percent. This trend should be continued, utilizing public funds to provide basic protection and private funds to intensify it as required by the owner.

Because forest pest control is a matter of combating natural causes, I believe it is the function of the federal agencies to develop ways and means of doing this job; but the operating funds should be provided by the

state, supplemented by private industry. This is what is being done on larger tracts, and the same service must be made available to small owners.

Public grants-in-aid were essential to convince the small owner that improved forest practices were beneficial to him at a time when the tree-growing business was not so attractive as now. The agencies have done an excellent job in this field. Industry is now employing hundreds of foresters working in this same field. If a particular state finds more demand than can now be met with the present public, industry, and consulting foresters management programs, then I think the state should provide the additional funds from its own sources.

Industry should continue to enlarge its programs of service because industry has both an obligation to the landowner and an advantage to be gained by continuing management assistance up to a point where the consulting forester can move in and sell the small landowner not only technical service but also business representation.

I see little need for expansion in grants-in-aid to promote a tree-planting program. Perhaps if federal grants-in-aid were deleted entirely, the national tree-planting program would in no way be curtailed. Where industry has not operated its own nurseries, it has actively supported increases in state funds to provide seedlings.

ALBERT D. NUTTING (Maine State Forest Commissioner): If the fact of multiple use of woodlands is recognized, then the federal government has a continuing responsibility to cooperate with states and owners in forest protection. Moreover, the hazard of war justifies increased federal grants for defense against forest fire possibilities. I come from a state where this is a particular problem, and I believe it is one that should be handled through the existing agencies which handle forest fire protection work.

I believe that federal grants-in-aid should be used as an incentive to states to set up pest detection services; but once well established, these services should be operated by the states and owners. In the case of serious, large control programs, the federal agencies should provide 25 to 50 percent of the funds needed. Basic research is essential, and is largely a federal responsibility.

Forest nursery programs are quite well established in most states. I believe a small amount of federal money is needed in order to coordinate state programs and encourage a few of the states in better nursery practices.

Federal assistance is needed to encourage further development in service or farm forestry programs and to maintain present programs in many states. I should like to see the federal government provide a more definite incentive by guaranteeing a fixed percentage of project costs. The allocations should have maximum limits to any state, based on woodland acreage and populations. This is a point on which I differ somewhat from Henry Malsberger; in the South they may have gone somewhat further in that respect than we have in the Northeast.

Certainly federal assistance should be based on long enough periods—probably five years—to provide for some degree of stability. I put quite a bit of emphasis on this.

CHARLES H. FLORY: In many states especially those producing 1-0 stock, and where nursery programs are well established and are efficiently operating, this program can be almost or entirely self-supporting. There is need for limited federal assistance, especially in continued research, methods to improve efficiency, etc.

W. D. HAGENSTEIN (Industrial Forestry Association): When the State of Washington was giving away free trees, we found we were not getting the trees in the ground. Since the state began selling its nursery stock, we have sold trees for $7.00 a thousand as far south as California, and in following up find that when the owner has a financial interest at stake the trees are getting into the ground.

GEORGE B. HARTMAN (Iowa State College): The time may have come in some states when the forest industry can be depended upon to carry the burden of growing and distributing forest planting stock and of giving assistance in forest management. There is no industry in Iowa to do that sort of thing. The same thing is probably true in Minnesota and, I believe, in many other states, particularly those that are primarily agricultural. Our forest industry in Iowa is largely made up of small operators who are not organized to help support forestry enterprise. So I rather expect that for a number of years we will continue to need federal aid.

What are the relative responsibilities of federal, state, and private agencies in obtaining more effective control of insects and diseases? Is legislation authorizing state agencies to force private owners to take control measures desirable?

ERNEST L. KOLBE (Western Pine Association): In many areas insects and forest diseases are imperiling the economic stability of the entire community. In the last 20 years, in my own region, an Oregon western pine area, insects alone have destroyed some 73 billion board feet of timber. A great share of this destruction is on public land. Public agency pest control work should be expanded. There are slight differences in the development of plans for fire control and for insects, but it is my feeling that a general pattern of cooperation between the federal government, the states, and the private companies or groups, along the lines established for many years on fire control, can be primarily responsible for the control of insects and disease.

Some states have legislation similar to the federal government's Forest Pest Control Act of 1947. Private owners have recognized their responsibility by paying their share and by participating in regional committees or councils. But to work effectively, these action groups need enabling legislation and also cooperation at federal and state levels.

Leadership is the responsibility of federal and state agencies. If progress in pest control is to be made in the manner of fire control, we must first of all have greater state authority, or specific authority for local groups to carry out control efforts. For voluntary local control is to a large degree the answer to the problem.

There is also need for emergency funds at

both federal and state levels. Many a project crew has been held back because the forest pest account had been set up on a lump sum basis and hence no area action could be taken.

JAMES A. BEAL (U.S. Forest Service): Control methods are very good for some of our forest pests; for some they are only fair; and for others no methods have yet been developed. Inasmuch as pests and diseases are not limited to federal lands, I feel that responsibility of the federal government is some form of basic research designed to improve and cheapen surveys and control. Much can be done in this field at state and industry levels. Some states and a few companies are starting research programs.

The federal government has been working on legislation with state forestry organizations, urging them to assist their state governments in drafting workable state pest control acts. The Council of State Governments is publishing a model pest law in 1954.

G. HARRIS COLLINGWOOD (Library of Congress): Two years ago I served on a committee appointed to study pest control problems for the Bureau of Entomology. While we all agreed that the federal government has a basic responsibility for research and developing ways and means of controlling pests, we concluded that the states, and industry in particular, were slow in picking up their part of the responsibility.

ALBERT J. RIKER (University of Wisconsin): Permit me to emphasize how important may be understanding by local men. Obviously, the research to control diseases or insects, for example, must be done where such pests are active. Then when control methods have been developed, their applications have been most successful with interested participation of well-informed local people. An unknown person, particularly one from outside the state, has little, if any, chance for success.

The state law in Wisconsin, for example, is ample for the needs. Property can be quarantined or destroyed. However, local men arrange for hearings and complete technical information. Almost always, when they once understand the situation, the local people encourage and participate in the necessary control procedures.

The Function of Research

In the protection and management of the nation's forest land, a primary role of the federal government is to provide the basic knowledge. No one questioned that. Such research, however, should not necessarily be confined to the federal establishment; in pest control, particularly, there is room for greater effort on the part of states and industry. With regard to fire prevention and suppression, it was thought that federal research in this field should be regarded as no less urgent than its more recent concern with insects and disease.

There is a growing awareness of the place of forestry in the larger framework of the watershed, and of the rich promise of the study of forest genetics. Both areas ranked high in the subsection's appraisal of research needs. Development of our second-growth timber economy was recognized to demand a great deal more research in utilization of low-grade hardwoods and waste materials. The fast-changing forest situation similarly requires faster progress in completing and bringing up to date the National Forest Survey. Providing information for its preparation is undoubtedly one of the useful contributions of the Timber Resource Review.

In view of the increasing demands upon our forests, it was estimated that total research efforts should double over the next 5 to 10 years. It would seem logical to expect the federal government, together with education and research institutions, to assume the major responsibility for fundamental research, and private industry to concentrate more heavily on research applying to its own processes. But so urgent is the need for basic research in all phases of forest activity that all agencies should be encouraged to step up their efforts.

FROM THE RECORD

In the expenditure of the funds for research, what should be the relative emphasis placed on protection, biology (including genetics), silviculture and management, economics, and utilization? What should be the character of the research conducted by federal, state, or private interests?

MR. GREELEY: In broad terms, our research in wood utilization, forest management and silviculture, and protection from fire is rolling on with so much momentum, with so many participating agencies and resources, and with such a constant interchange of results, that these fields need not give us special concern. In two other fields, however—insect and disease control, and water conservation and erosion control—management of forest resources is seriously handicapped by lack of basic know-how.

The Forest Pest Control Act of 1947 has provided an excellent base for mobilizing defense against a known enemy, but the law will be ineffective until it is backed by a much stronger research and intelligence service. To provide that technical leadership should be the responsibility of the federal government.

Increasing concern with water conservation and erosion is reaching the proportions of a crusade. The management demonstrations on some 65 small watersheds, to be carried out by the Department of Agriculture in cooperation with local agencies, are the type of practical work that should be duplicated by many states and private forest owners. [See Subsection D, page 115.]

There is another field of research that should be speeded up. After 25 years, the basic inventory of timber supply, growth and drain is nowhere near completed, and only

limited areas have been covered by the resurveys. I urge that the federal government give the timber inventory high priority in research appropriations and personnel.

We should also give much greater emphasis to forest genetics. The fact that our current expenditures for tree planting and seeding have reached $5 million to $7.5 million a year warrants greater attention to the sources and qualities of our plant material. It is a work that should be shared by all research agencies —official, educational, and industrial.

MR. DEMMON: The field of forest research that requires considerably more emphasis is genetics and tree breeding. At present we are planting about half a million acres a year, using about half a billion trees annually. An expansion in this program is not only justified, but very likely to occur. So there is urgent need to grow the best possible planting stock to assure the highest quality of material for the particular purpose for which it is planted. Very little is known about the hereditary traits of the hundreds of millions of seedlings being planted each year, but we do know that a large percentage comes from inferior stock. Breeding superior trees offers a vast field of relatively unexplored research. A little country like Sweden is spending annually $250,000 on this type of work, much more than is being spent in the United States.

Another challenge to research is to improve utilization facilities and intensify forest protection and management practices even further than in recent years, so that we can be assured of greater yields with less wasted material.

It takes a long time to carry on some of these forest research projects and you don't get an answer in a year or two. Total expenditures for forest research in 1949 were estimated at nearly $17 million, of which industry put up 32 percent, the federal agencies 29 percent, the states 24 percent, and private institutions and colleges 15 percent. I doubt if the proportions have changed very much since that time, but increasingly federal forest research is being undertaken on a cooperative basis.

Of the federal expenditures for forest research, 88 percent is devoted to applied, and only 12 percent to fundamental research. If maximum progress is to be made in the years ahead, a greater proportion of basic research is needed to determine natural laws or principles leading to new knowledge. In this, public agencies and educational institutions should take the major responsibility since it is to be expected that industrial organizations will, for the most part, concentrate their efforts on applied research, including pilot plant developments for promising fundamental research leads. Close cooperation between all forest research agencies should, of course, be maintained.

Research cannot wait until practice catches up with knowledge; it must anticipate future needs. Those needs indicate that all agencies should at least double their research efforts in the next 5 to 10 years. Backed by new knowledge, soundly applied, this nation need have no fear of a shortage of forest raw materials.

Mr. RIKER: In Wisconsin we have developed research teamwork in the Wisconsin Agricultural Experiment Station, the Conservation Department, the federal government through its various agencies, a number of private individuals, and various wood-using industries. Generally speaking, this cooperation between local, state, and federal agencies provides perhaps the best means of broadening the whole approach to resources research, and of achieving success in solving complex and far-reaching problems.

We are enthusiastic over the possibilities of forest genetics applied to disease resistance. We have some white pines resistant to blister rust and some poplars resistant to certain cankers. Other examples are available—but most of the work in breeding insect- and disease-resistant trees remains to be done.

FRANK D. QUINN (Texas State Park Board): I want to make two points: First, I have found in connection with a research project on which I have been working that there is indication of substantial fundamental research, particularly on the part of private industry. Second, the difficult role of the agricultural experiment station is not generally appreciated. If a station devotes its time to basic research in forestry problems, its people are criticized because they didn't spend their efforts on agricultural crops. They have a real problem.

HARDY L. SHIRLEY (College of Forestry, State University of New York): Colleges of forestry can be particularly useful to industry by doing research on fundamental problems. Our college has been very successful in research on pulping of hardwoods and on chemical debarking under joint college-industry sponsorship. Representatives from industry have reviewed work plans, discussed results, carried out pilot tests, and put results into practice. Fundamental research fits into academic work well; less well into industrial research. By concentrating effort on problems deemed of greatest immediate importance, forest schools as well as other research agencies tend to get involved in practical problems to the neglect of the fundamental approach that is essential to real progress.

Mr. KNEIPP: First things first should be one of the essentials in attacking the vast range of forestry research problems. And the only way we can arrive at that is to assemble the whole inventory of forestry needs in all phases of research, and evaluate it in terms of priority; then let everybody start working.

BENTON R. CANCELL (Rhinelander Paper Company): This seems to be one field in which there is no general disagreement. It may well present a proper initial study for one of the foundations.

Is the current type of periodic Timber Resource Review a desirable basis for the formulation of forestry policies?

WILLARD S. BROMLEY (American Pulpwood Association): All of us who are concerned with the forest resources of this country seem to agree on the need for basic figures on areas, volumes, growth, and drain. There is not, however, full agreement as to whether it is necessary to get this data on a national scale every 8 to 10 years, under a special project such as the Timber Resource Review. A major portion of our forest products industries argues that the Timber Resource Review will hold back the more useful current work and data developed by the Forest Survey. Most of the pulpwood and pulp producing portions of industry have concurred in the need for a periodic national inventory of our forest resources every 10 years but have questioned the desirability of collecting and presenting information much beyond the factual scope of the Review, covering timber drain and wood utilization, timber resource inventory, and timber growth. Many pulp and paper companies throughout the country are now contributing appreciable amounts of labor and money toward completing the inventory phases of the Review.

That part of the Review which presents long-term estimates of the timber product needs of the nation in 1975 and 2000, is based on highly theoretical premises, which will vitally affect all predictions. These premises begin by assuming a population of 193 million persons by 1975, certain per capita wood consumption trends, probable gross national production estimates, and other economic concepts which may or may not come close to a true prediction of what actually will take place. A similar line of reasoning was applied to an estimate of future pulpwood requirements by the Forest Service in 1924, when it was carefully predicted that we would need "about 15 million cords" of pulpwood in the year 1950. Our actual consumption of pulpwood in 1950 was, according to the United States Bureau of the Census, 23,627,000 cords, representing a difference of 58 percent.

I understand that the Forest Service plans to release the results of the Timber Resource Review in two reports, the first to present statistical data, and the second an interpretation of the data in the first report. I believe this will cause confusion in the reader's mind as to which information is based on demonstrable facts and which is based on speculation. If developed at all, the speculative portion of the Review should be presented separately from the factual portions which represent the primary justification for conducting this Review.

LEONARD BARRETT (U.S. Forest Service): The Timber Resource Review, as currently planned, consists of an introductory section; a study of requirements with a forecast of future requirements; a study of current timber cut, that is, the present timber cut along with a study of plant residues, including a determination of volumes used and not used; an inventory of current standing timber, with the usual volume and area figures; a growth forecast, detailing current and expected growth; a survey of productivity of recently cut lands giving also basic figures on ownership patterns; statistics and analyses of effects of fire, insects, diseases, and so on, on present growth and also the effect of the present destructive incidents on future growth; and, finally, a section dealing with planting, seeding, and artificial regeneration, predicting effects on growth in the future.

The sections on requirements and on growth predictions are companion tasks. They deal with this business of what some folks claim is not factual in that they make predictions, and make speculations. Of course errors have been made in the past and some predictions have not been fully realized, but it would seem to us unwise to stop with the so-called factual data, which do not attempt to look into the future, in examining present progress and relating it to a comparison of future growth and requirements.

The Forest Service has agreed to review the results of the Timber Resource Review—the statistical results—with our National Advisory Group, before publication of those results. We do plan to release two types of reports, first a statistical report, which will be just tabulations, and second an interpretive report. We will subject the statistics to interpretations, analyze them, and base our conclusions on those results. Others will be free to do likewise with the statistics to the extent they wish to use them.

There have been some statements that there is a large area of disagreement with the Timber Resource Review. This is mainly with regard to the survey of productivity on recently cutover land. I want to say only that we now have actual contributions in men, money, and equipment from public agencies of 30 states. On the productivity survey people of the Forest Service will probably do not over one-third of the field work east of the Mississippi River, where, for the main part, the land is privately owned. West of the Mississippi, or west of the great plains, where a large portion of the land is publicly owned, it will be higher, and a sub-stantial portion of the work will be done by Forest Service employees.

MR. BROMLEY: I was not saying these predictions should not be made. But for Pete's sake keep them separate from the factual data and the factual inventory that we all understand. Don't mix in the figures you develop from these statistics with the same class of data that you are bringing in from the field, on which there is little argument or dispute.

MR. BARRETT: It is self-evident that they are predictions in every case. If the heading of a given column of statistics is 1952 and that of an adjoining column is 1975, I doubt that any reader will have trouble in identifying the prediction.

Patterns of Land Ownership

Many people feel that a nationwide look at the status of forest land ownership would be beneficial. The subsection agreed with this view, and believed that a Congressional committee, working in cooperation with states, as recommended by the Fourth American Forest Congress, would be effective in getting the job done. (The proceedings of this Congress, which was sponsored by The American Forestry Association, are useful companion reading to the over-all discussions of the subsection.) Such a study would look toward adjustments to make the forest lands fully productive in the public interest.

FROM THE RECORD

Should the present pattern of forest land ownership be studied for the purpose of determining what adjustments, if any, should be made?

STANLEY G. FONTANNA (Dean, School of Natural Resources, University of Michigan; statement read by J. Willcox Brown): During the period when forest land was cheap and acquisition funds plentiful, the Forest Service acquired many million acres of land. Forest Service timber has become valuable to sustain private operations, and there is considerable controversy between big and small operators as to who shall get it. Sustained-yield contracts, which seem to be a natural to stabilize the operations of large owner-operators, are opposed by small operators. Much criticism is leveled at the Forest Service because, largely through lack of access roads, mature timber is not harvested and much timber has been destroyed because of insect epidemics in the over-aged stands.

It has been strongly urged by some that further acquisition of land by the federal government be stopped entirely; in fact, that the process be reversed, and that federal lands be disposed of to private owners. Private industry, it is argued, can do a better job of management. Undoubtedly, private industry increasingly is practicing good forestry, and will continue to do so as long as it finds it profitable. The primary objective of private industry is, and understandably must be, profit.

On the other hand, the objective of management of public lands is management in the long-run interest of the people generally. In the West in many areas the highest use for public lands may be management of the watershed; in the East it may be public recreation. Production of forest products, in many areas, may be a secondary objective. Most states do not have adequate state-owned areas for use as experimental and demonstration forests, and as recreational areas. These states should acquire lands to meet these needs—such acquisition may well include lands not paying their way under private management.

When it is clearly in the public interest, there should be no hesitation on the part of public agencies to alter boundaries and dispose of lands by outright sale or by exchange either to private owners or to other public agencies. The Michigan Conservation Department has used the exchange method successfully for many years to consolidate state forest holdings, while simultaneously assisting private owners and other public agencies to consolidate their holdings.

It would seem, therefore, that the time is ripe for a nationwide inquiry into the status of land ownership. Such was the intent of the Fourth American Forest Congress when it recommended establishment of a joint Congressional committee which, working in cooperation with states, would consider a desirable pattern for ownership of federal, state, and private forest, range, and other conservation lands; and formulate policies and recommend legislation to achieve this pattern.

MR. KAYLOR: I support the proposal that there should be a look at land ownership by a governmental committee. I believe that in any state where we have a program of rehabilitation, it is to our interests to have a complete look at the current situation.

Each state committee should be constituted of representative citizens of the state, and I don't mean just the industry. Sportsmen and industrialists alike are intent upon preserving some of our lands for recreational purposes, and often this may be the highest use to which the land may be put. But the problem of preserving our water supply stands above all conflicting interests. In the eastern industrial areas it is one of our gravest concerns. I know of no better way to build up the water-supply level throughout the United States than to put some of the lands now privately owned under some form of public management.

HARRY S. MOSEBROOK (Chamber of Commerce of the U.S.): Whenever we get into a study of land ownership patterns it becomes increasingly apparent that we do not have an accurate idea today of the extent of federal land ownership. The last session of Congress authorized the General Services Administration to prepare an annual compilation of federal land ownership patterns throughout the country.

MR. O'BOYLE: The federal government is doing a good job on its forest lands. But still from time to time further land is required for various federal projects—dam projects particularly, and some military projects—which leads to the acquisition of large tracts of good timberland and to consequent reduction of the amount of timberland available to private industry in any particular radius. One such tract in the east Texas area, for instance, ranged up to many thousands of acres; its acquisition by the government may eventually put a large sawmill out of business.

MR. BROMLEY: A proposal to curb that sort of thing was presented in the last session of Congress, and was very bitterly opposed because it was implied that industry wanted to grab the national parks.

MR. KNEIPP: You can't cut down a 25-year-old stand of timber and later find that you made a mistake and go back and pick up again where you left off. You have got to have absolute continuity in forest management. Recognition of this should be the basic principle guiding this study of ownership patterns. In cases of isolated holdings that cannot be managed economically, I believe adjustments by exchange can be made, so long as fair dealing is observed by both parties.

The National Forests
and Other Public Ownerships

Although the national forests are by now self-supporting, the federal government's handling facilities lag behind the rapidly increasing volume and value of their growth. The annual harvest of timber is still below the allowable cut. From all points of view, the greatest obstacle to attaining full utilization on a sustained-yield basis is lack of an adequate transportation system. Therefore, the rapid building of access roads was considered by the subsection to be a primary task. Inventory work and engineering and management plans should be stepped up. It was suggested that governmental timber sales procedure could be simplified with advantage to both buyer and seller, but at the same time increased market outlets for low-grade timber and expanded manufacturing facilities in underdeveloped areas are almost as necessary to full production as the development of better roads.

FROM THE RECORD

What measures should be taken to obtain prompt and full utilization on a sustained-yield basis of the forest resources in national forests and other public ownerships?

MR. HAGENSTEIN: Why aren't the national forests harvesting as much timber as they can grow?

The first and most obvious reason is that much of their timber is inaccessible. The problem of getting sufficient timber access roads in the national forests is a practical political problem because no congressman from a state without national forests sees any votes in support of timber-access-roads legislation or appropriations. It is an economic problem, too. More cannot be spent for roads than can be justified by the timber values created by their construction. Lack of timber access roads has the practical effect of creating an artificial timber shortage. This is reflected in higher prices for timber on the stump that are passed on to the consumer of forest products.

Moreover, without timber access roads the national forests cannot practice forestry. For example, the current estimate of the allowable annual cut of the national forests is 6 billion board feet. Only this last year has the cut reached 5 billion. Because very little cutting

has occurred in the mature timber on the national forests, there is very little current annual growth.

Another serious drawback is the cumbersome timber sale procedure. A simplified contract could still safeguard in every respect the interests of the government as a proprietor.

No one can manage a forest adequately until he knows how much timber he owns and how much of it is dead or deteriorating. But the timber inventory of the national forests is inadequate. So is the rate of advancement in engineering and timber management planning.

Additional appropriations may be needed for the development of an adequate system of timber access roads. But I sincerely believe that a realignment of the activities of the Forest Service with more concentration upon timber management would make the current level of appropriations go much further.

MR. STAMM: The people in the Forest Service, and in other interested federal or state agencies, give to the forests their best efforts. We have the finest kind of planning; but when it comes to putting the planning into effect there seems to be a lot of difficulty in making them all think of the same things at the same time. We should have some definite plans, not only for the cut today, but for many years ahead.

Timber sales need to be made in much larger volume. At least one government agency for which I reviewed the sales recently, showed for the last 10 years less than 2 million feet per purchaser, or per sale. The wasted effort in setting up the individual sales was just like the big boss man going out and selling peanuts on the street corner. The federal marketing units need to be set up on a realistic basis.

We are spending too much of the money that should be used in building roads, to landscape them; we need efficient roads and more of them, so that the timber can be removed with a minimum of loss.

EDWARD P. CLIFF (U.S. Forest Service): Before the last World War, the national forests were generally looked upon as a timber reserve and intensive management had not proceeded very far. During the thirties, there were strong sentiments to withhold the national forest timber in order to keep it out of competition with the timber of private industry and to avoid glutting the market. The industry was talking differently then than now.

It is the objective of the Forest Service to build up the national forest cut to the full sustained-yield capacity, working circle by working circle. Further expansion can be obtained only through installation of additional access roads and utilization facilities, the employment of more foresters, stepping up of inventory work and preparation of management plans.

Last year the United States lost about $20 million because the cut was 1½ billion feet less than it could have been under sustained yield. A five-year program of government construction of access roads at $20 million a year, plus roads built by timber purchasers, would provide the road system to market the full 6.6 billion feet annually. Timber access roads must be paid for from the timber hauled over them regardless of whether the government or the timber purchaser builds them, so in either event, access roads are self-liquidating.

The second major need to bring the national forest timberland into full production is increased market outlets for low-grade material now being left in the woods, for thinnings, for low-grade hardwoods, and the expansion of manufacturing facilities in underdeveloped areas such as the Rockies and Alaska.

Full production under intensive management, which should eventually raise the allowable cut to around 11 billion board feet per year, will result in materially higher costs of administration, but will show an excellent return per dollar invested. Expenditures of $11 million annually should produce receipts of some $110 million.

Indispensable prerequisites are: adequate forest protection from fire and pests; reforestation of an approximate 4 million acres of national forest land; and an expanded and continuing research program in forest management and utilization, disease and tree genetics; and development of economic methods of harvesting, transporting, and processing material of low grade and small size.

PERRY A. THOMPSON (Western Lumber Manufacturers, Inc.): One of the reasons the Forest Service doesn't make larger sales to the sawmills is because its stumpage prices are too high. At the present time, companies just can't risk buying national forest timber at appraised prices where they have to invest a million dollars in roads to get into an area. The profit margins are too small. Regional officers should have more authority to negotiate and process sales, and I think some local means of arbitration should be set up.

MR. GREELEY: In order to get an access road system with any continuity of construction and management, haven't we got to have something like the Ellsworth Bill?[2]

MR. CLIFF: Plans made by the Forest Service indicate that something in the neighborhood of $250 million could be used for roads in the next five years to bring the national forests up to full cut. The proposal is that the contractors will build the service and

[2] H.R. 4929 (83rd Congress) would provide timber access roads to and in the national forests through Treasury loans up to a maximum of $125 million, to be repaid through receipts from timber sales attributable to such road construction.

spur roads. The main line roads that tap the big bodies, we feel, should be built by the government.

MR. GREELEY: The urgency of some form of financing beyond the current annual appropriations is distressingly clear.

Subsection C

WILDLIFE, SCENIC, WILDERNESS AND OTHER RECREATIONAL AREAS

Recreation, as the word is used here, involves the use of wildlife, scenic, wilderness, and other areas by ever larger numbers of people. Increasing leisure, ease of transportation, and the impact of modern land and water utilization practices combine to make more vulnerable the resources that provide for the health and well-being of millions.

The basic question before the subsection asked if use of recreational areas can be intensified without impairing the resources. But discussion brought out a widespread belief that intensification, while helpful, can do only so much to check a worsening situation. More acreage, many participants concluded, must be added to the wildlife refuges; the national, state, county, metropolitan, and municipal parks; the wilderness and other natural areas. At the same time, they believed that the inroads of industry and of large-scale federal projects must be combated to prevent further shrinkage of our present recreational resources.

A prerequisite to attaining both objectives was seen to be cooperation in research, in education, and in programing among all the elements concerned— federal and state governments, and private organizations. Coordination of programs within the government was especially urged as part of the over-all need for a national policy.

Guidelines to subsection discussion separated the broad subject into five parts: (1) Wildlife Protection and Management, (2) Management of Scenic Resources, (3) Protection of Wilderness Areas, (4) Use of More Highly Developed Recreational Areas, and (5) Integration of Public Programs. The latter was concerned with compatibility of broad programs of drainage, irrigation, and flood control with efforts to develop the various recreational resources.

Wildlife Protection and Management

Providing adequate habitat for wildlife and controlling the numbers and enthusiasms of hunters are related problems, the answers to which lie more in the management of humans than of wildlife. Repeatedly, this thought was expressed in the discussion. If ducks are allowed to molest farmers' crops, their destruction is assured; strong effort is needed to reverse the trend toward shrinking habitat. Farmlands in game areas have about reached saturation point, so far as hunting is concerned. The problem, some participants thought, may lead to voluntary restriction on the part of hunters or a transfer of their activities to other areas or other forms of recreation.

Forest land was conceded to offer the greatest promise for increasing wildlife habitat.

Of paramount importance, the subsection considered, is the struggle to retain areas set aside for waterfowl which are threatened with virtual extinction if land acquisition for other purposes, together with increasing shooting, continues at its present rate.

FROM THE RECORD

What are the opportunities for increasing the habitat for wildlife by more intensive production methods on present specialized wildlife refuges and by considering wildlife requirements in managing areas devoted primarily to other uses?

IRA N. GABRIELSON (President, Wildlife Management Institute; paper read by C. R. Gutermuth): The amount of food and cover on wildlife refuges and management areas can be increased, but time and money are required to do the job. All such areas need management over a period of years to become of maximum value.

Outside the special areas set aside for wildlife, the forest lands offer the greatest opportunity for encouraging habitat with least interference with their main function. But efforts toward forest management practices that will increase wildlife habitat—particularly by methods of harvesting and artificial planting—have been and probably will be confined almost entirely to the public forests.

Range lands offer less opportunity, since they are largely in semiarid areas. But when well managed and not overgrazed, there is room for both livestock and the few species of game that are natural inhabitants of the areas.

Agricultural lands used for general farming, with a mixture of wood lots, cultivated crops, and pasture lands, are excellent. Wildlife interests working with soil conservation districts have produced hundreds of land management plans that allow for the introduction of wildlife food or cover plants. The development of farm ponds is an encouraging factor. These programs have been successful, but still the areas available for wildlife habitat development are much larger than those that have been treated.

HARRY D. RUHL (International Association of Game, Fish, and Conservation Commissioners): That the demand for recreation is rapidly increasing is shown by the U.S. sales of duck stamps, which have multiplied three or four times in the last nine years; by the increase in small game licenses, which in Michigan have multiplied by 28 over the last 40 years; and by constantly increasing visitation to state parks. Prospects for shorter work weeks and better means of transportation point to further demand, while simultaneously industry will be seeking more land.

What effect will this have on our wildlife?

We cannot rely on the limited established refuges and special areas to handle this problem. The loss of waterfowl habitat through filling, pollution, and drainage is going on at a much more rapid rate than all our efforts to restore or improve the areas. If we are going to have wild fowling as we know it, we must make careful studies of all existing areas. No drainage of waterfowl production units should be undertaken unless it can be clearly proved that the project will produce high-quality farm land at a low enough cost to justify both the cost of construction and maintenance and the destruction of the existing aquatic resource.

With regard to farm game, the problem is not biological, but social. If we are going to get good wildlife production on agricultural land, the people who want to use that land should police their own numbers; they may even have to pay for this privilege, because I do not know how long the farmers will continue to put up with the nuisance of increasing visitation without some compensation.

The cutting of timber as soon as it can be sold at a profit appears to be the most effective tool for managing a large portion of forest wildlife habitat. Moreover, if the hitherto neglected low-value "weed" species are harvested, there is apt to be a shorter cutting rotation, and this is favorable to wildlife because it results in a younger forest. But since there is conflict in the amount of timber and game you can raise on the same area of land, the greatest progress can be made when the timber-producing agency and the wildlife agency work together under a common administrative head.

HUGH B. WOODWARD (New Mexico Game Association): Two trends of changing land use in the range and forested areas of certain parts of the West affect the outlook for improved wildlife habitat. First, there is the growing trend to fence the range lands. I believe this will increase within the next several years. Then there is the fencing of accesses to roads to insure control of privately owned areas in northeastern areas of the Pacific Northwest. I believe that trend will advance rapidly down through Oregon and probably as far as California. Both of these trends pose problems in wildlife management. Perhaps primarily they are matters of human management.

Efforts to increase production of wildlife on farm land and public lands were seen to be closely tied to mounting hunting pressures. Much of the discussion at this point relates to both problems, and supplements discussion of the question on page 96.

C. R. GUTERMUTH (Wildlife Management Institute): Hunting, as a sport, and wildlife populations in general, should be maintained for the benefit of all Americans. I question whether the solution to the maintenance of wildlife abundance lies in its dollars and cents value to the man who is interested primarily in producing crops. Rather, we should try to educate the farmer to an appreciation of wildlife for its own sake, and the enjoyment that it affords to him and his friends.

CHARLES H. CALLISON (National Wildlife Federation): In most places the farm lands can't accommodate more hunters, even when able to produce more game. Perhaps we shall have to shift some of the farm-game gunning pressure to other land and other types of hunting or fishing sports. Since it is comparatively easy to create new fishing waters, many sportsmen who can't be accommodated on public shooting areas, may have to become fishermen rather than hunters.

The public forests hold some promise, since concentration of hunters for a short open season doesn't seem to damage timbered land. The possibility of increased fire hazard is a problem that, I think, can be solved.

RICHARD H. POUGH (American Museum of Natural History): There is a tendency in some national park areas toward growing fishing pressures. We may eventually have to consider whether fishing, as well as hunting, may not have to be relegated, at least in part, to special areas.

JOSEPH J. SHOMON (Virginia Commission of Game and Inland Fisheries): In the State of Virginia, we have been quite successful in shifting emphasis from one type of sport to another. We have a very large and growing deer herd, but we know that our food and cover will support just so many hunters. So we have successfully promoted archery. If we can somehow try to put a higher value on our wildlife—and it may be that we need smaller bag limits—we can get the maximum sport for every kill.

LESTER A. GILES, JR. (American Humane Education Society): Instead of trying to change men that hunt into men that fish perhaps a job should be done to educate them to other values. Far too many sportsmen take their vacations during the short crowded hunting season. The pressure could be relieved if vacations were planned for different times and reasons. Release from the complexities of civilization can be found in many wholesome recreative ways through an interest in the welfare and future of wildlife resources.

Can the present bag and possession limits and the present hunting seasons for wildlife (for example, migrating wildfowl along the Pacific Flyway) be maintained unless the areas of specialized habitat are kept intact or increased?

MR. WOODWARD: What is the future for migratory waterfowl on the Pacific Flyway and other flyways of its kind? To find answers to this question, I have written several hundred letters to game departments, regional biologists of governmental services, one of the ornithological societies, leaders of conservation, and sportsmen groups. The answers are unanimously gloomy. Almost all express the same thought: unless there is an immediate expanded program of land acquisition at state and national levels, the existence of wildfowl, as we know it now, in our country is doomed.

In 1935, there was one migratory duck stamp to every 194 people in the United States: this year there is one to every 70. During the intervening time, the habitat has steadily been constricted. Once there was something like 6 million acres of wildfowl habitat in the form of wetlands on the Pacific Coast. Presently, that has shrunk to some 200,000 acres. The same report comes from Maine to Florida, and from Alaska to Arizona and California—shrinking habitat, increased gunning pressure.

An executive order which would have set aside for permanent preservation a large portion of the Klamath-Tule lake area on the Oregon-Washington border is now being reexamined. Without that refuge, the last stand of the waterfowl on the Pacific Coast is going to be eliminated.

The new policy of the Department of Interior and Department of Agriculture provides for a minimum of outright purchase of land and a maximum reliance on securing the right to flood land by purchase of easements. This is in order to reduce real estate costs to the federal government and to benefit state and local government by the increased amount

of land left on the tax rolls. If that policy is carried forward, the only hope for the salvation of waterfowl—the acquisition and development of habitat on all the flyways and in the nesting areas—goes out the window. Thus, the intent of Congress, as expressed in the Coordination Act, has been nullified.

CLARENCE COTTAM (U.S. Fish and Wildlife Service): In the inventory of waterfowl taken last winter, 57 percent was shown to be in California. The birds are able to survive there largely because they are feeding on the farmers' crops. If we don't get some effective areas properly managed to take care of that tremendous bird population, the farmer may revolt. Either we are going to provide habitat, or we not going to have the resource.

Five lines of action can halt the grave trends of recent years:

1. Establish a more effective and coordinated land-use policy and program in government. There is urgent need to harmonize more effectively the conflicting programs and policies of bureaus within departments and between bureaus in different departments.[3]

2. Redouble the efforts of private and public agencies, the states, and the Fish and Wildlife Service to acquire and, by effective management, dedicate to wildlife uses the remaining wildlife lands.

3. Give support to the spirit as well as the letter of the amended Coordination Act of 1946. Unless public and government agencies do this, the fullest multiple use cannot be attained.

4. Follow up the wetland inventory now in preparation with action to dedicate the wetlands to effective wildlife use.

5. Make more effective the cooperative program between the federal Fish and Wildlife Service and the states, and between the public agencies and organizations, clubs, and private landowners.

JOHN L. FARLEY (U.S. Fish and Wildlife Service): For over 50 years there has been a coordinated cooperative arrangement between state and federal governments and, in

---

[3] See also the discussion relating to the integration of public programs, pages 106-7.

the main, the program has been successful. Educational effort is needed to prepare the public to accept the values of the program, so that if taxes or loss of personal shooting privileges are involved, resistance can be reduced. Long-range planning is essential to avoid delay, duplication, and unnecessary expense.

CLAUDE D. KELLEY (National Wildlife Federation): Specialized habitat has been of great value in increasing the wild turkey and deer population of Alabama. The game and fish commissions in the various states should obtain more areas for this purpose, and the U.S. Fish and Wildlife Service should also obtain more public shooting areas with specialized habitat, and more marshland, before these lands increase in value and are put into use for other purposes.

Since the passage of the Duck Stamp Act in 1934, something upward of $30 million has been received in the form of revenue. But only some $3 million has been spent to acquire land and water for waterfowl purposes.

MR. FARLEY: The Western Association of Game and Fish Commissioners has under study the possibility of cooperative game management in several million acres of West Coast timberland designated as tree farms, which are subject to a high order of management, utilization, and protection from fire in a continuous program. Next to the public ownership, that is the largest area available.

PHILIP F. ALLAN (Soil Conservation Service, Fort Worth, Texas): Of some 5 million acres of Gulf marsh area in Louisiana and Texas, at least half a million are suitable for nothing but waterfowl habitat. Though of low grade now, if suitably developed, that area could take care of most of the waterfowl likely to come that way for some time to come.

Areas of oversupply raise problems of game management that may lead to future rationing.

OLAUS J. MURIE (The Wilderness Society): There are places in the West where the enthusiasm of sportsmen's groups has resulted in large quantities of game animals that disastrously affect the forest forage, and overcrowd and degrade the hunting itself. In such areas we will have to look eventually toward a smaller game population and, perhaps, rationing of hunting in one way or another, to keep up the quality of the harvest.

JOSEPH W. PENFOLD (Izaak Walton League of America, Inc.): In Colorado, roughly west of the Continental Divide, we have few areas not overpopulated with deer. The problem there is to set seasons and bag limits to get hunting pressure in the areas that most require harvest. In one area we have for six seasons issued a two-deer permit on one license, requiring one of them to be a female.

But the country is still crawling with deer. We also have livestock. In the summer the deer have lots of summer range up above 9,000 feet; but come the deep snows, they must migrate down, where the grass has gone and the sagebrush and other brouse species are depleted, because the cattle work on it all summer and the deer all winter.

We are going to have to get the deer population within bounds; the cattle population too. But will the sportsmen be content to get a deer once every five years, instead of two years out of three? Are the livestock people going to accept the reduction in livestock numbers that may be necessary to preserve the area for both livestock and wildlife? I am inclined to believe that the real problem is one of managing humans, not wildlife.

JOHN H. BAKER (National Audubon Society): The fundamental reason for protecting wildlife is the role wildlife plays in maintaining the nation's ecological balance. The relative stress on harvesting and management from the standpoint of sport is one of the reasons we haven't gotten further with the protection of our wildlife resources. The time has come when it is imperative that our government adopt for all public lands a policy of restricted public use where fragile national assets are involved. I thoroughly agree that our problem is primarily the management of man.

Management of Scenic Resources

Chief among the problems of managing scenic resources are those of preserving the untouched quality of the wilderness and protecting the nation's "fragile assets" in areas of historic or prehistoric value from overuse by the millions to whom they belong. The subsection considered that a careful program of appraisal, acquirement, and disposal is needed to provide adequately for future generations.

It was pointed out that success of such a program must depend on concerted effort at all levels of government, not the least among which are the state park agencies.

Management methods are being improved to adjust to increasing pressures. As one participant said, "We have only begun to find better, more intelligent, more satisfying ways of increasing the use of the wilderness without bulldozing our way into it." Further discussion of wilderness preservation took place later in the subsection's meetings (pages 100-2).

FROM THE RECORD

How can we satisfy the demands of the steadily increasing numbers who visit the national parks and monuments, while still preserving these scenic resources for future generations?

CONRAD L. WIRTH (National Park Service): As use of the national parks increases, so does the complexity of our problem. In the natural areas, it is the fundamental difficulty of opening the wilderness to many people and still keeping its environment intact. In the historical areas, it is the related difficulty of retaining their inspirational qualities. Perhaps the acceptance of some restrictions by each visitor is inevitable, but the goal is to minimize restrictions.

The problem is not hopeless. Unspectacular but real progress is being made in the refinement of wilderness use techniques. Increase of facilities has not had to keep pace with increase in visitation because nowadays many services are performed outside the park. At Great Smoky Mountains, for instance, no overnight accommodations are included within the park boundaries but they are available at a number of places just outside.

More national parks and monuments should be established, especially in the East. On the other hand, certain areas that are chiefly of local or state interest or are below the established standard could well be eliminated from the National Park System.

The states and the federal government both have responsibilities in the park conservation field, and I feel very strongly that the federal government should not do anything in the park field that can be done as well or better by the states.

Roads into the wilderness can make the feeling of wilderness recede like a mirage. Some of the more recently established parks should be made more accessible to the public, but it is probable that they will need relatively less development than the older parks. I do not visualize new road construction into the major wilderness areas of the old and well-known parks. Rather, our efforts should be directed toward the more efficient use of existing development areas and increasing the facilities at some of the outlying areas, such as Wawona, Crane Flat, and Tuolumne Meadows in Yosemite. There will be greater use of the back country and trails as people learn more about them.

Perhaps the most promising method of developing park use techniques is through a more adequate interpretive program. People want to understand the places they visit; understanding increases their enjoyment. But such a program must be bolstered by adequate research into the many problems of park use.

Our prewar hotel and lodging facilities are grossly inadequate. However, we have made progress in simplifying concession policies and negotiating new contracts with the concessioners who, in turn, are doing their utmost to improve their plans to meet the public need.

BEN H. THOMPSON (National Park Service): A major means of conserving the national parks is through large-scale cooperative planning based on research that comprehends the natural resources. This involves the coordinated efforts of local, state, and federal agencies of government. It is an attempt to get away from the single-purpose method of resources planning.

Thus far, the provision of even minimum basic recreational facilities on federal reservoir projects has been largely deferred by lack of a national recreation resource policy. Such a policy would help to establish and differentiate the responsibility of the federal and state governments, in order that minimum basic facilities could be provided and necessary land acquired before costly and perhaps irrevocable damage is done to the public recreation potentialities of water control projects.

The Park, Parkway, and Recreation Study Act of 1936 directed the Secretary of the Interior to cooperate with the states, to gather data helpful in developing a plan for coordinated and adequate public parks, parkway, and recreation-area facilities. By now, enough information has been accumulated to make it possible to formulate such a plan in the not distant future, if the park and recreation agencies of all levels of government—federal, state, and local—will make an effort toward that end. The program would cover the wide variety of public recreational areas desired, from wilderness areas in remote regions to highly developed recreational areas near densely populated districts.

In such a plan, the importance of strong state park systems cannot be overemphasized. In 1921, when the National Conference on State Parks was organized, there were state parks in only 19 states. By 1953, there were more than 1,800 in 48 states. Attendance has mounted to exceed 159 million in 1953. This is encouraging progress, but still far short of what can be accomplished if the states provide adequate park and recreational areas in their systems. To a considerable degree, state park systems are the proving grounds for all park conservation policies and practices; people are apt to regard the sound practices adopted there, sound also for the national parks.

HARLEAN JAMES (American Planning and Civic Association): Some of the hordes that now visit national parks may go there for recreational activities having little to do with their true function. Probably those activities should be removed to other areas; that, in itself, would give us a little relief from the pressure on national parks. State parks already provide a large measure of relief. At all levels of government we have different types of areas in which we can develop activities.

Through the years, the National Park Service has developed standards for admission to the National Park System. But here is a word of warning: If we do not secure qualified areas that are still in the fairly native condition, we shall lose our opportunity. We do not expect, I take it, to expand beyond the size that our standards will permit; thus, we have a natural barrier limiting our expansion.

FRANK D. QUINN (Texas State Parks Board): How in the world do you expect to get your park programs across until you get the people who use the parks to demand proper facilities and provide the wherewithal to do it? We should establish a "Parks Parliament of America," where we can get all associations together with the local agencies which supply the funds. We must get the story to the people who vote the money for parks; until we do, we shall never get the speed and the volume we need.

MR. THOMPSON: The National Conference on State Parks is a lay organization that would do just that, if we could spread it over the nation a little bit.

Protection of Wilderness Areas

Recognizing the natural limitation on the acquirement of more wilderness areas, the subsection concentrated much of its discussion on the natural and wild areas that still can be brought into recreational use. In doing so, it touched on areas that might be set aside for educational purposes, particularly to help school children learn to appreciate wilderness values.

Of the numerous threats to the maintenance of wilderness areas proper, detrimental mining practices, the building of large water impoundments, and the continued existence of private holdings within the wilderness were taken to be outstanding. The subsection was referred to Section IV's discussion of efforts to adjust the mining laws (see pages 178-88). Measures to relate water impoundment projects with wilderness interests are dealt with more fully under the topic "Integration of Public Programs," pages 106-7, and some aspects were discussed in Section III (pages 131-33). Criticism of private holdings within the wilderness led to the voicing of an opinion that the best interests of the people as a whole would not be served by turning the public lands over to state control.

The view that true conservation may sometimes require the cutting of mature timber in wilderness areas was countered by the opinion, widely held, that the time is not yet come when such practices will be necessary to the country's economic welfare and that, in fact, swiftly changing scientific processes may avert this threat to our wilderness resources.

FROM THE RECORD

Are the present areas of wilderness in the national forests, the national parks, and elsewhere, sufficient to serve the purposes for which wilderness is set aside?

Mr. Murie: We have given recognition to the importance of our national park system by specific Acts of Congress. The time has come for Congressional recognition of all other types of national wilderness areas, just as the State of New York has done with the Adirondacks.

I am convinced that present areas will be inadequate for our children's children. But, instead of expansion, we are threatened by reduction: we are quarreling over boundaries; and those of us who are intent on immediate commercial prospects look upon our national unmarred scenery as something nice but of secondary importance.

We need more leisurely planning. We could well slow down on this process of invading every nook and cranny of the country with our commerce and give more serious attention to the job of conserving and increasing the yield of the land we already have put into production.

George B. Fell (The Nature Conservancy): We might say that wilderness implies a large tract where one can become lost from civilization. We need also to consider preserving smaller natural and wild areas. There are still many potential natural area preserves that should be set aside before it is too late.

We have come to realize the importance of the habitat—the biological community that is the home of a particular plant or animal. To preserve a species, we must preserve this community. Natural areas serve that purpose.

Natural areas offer important values. They provide opportunities for education and inspiration. They provide outdoor laboratories and check-areas essential for many fields of basic scientific research and land-use studies. They form a living storehouse of unknown but potentially useful raw materials. And they preserve the right of a species of plant or animal to a home on this earth.

There should be areas set aside to represent each type of vegetation or natural feature, and there should be a preserved area within reach of every community and every child.

KENNETH W. HUNT (Antioch College): Let's put that in educational terms and say we need such land for every school. Barring our great cities, I believe the land is available, even though it may not be what we think of as "natural." To restore a tract of poor, abandoned farm land to its natural beauty could well form part of a school's outdoor educational program.

Here I think we may have the means of developing an appreciation in the coming generation that will solve some of the problems of our wilderness areas. But how shall we reach outside our group to the educators and teacher-training institutions? And how can the schools be provided with the personnel who, themselves, will be eager to get into the outdoor education field?

MR. WIRTH: An interpretive program we have in the National Park Service is being adopted in many of the state parks, and I believe in some of the cities. But our experience in Washington is an example of what can be done with schools. During the slack winter season the six permanent guides assigned to the National Capital Park take the school children out in the park, and give talks in the classrooms. The demand for their services is now so great that they can't fill all requests. I think it is almost impossible to have a natural area by every school—certainly impossible in New York City. But there are areas not so far away that could be utilized for half-day outings with a naturalist.

MR. GILES: In the last few years, through the public school camping movement, school systems have acquired areas of naturalness or wildness which, while some distance from the schools, do provide for two-week periods when school children can become acquainted with

the soil, trees, and animals that are there. An extension of this idea would spread greater understanding of the problems we are discussing.

MR. POUGH: A part of our job which is largely unemphasized is to preserve minimum units of plant and animal life that are unique to a community, so that all the species that compose them can continue to exist. The research units of each of our park systems should have this strongly in mind. It is an important job for local groups around the country.

What are the primary threats to the maintenance of adequate areas of wilderness?

HOWARD ZAHNISER (The Wilderness Society): The threats to the wilderness ideal are specific, as well as related to our general attitudes. In the Olympic National Park, for instance, we are still contending against the lumbering industry and those who support it locally for the use of the marvelous rain forest for the production of timber.

Grazing of domestic livestock in wilderness areas should be eliminated wherever possible, because this use of high country vegetation destroys one of the ideals of wilderness preservation, and also because it results in competition for forage resources with pack animals used for recreation and wildlife.

In terms of urgency, one of the greatest threats stems from our outdated mining laws.[4]

Ill-considered building of large water impoundments, particularly by the federal government, is another outstanding threat.

Another danger is in the existence of private lands inside wilderness areas, leading to the demand for roads which can effectively destroy the wilderness. An especially hazardous threat is represented by the proposal of some to turn over federal lands to the states. Many of the states have excellent wilderness preservation programs, and there should be more. Nevertheless, moving a wilderness from na-

---

[4] Ways in which the mining laws affect the wilderness areas, and suggested steps to adjust them, are treated rather fully in Section IV, Domestic Problems of Nonfuel Minerals, pp. 185-86.

tional to state protection diminishes its security. When an area is in national ownership, conservationists throughout the nation have an effective voice in its protection, but when it is in state custody, the only *effective* voice is that of those residing within the state, who may not be so zealous in preserving nearby lands as they are lands farther afield.

Guardians of wilderness areas are often tempted to introduce facilities that will attract more people to the ranks of wilderness supporters. But a wilderness is not a developed recreation area; with development the wilderness recedes; and there thus develops the hazard of destroying an area, as wilderness, in an effort to protect it.

We are too slow in getting to work on the primary job of setting up a national system of wilderness areas. We need something like a zoning program to see that no inconsistent uses of the areas are permitted.

Finally, one of our great tasks, as wilderness preservers, is to cooperate with all conservationists for the production of commodities and the provision of outdoor recreational programs in areas outside of the wilderness.

HORACE M. ALBRIGHT (U.S. Potash Company): The wilderness areas in the national forests have never had a basis in law. They have been set aside by the Secretary of Agriculture for a good many years, and I am not sure that even now he can go to Congress and get such a law. Right away it would be asked: Would that mean the stopping of grazing, or of mining, or of cutting? But, just the same, law is the only means by which the areas can eventually be protected. The wilderness areas, or some of them and some of their characteristics, ought to be embodied in the law.

One participant suggested that we may be rapidly reaching the point where it will be necessary to utilize practically all our surplus crops, citing as an example of waste a mature stand of ponderosa pine in the Gila Wilderness of New Mexico. Part of this stand, he believed, under orderly and conservative Forest Service management, could provide continuous employment for a small community.

FRED M. PACKARD (National Parks Association): I testified at the hearing last year in which the future of that very stand of pines was discussed. The local communities were fighting mad at the proposal that this virgin forest should be cut, and vigorously demanded it be retained in the Wilderness Area. They consider its greatest value to be the benefits derived by the people, culturally and economically, from its preservation as a standing forest; and they won their point.

MR. PENFOLD: When we have reached the point where all of our available commercial timber has been put on a sound, sustained-yield and harvest basis, and we still need timber, then, and only then, might be the time to move into these little tracts of timber in our wilderness.

GEORGE MARSHALL (The Wilderness Society): The exciting promise of higher material standards of living through science's new raw material and power resources, strengthens us in demanding that our national parks, wilderness areas, and wildlife areas be maintained and extended. These regions now clearly not required for future economic development will be needed increasingly as an essential part of that spiritual and cultural environment which if lacking will make material advance futile.

Use of More Highly Developed Recreational Areas

The subsection looked first at the state parks. It was pointed out that more lands should be set aside for the benefit of more people whose enjoyment of public recreational areas is limited by travel time. Criticism of a tendency toward overloading state parks with facilities out of key with their natural function led to an opinion that this was a matter of public education and, also, of diverting to special areas recreational demand of a highly organized variety.

It was believed unlikely that local communities developing recreational areas could expect state financial aid, but some examples were given of methods by which some communities have successfully worked out their own recreational programs.

County recreation areas were considered to be far from adequate for even present-day populations. The importance of broad and long-term planning was emphasized again and again, as was the necessity of careful programs of research and of information to gain public support.

FROM THE RECORD

How adequately are the needs for the more developed recreational areas being provided for in national and state forests and state parks?

ERNEST SWIFT (Wisconsin Conservation Department): It is beyond debate that more money is needed for parks and forests on both state and national levels. In many instances the areas are available, but there is no money for maintenance. But on the other side of the ledger, do all the various demands have to be met? As our standards of living keep rising, our demands for fancier recreational gimmicks keep pace.

After dedicating some virginal solitude as a haven of rest for God's underprivileged, we proceed to gut it with roads; clutter it with overnight cabins; build dance halls, golf courses, tennis courts, knick-knack shops, and cut-throat eating joints; we reduce the wildlife to a WPA status; then we stand around and beam with pride.

It is my understanding that concessions are a necessary evil in national park financing. The same is true in many states; but even with adequate budgets I suspect many would attempt to justify concessions as something the public demands. Adequate budgets should produce better planning and management.

So long as we use the same formula of destruction in promoting recreation as we do in our economy, we will continue to lose ground. Our structure of government, our social philosophies, and our management of

national resources are inseparable. The future of our recreational resources will be determined by how well we control these three factors.

How is it possible to separate the sheep from the goats? People who believe water-power projects should be government sponsored are called Democrats and New Dealers. Those who advocate private industry are called Republicans. I cannot tell you what I am because I demand that both public agencies and private industry stay out of national monuments, national parks, and out of many of our rivers and streams. That includes the Army Engineers and the Reclamation Bureau.

VICTOR W. FLICKINGER (National Conference on State Parks): Because the nation's state parks are located closer to large masses of people, they get greater visitation than the national parks. Attendance for the year 1952, for instance, increased by 24 percent over that of the previous year. What are we going to do when we have some 200 million people to take care of?

The states are doing something about it. In 1921 there were state parks in only 19 states, 1925 acreage in 578 state parks was some 600,000 acres; in 1952 acreage in 1,787 properties in 48 states was approximately 2½ million acres. The county parks have increased from 67,000 acres in 32 counties in 1925 to 213,437 acres in 130 counties in 1950. The municipal parks have increased from 243,288 acres and 1,112 communities in 1925 to

430,630 acres in 1,208 communities in 1950. State forests have increased from 2,751,195 acres in 1928 to 12,933,242 acres in 1950.

Because of the crowded roads, people may no longer want to travel great distances. Consequently, it will be necessary to provide recreation facilities at various levels. County areas or metropolitan parks take care of the day-use areas for city people. State parks must take care of week-end or vacation use.

It is our job in the states to cooperate with the other levels of government in our planning. It is essential that we do some looking ahead and that we acquire suitable areas while we can. The development funds will come later.

A study should be made to determine who should do what on the various levels. A land classification to determine what is the greatest possible multiple-use of various types of land would disclose a lot of common ground. There is need, too, for restudy of the uses of presently available areas in our states. The over-all need, and one on which these other things depend, is more funds.

MR. THOMPSON: If we accept the premise that cutover and grazed lands or fluctuating reservoirs are as inspiring as virgin forests and meadows or natural lakes, this may well lead to the piecemeal impairment of the parks. If, on the other hand, we refuse to admit that such lands can provide much satisfying recreation, pressures will probably increase to develop the national parks and some state parks for kinds of recreation for which they are not suited. Spectator sports and other artificially created attractions can be provided in the multiple-use areas outside the parks. They can supplement park attractions, and probably the two kinds of programs will better serve the public than either by itself.

How adequately are recreational needs being provided for in smaller areas?

ROBERT R. MURPHY (Superintendent of Parks, Oklahoma City): Urban recreational resources are far from adequate to serve present needs, let alone the population of the future. More publicly owned ocean and lake frontage and land near the outskirts of our rapidly expanding cities should be acquired before the lands increase in value and are developed for other uses.

In 1943, Oklahoma City began its first real planning for a city of 500,000 in the year 1970. It took money, and before we could get the money, it took education.

In long-term planning there must be a general survey not only of the city proper, but of the land in and beyond its reaches. That means classification, and classification means zoning for residential, commercial, and park areas. This is the only possible approach to the problem that faces America today. Help and encouragement for the community that lacks finances for its own planning and zoning has to come from the state level.

In developing Oklahoma City's Master Plan of 1970 we have purchased new play areas in outer reaches that we will not develop for another 5 or 10 years. We have helped communities as far as 30 or 40 miles away from the metropolitan area to develop their own programs. For there is an allegiance we, in the larger communities, owe to our neighboring communities; what they are affects what we ourselves will become.

GEORGE D. BUTLER (National Recreation Association): We have sparse information on which to base our ideas of the adequacy of local recreation areas. In the first place, we do not know the acreage in our parks. True, we gathered some figures in 1950 but the last study of any comprehensiveness was made in 1940, and even that lacked particulars concerning the nature and distribution of the parks in relation to centers of population. We know a good deal about the types of facilities provided in both municipal and county parks, and surveys have measured what people think they would like to do. But the standards we have set up can bear examination.

We have a notion, shared by most city planners, that roughly one acre of park and recreational space should be set aside within the city for each 100 of the population. For metropolitan regions a somewhat less widely accepted standard allows for an additional acre of park and recreation space for each 100 in the total population of the region. But in the last few years, popular response to the availability of areas, particularly large properties developed for activities like boating, fishing, swimming, winter sports, and picnicking, indicates that our studies and standards provide no real clue to the extent to which people will use such properties if they are made reasonably available.

Reports from 550 communities of 2,500 to 5,000 show that 35 percent of them did not have a single acre of park in 1940. To the best of my belief, not more than one out of ten counties in the United States has since acquired park or recreational acreage.

Increasingly, we are educating our rural youth in consolidated schools where they are getting a taste for varied creative and recreational activities previously largely denied them. Unfortunately, many consolidated schools are far from where the children live. We are whetting their desires without satisfying their needs.

Mr. HUNT: These new consolidated school areas could be the means of providing many of the needs we have been advocating. Located between communities, they can not only supply our children with recreational areas, but also with natural areas for outdoor education (see page 101). Perhaps we can relate that to Mr. Murphy's plea for working with the schools to get support for conservation education.

Mr. MURPHY: It is essential for the municipal or county group of any community to meet regularly with the school officials to exchange information on land purchase or any other phase of recreational planning.

CHARLES A. DAMBACH (Ohio Department of Natural Resources): There are ways of getting money other than by voting a bond issue and having the legislature appropriate money. And there are ways of getting research done besides hiring an agency to do it.

The School Board of Worthington, Ohio, of which I am a member, faced with the problem of how most effectively to use the 80 acres of land at its disposal, obtained its most helpful information from the people of the community itself. Answers to a questionnaire sent to all local organizations gave us the means of measuring what recreational facilities the people wanted and a basis for framing a suitable program to meet most of those needs. They also provided a springboard for raising the necessary funds.

M. GRAHAM NETTING (Carnegie Museum): A few years ago, as part of a rehabilitation program in Pittsburgh, a group of us founded a recreation, conservation, and park council under the Allegheny Conference on Community Development. That council has interested itself not only in park facilities in the city, but in the broader problems of providing additional land in the county and in the western half of Pennsylvania. One of our actions was to assure all of the existing organizations that we did not wish to take over their functions or to eliminate them in any way. In that fashion we got their cooperation and have since succeeded in raising approximately $320,000, mainly in Pittsburgh, but to some extent in other communities. We have made purchases of land both north and south of Pittsburgh in the past three years that now total some 3,200 acres, with the idea that some, if not all, will eventually be offered to the Department of Forests and Waters of the Commonwealth.

Our is an interim operation to help out when legislative funds are not available. I believe the technique of listing the gaps in your own community, the functions that are not covered by existing organizations, and then bringing these organizations together to see how the gaps can be filled and the responsibilities shared, is a means of getting some of these things under way.

Mr. FLICKINGER: In Ohio we have set up an Inter-Agency Council on Recreation which is a form of state aid, though purely advisory. It is composed of members of various state departments—health, welfare, education, and so on. We limit ourselves primarily to certain situations upon request, select appropriate experts to meet with groups interested in developing a recreation project or improving existing conditions, thoroughly survey their situations, and come up with the kind of advice they need.

At present state aid for local communities is unlikely. It will be desirable later on, but undoubtedly there will be the usual fight to get appropriations. Perhaps it might be contingent on another form of aid—federal aid to state parks.

MR. GILES: A great deal of the problem has to do with the motivation of small com-munities. Vandalism, for example, is never found where entire communities are solidly behind a community program.

A community in Tennessee, where no sort of public park was available, got together, set to work, and eventually, with no bond issue, had an 18-hole golf course, a swimming pool, picnic tables, and everything the group had desired. If a community really wants something, it will get it, and the public won't be in debt for it, either.

Integration of Public Programs

Criticism of federal drainage, irrigation, flood control, and power genera-tion projects as harmful to wildlife and natural area values was voiced at various times throughout all the subsection's discussions. Suggestions had been made pointing to the need for a coordinated national policy concerning recreation areas in general.

Closer examination of this problem brought no disagreement with the view that the revised Coordination Act, which requires a review of water impoundment structures by federal and state wildlife agencies, was often rendered ineffective. Adequate review, it was thought, was hampered by insufficient funds. Creation of an independent federal department of natural resources was suggested as a possible solution. (See also Subsection A, pages 72-73.)

FROM THE RECORD

To what extent can public programs for maintenance of wilderness areas, national parks and monuments, and protection of natural habitat for wildlife, and public pro-grams to aid drainage, irrigation, navigation improvements, flood control, and power gen-eration be harmonized?

CARL D. SHOEMAKER (National Wildlife Federation): The greatest threat to our na-tional parks, monuments, and forests, is the federal government itself. Who proposes the dams—Green River, Echo Park, Split Moun-tain? The Department of the Interior. Who was sponsoring the Glacier View Dam? The Corps of Engineers. And yet the revised Co-ordination Act expressly authorizes federal agencies such as the Corps of Engineers and Bureau of Reclamation to cooperate with the Fish and Wildlife Service. If and when the Secretary of the Interior and the Department of the Army can get together on a program, some of the problems that beset the people in wildlife administration ought to be resolved.

MR. GUTERMUTH: More and more con-servation education to bring about changes in public concepts and philosophies is the an-swer to most of our problems—education not only in the public schools and universities, but also in the engineering colleges. The next crop of engineers should be taught something about the other uses and values of water.

Among the conflicts in public planning for the use of land and water, drainage has been about the most abused. Many projects have been justifiable, but other have destroyed im-measurable natural values and failed to yield the anticipated benefits. Millions of dollars of public funds have been spent in efforts to undo the destruction that has been wrought by unwise drainage. In the past few years, we have seen the federal subsidization of drainage by governmental agencies while other bureaus have been working frantically with other public funds to put water back on the land for use by livestock and beneficial wildlife. There are instances where the same landowner has been given a federal subsidy for draining a pothole and another payment for building a farm pond. One agency pays the farmer to clear trees and brush, while another gives him assistance in planting cover for wildlife.

As to major developments, in few cases do the long-term wildlife values and recreational values created on new reservoirs equal those destroyed by the impoundment. But benefits to wildlife frequently can be increased by incorporating appropriate measures in the over-all program at the time the projects are planned.

The joker in the amended Coordination Act is that most of the operating funds that the Office of River Basin Studies of the U.S. Fish and Wildlife Service gets to investigate those big impoundments must be doled to it by the construction agency that is promoting the project.

Another serious inconsistency exists in federal programs between the grazing fees charged by the Bureau of Land Management and the U.S. Forest Service.

Correction of the present somewhat chaotic situation can come only through one of two steps. One would be the creation of a real department of natural resources which would eliminate present interagency disputes and co-ordinate federal natural resource programs of all kinds on an impartial basis. The other would be the establishment of a citizen board of review with Cabinet status, similar to that described in the policy statement of the Natural Resources Council of America, upon which all interests involved would be represented equitably, and which could pass judgment upon the feasibility, desirability, and immediate need for federal dam-building projects.

At the close of the Conference, Mr. Ben H. Thompson added the following opinion:

MR. THOMPSON: Implementation of the Park, Parkway and Recreation-Area Study Act of 1936, which authorizes the Secretary of the Interior to cooperate with federal and state agencies in park and recreation planning, would also help to integrate and coordinate public land planning and management.

Subsection D

WATERSHED VALUES

Every piece of land drains into some stream or river, and small watersheds are parts of large ones. The work of farmers, ranchers, and timber operators, while aimed primarily at producing year-to-year direct income, also has wider implications in its effects on runoff, erosion, flood hazards, and other situations throughout an entire watershed. Operation of publicly owned land involves a similar situation, though sometimes with less occasion for conflicts.

This complex relationship is the source of the questions examined here. To what extent are the two ends—managing land for high immediate productivity and conserving and improving watershed values—consistent? What are the possibilities of conflict, especially between short-term private and long-term public watershed goals? What degree of cooperation seems to be required and what present methods are most promising? What are the most serious gaps in current knowledge that might be filled by research in the physical, biological, or social sciences?

These problems sometimes overlap the larger aspects of water resource management considered in Section III (pages 126-75), but only as the issues relate to the subject immediately at hand. The focus here is quite different; attention is centered on upstream programs and problems in the small, tributary watersheds.

Efforts to relate land management to watershed values are significant controversial events in current American history, and may turn out to be a distinctive step in the evolution of democratic processes in this country. Many questions are still unanswered. Among those considered here are possibilities of increasing water yields through direct efforts; the contribution land use and treatment can make toward flood prevention; how local watershed programs can best be fitted into larger efforts; and needs for further basic research.

Social and economic factors were seen to cut across all aspects of watershed improvement. The success of efforts to persuade upstream landowners to install and maintain land improvement measures depends largely on proof of a reasonable return on investment. Similarly, the community at large will be more enthusiastic in its cooperation when a watershed program can show benefits in the form of increased community income.

Many participants felt that a balanced national land and water policy would minimize bias in assessing the conflicting claims made for various projects and lead to a more equitable allocation of funds for research and operational assistance to benefit both upstream and downstream land and water resources.

Some participants held that lack of adequate stream-flow records on many of the smaller streams detracted from the value of pilot plant demonstrations, but this belief was countered by the view that research and action programs go hand in hand, and that since action often cannot wait upon the results of long-term research, much more attention should be given to all forms of studies in the watersheds—biological, physical, social, and economic—that are made concurrently with the initiation of action programs.

Improving and Increasing Water Yields

Water yields can be improved or increased by manipulating upland vegetation, controlling soil erosion; using water, including ground water, more efficiently for agricultural purposes; and controlling riparian vegetation. How can individual operators improve their practices in order to bring the greatest long-range benefits to their own lands and at the same time contribute to broader development efforts?

Underlying each specific suggestion advanced during discussion was the view that piecemeal methods to increase or improve water yields must take into account an evaluation of their effects on the watershed as a whole. "What we need," said one participant, "is management based on an understanding of the principles of hydrologic cycles, rather than concentration on various individual phases. We have manipulated water and soil without really managing it." The relationship of agricultural practices to ground-water supplies, discussed in this connection, also drew the attention of Section III (pages 135-36).

Lessons learned in 100 years of irrigation practice in the West can provide a basis for working out methods to increase water yields in the East, where shortages are already felt. Experimentation and research on the problems of both humid and arid areas are only beginning to provide some of the answers, and these, in turn, raise questions that involve social and economic problems as well as broader aspects of the physical sciences.

FROM THE RECORD

Manipulation of Upland Vegetation

MARVIN D. HOOVER (Rocky Mountain Forest and Range Experiment Station): In general, there are two possibilities of increasing water yields by manipulation of upland vegetation: increase in the precipitation that reaches the ground, and reduction in transpiration.

The most practical application of the first possibility appears to be in the Rockies and the Sierras, where experiments show conifers to intercept considerable snow. Replacement of conifers with hardwood species such as aspen will allow more snow to reach the ground. Other practices that will reduce snow interception are to create openings in the forest by timber cutting or to reduce forest density by thinnings. Naturally, there must be enough snow to satisfy the soil moisture deficiency before stream-flow increase can be expected. The impact on other uses of the forest must be considered. There may be serious conflicts between cuttings for increased water yield and management of forest land for recreation or timber values.

Reduction of transpiration can be expected to increase water yields in areas where growing season rainfall is sufficient to overcome soil moisture deficiencies. The substitution of shallow-rooted plants for deep-rooted plants reduces the total draft upon soil moisture.

In the Rockies, when trees were cut on a small watershed, the increase in runoff due to reduced snow interception was about 2½ inches the first year and averaged about 1½ inches for eight years after treatment. Increases might run to 5 or 6 inches in the Sierras, where there is more snow and more precipitation. Experiments in reducing transpiration losses in the southern Appalachians

by cutting vegetation resulted in an increased stream flow of 17 inches, or 65 percent, the first year after cutting. As vegetation became re-established the effect was less pronounced, but on a watershed cut 13 years ago the increase in stream flow is still between 6 and 8 inches a year.

LLOYD L. HARROLD (USDA Agricultural Research Service, Ohio): On crop and pasture land the type of vegetation greatly affects water yield. Grassland, for example, may have 40 inches infiltration of which 12 inches will percolate to the deep ground reservoir below, where it will be available for stream flow in dry weather. Cornland, on the other hand, may have 26 inches of infiltration but only 3 inches will percolate to the reservoir. While the yield of water from cornland through annual runoff thus is greater than from grassland, it is not usable, being silt laden and rather flashy in the runoff. The yield of water we like to think of as usable, in the streams, comes from water penetrating the grasslands.

If a farmer converts this grass, which is shallow rooted, to alfalfa brome, he increases his production, but he may also change the water picture. So there may be conflict between the farmer's use of water in his own economic interest, and the yield of usable water downstream. I cannot help imagining that in time, when we have a great downstream interest in water yield, those areas will help finance the land operations upstream to produce a better and more continuous yield of water.

MR. HOOVER: The first job is to get the soil in condition to handle the water. On soils with impermeable surfaces like many abused croplands in the East where there is much surface runoff and erosion, deep-rooted vegetation is needed to get them in shape. Then, as we need more water downstream, it may be possible by careful management to convert to shallow-rooted vegetation. In the western mountains where there is still heavy forest cover, we are perhaps ready now to take the necessary measures to improve water yield.

HAROLD WILM (College of Forestry, State University of New York): Some years ago, I asked an assistant state engineer whether, from the viewpoint of the people in Colorado and Wyoming who need water badly, it was more important for us to plan our research toward the management of forests for maximum infiltration or toward maximum yield, in view of the fact that the storage capacity of Colorado dams was, at the time, insufficient to handle all the resulting water. He recommended working toward ground yields and taking care of storage when the time comes.

CHARLES R. HURSH (Southeastern Forest Experiment Station): In temperate climates ground-water storage takes place principally during the winter months. At this time it is imperative to maintain maximum infiltration of storm water. Land management practices that lead to compaction of the soil thus increase the total winter storm runoff with a corresponding reduction of the total stored ground water during winter months.

Control of Erosion

REED W. BAILEY (Director, Intermountain Forest and Range Experiment Station, Ogden, Utah; statement read by Mr. Croft): There are two groups of major opportunities for improving the usefulness of water yields in the United States through the application of erosion control measures.

One is to stabilize already actively eroding lands on farms, forests, and ranges. Where accelerated erosion is occurring mainly by sheet erosion and the land is not deeply incised by gullies, soil stability and control of runoff can usually be accomplished by getting more plant cover on the ground. Extensively gullied lands

usually require mechanical aids as well as vegetation treatment. Unstable channels and slopes commonly require structural works even though runoff from above is brought under control.

The second opportunity is to maintain the stability of the land under the impact of use. Herein lie many difficult problems. Fundamentally, if soil stability and control of water yields are to be accomplished under the plant cover and soil disturbances that accompany farming, logging, grazing, road building and other structural works, those uses must be designed to leave the land in condition to withstand the destructive effects of the rare storm event.

A 17-year experiment we conducted in Utah on an area with an aspen-herbaceous cover is an extreme illustration of the ill effects of soil misuse. During the first 11 years, under normal conditions, 488 inches of water fell on the area and only a trace of runoff was found. Assuming those conditions had existed since the soil was built, it would seem that in 20,000 years a 20- or 30-mile column of water had passed through the soil, leaving the soil stable.

We then proceeded to change the conditions. Over a 6-year period during which 271 inches of precipitation fell on the land, we removed all vegetation. While this resulted in a runoff over the surface of about 3 inches, or approximately 1 percent, that 1 percent runoff created erosion at the rate of 60 tons of soil to the acre. In 36 years we could lose as much as one-sixth or 1 foot of the soil—one-sixth of its reservoir capacity.

I do not wish to imply that we can expect to use our land and keep it as stable as it was under pristine conditions. Some soil loss and some loss in the control of runoff may be inevitable. However, we must learn how to prevent such losses from being accelerated to intolerable limits. The determination of the safe limits of land use requires much more knowledge than is now available about the hydrology of our land. Let us therefore proceed to speed up our programs of erosion control where such needs are obvious and at the same time intensify our search for more accurate information about the hydrologically safe limits of land use.

EDWARD A. COLMAN (California Forest and Range Experiment Station): Is it a bad idea to reduce the reservoir capacity of the soil? Might not a reduction increase water yield?

A. RUSSELL CROFT (U.S. Forest Service, Utah): In general, it is a dangerous thing to attempt because of the sedimentation hazard. On the basis of onsite values it would not be good either.

MR. HURSH: The time factor to damage watersheds in the Southeast would be less than in Utah. There, loss of reservoir capacity of the soil does not take 6 years. By over-trampling wet clay pastures, for example, the macropore space (noncapillary porosity) can be reduced as much as 20 percent by volume in the first 4 inches of the mineral soil in 3 months. This will reduce the infiltration and result in a corresponding increase in storm runoff peaks.

MR. COLMAN: The mountain meadows in the West serve as natural regulating reservoirs for water flow. Some are so heavily grazed that the grass is largely gone. As a consequence, surface runoff has increased, and the meadows are deeply gullied. The gullies have lowered the water table, reducing the amount of detention storage capacity in the meadows. This has two bad effects: we have lost some control over stream flow; and instead of good forage, the meadows now grow sagebrush and other drought-resistant plants.

MR. CROFT: Loss of water control on the land in the West, especially in valleys such as that of the Colorado River, has also produced tremendous quantities of sediment to be carried downstream. Much of the sediment going into the Hoover Dam is so caused. There are many areas of high geological erosion in the Colorado, but there are also many that have been eroded by poor land use.

LOUIS GOTTSCHALK (U.S. Soil Conservation Service): In Illinois, where considerable study has been made of watershed erosion and sediment sources, we find generally that about 90 percent of our sediment is coming from sheet erosion and less than 10 percent from channel erosion. We have been struggling with land patterns in attempts to correlate research work on soil losses with work on the farms in the watershed. Where sediment loads are derived 90 percent from sheet erosion we can effect 60 to 90 percent load reduction through proper land use.

Changing the intensity of the land use is effective. During the last war, for example, when the acreage of soybeans was materially increased we found that sediment loads also increased.

Many of the stream sediment loads in Illinois are beginning to show decreases as a result of work that was done in the soil conservation districts not specifically for watershed improvement. The downstream water supply is improving. One of the greatest effects of a watershed program is on the quality of the water.

Better Practices in Agricultural Water Use

MR. CROFT: Two basic problems in irrigation have to do with storage between the time of high stream flow and the time of demand and conveyance. Conveyance confronts us with some of our biggest difficulties. Out of a rough total of 138,000 miles of irrigation canals in the country, less than 5 percent are lined. The estimated annual diversion from reservoirs and streams into those canals is 100 million acre-feet, but in conveyance from stream or reservoir to farm 50 percent is lost every year, and in applying that water to the land another 50 percent is lost. These losses are not corrected by return flow.

Drainage is a related problem. It is neither practical nor desirable to apply to the land the exact amount of water necessary to produce a crop. One reason we must apply more water is to prevent accumulation of intolerable concentrations of salt in the soil.

Waterlogging has taken a toll of irrigated land. Twenty years after irrigation began in the Imperial Valley, some 100,000 acres of land was waterlogged. It took 20 years' study to determine how to drain the land. About 5 years after that all but about 5 percent had been reclaimed.

Another waste in water use comes about through the way we are organized. Earlier canals were taken out low down on the stream. Somebody higher up took out another, and someone else took out another, until in many places we have great systems of parallel canals. Some consolidation of our irrigation systems will be necessary if we are to prevent this kind of waste.

G. A. HATHAWAY (U.S. Corps of Engineers): In many of our western valleys where there are losses from irrigation canals, the water is reused. Is some allowance made for that in the losses mentioned?

MR. CROFT: No, the figures are a summation of losses. When corrected for reuse, the total loss would not be so large. In the Sevier Valley, Utah, some water is used several times. Maybe we do not want to prevent all losses. That is another question.

Control of Riparian Vegetation

MR. COLMAN: There are thousands of acres of bottom land in the western desert and semidesert areas where the water table is quite near the surface and where there is a dense growth of water-loving vegetation that has no economic value. Interest has been growing in finding ways to reduce evaporative water losses in these areas, with the thought that the water thus saved would then become available for use elsewhere.

Preventing riparian water waste is not simple. One could ditch the area or put in drains and thus lower the water table; or one could pump water from beneath the riparian areas. Or, as is sometimes done, one could remove the willows, tamarisk, and other water-wasting plants and replace them with vegetation, such as alfalfa, which has economic use.

We do not yet know whether we can reduce water losses here simply by destroying vegetation. Instead of centering research at-

tention on methods of replacing water-loving plants with other species, perhaps we should find out whether, by treating the vegetation, we can actually reduce evaporative water losses in areas where the water table is near the surface.

A. W. MARION (Ohio Department of Natural Resources): I wonder if the problem of riparian vegetation is confined to the West. Improperly handled banks and meandering streams in the East have taken valuable land out of production. Planting the right type of vegetation along the banks might help control the situation.

More Efficient Use of Ground Water in Agriculture

R. L. NACE (U.S. Geological Survey): Important threats to our land and water resources stem from artificial disbalance of the hydrologic cycle. Proper management and utilization of ground water in agriculture in all stages of the cycle would increase the total effective supply by permitting use and reuse of the water, instead of allowing it to accumulate and ruin the land. Hundreds of miles of inefficient gravity drains in the West point to the folly of disrupting the hydrologic cycle without balancing it in a new pattern, involving ground-water utilization. Pumped drainage wells would help the reclamation of damaged land and would provide water for additional acres.

Irrigation with ground water often is relatively cheap, especially in comparison to surface-water systems which involve a cost for drainage and loss of cropland that is occupied by drainage works. In some areas, the cost of pumping ground water just to get rid of it is part of the price of irrigating by surface water.

Watershed management can improve soil productiveness in a watershed area about in proportion to the extent it increases soil-water storage on the watershed. By control on the watershed you are taking a cut out of water that is available for runoff or recharge of ground water that is used elsewhere.

Watershed Flood-Prevention Operations

What contributions to flood prevention are made by land treatment and improvement work on forest and range and crop and pasture land and by flood-detention structures? How can these contributions be increased?

Efforts to answer these related questions brought out one need common to all: More research and more experimentation is required before we can accumulate sufficient knowledge to help us evaluate the downstream benefits of upstream operations and determine the extent to which some of the measures practiced in one area can properly be transferred to another.

That there is total benefit to the watershed is clear, participants believed, but the degree to which these measures will minimize floods and sedimentation is determined by human factors which, by and large, are beyond the control of the technician. Ownership participation in land treatment projects—whether on land used for forest, range, crops, or pasture—is predicated on profit, or at least the absence of financial sacrifice. More convincing, realistic ways should be found, several participants thought, of persuading upstream owners to install and continuously maintain measures that will repay them in long-term onsite values and, at the same time, benefit residents downstream.

Some difference of opinion arose as to the purpose served by upstream structures. Was there a tendency to place too much emphasis on their contributions to downstream flood prevention? One participant pointed out that, while benefits downstream do accrue from the existence of small upstream structures, the main purpose of these dams is to supplement the effects of land improvement projects and to protect the upper tributary valleys. In defining their place in the watershed, the chairman said, "We should consider the whole of the statistics, knowing the proportion of the floods that start with a small flood damaging one farmer's acre, and at the other end, the so-called capital flood that occurs comparatively rarely in a large basin with widespread damage."

FROM THE RECORD

What contributions to the reduction of floods and sediment can be expected from treatment of forest and range land?

BERNARD FRANK (U.S. Forest Service): Potentially, the contributions of forest and range land treatment and management to flood and sediment reduction can be highly significant. Damages from the more frequent floods of lesser magnitudes can be reduced by 50 percent or more, and sediment production similarly reduced. Large floods from treated forest and range watersheds can be reduced in the order of 1 to 10 percent, and their damaging effects lessened.

If every watershed treatment automatically produced an immediate increase in the owner's income, contributions of this nature could be realized. Unfortunately, this is not likely to happen, nor are economic benefits to downstream areas likely to count for much with an upstream landowner. Programs have to be developed that are acceptable to the landowners, but initial acceptance carries little assurance that they will be fully installed as planned, and still less that a completed program will be maintained even for a decade.

For these reasons, I do not believe it is possible as of today to estimate the probable effects of watershed flood-control programs in years to come. About all we can do is continue along present lines, hoping that we can improve the predictability of watershed-treatment effects and develop more effective incentives for owner participation, especially in the day-by-day maintenance of the programs.

Our requirements toward this end are: First, continued installation on a widespread scale of the small watershed pilot demonstration programs to sample the physical and economic variations throughout the United States. (A minimum of 20 years following complete installation is needed to obtain objective evaluations.) Second, expanded and intensified watershed research, some of it on the demonstration watersheds, to throw further light on the natural laws governing plant-soil-water relations. Third, investigations by specialized scientific teams into the possibilities for improving the management of commercial timber and grazing lands, to increase and speed up economic returns from practices which are also effective in minimizing floods and sedimentation. Fourth, we may need to consider the application of technically sound financial incentives, preferably on a quid pro quo basis, to encourage sustained participation. Finally, we may want to re-examine more closely the need for social controls or other measures where the public interest is demonstrably affected.

MR. HARROLD: Fourteen years ago we reforested a small watershed and a watershed about 40 times as large. Results from the small watershed show that floods, which were numerous and rather high in the early stages of the experiment, are now subdued; but from the larger area we have floods as high as at the beginning of the experiment, and sometimes higher. We have much to understand before we can evaluate the effect of land operations on floods downstream.

What similar contributions can be expected from treatment of crop and pasture land?

CARL B. BROWN (U.S. Soil Conservation Service): It is only to a limited extent that land treatment measures such as contour cultivation, strip cropping, terracing, rotations,

and pasture management, are going to be applied on the land for offsite benefits. Yet those benefits can be rather phenomenal. If you convert bare land to grassland, small area plots will show decreases in surface runoff 100-fold or more.

In terms of averages, effects of land treatment measures on flood reduction down in the tributary valleys may range from less than 5 percent in some areas to 30 percent or, on a few areas, as much as 40 percent. The average effects on sediment reduction are even greater. Reduction will very commonly exceed 50 percent; in some areas where most of the sediment is coming from sheet erosion, it would be possible to obtain 75, 80, or even 90 percent reduction in soil loss.

CHARLES MARSHALL (Nebraska Farm Bureau Federation): It costs money to install a good, workable soil conservation program on a farm. It is easy to talk to the man in the bottom land, who has experienced a flood and knows the benefits of such a program. It is harder to talk to the fellow on the hill. You have to show him a profit motive for getting treatment on his land.

CARTER PAGE (U.S. Corps of Engineers): Is it not true that land treatment measures largely have quite an effect on small floods but not on large floods?

MR. BROWN: Certainly, land treatment measures could have relatively little effect when you get the type of storm that produced 1951's catastrophic flood in the Kansas River Valley. But the small, frequent floods that overflow several times a year in the headwater valleys, and maybe once every year in the larger tributaries, produce in the aggregate probably more than half of the country's total flood damage. The effect of land treatment in reduction of over-all flood damage is most significant in reducing small floods. That is where you pick up the kinds of averages I quoted.

MR. PAGE: The contribution of these measures should be understood because they are valuable in themselves. Perhaps we can lay too much emphasis on the admittedly smaller contributions they make toward flood-damage prevention.

MR. BROWN: We estimate that, on the average, land treatment measures have more than 90 percent of their benefits on the land where they are placed; less than 10 percent might be considered offsite benefits. But in terms of total flood-damage reduction, the percentage could be considerably higher than 10 percent.

What contributions can be expected from upstream flood-detention structures?

MR. HATHAWAY: Upstream flood-detention structures are in a twilight or intermediate zone between onsite land treatment measures and major downstream structures. In the main, they are substantial engineering structures of such importance to require a careful engineering analysis of each tributary area to determine the proper location of each structure, the most suitable type of structure, and the benefits to be derived from their construction. These upstream detention structures should not only be feasible from an engineering viewpoint but should also stand on their own feet insofar as economic justification is concerned.

C. V. YOUNGQUIST (Ohio Department of Natural Resources): In most cases the upstream structures are placed in areas where there are no previous records of stream regimen. That is one of the dangers in the proposed 65 pilot plant demonstration program.[5]

Is it feasible to design any structure in a river channel without considering its impact upstream and downstream?

RAYMOND A. McCONNELL, JR. (*Lincoln Evening Journal*): We cannot know the whole story of the big streams without knowing the story of the whole river basin. It is not a matter of trying to coordinate the so-called downstream with the so-called upstream, but of planning on the basis of a whole watershed, beginning at the top.

ANTHONY W. SMITH (CIO Conservation Committee): The way to handle floods is to prevent them by means of intensive watershed management before they get started. Country and city people have this problem in common and ought to work on it together. If we take the money now wasted on destructive single-purpose flood-control dams and put it into watershed management work under the direction of the Department of Agriculture, the expenditures will actually be less, and the results superior. The job should be done by the Soil Conservation Service, and that Service must have the funds, the staff, and the regional and national structure necessary for the work.

MALCOLM B. RONALD (Associated Missouri Basin Conservationists): We are up against a situation in which the conservationists had better start fighting. The Bureau of Reclamation and the Army Engineers between them have what might be called an automatic self-starting, self-perpetuating pork barrel. I do not think we can stop it. But we can insist that we get enough money to carry watershed research ahead somewhere near as fast as the big dam angle is carried ahead. I am not against big dams, but I am opposed to the way they build them in the Missouri Basin.

MR. YOUNGQUIST: Even before the Army started its operations, the Miami Conservancy District built a reservoir system of flood control. They first studied the alternative, which was to use some 50 small structures instead of 5 large dams. They knew little about land treatment measures but, from the standpoint of economy alone, they found that the 5 large structures could accomplish much more than the 50 small ones.

CLAYTON M. HOFF (Brandywine Valley Association): In Chester County, which is

---

[5] In 1953 Congress appropriated $5 million, to be spent on experimental watershed protection work on 65 sub-watersheds ranging in area from 4 to 400 square miles each. It is planned that programs would be installed within a five-year period at a tentatively estimated cost of $29 million to federal government and $30 million to state and local participants.

approximately 600 square miles in area, one half of which is drained by the Brandywine, conservation practices were adopted on a little over half of the farms in the period from 1945 to 1950. The result of this has been an increased income in agricultural products of $8.5 million per year. If we apply the price indices for the years 1945 and 1950 this still amounts to approximately $6 million per year increased income.

Downstream improvements resulting from upstream practices in agriculture are obvious, but difficult to measure. This applies both to reduction of flood damage and the improvement in the quality of water used for domestic purposes. However, in comparing the results from similar rainfalls, we find some quantitative evidence of considerable improvement. Comparisons made on this basis indicate that over a five-year period, runoff has been decreased by 35 percent and the loss of silt has been reduced by 75 percent.

MR. BROWN: According to criteria now used by the Department of Agriculture, upstream structures are detention structures ranging in size up to about 5,000 acre-feet and controlling areas behind them up to about 20 square miles. The average would be less than 20 percent of that size. To date, several hundred such structures have been constructed.

In many watersheds a land treatment program will not produce sufficient flood-damage-reduction benefits to the rural communities in the upper tributary stream valleys without the inclusion of these structures. Even so, such a program is not designed to give full protection against disaster type floods occurring in the main stem valleys. Adequate protection of Dayton, for example, could not be feasibly accomplished in 1913 or today by a system of very small upstream retarding structures. There is a different sort of economics, however, in looking at the unprotected area above the structure that protects Dayton. The Blue River Valley is a good example of a program which can be justified purely on the basis of protecting areas above the site of Tuttle Creek Dam, not below. We need to consider the kind of economics we are using, and not confuse

the purpose for which we are building dams.

LESLIE A. MILLER (Cheyenne, Wyo.): There are seven main stem dams on the North Platte River, starting down in Nebraska and on up the river into Wyoming. In about 20 years, one small power-producing dam, the Guernsey, had filled with silt to about 35 percent of reservoir capacity. So the Bureau of Reclamation conceived the idea of building a silt control dam above Guernsey, which would impound 150,000 acres of water when full.

After securing approval by Congress, the Bureau concluded that this small dam was uneconomical. So they finally came up with a comparatively large hydroelectric dam, entailing an 800,000-foot reservoir. They then looked around for some nonreimbursable features to reduce their hydroelectric power rates; and the Corps of Engineers obliged by finding they could allocate 275,000 acres to the capacity of the reservoir for flood control. Some of the residents whose lands were going to be flooded objected to the Wyoming Natural Resources Board, on the grounds that they no longer have seasonal high water.

They explained that in the years before the seven dams were built, spring rains and melting snows caused the water to go down the North Platte River with such volume and speed as to create a scouring effect, and caused a reasonably constant carrying capacity to be maintained in the channel of the river. When these irrigation dams were built, they held back the water so that the scouring no longer happened, with the result that the North Platte River has lost 20 or 25 percent of its former carrying capacity. Farm lands not previously subject to flooding would now be covered in the event of a flash flood in between any of the dams. Flood control features in the dam above Guernsey would not prevent this.

The question was asked: What is the answer—is this going to be a continuing thing? The answer given was—more dams!

So you see, when you perform one act you may create a further problem. We cannot make too many snap judgments in the early stages.

Small Watershed Programs

How much can be done to make efforts in small watersheds accomplish more in the interests of both individual operators and the larger public? Three major routes are considered here: better integration of local programs with broader ones, gains in research and education that will enable landowners and local officials to get better results, and improvements in program organization. Problems of integration, which lead quickly to regional and national levels, were examined here mainly from the local viewpoint; the question as a whole was discussed in Section III (pages 147-61).

Development of land on the basis of small watersheds brings onsite benefits, but you cannot plan a small area separately from the larger area; you cannot plan a single project inseparably from the rest of the basin in which the project is to exist. Many participants favored a national policy for land and water that would involve greater integration among agencies, on both federal and state levels, concerned with the nation's natural resources. Suggestions for integration included a commission to determine policy, creation of a department in which all agencies now in the field would be brought together, and a combination of both.

It was pointed out that the research being conducted today by no means comprehends all aspects of watershed work—the social and economic as well as the physical. More inventory data on land and water and more basic and applied research are needed, the subsection concluded, before watershed development work can be accurately evaluated.

In discussing ways to organize and operate watershed improvement programs, several participants told of methods used in watersheds in widely dissimilar areas. It was recognized that differing regional conditions make applicable only the broadest of principles, but emphasis was placed on the need to gain the active cooperation of every farmer on the home watershed and the interest of every water user in the larger watershed area. Many participants felt this to be an important reason for regarding the conservancy district as the most suitable mechanism for achieving integration of watershed efforts.

FROM THE RECORD

The Balanced Program

VAL PETERSON (Federal Civil Defense Administration): The idea of treating the upper watersheds is sound by any test you can apply. It is sensible to hold the maximum amount of water at the point at which it falls. We can produce better crops at that point; we can cut down the siltation in the dams below. But you cannot control floods by upper watershed treatment or soil conservation methods alone. If you want to control a river like the Missouri, you must build multiple-purpose dams to get the maximum benefit of the water you store in the way of irrigation, navigation, power, farming, water supplies, and sewerage.

There is no conflict between the two concepts; in fact, they complement each other. What we ideally need in all of our basins is a balanced program on proper watershed treatment and down-river structures. In the last two or three years we have made some progress, but we are working too slowly. The Department of Agriculture's appropriation for

1953—$5 million for upper-water river treatment—is not adequate, particularly in relation to the sums being spent by the Corps of Engineers and the Bureau of Reclamation. At least until 10 months ago, research in soil conservation methods and small watershed treatment was almost negligible.

MR. McCONNELL: A balanced national policy requires an integration of planning and action between land measures and water measures. If we are to plan better, we must know more of what can be accomplished by upstream and land conservation measures, and what is the relationship of upstream development to downstream structures. We have an excellent starting point in the pilot plant watershed development program initiated this year. It would be helpful if an unbiased private agency could parallel this program with an objective study of its effects.

An integrated national policy demands a true sharing of responsibilities. With a few exceptions, the states have not yet entered fully into watershed conservation activities. This is another way in which a private agency can help—by undertaking a survey of state responsibilities in balanced conservation development. The Council of State Governments might help along this line.

Two other essentials are (1) the provision, within the total budget for resources development, of a fair apportionment for the conservation phase; and (2) Congressional action to spell out the responsibilities of the federal agencies. Last, this whole problem of getting a balanced national policy cuts across so many agencies, federal, state and local, and involves a sharing of so many responsibilities in Congress and elsewhere that a way must be found of integrating the day-to-day actions that make policy. This implies the need for some kind of neutral Presidential commission, probably with its personnel drawn from all levels of responsibility.

Suggested steps toward achieving a balanced national land and water policy prompted several participants to question the amount and kind of research being conducted.

MRS. ROLAND C. BERGH (Garden Club of America): I understand that original plans for the 65 pilot plants called for making some studies as to their effectiveness.

MR. BROWN: Yes, thus far we have asked the Geological Survey and the Weather Bureau to cooperate with us; the Forest Service and state water resource agencies are also participating. The program is scheduled to be completed in five years, and the results will, of course, be made available publicly.

MR. McCONNELL: The federal government's pilot plant program certainly envisages study of such things as surface runoff and sedimentation. But I doubt if the federal agencies have the means for conducting comprehensive research on the economic and social impact of this type of program. We would like to know, for example, what the thing does in dollars and cents to the retail trade of Lincoln.

MR. MARION: I thought that kind of economic information was easily available. In Ohio we can almost predict in any trading area the average 10-year income we should obtain if the land were properly managed. But a great deal of research is still needed to determine runoff, erosion, and the structure and permeability of the soils.

MR. HARROLD: Increases in funds for action programs have not been matched by increases in research. In fact, it is just the opposite. In Ohio we feel the crying need for analysis of data that have been gathered so that they can be channelled into water programs.

Ignorance of watershed values accounts for most of this deficiency. When we have a measure of runoff results for five years on the pilot plant watersheds, we shall have a certain answer, but it will not provide us with the means of knowing what will happen in another watershed or of evaluating the effect of certain conservation practices. You have to get down to a much finer study of the way these things happen on the land, and thus build up a knowledge of how to determine and evaluate the actual effect of land operations of some other water control projects and integrate that into the whole watershed program.

Mr. Marion: Perhaps research of that kind and integration of planning and action are both important parts of the over-all job. In research, primarily we need a complete inventory of land use within our states. I know of no state that has one. Ohio is starting and hopes to complete it in 15 years. Water inventory is equally important.

We have been disappointed that in Ohio the state agencies had little to say in the location of the pilot plants. In one county a plant is located on a stream on which we have no stream gauge reference, no water inventory, although in the same county there is another stream which has given us the basis for some 30 years of accurate water records. In another county, the research will be somewhat similarly handicapped. Political expediency of this sort is going to return us less for our money than would integrated policy.

Integration of agencies has been handled in Ohio by putting all agencies having to do with resources in one department. A bipartisan Natural Resources Commission was set up to determine policy. An over-all plan of conservation requires similar integration on the federal level. And somehow the challenge of service should be emphasized.

Harold O. Ogrosky (U.S. Soil Conservation Service): The kind of evaluation we shall be able to make on the 65 pilot plant watersheds will largely depend on the kind of records we find of previously existing conditions, and on the degree to which states and local people cooperate. Where records are good, I hope studies can be continued beyond the five-year period now authorized.

Recent research work of the U.S. Department of Agriculture was outlined, particularly the pilot and small watershed studies having to do with the accumulation of basic hydrologic and land inventory data.

Mr. Ogrosky: A useful backlog of information has been assembled, but it is far from what is desired. Additional basic data are needed in every phase of watershed planning and development. Deficiencies exist in data on rainfall, infiltration, ground water, soil moisture, runoff, land use, and evapo-transpiration, to name just a few. And we need more soil inventory information.

With the limited public funds available, the strengthening of these data is going to be slow. The ideal program would be built around a national policy and organized in such a way that decisive planning could be exercised over the work. In the meantime, about the best we can do is to focus national attention on the fact that in order to do successful resource planning we must have sound basic data.

Adrian Williams (U.S. Geological Survey): A major problem is to find some way of getting together all these basic data that have been gathered in different parts of the country. And there is still the question of just how well we can transfer results of treatment measures in small areas to large watersheds.

The Federal Interagency River Basin Committee is very much aware of the problem of evaluating the related effects of measures taken in upstream and downstream development. While government agencies only are involved, this is at least an indication of recognition that coordinated efforts are needed to solve the problem. The study of treatment measures for an entire watershed, which would be involved, would cost quite a little money. But informal discussions with the Bureau of the Budget indicate very little likelihood that funds may be recommended for this purpose on an interagency basis.

Mr. Colman: In order to make research more effective we need to be more specific about research objectives. We also need better coordination between research organizations so that efficiency can be increased. Varying conditions across the country make some research overlap unavoidable, but there appears to be some unnecessary duplication in watershed research. Perhaps some nongovernmental group could coordinate research better than a strictly federal group such as the Federal Interagency River Basin Committee.

Greater participation in watershed research by organizations outside the federal government is also needed. I am thinking particularly of state and county water agencies, soil conservation districts, irrigation and drainage districts, conservancy districts, and water and power companies, because these stand to benefit from methods that may be developed for managing watershed lands. Their help can accelerate research and channel it in the right direction.

Watershed management is at present more of an art than a science. On the basis of experience, we can now make certain recommendations. But we still can appraise more easily the effects of land management on crop productivity than on water flow. We should be able eventually to write prescriptions for watershed improvement with the results of the improvements expressed in quantities (gallons, acre-feet, peak flow, or dollars) or in terms of human values.

The results of most present watershed research have mainly regional application. We need more research on the physical, physiologic, ecologic, and hydrologic processes which are basic to all kinds of watershed management. Only when we know a great deal more about the basic processes will we be able to carry on applied research in an effective way.

A change is needed in the emphasis of applied research to permit us to extend application beyond the borders of the plots or watersheds where studies are made.

In order to use available funds more effectively, we need a periodic appraisal of our knowledge in the field of watershed improvement. We must be more prompt in analyzing data, and we should terminate research that has outlived its usefulness.

Mrs. BERGH: I believe it has been established that no one formula can be followed for each and every watershed. If we have successful small watersheds, surely we should make their accomplishments and defects a springboard for basic research instead of holding back action programs while continuing to study in a general way.

WALTER B. LANGBEIN (U.S. Geological

Survey): Perhaps the answer is that a gamble is all right so long as the people putting up the money know the extent to which they are gambling. I have in mind ground-water projects which may enable a local interest to build up capital toward a more advanced independent undertaking. But where the error of a wrong decision is apt to entail great costs, it would be greater wisdom to wait for research. The problem is to put the dollar sign on the cost of the wrong decision.

How best can programs for watershed improvement be organized?

WILLIAM S. BEARDSLEY (Governor of Iowa): I think it is time for more than planning; it is time for constructive action. In Iowa, we believe that the way to treat this problem is on a conservancy district basis, which is the concept of the watershed program. Approximately one-third of our farmers today have individual, permanent, long-range soil conservation plans. We have increased our support money at the state level 450 percent in the last five years, but we need more technical assistance at the local level.

Now we have reached the stage where we should establish regional conservancy districts to encompass the whole watershed. This will require the cooperation of every individual on the land, with federal and state agencies cooperating.

MR. McCONNELL: The problem of relating local objectives with what is good for the larger river basin or region poses the clear need for correlating the planning and work of local watershed districts with river basin agencies. At the same time, a mechanism should be developed for correlating local and regional objectives and planning, with planning done in the national interest.

MR. HURSH: The development of the community center idea has been beneficial in the southeastern states for promoting better water resource conservation. Some communities have made more progress than others. Probably a survey of the organization and program of particularly successful community centers would be of value to any proposal to expand similar movements to other parts of the country where they do not exist.

MR. MARION: I can go along entirely with the idea of the development of the conservancy districts for watershed management. In the Miami Valley the idea that brought this about was flood control. Elsewhere in Ohio the emphasis is on land management.

We are using for industrial and municipal water supplies alone more than 5 inches of the total rainfall in Ohio. Our underground pumpage is tremendous. We need to manage the watersheds not only to conserve the quality and amount of water in the watershed, but also to replenish the underground aquifers. We must consider also the need for adequate pollution abatement and prevention along with the whole program of water supply.

If we are setting up conservancy districts there should be integration within and between districts. In Ohio we are having legal difficulties in some districts in connection with the collection of district benefits. The legal aspects should be thoroughly studied before legislation is passed.

OLLIE E. FINK (Friends of the Land): It is important to remember in talking of watersheds and conservancy districts, that the district itself is a legal machinery but overlaps your present legal machinery. Each state for the most part has federal, state, county, and town governments. The conservancy district is a fourth type of governmental agency which operates on the basis of the watershed perimeter. In the Muskingum District there are 16 counties cooperating, and all those people have a legal say in the matter.

GOVERNOR BEARDSLEY: The state-wide conservancy district largely looks to the states. Where a district overlaps state boundaries the practical way to treat the problem would be through interstate compacts. In Iowa in 1949, we created a Natural Resources Council. Participating are all pertinent agencies, state geologists, people from state conservation committees and the Conservation Commission. We have an agricultural economist measuring the

impact on business and future generations. Through that method we coordinate the over-all program. In fact, the man on the land, the scientist, the engineer, all joined hands in this endeavor. It works fine.

Several participants drew upon their experience in setting up and maintaining improvement programs on both small and larger size watersheds, such as Brandywine, Connecticut River, and Salt Creek, to illustrate ways of handling organizational problems.

MR. HOFF: People have more in common in a small watershed than they do in a large watershed, and this is the reason, I believe, that it has been expedient to divide the operations on large watersheds, say up to 12,000 square miles, into small watershed associations. These might be called tributary associations.

At the beginning there must be a sufficient number of civic-minded people interested to provide financial backing. Later, the scale of their contributions can be decreased as smaller contributions begin to come in. An educational campaign is essential to stimulate public enthusiasm, and as the work progresses the record of its achievement, in terms of specific dollar benefits to the community and to the individual within the community, must be well publicized. The active cooperation of the various agencies involved—local, private, county, town, state, and federal—should be persistently encouraged.

MR. COLMAN: In California there are deterrents to managing the watershed as a unit. As an example, the state has a central valley which receives most of its water from the adjacent Sierra Nevada. Between the mountains and the valley is a foothill area covered largely with unpalatable brush intermingled with grass, and used largely for livestock grazing.

In a few places, owners of the foothill land have used care and money to replace the brush with grass. In others, conversion is attempted by burning alone, resulting in a sparse cover of grass which provides a little feed for a few years until the brush comes back. Then the land is burned once more.

You cannot blame the ranchers for wanting to get income from their land. But when winter rains are heavy, which is frequently the case, the freshly burned lands erode and streams run muddy. A number of reservoirs are silting, streams flow more erratically, and the lands in the valley are suffering.

How can the ranchers be made aware that their work in the hills is affecting the welfare of people below and, therefore, eventually their own welfare?

MR. HOFF: I can but suggest a method which in itself may not be a solution to this problem, but it has worked in many cases. A watershed organization, even if it is large, will provide different interests therein with an opportunity of meeting under conditions in which they can discuss frankly, without bias, their mutual problems. This in itself may lead to a satisfactory solution.

MR. MARION: If the watershed will not support a profitable agriculture and the use of the water down below is of sufficient value, it may be possible for the interested users to buy the watershed and develop it.

MR. WILM: That has been done in two or three places in Utah.

MRS. ALFRED S. GRIFFITHS (General Federation of Women's Clubs): Smaller but somewhat similar problems have been solved in Utah and New Mexico, where groups of women raised money among themselves, 10 cents apiece, to have a reseeding project. Three years later people came out to see the grass; now they are raising cattle on it.

MR. MCCONNELL: I have participated in the organization of some nine watersheds covering perhaps 20,000 square miles. The problem in each has been to get city people and farm people to see that they have a common problem. A good nucleus for effective organization can be formed by city bankers and soil conservation district supervisors. The rest of the business community will come in when they are shown that the stability of their retail trade is at stake. After that you can solicit smaller contributions from the rural population. But the problem is this: while you are asking the rural people to do a lot of things voluntarily, there is not a great deal that city people can contribute other than money. In our Salt Creek area encompassing 135,000 people, of whom 100,000 live in the City of Lincoln, city people provide the major financial support of the promotional effort. Farmers do their share in applying conservation to their land.

The nucleus in your agricultural area generally is the people most active in conservation on the land. In our own movement almost every farm organization is represented.

MR. WILM: Do you have anything in your organization to insure continuity of the work on the land?

MR. MCCONNELL: Yes, we rely on demonstration. Once you begin to show results you can broaden the support. At the outset we spent a good deal of money taking farmers on bus tours from some of the more backward areas to a few places where a good complete job, on a small scale, had been done. That is tremendously effective.

To keep the job rolling, some kind of governmental subdivision is essential. The soil conservation district is inadequate when you are talking of rural-urban problems. It has no tax power in most places.

We found it necessary to draw heavily upon Ohio's law, but we had to rewrite it to suit our local people. Initially we ran into opposition in our Legislature from arid-area citizens who were afraid of conflict with the Reclamation law. The week after the Legislature adjourned a flash flood in an irrigation area caused about $1 million damage to the canals. Some of our most effective support for passage of the watershed law subsequently came from that area, and there is being developed there a small watershed project with a system of gully checks and retention structures designed primarily to stabilize and protect the irrigation canals.

E. H. TAYLOR (Curtis Publishing Company): How can the watershed movement be facilitated by state enabling legislation? And what type of state resource organization would best facilitate the initiation and operation of watersheds? It seems to me that in a large majority of states the resource agencies are not organized to handle such a responsibility.

MR. MARSHALL: Mr. McConnell mentioned the law we have in Nebraska. So far as the organizational approach is concerned, the method used in Nebraska is effective because we did not have a formally established head group. Instead, some influential leaders secured the support of other groups with kindred interests. This drew the spotlight and made the venture more of a cooperative one.

The right person-to-person initial approach is important when you are dealing with the average conservation-minded farmer. You can have the best research and the best machinery, but unless public opinion works for it, no project can be effective. One of the things we need in the research field is to find out what the more progressive farmers have been doing. A lot of research is being conducted outside the laboratory by fellows with ideas.

MR. HOFF: I should like to suggest six basic philosophies based on this subsection's discussions of eight or ten different watersheds: (1) the watershed is the logical unit within which people can work together on the conservation of their resources—based on the belief that people in watersheds have more in common than people in other political units; (2) it is the responsibility of all the people in the watershed to participate actively in the preparation and prosecution of their own resource program; (3) to be effective, watershed programs should deal with all re-

sources and all related problems, preferably simultaneously; (4) people of watersheds should secure cooperation between all assisting agencies—federal, state, and local—but retain control of the program for the people of the watersheds; (5) watershed work should be directed toward the greatest benefits of all interests in the watershed; (6) costs of watershed programs should be borne principally by local people (individuals and organizations) and by the various watershed interests, in proportion to the benefits received.

JOHN D. BLACK (Harvard University; comment submitted after the Conference): Nearly all aggregative land-use and conservation activity is now and surely will continue to be organized by county and state units. The Soil Conservation Service started out favoring the small watershed as a unit for its districts, and got nowhere with it.

This does not mean that there is no place for watershed-unit organization. Indeed, it is badly needed. But it must be an aggregation of county units, grazing districts, and the like within the state, or sometimes more than one state. The actual carrying out of the watershed plans will be mostly by the county soil conservation, agricultural extension, and forestry units, grazing district units, and the county governments. A watershed planning unit is needed to plan these operations and work out administrative, financing, and other arrangements with the county and state governments involved, within the federal framework.

To integrate planning and operations in the various tributary watersheds on a main stream, an aggregative organization of the smaller aggregates is needed.

CHAIRMAN'S SUMMARY

The four subsections of this section, working independently, have made significant progress in detailing steps that might be taken to solve some of the problems concerned with the nation's renewable resources.

Food and Nonwood Fibers

It appears likely that during the third quarter of this century the need for food and nonwood fibers will increase 40 to 50 percent.

This means that production must be increased as much during that period as it was increased during the preceding 25 years. How can the output be increased efficiently and at low cost? The amount of increase of cropland will, of course, depend on economic conditions and needs. But the consensus seems to be that the answer largely lies in increased productivity on land now in agricultural use.

Research, particularly basic research, appears to offer the greatest long-term promise. This must be coupled with intensified efforts to bring improved techniques into application —increased use of fertilizer, machinery, and many other technical aids. There is considerable opinion that neither past nor current organization of soil and water conservation activities, in the form of engineering and other technical aid, is satisfactory for meeting needs; and that selective financial assistance, based on lasting good practices, is needed for some areas and certain types of farmers. Fertilizer use and pest control should be expanded as means of lowering the relative costs of agricultural production.

Unexpected agreement has been found that present public ownership probably is the most desirable arrangement for upbuilding and protection of range lands. There is strong sentiment for combination of all federal activities relating to federal lands not in specialized use. Understanding of the optimum combination of uses for open land is generally considered far below what is needed.

The immediate value of our 30 million acres of water-surfaced lands is for recreation, but their potential value for food and fur production is significant.

Timber and Wood Products

It is certain that needs for forest products will increase materially during the next quarter-century. At the same time, watershed protection and recreation values must be regarded as an integral part of forest development. While the area of disagreement steadily

has been narrowed, sincere philosophical disagreements are likely to continue as to how both requirements are to be met.

The principle of federal, state, and private cooperation, which, on the whole, has worked well in fire control, should also apply to pest control. There is disagreement over apportionment of responsibilities, but general approval of a trend toward increased state contribution.

The greatest need for research appears to be in pest control, watershed management, biology including forest genetics, utilization of low-quality woods, and economic aspects of forest management. A major increase in public financial support for basic research therefore may be necessary.

Opinion on federal grants-in-aid for forest management vary from full federal support of technical services to exclusively private support. Consensus favors federal research and financial assistance to states, with states taking primary responsibility in education and demonstration. There is little sentiment favoring close federal regulation of cutting practices, but some tendency to approve minimum state control. Education remains the primary need.

A good transportation system appears to be the most urgent need for prompt and full utilization of resources of our national forests. Other needs mentioned during discussion are simplification of timber sale procedure, speedup of timber inventories, and more advanced engineering and timber management planning.

A specific suggestion that a joint Congressional committee should make a study of the pattern of land ownership has had general support, provided the basic integrity of structure of the national forests is maintained.

Wildlife, Scenic, Wilderness, and Other Recreational Areas

A primary question centers around the various means by which wildlife can be increased to meet probable future demand, in face of parallel trends toward destruction of habitat and mounting hunting pressures. Throughout the discussions human considerations in wildlife management have been stressed. Production of game should be maintained and in some cases increased, but sportsmen should be influenced to find satisfaction within the limits of available supplies.

Additional parks and monuments, embracing outstanding scenic areas, important historical areas, and areas to fill other significant gaps, are desirable in long-range programs if we are to meet the current, let alone the future, needs of our increasing population. Opening of some additional areas in existing national parks and monuments may be necessary.

If we are to maintain the high level of scenic values in our wilderness areas, national parks, national forests, and certain state parks, we must provide more protection and resist the destructive pressures of lumbering, grazing, mining, motorized transportation, and construction of reservoirs. Increasing competition for the use of these lands should lead us to recognize the importance of managing them for the greater benefit of the greatest number of people. There is further need for small "natural areas" near populous districts, where animal and plant communities may be preserved for study and enjoyment.

In connection with the fast-growing demand for small recreational areas for urban, suburban, and rural sections, it is urged that such areas should be acquired soon, before land values increase further.

Suggestions for integrating public programs for maintenance of wilderness areas, national parks and monuments, and wildlife habitat with those to aid drainage, irrigation, flood control, and power generation include: better implementing of the Coordination Act of 1946; government agency reorganization to provide more balanced resource development planning; and increased efforts to educate the citizenry concerning the economic and social values which lie in the protection of nature.

Watershed Values

Consistently throughout the sessions of the subsection, the human and social aspects of watershed conservation and development have been emphasized. Similarly, all sessions of the subsection have heard repeated presentations of the need for additional research, both basic and applied, in all pertinent sciences, to add to the fund of available knowledge about watersheds. Voices have been raised, however, to urge that the time is at hand when actual watershed operations are now at least as necessary as additional study.

Upstream watershed operations are essential, according to presentations made before the subsection. Among other things, they reduce the frequency and damage of "smaller floods" on the smaller streams in rural areas, where more than half of the total United States flood damage occurs. They also improve agriculture and farm productivity; help protect and prolong the life of downstream flood control, power, and similar installations; and reduce the accumulation of silt in river channels and reservoirs.

Specific suggestions include: (1) establishment of a neutral, nongovernmental body to evaluate the progress of the recently inaugurated $5 million pilot plant operations on some 65 watersheds; (2) greater participation by the several states in watershed programs, together with revision of state laws to facilitate such effective participation; (3) clarification of the statutory authority and responsibilities of the federal agencies working in the conservation field; (4) establishment of a Presidential commission, or a body operating in the Office of the President, as a means of achieving balance and coordination in the activities of federal agencies in the conservation field.

LLOYD E. PARTAIN
December 4, 1953

Chairman

GILBERT F. WHITE
President of
Haverford College

Co-Chairman

ABEL WOLMAN, Professor of
Sanitary Engineering at
Johns Hopkins University

Steering Committee and Advisers

Steering Committee: JEAN S. BREITENSTEIN, Attorney, Denver · J. M. CLARK, Professor of Economics, Columbia University · WARREN T. HANNUM, formerly Chairman of the California State Water Pollution Control Board · W. W. HORNER, Consulting Engineer, St. Louis · CLAUDE D. KELLEY, President and Chairman of the Board, National Wildlife Federation · SAMUEL B. MORRIS, General Manager and Chief Engineer, Department of Water and Power, Los Angeles · CHARLES A. SPRAGUE, Editor and Publisher of *The Oregon Statesman*, Salem · *Assistant to the Section Chairman:* PERRY R. TAYLOR, Assistant to the Chief, Division of Water Pollution Control, U. S. Public Health Service · *Section Consultant:* RUSSELL LORD, Editor, *The Land* · *Steering Committee Assistants:* HENRY ERLANGER, Resources and Civil Works Division, Bureau of the Budget; HOWARD E. BALL, Resources and Civil Works Division, Bureau of the Budget · *Section Rapporteur:* MAYNARD M. HUFSCHMIDT, Technical Review Staff, Office of the Secretary of the Interior

Subsections

A. SUPPLY, USE, AND COMPETITIVE DEMAND

Chairman: THORNDIKE SAVILLE, Dean of the College of Engineering, New York University

Rapporteurs: STEPHEN BERGEN, The Conservation Foundation; JOHN LUDWIG, U. S. Public Health Service

B. DIVISION OF RESPONSIBILITY

Chairman: W. S. ROSECRANS, Chairman, California State Board of Forestry

Rapporteur: HOWARD L. COOK, Corps of Engineers, Department of the Army

C. EVALUATION AND REIMBURSEMENT

Chairman: M. M. KELSO, Dean of Agriculture, Montana State College

Rapporteur: MELVIN E. SCHEIDT, Resources and Civil Works Division, Bureau of the Budget

About 300 persons participated in the work of Section III. The 262 who registered formally are listed on pages 389-94.

WATER RESOURCE PROBLEMS

CONSIDERED NATIONALLY, water is still abundant, but in the face of ever-increasing demands adequate supplies can no longer be taken for granted in many parts of the country. A huge task of conserving and developing water resources lies ahead, one that will require the best efforts of individual citizens, private organizations, and federal, state, and local public agencies. We will be dealing with a complex of area problems rather than one nationwide problem. Watersheds and drainage basin units present an infinite variety requiring individual treatment rather than the wholesale application of any single approach.

The problems considered here concern supply and use of the nation's fresh water resource—flood control, irrigation, drainage, navigation, and pollution control, and, in fact, the whole range of situations and issues from precipitation on the slopes to the final flow of water to the sea. Problems of marine resources are not considered. Development of hydroelectric energy is touched only lightly since it bears on the problems discussed in Section V (pages 228-36).

The line between problems of fresh-water resources and those of soil conservation and land use is faint at best. Land and water are inseparably linked by nature. Within a watershed and on a continent, land and water problems interlace. The relationship with the discussions of Section II (pages 107-23) is close.

In the discussions that follow, water resource problems are examined from three points of view that reflect the organization of subsections: Supply, use, and competitive demand; division of responsibilities; and evaluation and reimbursement.

Subsection A

SUPPLY, USE, AND COMPETITIVE DEMAND

How can we as a nation assure at reasonable cost adequate supplies of water for all essential uses during the foreseeable future? The subsection examined this question from many angles. For convenience, the record of discussion is presented here under five main headings: (1) Supply in relation to use: now and in the future; (2) fundamental problems of competing demand; (3) ways of increasing the usable supply; (4) problems of pollution control; (5) basic data and their analysis.

Supply in Relation to Use: Now and in the Future

A number of areas in the United States, some of them large, are experiencing shortages of water from causes other than drought; more areas are likely to feel similar pressures in the future. Strong forces are working to increase total demand for water—growth of population, particularly in cities, expansion of industry, and higher living standards that raise per capita consumption. On a national basis, our total of available water resources is huge—the steering committee suggested that it exceeds foreseeable demands for at least 100 years. But this has little practical meaning even if true. The problem of supply is predominantly geographical, or related to particular uses.

The continuing expansion of industrial use of water and the rising quality requirements of a number of industries stand out as major factors in prospective demand. And the rapid emergence of air conditioning and supplemental irrigation as large users of water may have large significance in the future. Some far-reaching implications were noted here, including the possibility of tighter supply-use relationships in areas of the East.

A working definition of consumptive use was arrived at for purposes of sub-section discussion,[1] but some questions of its practical application remained unresolved. In fact, one of the clearest conclusions to be drawn from the discussion was how often deficiencies in basic information and its analysis stand in the way of useful appraisals and projections.

For instance, how renewable is ground water? This is a major question of supply, but while some people feel that in some areas the mining of ground water is an unmistakable long-term trend, others hold that in other areas records do not yet go back far enough to tell us much. To what extent may available supplies be increased through greater knowledge of conditions under which ground water can be replenished? Also, while we know that rising costs will affect future demand by discouraging wasteful use of water, there is no agreement on how much.

FROM THE RECORD

Local Situations

From a practical standpoint, problems of water supply are so localized that there was no attempt to sum up the national situation.

But examples were given from a number of areas. A few of them follow.

ROYCE J. TIPTON (R. J. Tipton and Associates, Inc., Denver): Very definite mining[2] of water is going on within the Central Valley

---

[1] Water lost to future use, such as water transpired by vegetation, incorporated in manufactured products, used up in industrial processes, or rendered unfit for any further use.

[2] Here, and throughout, "mining" of ground water is used in a general sense to denote withdrawals that exceed replenishment over long periods.

of Arizona. A million and a half acre-feet per year are being withdrawn, and the natural recharge is on the order of 100,000 acre-feet or less. The Pecos River area in New Mexico and Texas is very short of water due to encroachment of natural vegetation and withdrawal of ground water.

JACK R. BARNES (Consulting Ground Water Engineer, Austin): In the high plains of West Texas water is being mined at a rate probably 30 times that at which water is going into the ground. Some two years ago I put together some U.S. Geological Survey statistics on the use of underground water. At that time it seemed that approximately one-half of all ground-water use in the United States occurs in the southern tier of states from western Texas through southern California, and that approximately one-third of that amount of water was in excess of the amount of recharge.

RAYMOND A. HILL (Leeds, Hill and Jewett, Los Angeles): If the entire flow of the streams that enter the Central Arizona Plain were put underground it would still take care of only half the draft upon ground water; but those streams are now used to their utmost by surface irrigation. The situation in California is not so acute, but if it were not for the regulation and diversion of the surface streams and the returns from irrigation, the ground waters of the great Central Valley of California would have long since been exhausted.

HOWARD T. CRITCHLOW (New Jersey Division of Water Policy and Supply): In certain areas of New Jersey the water table has been lowered seriously. We are requiring the return of uncontaminated water used for cooling to the ground-water table to help replenish it. This experimental program is working in some areas. But in the coastal area there seems to be a permanent lowering of the water table, and we are fearful that an overdemand is going to bring in salt waters and ruin the whole thing.

None of the local examples was contested,

but there was considerable debate over how some of them should be interpreted.

WILLIAM S. WISE (Connecticut State Water Commission): The rate of producing water from underground in many places is a mining proposition; some withdrawals are being accompanied by evidence of complete taking out of storage. In such areas, water certainly does not represent a resource for the future under the present system.

JOHN C. FRYE (State Geological Survey, Kansas): We need an exceedingly long record to determine whether an area is being mined of its ground waters. An area in western Kansas would have been considered to be seriously mined of its ground-water supplies as recently as three years ago. Water levels had been lowered many feet. Since then we have had a period of unusually heavy rainfall. Water levels are higher than they were 20 years ago.

ABEL WOLMAN (Johns Hopkins University): The water situation, even in the West, is related to location and to competitive demands and needs. I doubt whether any general summary is completely characteristic. For example, as I read the most recent State Engineer's Report on the Potential Water Resources of California, these resources, no matter how measured and no matter how desired or supplied, are far in excess of their foreseeable demands or needs for many a decade. Generalized statements should be subjected to some quantitative scrutiny.

Two Fast-growing Uses: Supplemental Irrigation and Air Conditioning

The record of recent years, several persons noted, points to a continued rapid expansion of supplemental irrigation.

PAUL WEAVER (Texas A. and M. College): In 1948, I heard it said that we should probably use more water in agriculture east of the Mississippi when full development has taken place than we are now using west of the Mississippi. Some recent developments tend to support that then-radical statement. Irrigation should be considered an important future competitor for water east of the Mississippi.

J. W. Dixon (U.S. Department of the Interior): I recently was sent to New Jersey by the Bureau of Reclamation to confer with some local sprinkler irrigation people. In that area they dig huge pits in the flat, sandy lands and pump the irrigation water supply from the pit. They find the operation to be very profitable. Then the neighbors put down pits too. Too often this results in an overdraft of ground water, and then there is no water for any of them. Water codes *are* needed in the eastern states.

The continuing spread of air conditioning could significantly affect future patterns of water use. Since the technology of this relatively new development is still changing fast, operating methods were discussed in considerable detail.

Stifel W. Jens (Consulting Engineer, St. Louis): Air conditioning is an emerging competitive use of water that raises some serious problems, particularly those of regulation. More and more builders are contemplating complete air conditioning of entire homes. Water costs so little that for most householders it will be cheaper to use a once-through cooling and then discharge this into the sewers. Serious overcharge of separate sanitary sewers can be a corollary problem. I understand that in some places one response to the problem is to make water so expensive for air conditioning use that it will be more economic for the householder to go to some recovery type of system.

Harry E. Jordan (American Water Works Association, Inc., New York): The water works industry is learning that air conditioning uses of water can be held within reason by a proper rate structure.

Mr. Jens: In most communities there is no knowledge of how many water-using units for air conditioning have been installed. (Suggestions that permits for such installations be required are practical.) Even if no other measures were taken, a community would have accurate knowledge of its situation for use at whatever time the problem became critical.

M. B. Cunningham (American Water Works Association, Oklahoma City): Many cities are requiring installation of cooling towers and water-saving devices for air conditioning equipment down to five-ton size. There are many systems that does not reach—there is widespread use, especially beginning this year, of the one-ton unit. We need to go all the way on this problem.

Richard Hazen (Hazen and Sawyer, New York): Both New York and New Jersey have restrictions against the wasteful use of water for air conditioning, and in those areas where it is at all feasible to recharge, recharge is generally required. The economic factor is important in air conditioning. With competing demands for water, we have to make up our minds that we cannot have everything cheap, as much as we may want it. Sometimes I think air conditioning is carried further than it has to be, and that if we get to a point where there is a real shortage of water, air conditioning will take its proper place.

Interpreting and Using Data on Supply

W. W. Horner (Consulting Engineer, St. Louis): The supply figure in most instances is the rainfall that reaches the ground. That is all potential supply, a flexible figure whose meaning depends on how much of it we prevent from getting away from us.

Mr. Hill: Many grave errors in project planning have resulted from the assumption that the long-term averages of precipitation and runoff can be used safely. In 1922, the Santa Fe Compact divided the waters of the Colorado River among Upper and Lower Basin States. It was then thought that there was a large surplus above the allotted amounts. But the long-term average has not worked out and will not work out. The average flow of the Colorado River from 1915 to 1930 was approximately 16 million acre-feet per year. The average since 1930 is approximately 12 million acre-feet per year. You cannot derive a meaningful long-term average; as one old farmer in Arizona said, you cannot irrigate with averages.

MR. TIPTON: The situation on the Upper and Lower Rio Grande could also be cited. In making water supply studies for the development of new water supplies by storage, the longest record should be taken and then considerable engineering judgment should be exercised because, unfortunately, we cannot accurately forecast the future water supply based on historical happenings.

Influences that are hard to gauge can have large effects on future situations. Costs, for instance, can affect use, and gains in research and methods can enlarge available supply.

MR. HAZEN: Water is essential, but like salt on the dinner table it is cheap, even though today we are paying two and three times what we paid 20 years ago. People could spend a great deal more for water and it would still not be a burden. In estimating future uses of water we tend to overlook the fact that as the costs go up waste goes down. That and the enforced treatment of industrial wastes should be forceful brakes in reducing the amount of future water consumption.

C. G. PAULSEN (U.S. Geological Survey): The interrelation between surface water supplies and ground-water supplies changes from time to time depending on a great variety of conditions. While we have problem areas, the ground water will replenish itself in due course if given an opportunity; that is the reason we need to know more about the conditions, the variations, and so on.

How Long a Look Ahead?

TOM WALLACE (Editor Emeritus, *Louisville Times*): Most of our discussions have related to the immediate or shortly foreseeable use of water and to ways of using water economically at this time. Shouldn't we stop somewhere and leave something for the people that are going to be born 1,000 years from now?

Fundamental Problems of Competing Demand

Most competition among water uses is either geographical (as, for example, the conflict between California and Arizona for Colorado River water) or functional, involving conflicts among different uses in the same area. Both types were discussed, but functional competition received the most attention.

Multiple-purpose projects were discussed as a means of resolving some of the conflicts in water use. It was noted that generalization is hazardous—that the extent to which multiple-purpose reservoirs can reconcile competing demands must be examined on a project-by-project basis.

The importance of recreation as a purpose of water resources development was pointed out by a number of participants; so was the necessity for safeguarding the essential characteristics of national parks and monuments and wilderness areas. The desirability of preserving sea beaches, especially from the standpoint of recreation, also was mentioned. The competition between reservoir storage sites and recreation and wildlife areas was discussed. (See also Section II, pages 101, 106-7).

How much weight should be given to noneconomic values? No one suggested ignoring aesthetic and recreational benefits of water development, but some laid particular stress on measurable economic aspects. Others believed that at least equal consideration should be given to those values going beyond economics.

FROM THE RECORD

Basic Values

Any discussion of competitive demand leads eventually to ultimate values. What are we really looking for in water development? And what relative weight should we give the different aims?

MR. TIPTON: The use of water for irrigation is basic. Generation of energy by water is a service use. If necessary, energy can be generated by other means. Navigation is a service use of water. Transportation can be provided by other means. However, food and fibers cannot be produced in the West except by irrigation. Irrigation in the West as elsewhere will become increasingly important to the whole country as the population grows. For this reason recreation where adversely affected by irrigation should give way to the use of water for that purpose. However, the uses of water for both purposes are usually perfectly compatible.

There is a segment of society which thinks that some sections of the country should remain in the forest primeval state; there should be no development; there should be no scars on the landscape. However, scars on the landscape will continue to be made if we are going to have development. The flooding of such areas as those situated within Echo Park and Split Mountain reservoir sites in the Dinosaur National Monument[3] will not detract from the scenery; it will add to it. It will make that area more accessible to the public and at the same time will make water usable for consumptive-use purposes and power development.

WILLIAM VOIGT (Izaak Walton League of America, Inc.): There is no broad acceptance of certain of the things Mr. Tipton has said by that rather large body of opinion in the United States that is embodied in the

---

[3] Dinosaur National Monument consists of about 200,000 acres lying in Utah and Colorado and is characterized by fossil beds and rugged canyons of geologic and scenic importance. It is administered by the National Park Service.

Natural Resources Conference, which I represent. He indicated that the impounding of water in Dinosaur Monument would not be damaging. There is considerable and growing technical opinion to the effect that the purposes of development which we all favor can be accomplished by going elsewhere. As to the forest primeval, yes, we want to reserve some of that, for watershed protection primarily.

Several of the comments on values to be considered among competing uses of water dealt specifically with recreation.

GENERAL U. S. GRANT, III (American Planning and Civic Association): We should distinguish between organized recreation, such as you have on a reservoir where people rent boats and things are commercialized, and the kind of recreation which you can get in Dinosaur National Monument, which cannot be reconstituted. There is a cultural benefit in the preservation of natural wonders of watershed areas which can be used by large numbers of people.

GEORGE E. DICKIE (Federal Interagency Committee on Recreation): More emphasis should be given to the recreation potentialities of water developments. Generally speaking, it is a compatible use. Millions of people are now using the newly created reservoirs of the West for recreation and not interfering with their other purposes.

DAVID R. BROWER (Sierra Club, San Francisco): Dinosaur is a unique scenic asset which cannot stand the program for its development in the Upper Colorado Project and survive as anything but a common reservoir, which is fine, but which falls far short of what the area now offers.

In other units of our national park system, demands for water development are threatening areas devoted to recreation and to preservation of wilderness qualities. These areas should be preserved, considered unavailable for this type of development, so that they will be there for our children. I think that science is going to solve some of these water reservoir problems by further studies in hydrology, by the anti-saline program, and by other means. Let us find the solution *before* we lose these scenic areas.

JOHN G. BAKER (*Milwaukee Journal*): In some instances river development is entirely incompatible with the best interests of recreation. In the Namekagon Dam case decided by the Federal Power Commission, the state of Wisconsin has so far been able to save an 11-mile stretch of free-flowing river with wilderness banks because of its peculiar attraction to people who like to fish and canoe in fast-moving water. The damming of that water would destroy for all practical purposes these recreational values; it would just make another lake, of which our state has 8,000.

EDWARD J. CLEARY (Ohio River Valley Water Sanitation Commission): While priority in terms of quality requirements may be listed as public and industrial water supply, fish life, agriculture, recreation, navigation, power and waste disposal, such listing does not necessarily establish priority of stream use in terms of economic usefulness. In some cases the use of a stream for waste carriage purposes may best serve the public interest. This does not mean open sewers—it means that treatment requirements for waste discharge would not be so rigid as for streams used for other purposes.

No one questioned the need for considering aesthetic values, but several participants regarded them as something completely apart from economic values. This drew dissent from two angles.

MR. WALLACE: The word "aesthetics" has been used pretty frequently. I have heard it for 25 years. It is intended to make those who want to do a practical thing look impractical. Of course we all depend on manufacturing. But the utilitarian values of water include its fitness for mules, men, birds, and others, including bass and manufacturers.

FRED F. HORNE (Carmel Valley, Calif.): Industry and private enterprise should take a new look at the aesthetic value of water or the recreational value of a stream, or a beach. When you have a community that offers recreation, you will find people traveling from afar to use that recreational facility and you will soon find your community benefiting.

FRANK W. SUGGITT (Michigan State College): We in Michigan feel that recreational use of water is not necessarily a secondary use. We evaluate recreation as our second most important industry in dollar terms.

The Multipurpose Approach

MR. TIPTON: During the single-purpose project era we in the West could visualize all kinds of conflict between uses of the water. When we entered the era of multiple-purpose projects we found that this conflict we had visualized generally was not real. The Lower Colorado River development is an excellent example of providing a number of uses of water by the coordinated operation of interrelated multiple-purpose projects.

MR. HORNER: The multiple-use reservoir is a tool we can use in problems of competitive demand, but only to the extent that a coordinated development of an area's water resources can be achieved at less expense with one site than with several sites for different purposes. Under some circumstances the multiple-purpose project can accentuate some of the differences. I have seen a recent example. Congress had authorized the construction of a multiple-purpose reservoir in one of the Ozark valleys for the purpose of flood reduction, aid in low water flow to the Mississippi, and recreation. It is a 200-mile running stream with rather cool, spring-fed water. State and regional groups in the area reached the unanimous opinion that the value of that stream as a continuing river for recreation and wildlife far exceeded the recreational benefits alleged for the reservoir; so the multiple-purpose reservoir did not satisfy all the needs. The project is now on the shelf. I do not think we can discuss the multiple-purpose reservoir as a generality.

133

Ways of Increasing the Usable Supply

The subsection considered ways of improving the quantity and quality of available supplies, and of reducing waste in industrial use.

Improved land management, especially better care of watersheds, was emphasized as the key to improving supplies of surface water. Further basic studies of stream ecology were suggested, with a view to learning more about natural processes by which water quality is regenerated.

Methods of replenishing ground water that were considered included natural recharge through tillage and other land management practices, and artificial recharge with flood waters, treated sewage effluents, or ordinary surface waters. It was suggested that in some localities the only feasible storage is underground. Salt water intrusion was seen as a threat in many coastal areas. Examples of state efforts to conserve ground water through regulatory action disclosed little uniformity among states, although it appeared that there are more such regulations in western than in eastern states.

Is the mining of ground water necessarily bad? Some people believe that this practice is always a threat to the long-term economy of any affected area. Others see no basis for so sweeping a judgment, point out that many communities have built up thriving economies by this means and then used accumulated capital to obtain water from other sources. According to this view water mining is not intrinsically wrong; the real mistakes come from failure to recognize that depletion is taking place.

Discussion of water conservation by ultimate users touched mostly on industrial use. The Fontana steel plant in California was seen as an example of how greatly total requirements can be reduced by operators geared to reuse of water. Use of the treated effluent of Baltimore sewage by a nearby steel plant indicated that large additional supplies can be obtained from water that otherwise would be wasted. Present data on industrial use and reuse are fragmentary and unreliable; it was suggested that fuller information might show significant advances in reuse, and open the way to further gains.

Weather modification was considered with a full awareness that research still is in an early stage. The U. S. Weather Bureau, which is interested in evaluating as many weather modification experiments as possible, reported that not enough data were available for a definite determination of practicability. Some participants were confident that new research holds promise for highly significant modifications in the future. (Other aspects of weather modification were discussed in Section VII, Problems in Resources Research, see pages 316-19.)

FROM THE RECORD

Care of Watersheds and Surface Waters

MR. WALLACE: Everything depends on what happens to water after it lands on the ground. Not enough interest is taken in what happens to the watersheds. There is at present a widespread move to go into the watershed forests created under the Weeks Law legislation and strip-mine the watershed forests; that ruins the water for various uses. We ought to consider very seriously the need of a Supreme Court decision that a person cannot sell surface rights to a national forest and then because he has retained mineral rights come back and destroy what he has sold.

GENERAL GRANT: The natural condition of the watersheds should be preserved, and the watersheds which have been denuded should be reconstituted.

RICHARD D. HOAK (Mellon Institute of Industrial Research, University of Pittsburgh): I would like to see more basic research upon ecological factors; only when we understand the interactions of the various things which are present naturally in stream water and those that are introduced can we draw sensible conclusions upon establishment of quality standards. In a study of tastes and odors which Mellon Institute has had under way for a year, we are appalled by the meagerness of our effectual information. And taste and odors are only one feature of the ecological problems of streams.

MR. VOIGT: A survey of a presently polluted stream, perhaps like the Mahoning, might be desirable, just to see what the economics would be. It would be a question of increasing the supply of usable water by more complete treatment of the water used and examination of the comparative costs of the treatment as against the costs of developing new supplies or the costs of doing without the needed water.

Ground Water Storage and Recharge

ADOLPH F. MEYER (Consulting Hydraulic Engineer, Minneapolis): We have not paid enough attention to the possibilities of storing water underground. We [in Minnesota] have streams like the Red River of the North. In floods, most of the water goes to waste. No large percentage of it could be stored on the surface for most of the valley is flat. We are working on the possibility of storing some of those waters by recharging the underground supply.

MR. HILL: The use of effluent from the Hyperian Activated Sewage Treatment Plant in Los Angeles County to halt the intrusion of saline water is pretty much of an experiment. The plan has been to drill a series of wells near the coast and introduce the water from the sewage treatment plant. The limit of the hope is that this will interpose a fresh water barrier between the ocean and the valley lands, which are highly developed, largely for industries and homes.

The city of Pasadena and two of its neighboring communities had an activated sludge plant whose waters went to recharge one of the ground-water basins. That has been abandoned because of operation costs, and the sewage from Pasadena and adjoining cities is now carried out to the ocean. The trouble is that in seacoast cities the sewage plants are down at the shore line; to get the water back to where it will recharge the aquifers is an almost insurmountable economic problem.

A. NELSON SAYRE (U.S. Geological Survey): Recharge by sewage is only a small part of the recharge being practiced. For example, around Whittier Narrows in the West Coast Basin of California recharge basins are taking large amounts of surface water into groundwater reservoirs. A very effective exchange of surface water and ground water is taking place in the Salinas Valley. In the Los Angeles basin a good bit of the flood water has been captured temporarily and put into underground reservoirs. An example of unintentional recharge was the irrigation in the Salt River Valley which raised the water table until substantial areas were waterlogged. In Sweden, there are about 150 artificial recharge projects where water is put into sandy glacial formations. In our own country, it would be possible to use recharge methods much more extensively, but the places where they are used must be selected with primary attention to geologic conditions.

WARREN T. MURPHY (U.S. Forest Service): In some water-deficient areas a conscious change in the tillage practice and the use of the land can bring about a substantial amount of recharge of underground aquifers with water which would otherwise run off and be lost. In Davis County, Utah, we have retarded flows primarily by reintroducing grass covers. In the lower Appalachian Mountains, we have noted an increase of flow through the subsurface strata; quite evidently a recharge has resulted from manipulation of the surface cover. It is dangerous to generalize too far. I wish only to point out that in addition to specific engineering projects, other efforts are under way.

MR. HORNER: There must be many marginal areas where, although land treatment practices do introduce more moisture into the soil, more intensive crop production takes a good deal of the increase. I do not think you can generalize.

THORNDIKE SAVILLE (New York University): We would be helped in this discussion by some concrete facts, particularly if they were not confined to plots, that in a given area conservation practices on the land had produced a given increase in water yield.

MR. BARNES: Although no generality should be extended over a great area, I might point out an example that supports Mr. Murphy's view. When a sandy area in West Texas was first settled some 50 years ago, it was covered with mesquite growth. The water table was at the base of this sandy material. Following the removal of the water-intercepting mesquite and the initiation of farming, the water table has risen in that area as much as 30 to 40 feet.

MR. SAYRE: You have to consider the geologic conditions of an area in determining whether certain land practices might be beneficial or harmful. Increased infiltration does not necessarily mean increased recharge of ground water. Unless you are in an area where a ground-water reservoir immediately underlies the land surface, the infiltration of rain water into the soil is likely to do nothing more than add to the soil moisture which supports evaporation and transpiration by plants. An experiment on artificial recharge on the Black Prairie of Texas would be a waste of time.

Can Water Mining Be Sound Practice?

MR. HILL: Twenty years ago I would have said the mining of ground water was sinful, but I have since observed the development of substantial economies based deliberately upon mining of water. There are at least half a million acres in the central part of Arizona from which tens of millions of dollars of agricultural products have been produced; 95 percent of their water has been mined. If the people of such a region recognize that they are mining water and take steps to develop some other economy while the mining operation is carried on, they have done a good thing. The sin lies not in mining water, but in failure to recognize a mining operation for what it is.

MR. WOLMAN: There are innumerable areas in this and other countries where the mining of underground water can create an economy that will support large capital investment in water development. They can then go greater distances to their own watersheds. Southern California is an excellent example. If there had been some omniscient planning board in southern California in 1880, which had laid down regulations that ground water be withdrawn only up to the point where it would not deplete the resource, there would not be a Los Angeles.

MR. BARNES: [Comment submitted after the Conference.] I agree that mining of ground water has in many cases created sufficient wealth to enable users, upon exhaustion of ground-water reservoirs, to seek more expensive sources of water. However, I do not think we can generalize and say that the depletion of ground-water supplies is not a serious problem. In many areas where ground water is used for irrigation any substantial increase in the cost of water would mean abandonment of much of the land.

T. J. McFARLAND (Lubbock, Texas): I am manager of a ground-water irrigation district in Texas. We are irrigating, and supplying our municipalities and industries solely from ground water. The people in my section do not believe in creating a false economy by pumping a lot of water, encouraging a lot of industry, and building a lot of cities and eventually having the well go dry. We are trying to avert the tragedy of a resource that has gone forever. We have tried to figure out in our area what people in 1975 are going to use for water.

MR. TIPTON: The mining of water in some localities can be a good thing. In some instances ground water is a resource the wealth of which cannot be obtained unless it is mined. If people know what they are doing, and the rate of withdrawal is such that there will be full amortization of all investments, it ought to be done if people decide that way. The farmer's investment generally is amortized very quickly; but investments in public works are amortized over three or four generations. People that move in and establish businesses know that these businesses are subject to the same kind of processes that operate in a metal mining town.

PAUL WEAVER: Where the mining of water takes place in poorly consolidated rocks we must consider the so-called compaction phenomenon. That is the most important reason for trying to reduce the mining of water in the Houston area. The land surface there is subsiding at the rate of about 1 percent of the lowering of water table. The water table is lowering by 20 feet per year. The surface subsidence is about two-tenths of a foot. That effect should be taken into consideration when people decide whether to withdraw ground water. In the case of hard rock, such as the Twin Cities, these considerations do not apply; but they apply more generally, I think, than is recognized.

MR. BARNES: [Comment submitted after the Conference.] The aquifers in the Houston area are still fully saturated and capable of continued high production. The subsidence noted is a result of the lessening of the pressure in the underlying formations and occurs to a certain degree in every area where ground water is obtained from artesian wells. In only a few areas of local extent, such as in Mexico City, have compaction of aquifers and the resulting subsidence of the land surface caused serious engineering problems.

Industrial Reuse

MR. HOAK: Industrial concerns are becoming increasingly aware of the necessity for reusing water, largely because of the rising cost of purifying natural water. It is difficult to summarize present methods of reusing industrial water because no one seems to know how widespread such practices are. But we do find, from time to time, references in the technical literature to methods employed in one industry or another for reconditioning water that has been used by another plant, or for using water for a purpose requiring lower quality than the first use.

MR. WOLMAN: Reuse of water in the steel industry and in many others like it is much more extensively practiced than we might gather from general discussion. A summary of those practices would be extremely enlightening.

Discussion here brought out some details of two outstanding examples of reuse of water by industry: Fontana and Sparrows Point.

MR. HOAK: The Fontana plant of the Kaiser Steel Company has little water available. They have two wells on the company property, and there are two nearby wells owned by a private water company from which they can obtain a limited amount of water. Through an ingenious system of reuse whereby each successive use requires water of lower quality than the one preceding, they are able to manufacture steel with a net consumption of, if memory serves, about 2,500 gallons per ton. In the East, the average water used in manufacturing a ton of steel is 65,000 gallons.

RAYMOND C. KELLY (Cooling Tower Institute, Palo Alto): I happened to be in the original discussion of the water utilization problems of the Fontana plant. Cooling towers were used extensively. The plant now has 18 cooling towers and I believe the operation is entirely satisfactory.

MR. WOLMAN: Do the steel-making processes at Fontana cover the variety of operations carried on, say, by an integrated steel plant in the East?

MR. KELLY: As far as I know the Fontana plant has a complete chemical problem just as any other plant.

MR. WOLMAN: The largest use of waste water for industrial purposes is, I believe, that of the Sparrows Point tidewater plant of the Bethlehem Steel Company. It now uses for steel-making purposes between 55 and 60 million gallons a day of the Baltimore City sewage after treatment and after secondary processing. Also, preparations are under way to take the entire flow of sewage from the city of Baltimore. The effluent is used for all industrial purposes in the plant.

The arrangement provides cheap industrial water for the steel company. It relieves Baltimore of a difficult disposal problem involving additional expenditures which it has been estimated might exceed $15 million for additional pipeline and discharge. It now returns to the city about $38,000 a year for a waste material and will return something in excess of $100,000 a year.

Weather Modification

MR. CUNNINGHAM: Several cities in the Southwest have had contracts with cloud-seeding, weather modification companies.

Last year Carl Hopewell, water superintendent in Dallas, said that the 80,000 acre-feet of water in his reservoir were convincing proof to him. In Oklahoma City we have had one large rain since a contract was made, but I doubt if the cloud-seeding operation had too much influence on it. However, in the watershed of the North Canadian River where Oklahoma City gets its water supply, all of the runoff from precipitation came from the area in which the cloud-seeding operation has been carried on. There have been no complaints from areas to the leeward that cloud seeding has taken rain that otherwise would have fallen on them.

MR. MEYER: There is no doubt that rain making has been successful in certain instances. But how are we going to increase the *total amount of rain* that can fall on the land if we cannot affect the sun and its evaporative power over the ocean? I have not the least confidence in the ability of man to do so. We are in a region of prevailing westerlies. What happens to the areas to the east?

WILLIAM HIATT (U.S. Weather Bureau): I do not question, personally, that operators with reservoirs to fill have gotten results from hiring weather modification people. However, in the Weather Bureau, after evaluating as many operations as we have been able to, we take the position that not enough significant information is yet available to prove or disprove whether precipitation can be brought on by weather modification practices.

A. D. EDMONSTON (California Division of Water Resources): California has for two or three years provided funds for evaluating rain-making activities. Information was obtained from various organizations that were experimenting in rainmaking. Thus far in our evaluation, we cannot say whether the results are positive or negative.

Problems of Pollution Control

It was generally recognized that serious situations in many parts of the country call for continued efforts to combat pollution of water supplies. Differences of opinion came over how clean we should try to make our streams, what methods are best, and where the chief responsibility lies.

The ultimate aims of pollution control were sharply debated. Some believe that the national interest calls for continued upgrading of water quality in all parts of the country. Others feel that goals should vary with circumstances; the best uses of a stream should be determined in the light of all interests concerned and quality standards set accordingly. There were differences, also, as to practicability: what degrees of cleanliness are really within reach?

As to method, there were differences over how to determine the public interest. Are economic and technical criteria more important than the broader political and social considerations? Support of uniform regulatory laws, with classification of streams over large areas, was countered by the belief that such classifications tend to become frozen and that they may overlook important local situations and relationships. To some it is clear that industry should at once assume a greater share of the burden of abatement. Others are convinced that in general industry's treatment of waste is keeping pace with needs through technological advances. Suggestions for financial inducements through federal tax legislation were noted.

The need for more research was widely recognized.

FROM THE RECORD

The Situation: Bigger Cities, More Industry

There was little discussion of the nation's pollution problem as a whole; its seriousness was taken for granted. But many bits of evidence were cited, and the Assistant Surgeon General of the Public Health Service briefly sketched some trends he found disturbing.

MARK D. HOLLIS (U.S. Public Health Service): We are becoming an urban, industrial nation and the streams simply can no longer take the load of pollution that we are putting on them. About 100 million of the country's people live in cities. Twenty-five million of these live in cities served by adequate treatment. Thirty-one million are in communities with no treatment at all. The rest are served by forms of treatment that are considered inadequate by their state authorities. We have had some 700 percent increase in industrial production since 1900; over half of it has occurred in the last 10 years. Especially because of the rapid development in chemicals and synthetics, the rise in industrial wastes is producing a chemical burden on the streams that we as yet do not even know how to appraise or measure. I would certainly hate to have the record imply that perhaps we have gone too far in pollution abatement measures.

How Much Cleanliness Should We Aim At?

MR. CLEARY: The basic reason for pollution control is to safeguard certain uses of a stream. Therefore, what justification exists to require treatment of wastes beyond that necessary to safeguard those uses of a stream which will best serve the public interest? How do you determine the public interest? This is a matter of engineering evaluation subject to final determination on the basis of a public hearing.

MEREDITH F. BURRILL (U.S. Department of the Interior): If I gather correctly, you have said that the determination of public interest is a matter of engineering judgment. I am not fully satisfied with that answer.

MR. VOIGT: I do not believe that any stream, no matter how grossly polluted it might be now, should be considered as completely incapable of being upgraded and improved in quality over some period of time. The objective of every control agency should be the ultimate lifting of quality classification of every stream or other body of public water in its jurisdiction. Any other provision is a denial of the national characteristic of continually seeking all kinds of improvement both cultural as well as economic.

Samuel S. Baxter (Water Commissioner, Philadelphia): I am aware of the importance of economic factors, but in addition we should not forget the aesthetics or the amenities of the situation. Streams flow past our municipalities—I think that we ought to put a little bit of our economic effort into cleaning up those streams just for the sake of cleanliness itself.

Mr. Cleary: Aesthetic considerations do represent an important stream use, and quality standards for this purpose—such as no visible solids—would be established as part of the engineering evaluation of pollution control requirements.

Mr. Wallace: Is it all right to swim in and drink if the solids are not visible?

Mr. Cleary: It depends on proximity of the sewage outfall. To provide swimming-quality water directly below Louisville's proposed sewage plant it would require additional treatment for disinfection that could cost $100,000 yearly. Are the citizens willing to pay that price for the dubious privilege of an occasional swim?

Another phase of the problem: limited treatment for purely local benefit or treatment designed to improve water for downstream users?

Harry LaViers (South-East Coal Company): I live in an eastern Kentucky town of about 4,000. When we came to build a new water plant we included an appropriation of $100,000 for a swimming pool. We did that after examining the possibilities of cleaning up the sewage and waste in our community and in the streams that go by there. We found that this was a much cheaper way; it would cost us a million dollars to do it some other way. We still have a health problem which we are working on, but we do provide recreational facilities through the municipal water system.

Mr. Wallace: How about downstream?

Mr. LaViers: The next community below is considering or planning the same program that we have.

Thomas F. Barton (Indiana University): I had not expected to hear remarks to the effect that we are going to skimp on some dollars, let the sewage go, build a swimming pool in the city, and dump our sewage on the farm people and on the smaller cities and villages down the river. That is no solution of the problem. It delays the solution while the population doubles and triples and goes still higher.

Federal programs of the Public Health Service came into discussion at several points, especially those concerning uniform regulations and stream classification.

Mr. Hollis: The principle of the suggested uniform state law is to encourage a comprehensive approach by the states to water pollution problems, considering all of the legitimate water uses. It contains a recommendation for an administrative entity that would vary depending on the wishes and structure of the state government—either a board with authority, or a director or administrator with an advisory board. Whatever the administrative entity, we suggested that it have the power to classify streams and to set up standards of water quality, based on major uses. We strongly urged some enforcement provision in the end. This went out about two years ago and 22 states have used the document either in whole or in part in new legislation or amendments to their existing laws.

I would like to emphasize the extent to which industry itself recognizes the need to protect our streams. Obviously, that is not 100 percent true, but industry has organized itself into the National Technical Task Committee on Industrial Wastes, which committee represents some 10,000 industrial plants.

Mr. Hoak: Despite a uniform state law, any attempt to establish uniform water quality standards over an area as large as a state would, in the long run, not be in the public interest; any such standards would have to be relatively rigid in that they would be designed to correct the worst possible condition. The principal objection to stream classification is its tendency to become permanent and in a sense self-defeating. The more firmly stream zoning is fixed in the public consciousness, the more difficult it is to upgrade a lower class to a higher one.

Any effort to control the discharge of wastes into a stream should be based upon a recognition that the purpose of such control is to provide water of a quality which will serve a specific use in a definite locality. Those in a position to promulgate regulations on stream pollution control often seem to think too much about waste treatment and not enough about stream water improvement.

RICHARD W. EVERETT (McGraw-Hill Publishing Company): In any kind of classification covering a whole state, you would have to assign more or less a whole area permanently to specific uses—residential, farming, and so on. I wonder if anything already has happened along these lines; if so, it could be a very dangerous thing.

Where Does Responsibility Lie?

Industry, municipalities, urban fringe communities, and denuded watersheds were identified as major sources of pollution. Most of the differences of opinion concerned whether industry can or should do more toward control.

MRS. JAMES MUFFLY (General Federation of Women's Clubs, Lewisburg, Pa.): Boys and girls like to swim and fish. I live in a rural community where we do not have swimming pools, and we have to think of the fact that the chemical plants are disposing of all their sewage right there in that stream. You people who put in sewage or waste matter have a definite responsibility; the government— state, local, or federal—should not be responsible for your debts. You are making the money and asking us, when we buy your product, its full value. I would be willing to pay you 10 cents more for that article if you take your responsibility seriously in every respect. Some industries do; some do not. This is a beautiful America. I want to keep it that way, and I am willing to help industry in every way. But I do feel it is *your* garbage and your responsibility to dispose of it at your own expense, as a housewife does in carrying out her household duties.

ALLEN ABRAMS (Marathon Corporation): I have a great deal of sympathy for Mrs. Muffly's point of view. I happen to be a fisherman. I also have children who are fond of the lakes and the woods and the streams. At the same time, I am in industry. The fact that the public demands certain products is to some extent the cause of our pollution. I am connected with the pulp and paper industry which, in our state, is primarily centered on the Wisconsin River.

Some 27 years ago my own company realized that there was a pollution problem. At that time there was no legislation, but we determined to work toward a solution. In the course of those 27 years we have spent some $4 million and have developed a method that substantially reduces the amount of oxygen demand occasioned by our liquors. Marathon uses the sulphite process which is typical of a number of the mills in the state. Some 14 or 15 mills have banded together in the Sulphite Pulp Manufacturers Research League.

The pollution problem is not simply one of economics or of aesthetics. It is a matter of engineering. Until very recently there were no feasible methods to do this job. We are learning more about it today and I think we will find the solution.

PAUL WEAVER: Municipalities have a great responsibility, and their backwardness can be appreciated by looking at the situation in the Houston metropolitan area, which has 380 sewage treatment plants varying in size from 15 million gallons down. According to a recent survey by the Public Health Service, about half of these plants were inadequate as to capacity, and about half, not the same ones, were inadequate in that they did not give any secondary treatment. This is a fundamental engineering problem. Plans have been made for correcting the situation by a consolidation into units of manageable size, involving complete realignment of sewage lines.

MR. JENS: Another potential and actual source of pollution is the small sewage treatment plant. The big problem is adequate, competent operation. Many plants in the Middle West were well designed and constructed in their time, but because the community apparently has either not seen fit or had the economic ability to provide competent operation the effluents are in many cases almost as bad as raw sewage. In few places is it feasible to combine several such small communities into one efficiently operable plant.

MR. BARTON: It is time to take another type of person to task for the pollution both of rivers and lakes. I am speaking of those individuals who think they want to live with nature and yet avoid the high taxes of the city. They scatter themselves over the land, along brooks, intermittent streams, and even our best recreational lakes. They build so-called septic tanks in their fields and are responsible for an untold amount of pollution. This family pollution of areas is becoming greater and greater as more and more people move to the country. I shudder to think what the result will be in 25 years when we double the population.

MR. HOLLIS: [When asked if the proposed uniform state legislation includes any financial incentives to industry for reducing pollution.] Proposals for state action along those lines were omitted entirely. We felt that was a prerogative of the states. There have been federal proposals for tax relief for waste pollution control on the part of industry. In general, they have suggested an accelerated amortization for tax purposes of treatment works in industry.

MR. WOLMAN: In 1937, the Stream Pollution Abatement Commission included in its report to Congress an analysis of accomplishments, state by state, in relation to the adequacy of legislative control. One of the disconcerting results of that study was that it did not appear that the states having the best regulatory legislation showed the best performance in stream pollution abatement. Something deeper than that was involved. Is there any consistency of accomplishment, or does

accomplishment rest on the economics of the area, on the capacity of your state engineers, their leadership, their enthusiasm, and the like? I suggest that the Public Health Service consider running a study of what is accomplished by these measures on which we pin so much of our hope.

Where Are Some of the Gaps in Technical Knowledge?

Besides the research proposals already noted, suggestions were made for studies along particular lines where lack of basic knowledge is seen as a major obstacle to pollution control.

RUTH PATRICK (Academy of Natural Sciences of Philadelphia): There is need for fundamental research on the effect of various kinds of pollution on the rivers. By that I mean a better understanding of the physical structure of a river, the chemical and physical properties of water as they affect the severity of a given pollution. Certain organisms that are in every stream do a great deal to put the water back into good condition. The point is not to use a river in ways that destroy the bio-dynamic cycle. We need to gain greater understanding of this cycle of life in the river which brings about rejuvenescence.

The steering committee working paper had mentioned current concern with viruses in water and asked whether more research was needed.

MR. JORDAN: I agree that research is needed. But we should not draw conclusions from the research before we make it. Until someone has demonstrated with some degree of objectivity that public water supplies can be definitely associated with virus diseases, we should carry on the research and not announce a conclusion.

MR. CLEARY: Our much maligned Ohio River apparently will not even tolerate viruses. A certain type virus being studied at the Cincinnati research station of the U.S. Public Health Service is reported to live quite happily in distilled water but disappears within 24 hours when placed in Ohio River water.

A matter of great importance in water quality—about which we lack proper information—is the potential chronic toxicity of substances reaching our rivers. The Ohio River Valley Water Sanitation Commission is sponsoring a project at the Kettering Laboratory in Cincinnati in an endeavor to determine, if possible, what toxicological effects may result from trace amounts of various substances. These findings will be employed in the drafting of regulations for industrial waste control.

Basic Data and Their Analysis

Research has been mentioned many times already in this chapter, for often it was clear that one of the main reasons for delay in overcoming problems of supply and use is simply that we know too little about them. When the group turned to a direct consideration of the present status of research in its field, there was wide agreement that much should be done, and quickly, toward further collection and analysis of data and speedier publication of findings. Issues arose chiefly over priorities.

Analysis and publication were seen as the weakest spots on the supply side; much primary information already is being collected on precipitation, stream flow, and ground water reserves. While additional basic data on supply would be helpful, many people feel that worse gaps elsewhere ought to be attended to first. Others believe that some of the bare spots in supply information should be covered right away. It was evident that much more should be done to interpret and use data already in hand. Water-land relationships, weather cycles in the West, and uniform presentation of material in maps and atlases were among the subjects proposed for immediate attention.

On the consumption side, the general lack of basic data caused the most concern; reliable information on industrial use was seen as almost nonexistent. However, the urgency of collecting comprehensive data on consumptive use in the humid East was disputed. With fewer data to interpret, there was less talk of analysis, although its importance was recognized and some specific lines of study proposed.

In consideration of methods, a larger role for states and units of local government in collecting and analyzing data was suggested, provided coordination on a national basis could be maintained. Recent advances in this direction by some states were noted. Centers at a state level were suggested as a means of coordinating public and private research and directing it to local problems.

FROM THE RECORD

Collection of Data

MR. HILL: A tremendous amount of data is still needed. We can rely largely on the U.S. Geological Survey for the basic data as to stream flow and ground water reserves, but there is a great dearth of information as to consumptive use.

As an illustration, I had a problem this past summer of estimating the probable stream flow depletion which would result from creation of an industrial community of perhaps one million in western Colorado where the tremendous oil shale reserves are. How much water would be consumed in an industrial community of that size? There were substantially no data available. Most cities know how much water goes into their systems; few can even approximate how much of that same water is actually consumed.

Although everyone agreed that much more is known of supply than use, some felt that "better" in this instance is far from "good enough" and cited urgent needs of improving basic data on supply.

MR. EDMONSTON: We cannot get too much basic data as to stream flow or precipitation. It should be adequate and continuous. As for precipitation records, the Weather Bureau has been inadequately financed on establishment and the operation of basic rate rainfall and precipitation stations.

MR. BARTON: There is great need for studies concerning water storage in the glacial materials and the underlying bedrock in the great glacial area between Missouri and the Ohio. Many cities in this area depend upon glacial deposits. Some cities in Indiana depending upon glacial deposits have run short this year. Did drought simply bring to a climax a shortage that has been developing over a number of years?

MR. JENS: One of the worst gaps in data from the standpoint of urban drainage is the lack—with a few exceptions—of information on relatively small watersheds. We need data on watersheds from 1 to 50 square miles in urban areas preferably. This is important: every sizable concentration of population has hundreds of millions of dollars invested in storm water facilities. Highways have large aggregate costs for culverts and other small drainage structures. There are currently no good empirical data on which to base designs of that character.

There is another regional problem in the big alluvial valleys like the Mississippi and the Missouri. We have no information on runoff in these very flat bottoms. A great many levee and drainage districts have a serious problem of internal drainage. The engineer working

with that often has to lean more heavily on judgment than most of us like to.

C. V. YOUNGQUIST (Ohio Department of Natural Resources): The Department of Agriculture has a program of demonstration areas for upstream flood control. There is a need for an expanded program to check on some of these demonstration areas both prior to and after the installation of some of these structures.

Industrial use was seen as by far the darkest area of basic data on consumption, even against the background of general inadequacy.

MR. SAVILLE: Background statistics in the steering committee paper show a substantial divergence of opinion with respect to the amount of industrial use. One of the authorities cited estimated industrial use in the United States at from 20 to 25 billion gallons per day. Another authority estimated it at around 80 billion. That is roughly a 300 percent difference.

MR. JORDAN: A major problem in industrial water use is the extreme unreliability of the data we have at present. We are assuming upon the basis of information from a variety of sources that, for example, it takes *x* gallons of water per ton of steel produced to operate a steel mill. These figures are of the "spot check" variety and do not differentiate between *intake* and *consumptive* use. I hope that we may set our sights on a correlated study of industrial water requirements that will supply basic, reliable information that covers a large territory and can be consolidated through some agency to the point where we can make an intelligent estimate of the future needs of industry for water in the United States. We do not have those figures now.

Granting the need for further information on water consumption, should immediate efforts to collect more data be broad or selective?

MR. HAZEN: In the West, consumptive use is all-important. In the East, it is not nearly so important as the quality of water, and what happens to it as it goes down the stream. I would hate to see us spend tremendous amounts of energy and money in trying to get detailed statistics on consumptive uses. In some parts of the United States I don't think anything particularly useful would come of it.

MR. SAVILLE: I believe that farmers, particularly in Mr. Hazen's neighboring territory of Long Island, are going extensively into spray irrigation and drawing on ground-water levels very extensively. Is there no need to bother about that consumptive use?

MR. HAZEN: If you set out on a program of making a complete inventory of consumptive use of water in the eastern states you are going to spend about 75 percent of your time on things that will not be useful. I do not mean to say that there are not some consumptive uses that should be inventoried.

Evaluating and Publishing Data

MR. SAVILLE: I have heard from several members of this group about enormous amounts of data that have been collected over the years as a result of experiments and are now lying unanalyzed and useless in the archives of the several agencies.

MR. HIATT: It is true that many, many types or files of data are not in their most usable form. It is the feeling of all the federal agencies that have been collecting these data over the years that some summary and analytical work would go far toward solving some of the problems with which we are all familiar. Speaking of the data we have in the Weather Bureau, it would not take too much effort to put many of them in more usable form; and that is equally true, I am sure, of many other types of data.

One of the basic requirements in appraising our total water supply is to know more precisely how much precipitation we have. We in the Weather Bureau for many years have tried to do as much as we can toward the development of adequate isohyetal maps. There is none available now, certainly. To really develop an adequate isohyetal map is a job. Topography affects the norms and many other

variables go into the annual precipitation figure which in turn would give annual potential water yield.

MR. BROWER: I would like to underline what has been said about the undigested data. But we cannot digest the present data, let alone get more, without spending more—more appropriations for the government agencies themselves, more grants to the universities. This would not produce immediate economies in government. Also, gathering and digesting data is not enough. Often in my experience with a university press I have seen thousands of dollars for research and not one cent for publication. The communications fall down.

How useful are the available data that bear on watershed treatment and other aspects of the water-land relationship? Are they on a large enough scale? Paul Weaver said that since most of the research has been based on studies of small plots, some results are useful guides to management of whole watersheds, but many of them are not. He emphasized the need of pilot studies on a watershed scale; they will be slow and expensive. He made his points by quoting from E. A. Colman's book, Vegetation and Watershed Management *(published by the Ronald Press under the auspices of The Conservation Foundation). Two other new books were mentioned by Mr. Wolman as authoritative analyses of previously scattered data:* Floods *by Langbein and Hoyt (Princeton University Press) and* The Flood Control Controversy *by Leopold and Maddock (Ronald Press under auspices of The Conservation Foundation).*

MR. HORNER: One of our greatest lacks today is knowledge of the interrelationship of land and water. Certain federal agencies, starting in the early thirties, have spent millions of dollars on collecting factual information in that field. This effort has not been accompanied by any reasonable expenditure for data analysis and interpretation. The material may not be what you want if you are looking for precision, but I think an intelligent person, with proper selection, could analyze the material and get a reasonable quantitative value out of it. We cannot wait for large watersheds to change from one class of land management to another so we can compare data on what occurred before and after. We have to do something to arrange for a review, analysis, and publication of a tremendous amount of data on water and land relationships that has already been collected.

SAMUEL B. MORRIS (Department of Water and Power, Los Angeles): In the West particularly, in areas where near-complete use is being made of water supplies, and where the accumulated departures from normal may be substantial over a considerable period of years, the possibility of knowing more about departures from normal in weather cycles in the world's history is really an important subject.

MR. YOUNGQUIST: In the East particularly we have been slow to realize that we must get into these water inventory and interpretation programs, both as to water supply and water use data; and that after we get that information we must analyze it statistically and by other means to properly utilize it.

Methods and Approaches

Federal government, the chairman noted, generally has taken the lead in collecting the older types of data, usually in collaboration with state and local interests. How should the newer types of data be collected?

MR. JENS: We ought to get basic data on small watersheds at as local a level as possible. Some large cities have set out extensive rain-gauge installations; few have gauged sewer flows. A lot more of that should be done. The states could very well assume a great deal of responsibility. The Bureau of Public Roads has been educating highway engineers on the importance of what offhand seem like minor structures. I think the federal government could well give guidance in that field with the states and local areas doing the actual work.

PAUL WEAVER: In Texas, we have organized what we call the Water Research and Information Center. This is to be operated by the Texas A. & M. College System. We feel a need for collating and correlating the work the federal agencies are doing, appraising the applicability and the adequacy of their data in terms of the problems in specific localities. We are making an effort to collect the information from all sources. We find that there is a tremendous amount of private data. For example, we have some 35,000 analyses from streams, and only about one-third of them were taken by public agencies.

WALTER B. LANGBEIN (U.S. Department of the Interior): The record of publication and dissemination of data collected by local authorities has not been too good. It speaks rather urgently for a coordinated kind of basic data activity. Basic data programs cannot be haphazard in design and purpose. The designer of a program of basic data must commit a large part to urgent current needs for information, but he still should have a large flexible component in the program so that unforeseen needs of the future can be accommodated.

MR. MURPHY: The federal agencies that gather data here and there on a small watershed or plot all realize the desirability of bringing that material together and evaluating it. The Federal Interagency River Basin Committee has designated a committee to study the possibility of establishing among the interested agencies of the federal government a general, national hydrologic survey group that would act not within any one federal department but as a rather independent group. They found that it would be a multimillion dollar task running over several years to do what really should be done. They have trimmed their sights down to the point where it would cost but a few thousand dollars in any one year. But even so, we find that we are still running into the problem of finance.

MR. HORNER: We have been relying for the primary data programs on the federal agencies that have been designated for that. Except for stream flow measurements on which the states cooperate with the U. S. Geological Survey there has been very little organized data collection by other agencies. I wonder why, in areas where more intensive data collection, processing, and publication is needed, we cannot begin to see more active cooperation from the states. It should be possible to enter into more cooperative programs in which local sources not only supply the data available to them, but take some part in any additional data collection, processing, and publication that serves the needs of the particular area. I realize that a good deal has been done. In the Middle West, for example, the work done by the Ohio and Illinois agencies has been extremely helpful to everyone.

Subsection B

DIVISION OF RESPONSIBILITY

With such a large task of water development ahead, there is plenty of work for everyone—industries and other private organizations, and government at all levels. Nevertheless, the way in which the total effort is organized can have great influence for good or ill. Certain kinds of agency are particularly adapted for certain phases of the work and poorly suited to others. Wise division of responsibility and efficient machinery for coordination can make progress smoother and swifter; while mistakes in these areas mean lost motion and needless friction.

Need for coordination somewhere between the local and national levels was recognized. Interstate compacts were examined for strong and weak points. The valley authority method was frequently cited as a desirable approach, a point that turned discussion to the relative merits of prompt action as opposed to delay when there are conflicts in state and local opinion. The same issue arose in consideration of interagency basin committees and of more formal regional organization such as the proposed Missouri Basin Commission.

A major source of concern in discussion of federal organization was the fact that the different agencies concerned with water development operate under different policies, established by different laws, and have different objectives and administrative procedures. There was considerable support expressed for a reviewing and coordinating mechanism, often referred to in the discussion as a board of review. However, others held that unification of national policy and improvements in organization would obviate the need for such a device.

Throughout the subsection discussion, there were several suggestions for research into present patterns of dividing responsibility, and wide recognition of the need for a clearer, more comprehensive national policy on water development.

The record of discussion is presented here under four major heads: (1) general principles of dividing responsibility; (2) interstate compacts; (3) regional organization; (4) federal organization.

General Principles of Dividing Responsibilities

No one questioned the desirability of greater local activity by both private groups and local units of government. The issues concerned practicability: how many of the tasks can be handled well by local agencies and how many of the jobs are they willing to take on? Is there a point beyond which too active federal participation leads to encroachment on local rights and to bureaucratic rigidities?

FROM THE RECORD

The Nature of the Job

The need for an orderly division of responsibility was brought out by two appraisals of the problem from the local viewpoint.

MRS. ORVILLE FOREMAN (League of Women Voters of the United States): My city of Jacksonville, Illinois, has about 25,000 people, and a couple of new factories that use much water. Air conditioning and other gadgets have been taking a lot of water. We have not had enough rain for a couple of years.

Our engineers have suggested that one way of getting supplementary water is to run a pipeline from wells in the Illinois River bottom some 20 miles away. This sounds fine, but I am disturbed by what has happened to the water holes in New Jersey. Also, since the Illinois River is navigable, the federal government has an interest in it; and since the watershed lies almost wholly within Illinois, the state is a good deal concerned with it. And let's not forget about Hiram Walker of Peoria who is a very great private user of water. Who ought to start planning for water use so that Jacksonville will not spend several million dollars setting up a water hole and then see that water hole presently going dry?

N. R. GRAHAM (Oklahoma Planning and Resources Board): Someone, at some level, must control the dam sites or you are going to have 10, 20, or 30 percent use of a dam site on a basis that it can't be increased.

It is always best for the local interests to handle these things where they can. If hydro power is economically feasible, private industry can handle it as well as anybody else. But some little communities with fine water resources just can't do the job themselves. We say in Oklahoma that such situations are problems for the state. You elect a man to office for two years in a town, and he is just going to pray that the water is going to last until he gets out; nobody is going to think 50 years ahead. Yet you can't develop water in less than 25 years at best.

Responsibility at the Grassroots

Granted that local interests should take a large part in planning and carrying out water development programs, how far is it practicable to go in this direction? What jobs can local groups, public or private, do better or as well as anyone else? Is there enough local activity and responsibility now?

J. E. STURROCK (Texas Water Conservation Association): These are some of the answers to the question of how to divide responsibility: First, taking in private enterprise as a partner in the planning, developing, and use of our water resources and giving it an equal chance of sharing the benefits from a project; second, working in copartnership with local and state governments in planning, development, construction, distribution, and use of water resources and giving assurance that operation and management will be by local or state agencies; and third, assuring that when the federal government investment has been repaid, the products will belong to local and state agencies. The water does not belong to the United States; it belongs to the people in the state.

A special act of the Texas Legislature about four years ago created districts to handle multi-city projects, where one city could not finance the project alone. Three or four or up to 10 or 12 cities go in and pool their resources and finance the project with the assistance of the private industry within the area. When private enterprise is taken in and can participate in the benefits, you will find that it will go along with your local community, your state agency, in developing these projects, and we won't have to go to Washington for help.

BRIG. GEN. HERBERT D. VOGEL (Corps of Engineers): The Corps of Engineers has been working closely in Texas and the Southwest with federal and state agencies and with private industry—not only with power companies, but also with representatives of railroads. Starting with the individual, every element of government should do as much as it can within its own resources before calling upon the next highest.

HERBERT S. MARKS (Washington, D.C.): I wonder if, apart from financial functions like floating revenue bonds, there is much room for private interests in the development of water resources except for power? The interests seem to me primarily state and local governmental interests and federal interests.

MR. STURROCK: Power is not the only question. The chemical industries coming to the South all are large water users and they are willing to contribute their share to the development of water resources. In several instances in my state they have joined oil refineries and other types of industry to help cities and districts develop water supply projects. In Texas about 3 million of the 3.7 million acres of land under irrigation have been developed by private enterprise and municipalities.

IRA L. PORTER (Peoples Banking Company, Oberlin, Ohio): There are broad expanses of the United States where multipurpose dams will not be built, where the topography is such that water development is a local problem largely. The states and local communities will have to assume responsibility; it is not a federal job.

DONALD W. VANTUYL (Chamber of Commerce of the U.S.): What are the capabilities and interests of private enterprise? Private enterprise doesn't ordinarily go into any kind of a development unless it can see a return on its investment.

W. S. ROSECRANS (California State Board of Forestry): I don't think there will be any answer on a national basis to the question of capability of private industry. It will depend on location.

Is there need for greater attention by local interests to these problems? Is there a greater need for the individual responsibility of the citizen of a local area?

Local people can't do planning on an engineering basis without engineering experience, but they can determine the adequacy of a plan to their needs and follow through. In California we have found generally that if the local folks take an interest, the problems don't get so serious.

What are some of the limitations of, and obstacles to, local participation, and how can local participation be encouraged?

CHARLES W. ELIOT (Ipswich, Mass.): When we come right down to it, everybody would like to have local participation, business participation, to the greatest degree. But are the people we all want to participate ready to really participate? Are they ready to take their share of the financing and the costs, or do they just want the cream?

G. L. BEARD (Department of the Army): The Corps of Engineers is making a study of ways and means to get greater local participation in flood control projects, particularly the local flood protection projects. There are two sides to that, of course. If you try to saddle the whole thing on the local people, the program probably stops. The federal government has a serious practical problem of increasing local participation without stopping the program.

OLIVER L. NORMAN (National Water Conservation Conference): For local communities and states to assume these responsibilities, most states will need different organization. One of the few states that has legislation that provides an opportunity to really get in and pitch in this program is California.

STIFEL W. JENS (Consulting Engineer, St. Louis): The crux of the sharing of responsibilities for the control, use, and development of water is the sharing of costs by the various interests. This has been profoundly affected by the pattern of federal financial participation in bearing the costs of water projects even when they were so patently local as water supply and waste disposal. Many local interests take a do-nothing attitude in the hope that more federal money will be forthcoming.

The withdrawal or minimization of federal participation in regional or local water projects where beneficiaries are readily identified would, in my opinion, restore a considerable assumption of real responsibility on the part of local and regional interests.

MICHAEL W. STRAUS (Washington, D.C.): Is the basic reclamation proportion of federal assistance sufficient to meet the needs of today? Many good projects cannot qualify under existing reclamation law with 100 percent repayment without interest, but many people want those projects to go forward. I think many of them should go forward, but they will not qualify financially under the present law.

There are many opportunities now for those who believe in more local control to exercise that local control without any new laws.

For example, the determination of water rights—a state function—is not being discharged now as a rule. Also, the acquisition of rights-of-way can be a privilege of local bodies. I never found one yet that really rushed in to take that piece of drudgery. Third, under certain federal laws now, there is full provision for taking over operations. I have spent a lot of my life trying to get local districts to take over the operation to which they are entitled under existent law.

BERT L. SMITH (Irrigation Districts Association of California): Texas has 40-odd conservation districts. Is that a good thing? Should it be the pattern through the West? We don't know. The experience of Texas, California, and other states that have tried and missed or tried and succeeded should be brought together in summary form for the benefit of folks elsewhere.

MEREDITH F. BURRILL (U.S. Department of the Interior): A critical summary of water laws would be very useful to a great many people in understanding the whole question. The need has been mentioned particularly with reference to the East. I think it is equally applicable to the West, especially for laws relating to ground water.

Are enough avenues open for local groups and individuals to make their opinions known? Do local people take full advantage of existing opportunities?

HARRY A. STEELE (U.S. Department of Agriculture, Lincoln, Neb.): The Kansas River situation is an example of a serious problem. Flood damage has been heavy and local people and various interests disagree as to what should be done. There are also conflicting engineering recommendations.

In this type of situation, who speaks for the public? How can the public interest be expressed so that everyone knows what it is?

The Tuttle Creek Dam part of this controversy has become nationally known. We have a $5 million investment there in an unfinished job that many say should never have been started. This pile of dirt is a kind of monument to this disagreement. We need organization and procedures which can resolve these conflicts and solve this problem.

MRS. CHARLES E. KERR (Wichita, Kansas): The State of Kansas ordered an independent survey, which recommended against Tuttle Creek Dam. The Missouri Basin Survey Commission reported against Tuttle Creek Dam. If the people cannot control 55,000 acres of their own land, then we are going to have to give up.

COLONEL WILLIAM WHIPPLE (Corps of Engineers): Tuttle Creek is to all intents and purposes stopped. There are certain contractual obligations that have to be carried out, but the local people very successfully stopped Tuttle Creek under the present setup.

FRED F. HORNE (Carmel Valley, Calif.): We have a bureaucracy in this government that has done us great good. But in its arbitrary administration it also has done us great harm without even knowing it, because nobody ever yelled. In Los Angeles County the houses and streets were built on land that used to collect and store ground water in our rainy season. Why were they built there? I will tell you one reason. The FHA can say to a man: "You can't build a house on this slope because the percolation rate from your septic tank isn't right; find another site where the water flows into the ground faster."

The whole question of what the public interest is came up again in the December 4 meeting of the whole section.

NORMAN I. WENGERT (North Dakota Agricultural College): In this discussion we have skirted the very important question of the public interest. I am very sorry for this because I think many of the problems of organization, cost-benefit, and public action might be resolved if we went back to the fundamental question: Wherein does the public interest lie?

EDWARD A. ACKERMAN (Tennessee Valley Authority): Aside from a few individuals, there seemed to be a singular lack of disposition to take up the question of the public interest in relation to water resources. The reason, I believe, was that it is peculiarly difficult to distinguish the federal interests from state and local, and private interests.

How Much Should the Federal Government Do?

C. I. WEAVER (Ohio Fuel and Natural Gas Company): I do not think you can do this job completely without the federal government being in as a referee. To get cooperation you have to divide the power. The power of the United States Government should not be complete, and the power of the states should not be complete. The right of the states and the agencies of the states and of private enterprise in the states to initiate projects is a very healthy thing. But the federal government should use initiative, too, and call attention to problems and possible lines of action.

MERTON BERNSTEIN (Office of Senator Morse): I gather from the discussion that there is not undue concern about the past role of the federal government. I think that the problems of water supply are practical ones of grappling with forces of nature and making what seems to be too little go around. The federal government, after all, is not something divorced from the people in this country. The basic difficulty seems to be in getting practical solutions and not in making sure that private enterprise will participate. There seems to be enough work for everyone.

F. W. SCHEIDENHELM (Consulting Engineer, New York): [At the December 4 session.] As a question of fundamental law, how much authority has the federal government to engage in water development? There are those who are convinced that the federal government, under the so-called general welfare clause of the Constitution, may undertake any kind of development or project in the water resources field. On the other side, there are those—I am one of them—who feel that the Supreme Court has not yet decided that point. This whole area should be clear; the safe way is through an amendment to the Constitution.

Tangles over water law, it was pointed out, hamper both federal and nonfederal efforts at development through cooperation.

MR. STRAUS: The wonderland of water rights, which is largely a legal problem, has been a great trouble to all of us. Everybody wants to develop water resources. How are you going to get maximum opportunity? Everybody wants the state water law to apply, but you cannot get the verdict as to what water is whose.

JEAN S. BREITENSTEIN (Attorney, Denver): That is a definite problem. You people in the East who think you do not have it should realize that more and more the eastern states are turning away from riparian water law to appropriation water law. Before very long, you are going to have the same problems that we have had in the West for 50 years. We haven't solved them yet.

The recurring controversy of whether the federal government or the state governments shall have jurisdiction to control the use of water is a live subject in the West.[4]

For all of the unsolved questions and remaining obstacles, a man who has been around a long time looked forward with hope.

DAVID C. WARNER (Ohio Department of Natural Resources): A process of evolution is going on in water development. I have been

---

[4] Under the doctrine of riparian rights the waters of a stream must be permitted to pass downstream essentially undiminished in quantity and unimpaired in quality. Otherwise downstream owners may have a legal claim for damages. Under the appropriation doctrine a right to divert and consume water may be acquired from the state on a "first come, first served" basis. Downstream riparian owners cannot collect damages even though the entire flow of the stream is taken. In the eastern states the riparian doctrine is in force; in most of the western states the appropriation doctrine controls.

studying it for 60 years. I will be 81 years old next Saturday. I have watched this thing grow. In June, 1933, I organized the Ohio Valley Conservation and Flood Control Congress. In June, 1936, we got the first federal flood control law that authorized the Army Engineers to build headwater flood control reservoirs. Only last year we got an appropriation for the handling of little watersheds—upstream engineering. It has taken all that time to get this combination coordinated.

It is evolving; it is growing. I am not scared. I have waited a long time to see it happen. Men, it is coming. I am glad to see it coming, and I pray to God that in the next 20 years we will see our water resources developed and conserved as a coordinated whole. I don't care whether it is a conservancy district, an interstate district or what it is. Let's get it done! We must do a coordinated cooperative job.

Interstate Compacts

While most of the participants agreed on the value of the interstate compact as a device for apportioning water among states, there were wide differences of opinion over its range of usefulness in planning, development, and operation. It is a slow and often cumbersome method; some view these limitations as serious flaws, some as positive virtues. The broad question of efficiency for its own sake as against constitutional checks and balances came up.

Comparisons and suggested alternatives often led to the other major areas of subsection discussion, particularly to the general issue of regional and field organization.

FROM THE RECORD

MR. ROSECRANS: Is the interstate compact type of organization a suitable vehicle for water resource development planning? For financing? For construction? For operation?

MR. STURROCK: Originally the interstate compact theory was used to apportion the waters among the several states. In later years we have been conferring more authority on these interstate compact commissions of the West.

In the Pecos River Compact, for instance, the compact commission is actually developing plans for increasing the water supply of that stream. Through appropriations from the Texas Legislature and the legislature in New Mexico, it can study and make plans for eliminating loss of water from salt cedars.

I see no reason why one of these interstate compact commissions could not be the authority—through cooperation with local districts, irrigation districts, conservancy districts, cities, towns, industries, and federal agencies to develop programs and actually construct projects for the development of interstate streams. Then, in the interagency basin commission, we have a vehicle for bringing all of the interests together—the interstate compact commission, federal, local, and state agencies having to do with water development and conservation.

RONALD B. PETERSON (New York State Department of Commerce): We have had experience in New York with both the interstate compact and the interagency commission. The interstate compact holds out one thing that we think is worth the difference. That is freedom on the part of the states and the localities to designate in the first instance what the problem is; freedom to go ahead and study it; freedom to make the plans; freedom to make fools of ourselves if we want to. We still value that.

ROBERT M. BROWN (Maryland Department of Health): The interstate compact arrangement is an interesting and useful one, but is it the beginning or the end? In Maryland, for example, we can't get people to think and talk in terms of interstate problems until we tell them what we can do about their intrastate problems. Do we not have to provide something of an over-all plan for a state, taking into consideration both interstate and intrastate problems, before we can go ahead with negotiations with adjoining states to solve the major problems?

LEE S. GREENE (University of Tennessee): Although it would be incorrect to say that the interstate compact is not a suitable vehicle, its faults should be pointed out.

In the first place, the method is a slow one. Oftentimes this is very good. Perhaps some of these things should be developed slowly. But I am afraid that if we in our area had relied on interstate compacts, I would be gone before I had any benefits from the development of the Tennessee River. Secondly, I think the interstate compact is very uncertain. It gives rise to controversies which are not settled. Finally, it doesn't seem at all realistic to suggest that streams can be divided between those that are intrastate and those that are interstate. Development of water power should be on the basis of a river basin.

There is at present only one agency that is in itself a river basin agency and not a diplomatic agency or a diplomatic corps, such as I think is true of the interstate compact and the interagency committees. That agency is the TVA.

MR. STURROCK: Apportioning water rights through an interstate compact is no more of a long-drawn-out process than filing a suit in the Supreme Court. To settle one of these interstate lawsuits in the United States Supreme Court takes from 10 to 15 years. The Supreme Court has recommended in every interstate case that has been before it that we settle these matters around the conference table by the interstate method. The interstate compacts will work from the grassroots up if the local people will attend the meetings and take an interest.

WILLIAM S. WISE (Connecticut State Water Commission): An interstate compact provides a vehicle which gives the local people who are affected in any way the maximum chance to give their views and to help to plan for the solution of their problems. Obviously there are many differences of opinion. But an interstate compact recognizes that.

MR. STRAUS: Speaking as a man who has always supported interstate compacts, I would like to report that they are a very poor, slow, and delaying method. But despite all the handicaps, the compact is the best method yet found to find out what water is whose. Until that is found out, you can't have development. One alternative has been tried: direct action before the Supreme Court. The Supreme Court doesn't like to take these cases, and its footwork is very good.

ALLISON V. DUNN (National Park Service): There are different kinds of existing compacts for different situations. The compact medium should not be universally adopted or rejected because of individual cases of past success or failure.

MR. ACKERMAN: There is no question that some compacts work, or that it is highly desirable to have maximum local participation and the views of as many local people as possible.

The real problem here relates to the interstate river basin compact as an instrument for planning, construction, and operation. How well does the compact method work when it comes up against a really tough problem, such as having to perform in a hurry? During the last war TVA was asked to construct a certain quantity of power capacity as rapidly as possible. The result was the construction of Douglas Dam in 12 months, and the 480-foot high Fontana Dam in less than 3 years. I wonder how the campact approach would have handled that problem.

MR. STURROCK: Of course a strong centralized government can act fast. A democracy in action is where you get the views of the people instead of just going ahead and doing the job without consulting the people. An interstate compact is democracy in action, whereas TVA and some of these other authorities go ahead and get the job done and to hell with the people.

MR. GREENE: I would like to suggest that democracy is not necessarily synonymous with anarchy.

MR. STRAUS: Three years ago, when we passed the silver anniversary of the Colorado River Compact, there was still a violent dispute; Arizona and California had not agreed as to what the compact meant. Since then the Upper Basin states have been added and they are in violent dispute. After nearly 30 years of that compact, most of the major questions are not yet settled. In supporting interstate compacts we have to recognize the delay they can entail.

MR. GRAHAM: Doesn't the fact that sovereign states are now in dispute on the North Colorado River go back to the idea that when you use the compact beyond an attempt to get together to do some very definite thing, you get into trouble? In the Delaware River Compact, for instance, all the states don't seem to be in agreement. When you ask the Congress and various state legislatures for an interstate campact, you have to have a definite objective in view.

MR. PETERSON: It is probably a good thing that interstate compacts offer opportunity for disagreement. You could superimpose a regional authority which would make final determinations in an arbitrary manner.

The question here is whether states and local governments can get together and cope with the problems which they themselves have identified. I don't think that you should measure their ability to do so by how well they can handle an emergency. I admire the TVA for being able to build this tremendous project in Carolina but I think the South Podunk Rod and Gun Club could have done it equally as well if they had had the United States Treasury to depend on.

MR. GREENE: "Arbitrary" means "unreasonable." I suppose that all governments act in an unreasonable manner from time to time but I believe that the quantity of unreasonableness at the state level is about equivalent to that at the federal level. There are plenty of reasons why things should be done at the state level, but the boundaries of many states were not designed to outline a setup for resources administration. We cannot change the state boundaries; neither can we do fully what has to be done by means of the interstate compact because it is so clumsy and so slow. I am not suggesting that the interstate compact should be thrown out of the window, but neither should the authority idea.

Further comment on the values and limitations of interstate compacts led to a suggestion for exploring an additional kind of organization.

MR. ELIOT: The interstate compact is a very useful instrument to obtain agreement on what we have—the quality and amount of water and the responsibility of the different participants; but perhaps it is the wrong instrument for financing, construction, and operation.

It was a great contribution when Herbert

Hoover finally got the states together in the Colorado River Compact. It was another great contribution when the Tennessee Valley Act opened another way of operating and developing our river basins. Perhaps we have now come to the point where still a new method should be developed and experimented with.

Some years ago the National Resources Planning Board suggested the possibility of combining the interstate compact with the authority procedure in a mixed corporation, in which private enterprise, state and local gov-ernment and the federal government would all participate in about the same pattern used by the great East India Company. India was developed by such a joint effort, and the same method is worth considering today as a way of seeing that all those who participate financially have a definite voice in accordance with the amount of their participation. Perhaps this is a means of opening the way to everybody concerned enough to participate financially. We should keep the doors open and not try to choose between all of this or all of that.

Regional Organization

What form of forms of organization seem best to bring about coordination within regions or major river basins? What are the advantages and disadvantages of those now in use?

Much of the discussion centered on two kinds of organization—the interagency committee (including state representation) and the basin commission. TVA, as the one going example of the valley authority, was discussed pro and con. It was pointed out that regional mechanisms cannot be fully effective without a unified national resources policy. This need, while expressed clearly here, was emphasized even more strongly in the discussion of federal organization (pages 158-61).

FROM THE RECORD

MR. ROSECRANS: How should our administrative talent be organized at the regional or field level? What type of structure, and what set of powers, would best serve the combination of private, local, state, and federal interests?

MR. STEELE: You may be interested in the recommendations of the Missouri Basin Survey Commission which last year studied the present organization in the Missouri Basin and concluded that some change was needed.

They recommended a new central agency that would direct planning and suggest budgets, with the advice and assistance of the agencies. It would work through the agencies, but it would schedule the investigations and have the direction of when and where agencies were to plan. It would then present the projects to the Congress for authorization and would submit the annual budgets. Construc-tion would be turned over to the agencies.

In the field of operation, they recommended that the proposed commission have jurisdiction only over those things that have some basin-wide significance and that other parts of the development be turned over to the local districts or state agencies. However, they suggested that the central commission have some sort of applied research and extension program in the field of maintenance and operation to assist local districts.

One goal set out by the Survey Commission was that the program should be comprehensive, covering all the land and water resources of the whole basin. They found that the Missouri River Basin lacked an adequate watershed program.

The Commission felt very definitely that the states should be partners in the development because the facilities and powers of both federal and state governments would be needed. They found, too, that the local people and the state governments are not contributing very heavily to the present program.

MR. STURROCK: I favor the interagency basin setup. I understand some basin commissions haven't been altogether satisfactory, but from my work with the Arkansas-White-Red Basin Commission I think that is an ideal setup to bring together all interests and groups and plan basin development.

MR. GRAHAM: The interagency committees have great possibilities. I have jotted down four essentials; there may be others: First, real participation by the states as equal partners; some of our states are intensely interested in the studies and some are utterly indifferent. Second, top-level agreement among the federal agencies on the approach to economic problems; that has got to come from the top. Third, freezing of a policy, once adopted, for the duration of the study; when a policy is changed in the middle of the stream and you go back and do the work all over again, it's pretty wasteful. Fourth, sufficient funds to employ competent engineers and economists who, aside from the restrictions of agreed economic policy, shall be free to do their work.

HERBERT G. WEST (Inland Empire Waterways Assn., Walla Walla): If we are seriously considering the interagency commission, we should also consider the need for removing the requirement of unanimity of action.

FRANK L. WEAVER (Commission on Organization of the Executive Branch of the Government): The New England-New York Interagency Committee has never invoked the unanimity rule. It is on the books, but no one has ever raised that question. We had one division of 7 to 5, and the 7 vote ruled. The states had equal vote with the federal representatives. You can't get 10 or 12 or 15 people around a table and expect them always to agree.

MR. PETERSON: A few years ago someone decided that New York and New England had a community of interests that should be handled on a river basin basis. The state of New York didn't agree, nor do we yet agree, that we have any common problems in river basin development. We have gone along on a cooperative basis. We are delighted to help, but we don't see how we can help on a river basin basis with the development of New England.

The second thing we dislike about the NENYIAC or interagency approach is that they don't talk just of water development with ancillary benefits of power. They go into the whole background of the economy of an entire region, which may be completely unassociated on an economic basis, and get lost in a welter of studies on economy, insect control, forestry, and recreation.

FRANK L. WEAVER: As I understand the Missouri Basin proposal as outlined by Mr. Steele, you would bring the states into it and keep the federal agencies as they now exist doing the pick and shovel work. Then on that would be superimposed this commission. Just what will that accomplish that isn't being accomplished now, assuming that the interagency effort can work?

MR. STEELE: The Survey Commission report pointed out several unsolved coordination problems. One dealt with cost allocation. The Corps of Engineers has one interpretation and the Department of the Interior another. The difference is some $500 million and is either reimbursable or nonreimbursable according to whose interpretation is chosen. That problem is still not solved. This is one example of the need for a responsible central agency that speaks for all of the basin and all of the resources.

Here is another type of problem cited by the Survey Commission: In the Salt Creek area adjacent to Lincoln, a local association tried to get a joint flood control program from the Corps of Engineers and the Department of Agriculture. That effort failed partly because the two agencies never got in at the same time with a budget for planning. One year, only one of them had a planning budget; the next year when the other agency had a budget, the first one didn't. There are now two separate, uncoordinated reports on that area before Congress.

C. I. WEAVER: If we have a strong central agency—though limited in its scope—in an area, we can be assured that when a power company wants to build a dam, somebody will say: "No, don't build that dam yet. There are a lot of other uses that need to be reviewed." Whoever is the first in with a proposal should state that they want to build a dam or a housing project or what not. That brings the whole family in to take a look. You will save many embarrassments if you study the whole thing.

MR. BEARD: Mr. Steele's mention of cost allocation brings up questions of uniform policy and of administration, at whatever level, of the policies established. It is quite a delusion to think that simply changing the administrative setup or changing the faces in the administrative setup will settle those questions. It takes a lot of scientific analysis and soul-searching, but once we get there—and we are making progress in my opinion—a lot of these conflicts between administrative setups will resolve themselves.

There seemed to be rather general support for the development of broad, coordinated and multiple-purpose plans for major river basins. The differences of opinion came over how to do it.

J. W. DIXON (U.S. Department of the Interior): The basin plan is the only solution I can think of to water development through cooperation. Developing such a plan is an expensive and complicated job. The machinery for doing it is unwieldy at the moment. Nevertheless, once you have an over-all basin plan developed with full participation of the communities, states, and federal agencies concerned, you have a fair idea of who is going to do what and when and where and how. Until such plans are developed it is all too probable that somebody will be doing something to help himself, which may be to the hurt of another.

VERNON NORTHROP (Lester B. Knight and Associates, Washington, D.C.): Our waters are in basins and the basins know no state lines. This is something to bear in mind in considering how private or local interests can contribute to sound water resource development. There is no current device that either by state law or by federal law provides a basis of contribution. If we can find a basin approach to the problem, then we can fit the pieces together.

MR. WEST: We all want water development, but there seems to be a little division as to whether to accept the best engineering or the most expedient engineering. I reject very definitely for our Northwest areas the valley authority approach or a straight engineering approach. The good legislation on our books today has been the result of many years of debate in the Congress; it has stood up. When we have adopted expedient legislation to cure a problem for the moment, we find ourselves in hot water—we have manufactured many other problems.

MRS. FOREMAN: There is a national public interest involved in much of the planning that goes on on a regional basis. I have a fishing hole up on the upper waters of the Columbia River. The kind of interstate planning for the valley that has been described earlier has taken little account of my interest in my fishing hole, which is bounded on one side by Glacier National Park, a good slice of which some of the people in the Columbia River Valley would like to flood. In considering what they are going to do downstream with their water, they are being extremely casual about the recreational interests of the people of the whole country. If interstate agencies are going to do the planning, somebody who can represent the national interest ought to sit with them.

PHILIP SCHIFF (National Jewish Welfare Board): As one concerned with sociological problems, who has talked to the farmers in the backwoods all through the Tennessee Valley, I would urge that the more we think in terms of integrating those programs on the federal, state, and local level, with private enterprise having its fair share of it, the more we come up with this integrated plan and not this piecemeal business that some of us have found over the years in different parts of the country.

Federal Organization

Discussion of federal relationships with other levels of government and with private agencies made it clear that to regard the whole federal establishment as a single factor in water development often could lead to meaningless oversimplification. The Bureau of Reclamation, the Corps of Engineers, the Soil Conservation Service, and other federal agencies active in one or more phases of water development have different major objectives, operate under different laws, and are fitted into the organizational structures of different departments.

Would better federal organization improve working relations at all levels? Is there need for a national board of review? Persons who saw the need for a national board of review had some varying suggestions on how such a body might be set up. Others suggested that better coordination of present machinery would reduce or remove the need for a new board at the top. Quite a few people appeared to doubt that formal organization is the real key to consistency at the national level, and emphasized needs for a clear, comprehensive national policy and more consistent legislation, and for more and better apportioned funds for planning water development.

FROM THE RECORD

WILLIAM VOIGT (Izaak Walton League of America, Inc.): Several federal agencies now deal with the development of water resources. The Civil Functions Branch of the Army Engineers, the Bureau of Reclamation, and the Soil Conservation Service are the principal ones that plan, construct, maintain, and operate. Would there be any genuine validity in a functional approach rather than the present all-embracing approach of these agencies? For example, each of the agencies plans. Perhaps there would be more economy and less confusion if we put the planning together. If there were a constructing service agency to build the physical structures, operation and maintenance could be given to a specific separate service. Then there certainly should be a board of review between the planning agency and the Congress as the representatives of the general public. This kind of organization might bring a bit more efficiency; a little more safeguarding of all of the public interest in all of the resources affected. Some of our agencies, we must admit, have a limited viewpoint.

MR. WEST: I believe that the greatest economy will come if more money is appropri-

ated for planning. Often projects are authorized 10 years before the appropriation actually comes through. Many projects that were estimated on cost indices of years ago have no business being authorized projects today. But they can be weeded out only if there is enough money to keep the planning completely up to date so that when the final determination is made by the Congress the estimated cost will be the current construction cost.

The problem is one of strengthening our present organizations. I believe that the proposed board of review definitely should be in the Bureau of the Budget, the agency that has to fit the appropriation into the President's fiscal policy.

MR. ELIOT: The suggestion that the Bureau of the Budget might be a board of review to coordinate planning for watershed and drainage basin development in the federal government is good, but limited. The Bureau of the Budget is primarily concerned with appropriations and the economic side of every project; but there are other considerations that should be taken into account before a decision is reached. Social purposes—recreation is just one example—do not appear on a balance sheet, drawn up in money terms. Besides the Bureau of the Budget review, there should be some other kind of an appraisal and coordination of planning.

One other thing about centralized planning: Separate investigations are sure to come up with separate answers; and once a man has put his name—or an agency its name—to a report with a solution, it is the very devil to get him to backtrack, whether his connections are federal, state, or private. The coordination process has got to take place before the distinguished engineer or the distinguished head of a bureau takes a stand, not afterwards. To me this means that somewhere in the government there has to be a single agency that will coordinate the planning, and not come up with three plans and then leave it to Congress to decide on a political basis what may be an engineering question.

MR. GRAHAM: Either Congress will get to a point where it can agree that one agency might solve all the problems of water development, or you have got to solve them in front of the committees of Congress. After all, this is a democracy and we are allowed to have differences of opinion. The only forum we have is the forum created by the people, not a group set aside and given some power to make a judgment over it. To set somebody off like that is to make a master for me, and I don't want a master.

MR. ELIOT: I had no intention of bypassing or opposing Congress. This is entirely a question of service to Congress in developing proposals for its consideration.

MR. NORTHROP: The geographic unification of water basin planning must come before you decide whether or not a functional national organization will work. I don't think you will find any top decision on organization of federal functions that has a prayer of working unless it is tested against the way in which it works in the locality.

MR. STRAUS: I don't believe that complete separation of planning, construction, and opera-

tion is a realistic suggestion. When you have your planners, builders, and operators entirely separate, you run into the most objectionable type of buckpassing. The builders say, "How in the hell can we build that thing? The planners planned it all wrong." And the operators say, "How can we operate it right if it was built wrong?" You have to have somebody that the public can put a finger on.

Organization, of course, can be improved, although I think there is less cause for worry about conflict than for wonder at how little conflict there has been against the handicap of built-in conflicts in law and policy.

To cite the leading example, the government has created two agencies, one—the Corps of Engineers—consecrated to getting into the sea a lot of surplus water that is doing flood damage. The other—the Bureau of Reclamation—is consecrated to keeping as much water as it can out of the sea and saving it for use. This is a direct conflict. It has worked out pretty well only by the good sense of the two agencies, but still there are troublesome difficulties of operation. Many of the built-in conflicts in law and policy can be eliminated. It would be a most fruitful area to work in.

Discussion of the federal structure had included a number of comments on a board of review even before the subsection chairman raised the direct question: "Is there need to establish a national board of review?"

MR. ROSECRANS: I think we should discuss the question under the status quo of existing multiple agencies. If we change the status of these organizations and put the over-all planning in some large organization, that in itself might constitute the board of review.

MR. NORMAN: I would favor a board of review if it could be taken completely out of politics. If the members were designated—not appointed, but designated—by the Engineers Joint Council, say, for ability, and were appointed for a definite number of years and not subject to reappointment, that would be all right. Otherwise, I think all we would have within the board of review would be another political agency.

MRS. FOREMAN: I think we are talking about an organization for clearing plans in advance, rather than a board of review that would come along and try to arbitrate after each separate agency had made up its mind.

C. I. WEAVER: Reviewing somebody else's work after all the plans are made just creates delay. Get the best organization that you can, central and strong, which will have authority to initiate things, the authority to coordinate things, and establish a procedure under the law where you can proceed. When you do that, you don't need a board of review. If you have wibbley-wobbley committees then maybe you do need one.

GENERAL WARREN T. HANNUM (formerly chairman, California State Water Pollution Control Board): A board of review is another cog in the wheel, and it is bound to delay action. After all, if you have a board of review, its work will be reviewed again by a committee in Congress before you can do anything. Therefore I think that the Congress should reorganize its committees so that one committee would handle all these various projects; and that this committee, through Congressional action, should establish identical procedure for the various agencies for investigation, and review, and approval of projects.

MR. WISE: We are talking here of large projects. Generally in large projects you don't get in very far before you find a great many collateral problems that weren't anticipated. There ought to be some agency to solve these problems as they crop up in the course of the study. For something of that sort a board of review might be very beneficial.

MR. WEST: A board of review would have to go back and take over the steps that the various agencies now take. The greatest safeguard we have in a water resources program is the fact that there must be public hearings out in the area that is affected.

MR. GRAHAM: It seems that there is a trend toward more state participation. I don't know whether the states would participate if someone other than the Congress is going to do the reviewing. The final board of review is the Congress of the United States. We just can't get away from that.

MR. DIXON: For several years the coordination of proposed project reports among local, state, and federal agencies has been a part of my job. At the present time, due to a complex of laws, executive orders, interagency agreements and so forth, every one of our project reports has to run the gantlet of at least 16 agencies of one kind or another. This takes about a year, and if prices of construction are fluctuating the cost estimates of the projects become either too high or too low before any conclusion can be reached concerning the proposed project. If a board of review could simplify this procedure, I am sure that it would find a great deal of support.

MR. NORTHROP: It is idle to think that any board could do what agencies working together have been unable to do heretofore, even with the partial kibitzing from time to time by the Budget Bureau or other agencies. Each agency feels compelled to carry out its provisions under the terms and understanding with its Congressional group. Until the situation is changed, the limitation created by basic differences in the laws will produce almost insurmountable barriers.

ARTHUR MAASS (Harvard University): The task force on natural resources of the Hoover Commission proposed the board of review originally; its function is primarily that of coordination. In any plan for water development, according to the task force report, the interests of departments other than the department making the plan are involved inevitably. Obviously, the organization level for taking into account the interests of the different departments must be higher than that of any one of them; and therefore the task force proposed a coordinating facility in the President's office. Any agency intending to survey a water resource situation would submit to the coordinating office a prospectus of its planned survey. This prospectus would be distributed to the other agencies of interest for comment, and consequently they would be in on the planning from the very beginning. The review and coordinating board would then check several times during the conduct of the survey to insure that all interests are in fact being considered in balance. With such a focus, you have a good case for establishing a review function. I think the review would be carried out better by a special board in the President's office than by the Bureau of the Budget. But this latter is a matter of opinion.

MR. ACKERMAN: If you achieve coordination in the basin, perhaps some of the problems that would otherwise go to the board of review may be taken care of. We feel that in the Tennessee Valley we have not had since 1933 the more difficult problems of coordination described for some other parts of the country.

The Need for a Clearer National Policy

The need for a better defined national policy of water development was implied by several persons, and brought out directly by others.

BRIG. GEN. THERON D. WEAVER (Department of the Army): I agree with the necessity of getting the plans coordinated in advance. I think that can be done by the present machinery of the government, given a clearly enunciated statement of national water policy. I think we can do a job economically and efficiently with the existing agencies the way they are. So far as I know, there is not at the present time a clear national water policy. There are many policies, but they haven't been coordinated.

MR. STURROCK: I think Congress should adopt a national water policy. The lack of a national water policy has resulted in Congress' delegating to certain administrative agencies policy-making powers and other authority, which has resulted in a law by secretarial order or solicitor's opinions and so forth. Congress should reassume its authority.

MR. GRAHAM: Such a policy having been adopted, you can't stop the next Congress from undoing it. Congress adopts water policies every session. The real difficulty is to find enough money to study the problems; and you still have to go to Congress to get it.

MR. BROWN: We can't legislate or pass regulations that will make people work together; but if we strive to work together as men of good will, we will achieve the objective that we seek. We can't base our hope completely on improvements in government structure.

Subsection C

EVALUATION AND REIMBURSEMENT

Even if the most cautious counsels are followed, a tremendous job of water development lies ahead. As the steering committee pointed out, the range of estimates for projects and programs during the next few decades is from $50 billion to $100 billion. In whatever way this task may be shared among private groups and local, state, and federal public agencies, a considerable part of the cost will be borne by the federal taxpayer.

Thus, evaluation and reimbursement principles and procedures as they relate to federal water development programs raise significant questions. What determines whether or not public investments in water resource projects and programs are justified? To what extent is economic evaluation a useful tool for making such determination? What is the relative importance of the direct and tangible benefits of water resource development as compared with the indirect, secondary, and intangible benefits? How should the costs of water resource development be shared? The focus throughout the discussion was on federal projects and programs.

Major points developed in the discussion concerned emphasis and methods rather than sharp issues of principle. In examining the justification of public investments, significant differences of opinion arose less over whether financial feasibility or the public welfare should be the chief criterion than over what combination of the two is best. Debate on economic evaluation centered not on whether it should be used, but on when and how. No one questioned that individual recipients should pay for benefits insofar as practicable; the differences came over what benefits can be traced to individual beneficiaries and how much persons should be expected to pay for different kinds of benefit.

Evaluation

There was wide agreement that both financial feasibility and public welfare should be considered in determining whether federal investment in a proposed water development is justified. There would be small reason for supplementary private investment if reasonable expectation of profit were the main criterion. On the other hand, many participants felt that financial prospects should be examined carefully in any decision to use public funds. Consequently, the place of economic evaluation drew much attention. How trustworthy are present methods, particularly the benefit-cost ratio? What are their strong and weak points? What improvements are most needed?

In exploring problems of how to measure the probable tangible effects of projects, questions of secondary benefits received most attention as the more complex and pressing, but no one contended that all important questions of primary benefits have been solved.

FROM THE RECORD

What Justifies Federal Investment?

M. M. KELSO (Montana State College): Should we apply the test of financial feasibility to the question of whether the public should sink capital in water resource development? Is it enough to ask whether a project will pay financially?

MARK REGAN (U.S. Department of Agriculture): I think it is not. If you insist that a project be financially feasible, why should there be any federal interest in developing it at all? It is the widely distributed benefits that accrue over broad areas that justify public participation.

WILLIAM J. HULL (Ashland Oil and Refining Company, Kentucky): Each individual project should bear a relationship to the whole problem of conservation and proper use of water resources in a large area. Any attempt to analyze the feasibility of a project in strict financial terms would be much too narrow and quite inappropriate.

HAROLD H. CHRISTY (The Colorado Fuel and Iron Corporation): I question whether you can inventory and develop certain areas over the next 5 to 10 decades if you do it strictly for profit. From the long-range viewpoint, certain areas have been neglected in their development. There are areas where private financing has developed everything that is feasible, but for the long pull the terms of private investment may not be applicable to the needs of coming generations. They might find themselves with all the water developed in a pattern that is no longer best for the entire community.

Several other persons suggested types of desirable water development which offer little prospect of immediate profit or appear beyond the capabilities of local or state units of government. The chairman then posed the question from the other side: Is the public welfare in itself an adequate reason for federal investment?

J. R. BRENNAN (Department of the Army): In water resource projects, we are faced with benefits of two kinds: those which are direct and tangible, and those which are not. The reason for not going on financial feasibility alone is recognition of other values not appropriate to private investment. The reason for not discarding financial feasibility is that in water resource programs we have that kind of values, too. There is no reason for not using some combination which considers both of those values.

MORRIS E. GARNSEY (University of Colorado): The differences which seem to exist in this area really spring from differences in fundamental values. I think many of the difficulties would be resolved if everyone who stated an opinion about cost, benefit, and reimbursement policies would preface his opinion with a statement of the values or the ethical concepts upon which his conclusion is based.

I will offer one example. The Army Engineers have said that they could control floods on the Kansas River by a series of 24 reservoirs and that this would cost roughly $1 billion. The report of the Board of Engineers for the Kansas Industrial Development Commission offered a plan that would cost $350 million. That would be a net saving of $650 million. Now I am not attempting to judge the merits of the two plans, but $650 million is a very respectable sum of money. All alterna-

tives ought to be examined and the cheaper alternative chosen, except on the basis of a set of values explicitly stated and commonly recognized by all concerned.

HORACE M. GRAY (University of Illinois): I like the general welfare approach, but we are in a very vulnerable position if we allow a lax system of financing to enable certain strategically situated groups to derive direct, localized tangible benefits from public expenditures. That is regarded as unjust and arouses bitter political opposition. Where the benefits are direct and accrue to local beneficiaries, the pay-out principle is sound. But other benefits which are not localized must, I think, be borne by the general public.

CHARLES D. CURRAN (Commission on Organization of the Executive Branch of the Government): We have just so much energy, materials, and money to put into the development of water resources in any one period of time. One of the easiest measures of priority is to pick first those projects which most clearly are going to bring the greatest return to the community. I think you will find that the benefit-cost ratio on the basis of direct measurable returns is of greatest help in dealing with the immediate problem. In the ultimate problem, of course, you can consider all benefits including vagaries ascribed to the general welfare. There is no way of legislating good judgment or finding a mathematical formula as a substitute for good judgment. A benefit-cost ratio is only a guide. When you get to the abstractions of vague indirect benefits, I think you will find that those that are not real and measurable are not worth considering in economic evaluation. The greatest increases of wealth will tend to bring the greatest improvement in the general standards of living.

C. EDWARD BEHRE (U.S. Forest Service): The criterion of a benefit-cost ratio falls down from the national standpoint. We may find that all the projects that offer the biggest monetary returns are in the Pacific Northwest. Is it sound public policy to develop the Pacific Northwest and neglect the Southwest or some other area?

WILLIAM J. BURKE: (U.S. Department of the Interior): I have worked on water problems for almost 30 years. I have rolled up and down the Missouri River Basin from one end to the other. I have heard today's discussion repeated for the past 30 years.

As to whether you are going to approach resource development from the welfare standpoint or some other standpoint, all you need to do is look back into history. You have already approached it from the welfare standpoint, and irrevocably.

REGINALD C. PRICE (U.S. Department of the Interior): It is well established that general welfare must be the basis for substantial federal interest in the river basin programs. But the need must be presented in a way convincing to those who finance it, and they have shown a predisposition to require not only a general justification in terms of welfare but also an economic justification of individual projects. I would assume that general welfare must be the basic justification of our major programs, but that in addition there must be a benefit-cost analysis justification, embracing all benefits and costs, tangible and intangible, so that we have a measure in terms of the increase in useful goods and services to the entire community.

F. W. SCHEIDENHELM (Consulting Engineer, New York): There is real need for understanding the distinction between financial feasibility and economic evaluation. While I do not believe there is any constitutional backing for the federal government's entering into projects for the sake of making money, it seems fairly clear that the judgment of the Congress has got to be, as far as it can, on the basis of "Will it pay?" An economic evaluation surely must mean an evaluation on the basis of dollars and cents. Still another reason for economic evaluation in dollars and cents is to compare projects. If one does this only on the basis of general welfare the measuring stick is something intangible that even our economist friends have their doubts about. If the benefits do not exceed the cost, then we are merely swapping dollars. We are not increasing the national wealth.

SIDNEY T. HARDING (Engineers Joint Council, Berkeley, Calif.): If we build water projects that do not in some way or other produce benefits in terms of public welfare, a very pertinent constitutional question is raised. The fact that benefits to the public may be intangible does not mean that they don't exist, or that we should not compare them so we can judge between projects. We should get the most for our money by selecting those on which the apparent benefit-cost ratio is highest.

WALTER C. LOWDERMILK (Berkeley, Calif.): We sought to require farmers of irrigation projects, both privately and publicly financed, to reimburse the entire cost of an irrigation project. This we believe now is unsound. For when we eat cornflakes for breakfast we are paying about $36 for a bushel of corn, for which the farmer got about a dollar. This bushel of corn was a raw material that gave rise to a lot of economic activity with profits made several times along the way by the time the cornflakes were served at my breakfast table. The food-growing division of labor is the foundation on which is built a great superstructure of industrial and service enterprises. It would seem that the entire development should pay for an irrigation project, where a project is justified; the costs should be apportioned against the farmer, business enterprises, in fact the social structure that arises on this foundation, on the basis of fair shares of the cost of the irrigation project.

MR. GARNSEY: We talk about the effect on regional development and about growth and stability of the economy and then throw all these things in as factors justifying a project. We develop a figure, but what I am afraid of is that people will look at it and think it settles everything. The fact is that the benefit-cost figures are just arbitrarily developed as a result of some other concept of values.

General Problems of Economic Evaluation

MR. KELSO: What are the relations between the intangible benefits and economic evaluations?

IRA A. WATSON (U.S. Department of the Interior): I think we can say that water resource development is the economic application of science to social purposes. On this basis, evaluation is a task for a combination of professions, including the various branches of engineering involved in design and construction, the accountants concerned with repayment, the economists and other social scientists. There are other ways of assessing economic implications in addition to the benefit-cost ratio, such as comparisons identifying the most economic alternative for achieving a purpose. I would like to suggest that the purposes of resource development are essentially social rather than economic, public rather than private. This fact is very important in project evaluation and implies that social sciences other than economics can help us. For example, there is an opportunity for geographers because needs and project effects vary in time and place.

S. V. CIRIACY WANTRUP (University of California): There is no difference between economic evaluation and welfare evaluation. Economic evaluation is only a system of principles and methods to help in achieving welfare. If a bridge collapsed, we would blame the engineer, not the discipline of engineering. Instead of blaming economics for mistakes in present evaluation procedures, we should blame some economists. Economic evaluation is not confined to some prices directly yielded by a market. We want to evaluate the preferences of *all* people concerned with respect to *all* benefits and costs of a project. This does not mean that we have to replace economic evaluation with some vague personal philosophy, nor that we have to look beyond economics to evaluate some of the benefits of water development which have been called "intangibles." Power and water are usually called "tangibles." In social evaluation they are no more tangible than recreation or wildlife or other "intangibles." In some respects, evaluation of water and power is even more difficult than that of other products of multiple-purpose projects.

MR. GARNSEY: Just what is the general welfare or just what social values can be generally agreed upon? I do not believe there is any generally acceptable set of values or any way for economists to measure one set against another. This does not mean that I substitute my personal values for anybody else's. What you have to do is to find out what the people concerned hold as values or purposes or desires, and this needs to be tied specifically to the particular objective. For example, in the Upper Colorado River Storage Project it is proposed that irrigation will not pay a cent of the cost of this project and will only be able to pay operating costs and maintenance costs. It is also conceded that there are very large values to people in terms of recreation, wildlife habitats, and wildlife protection, and, I assume, flood control. Yet according to the benefit-cost ratio, the only thing that pays for anything is the power.

MR. WANTRUP: Any economist will realize that in water resources development final decisions—as distinct from evaluation—are political and not economic decisions. The water of the Upper Colorado River Basin is of interest not only to the people of the Upper Colorado Basin; it is of very great interest to the people of southern California and to people all over the nation. The Upper Colorado Basin Project should be evaluated by proper professional tools. Then, the political bodies of a democracy decide where the water should go. However, economic welfare is not just a goal which economists have invented. It is a lodestar toward which our whole price system, in spite of its serious shortcomings, is oriented. Some of these shortcomings can be taken into account and compensated for in evaluation.

GILBERT F. WHITE (Haverford College): There is a problem here that concerns the attitude of many persons toward professional economists, when particular evaluations are presented to the public.

Insofar as the individual who presents these evaluations gives specific findings of values for certain features of the undertakings, and disposes of the others with vague statements which are excluded from final statements of benefits and costs, the implication is that all those for which there are no specific estimates are somehow less important, or are in the political sphere.

Also, there is an uneasy feeling that the specific estimates of values which would accrue in such areas of social activities as flood control or power or irrigation in many instances are somehow manipulated so as to give a socially acceptable result. This impression is due, in part, to the fact that the methods used differ so much among agencies and parts of the country, notwithstanding the very earnest efforts which the interdepartmental committee has made to suggest uniform methods.

MR. SCHEIDENHELM: Many of the decisions on federal water resources and power development are political, being made by Congress. But I am convinced that the more one keeps to dollar and cents evaluations, the less there will be of what we usually think of as political pressure. I believe that flood control and navigation benefits can be interpreted in monetary terms just as well as can power with its salable output. What ought we do about intangibles if evaluations are to be made in terms of dollars and cents? There are, of course, many detriments just as there are many benefits. That is true of both intangibles and tangibles. Therefore, what we have left to dispose of is the net benefits.

For myself, I would rest upon the recommendations of the Engineers Joint Council, according to which the net benefits that remain in the form of intangibles would be used to determine the choice as between projects or objects of expenditures. This applies, at least, in situations where there is an alternative.

MR. BRENNAN: The purpose of economic evaluation is to determine not only the merits of a project, but also its relative priority. The analysis should determine which project produces the greatest possible benefits at this time, or in the future, and which fits in best with the national policy from a long-range point of view.

MR. BEHRE: The benefit-cost ratio as applied to land programs is misleading and unreliable. It can be derived only from benefits and costs that are measurable in monetary terms and so gives only a partial measure of the total relationship. It gives a distorted evaluation of a comprehensive agricultural program because a larger portion of all costs can be generally expressed in monetary terms than is the case with benefits. The attempt to translate the complex interrelationships involved in a comprehensive agriculture program to a simple mathematical criterion creates a false impression of accuracy. Even for those aspects which can be expressed in monetary terms, the data which are available, or which it is feasible to compile, are inevitably inadequate. For many segments of a comprehensive agricultural program it is impossible to associate a firm increment of benefit with a specific increment of cost. Also, identification and evaluation of all associated costs become an insuperable task. The sheer volume of work involved in testing alternative proposals to determine which combination of measures is most economical renders that basic aspect of the theoretical procedure prohibitive. Furthermore, the value of benefit-cost ratios in determining priorities of programs or projects is open to question because there is no way to test the significance of differences.

ALBERT R. JOHNSON (U.S. Department of the Interior): I cannot agree that the benefit-cost analysis should be thrown out simply because it has often given misleading results.

If the items that go into the benefit-cost ratio are items that we can measure with confidence, the ratio can be an extremely useful tool. We should not permit money valuations that we cannot defend to be included on the benefit side of the equation. If we limit our benefit estimates to those we are confident of, we will end up with a defensible mechanism, one that will narrow down reliance upon the nonmeasurable items.

JOHN SHORT (U.S. Department of Agriculture, Tulsa): The science of economics has not advanced to the point where we can tie all of the factors down. Research in economics and financing is badly needed. The benefit-cost ratio may be a trap we have fallen into through insufficient economic research and knowledge. While costs are tangible, benefits are not always tangible. And even some of the tangible benefits are not amendable to monetary evaluation. You are then throwing apples and peaches together into a benefit-cost ratio which does not mean much. I do not think the science of economics has gone as far as it should. In fact, our present procedures probably do not take full account of the extent to which it already is developed. For example, under the present benefit-cost analysis procedure we in the Arkansas-White-Red area have been given some price projections which we use in our economic analysis. We find a million acres in Arkansas that we can put into rice. The water is available and we show wonderful cost-benefit ratios. But then we wonder how many Chinese restaurants we have to put in to take up all that rice. If we were evaluating 1,000 acres of rice in Arkansas, perhaps the projected prices would not be disturbed. But to use them for a million acres of rice would be ridiculous. On the other hand, there may be benefits beyond what you can put in dollars and cents terms.

The importance—and difficulty—of appraising intangible benefits were emphasized.

MR. GRAY: The social values which came over the horizon only recently will ultimately be much more important, difficult, and diversified with the increase in population and the increases in demands for goods and services, the rising standards of living, and the desire to develop some of these areas which have not been fully developed as yet. At our present stage of development, perhaps the best we can do is to identify and describe as fully and as accurately as we can the nature and general extent of these social values.

Primary Benefits

MR. REGAN: The Benefit-Cost Subcommittee describes primary benefits in terms of the values to the immediate beneficiaries. For instance, the primary benefits from wheat pro-

duction would be the value of the wheat to the farmer who produces it. Everything beyond that would be a secondary benefit—for instance the benefit to the local elevator operator from handling the wheat. Not all primary benefits have to have market value. Intangible benefits like recreational values are primary when they accrue to the immediate user. The basic purpose of an analysis is to formulate proposals that are of proper scale and scope, and your principal reliance has to be on the primary benefits in order to maximize the net return from the investment. In order to do that, you have a host of standards to apply and the selection of those standards raises a whole series of questions. What is the proper interest rate and price? What is the projected price? How should you treat any number of special problems such as taxes and the acquisition of local facilities?[5]

Secondary Benefits

MR. KELSO: Can we determine the effects of a local investment for development on the national total of goods and services?

G. ROBINSON GREGORY (University of Michigan): We need a time reference. What we are concerned with in the secondary benefits are real costs and not monetary costs. The real cost of a multipurpose water storage reservoir can be expressed in terms of what the concrete would have been used for as an alternative, but this means one thing under conditions of reasonably full employment and another during a period of depression.

MR. REGAN: Mr. Gregory has raised a basic issue—what assumption do you use with respect to resource employment conditions? In an analysis, you have to take account of the secondary benefits that would have come from other uses of resources and claim only the difference in net benefits between your project and the other uses. If you assume that re-

---

[5] The Federal Interagency River Basin Committee's Subcommittee on Benefits and Costs defines primary benefits as "the value of the immediate products or services resulting from the measures for which project costs and associated costs were incurred."

sources are diverted from other productive uses, the answer on secondary benefits is entirely different from the answer based on an assumption that the resources will be under-employed in the absence of the project.

MR. PRICE: Not to take account of secondary benefits would be equivalent to evaluating them at zero. The major problem in taking account of them is alternative use. To complicate it a little further, there are two different factors. The first is the construction itself; you can identify the utilization of labor over the short run with a considerable degree of accuracy. Second, after a project is constructed, there are the commodity types of secondary benefits which increase the national product over what it would be without the project. If you assume that there would be full use of alternative resources without projects, the secondary benefits of the commodity type would amount to zero. If you assume that there would be no use of resources in the alternative, then they would amount to 100 percent. Usually, the answer lies somewhere between.

MR. JOHNSON: If there is a deficit of primary benefits, for a given project, does not the analysis in effect indicate that another project or a general use of the resource might have more primary benefits than this particular one? I have a feeling that under situations with a relatively full employment of our resources, no deficit of primary benefits can be made up with secondary benefits.

MR. GARNSEY: We should think of the multiplier effect not in terms of the employment generated by the construction phase, but in terms of the potential contribution to the gross national product of the economy over a considerable period of time. We should think in terms of the conservation of resources, using that word to mean wise use of resources over time. We should relate resources to total population and the standards of living projected to 1975—the resources and demands of the American people at a higher plane of living than they enjoy in 1953. In that way we would end up with a justification of water projects based perhaps almost entirely on these large intangibles which are none the less real, none the less vital, and none the less important. I realize this might open up the possibility of spending billions of dollars in all directions which many of us would strongly oppose. But it also opens up the basic reasons why we have water projects in the first place.

MR. GREGORY: If you start out with a predetermined justification, there is not much point in making an analysis in the first place.

MR. SCHEIDENHELM: The poorer a project is, the further we go out for benefits, the cleaner we scrape the barrel.

The need for concepts of evaluation that will hold up over the long pull was brought out, and further research was urged as a means of improving techniques.

MR. GRAY: Primary and secondary benefits are going to be determined pretty largely by what we decide to do about resources over periods of time. In examining some of the basin studies, it has struck me that we lacked sufficient data on the potentialities of long-range industrial development in areas where the water might yield primary and secondary benefits far beyond anything you can justify in terms of rice or more potatoes or wheat. It seems to me that the industrial potentialities of the Missouri and Arkansas Rivers should be much more fully explored. I have an uncomfortable feeling that we tend to do more and more of the same things we have been doing.

NATHANIEL A. BACK (Department of the Army): Wise use of resources is not necessarily the same as total development of resources, at least not in any given time span. I cannot agree that we are under any compulsion within the next 10 or 20 years to fully develop all of our water or land resources. With our present methods of looking to the future, we may be doing a much smarter thing to defer development of some resources. We may find 20 or 25 years or 50 years from now that we are going to need them mighty badly for higher uses.

Problems of Reimbursement

Who should pay what for benefits from water development? Subsection C considered only problems that concern federal projects. How closely should reimbursement be related to evaluation; do the same factors apply to both, or are the two essentially different? Should receipts from one line of development—notably power—be used to finance other phases; and if so, to what extent? How logical and workable is the present pattern of procedures; in particular, does it tend to obscure subsidies to certain types of water development?

FROM THE RECORD

How Closely Tied Are Evaluation and Reimbursement?

MR. KELSO: Is repayment or allocation of costs an integral part of the evaluation of the project that is made for the purpose of justifying it in the first place? Do you consider the same things in allocation of costs and reimbursement requirements as you considered initially in determining whether a project should be built?

MR. BRENNAN: These are distinct fields, but interrelated. There are basic differences. A completely different set of standards may be used in one case as compared to the other.

MR. SHORT: I think the common practice is sometimes mixed up. Reimbursement is a valuable tool in economic evaluation. What the people are willing to pay is a useful measure.

MR. SCHEIDENHELM: I see no reason why the measurements in cost allocation and reimbursement should be different from those in economic evaluation on a dollar and cents basis.

MR. REGAN: The secondary benefits in a local area may be quite different from the secondary benefits from a national viewpoint. There may be a whole set of offsetting factors that would reduce the secondary benefits to the whole country, so that they should be cancelled out in the evaluation, yet perhaps used for purposes of reimbursement.

MR. WATSON: I don't mean to say that the standards should be the same throughout, but where they are not the same you get into difficulties in reconciling the whole process of economic analysis with the financial arrangements. Suppose that you were using a figure of $2\frac{1}{2}$ percent in making a benefit-cost analysis and determining justifiable investment. If later you try to repay that investment at 3 percent over the same period as that used in the analysis, you are going to run into difficulty.

MR. HARDING: In irrigation developments we often have a report which shows that the land has a lot of direct benefits but it does not have the ability to pay. Theoretically, the ability to pay is the net income from the land. But, actually the landowner often has to put in a lot of investment to get the ability to pay. When people come up with the big benefit to the land yet say that the land cannot pay any more than it pays now, they are contradicting their own benefit determinations.

MR. GARNSEY: Economic evaluation and reimbursement should not be tied together. Whenever costs can be directly assigned to a benefit, and the benefit can be ascertained with some degree of certainty, then reimbursement should be called for. The balance should then be made up from either general tax revenues, or revenues from the other commodities or services in the multipurpose project for which the reimbursement exceeds the cost. You cannot talk about reimbursement or no reimbursement. You can only talk about more reimbursement or less reimbursement.

MR. JOHNSON: To say that evaluation and reimbursement are separate is really to throw away the reimbursement criterion and substitute an economic evaluation. Economic evaluation methods should be sharpened up and made much more defensible than they have frequently been in the past before we fully abandon the reimbursement criterion for use in selecting projects. I subscribe, though, to the idea of setting charges independent of project cost, and that would apply clear across the board for power, irrigation, and other vendable products or services of a project. There is one additional point. Using the value of the service as a basis for charges would remove some of the problems in the economic phases of project analysis. There would be no need for cost allocation except insofar as it be advantageous administratively to have the cost of the project split up among different purposes.

MR. SCHEIDENHELM: Where a direct benefit can be ascribed to a beneficiary, he should pay something for it. As soon as an individual has to put up some money in payment, he looks twice at the project and thinks four times before he agrees to do it. The result will be, I have not the slightest doubt, to eliminate many projects which are not worth carrying on. The result would further be to scale down the evaluations put on them, on the benefit side of the ratio of the benefits and costs. That, in itself, is worth a great deal.

MR. WHITE: What do members of this group consider to be the desirability and feasibility of attempting to apply, more generally, the principle that a basic test of financial feasibility is the willingness of some of the local beneficiaries to contribute some part of the cost?

EUGENE W. WEBER (Corps of Engineers): The Corps of Engineers has officially stated that it believes that principle is one of the factors which should receive further study by all of us. The problem of applying the principle is very complex, especially for navigation and flood control. But putting it into effect to some reasonable extent would provide a check on the accuracy of our knowledge of the benefits, facilitate the analysis in formulating projects, and help to show how much weight should be given to various uses and the resources.

DAVID CUSHMAN COYLE (Washington, D.C.): The importance, in evaluation, of the willingness of beneficiaries to pay depends partly on how widely the purpose of the project is accepted. About 125 years ago the public schools were not considered important and it was thought best that people should pay directly for part of the cost of schooling. Now, that matter is less controversial and schools are public. People today think transportation is important and that is why we subsidize the steamships and highways and all other sorts of transportation, including railroads. You don't pay anything, specifically, for not having your water poisoned with typhoid germs. We agree that these things are so important that we charge them to everybody. Many of these water projects are at present halfway between public acceptance and public rejection. Willingness to pay for benefits is a criterion to be used in places where there are things that are controversial and dropped when they cease to be controversial.

Bases of Repayment

Two large questions were examined here. The first concerned principle: How much of an effort should be made to recover part of the cost of water development from specific individuals? The second concerned methods of collecting from individuals.

MR. KELSO: Should all beneficiaries be asked to reimburse the cost of federal water development? If so, on what basis?

MR. WATSON: You cannot ask all beneficiaries to pay in relation to the benefits received. Present procedures do not permit us, with any large degree of accuracy, to determine precisely where all the benefits will occur, because some of the benefits are intangible and others are estimated in dollars but by generalized procedures which do not identify individual beneficiaries.

Mr. Kelso: When we decide to sink liquid assets into any given fixed asset we lose the alternative use value of that asset. How far can we go in assessing those costs against specific individuals on some specific basis, rather than against all of us in the incidence of general taxes?

Mr. Coyle: Self-liquidation in a project does not prove anything—except that it is of a commercial type. This country has got so much more prosperous in recent years that you cannot determine who made whom a beneficiary.

John J. Harrison (Washington, D.C.): Man and water both run downhill. Unwillingness to come to grips with the identification of beneficiaries is one of the real bottlenecks. Nowhere is it more evident than in the field of flood control. I think a great deal more can be done toward identifying beneficiaries and allocating costs to them.

Assuming known beneficiaries of water development should pay, what should the principal basis be—cost, or ability and willingness to pay?

Mr. Harding: We have, in actual practice, a tendency to charge what the traffic will bear. Under the Reclamation Law, they are selling water for municipal uses in a section of California for $10 per acre-foot right alongside of water for irrigation for $3.50 per acre-foot. In the main, municipal use has the capacity to pay more than the cost. Irrigation is in the reverse position. Whether irrigation should pay interest on money spent in its behalf is academic; it cannot pay the principal.

Mr. Garnsey: The practical thing to do is to charge what the traffic will bear. If you try to push reimbursements very far on the specific or separate basis and on a cost basis, you end up by choking off the whole process. On the other hand, the principle of all the traffic will bear implies distortion when pushed too far. You can't combine the present political efforts to promote cheaper power through federal projects and also charge for that power the marketable value. But if a number of products are sold at cost of the next alternative to the consumer, the income will carry part of the products which cannot carry their own weight.

Mr. Hull: The concept of what the traffic will bear relates to pricing in a competitive economy. It is very difficult to imagine an interplay of competitive forces with respect to most of the goods and services offered as a result of federal water resource projects that would enable anyone to establish that kind of a figure with any degree of economic sanity. As for the other approach, the whole idea of allocating costs for benefits from a multipurpose project is extremely tenuous and arbitrary.

I wonder if it is very fruitful to invoke this kind of consideration when our primary concern is with what we should be doing to maintain a margin of water resources. Narrow engineering concepts should not be permitted to interfere with the much broader objective of preserving and enlarging the water projects that protect the nation against waste of resources.

Also it seems to me that questions of charges for water resources services get you into fields of public policies far removed from national resources considered alone. I am thinking particularly of navigation. There, you get the complex question of relationships with competing forms of transportation. There is a sort of superficial plausibility in letting the direct beneficiary pay, but it is an oversimplification. There are many problems in this field that require the most careful sort of study.

Mr. Back: As a broad guideline, the statement that the beneficiary should pay does serve a useful purpose, even though we all recognize that we are not going to achieve the goal 100 percent. In discussing the concept of basing charges on the value of service, we might take note of the fact that our legislation is all based on the other theory—reimbursement of costs incurred. There would be a political hurdle to overcome to put it on the other basis.

Charles A. Sprague (*The Oregon Statesman*): Beginning in the 1930's, when

Congress began to appropriate directly, instead of from the Reclamation Fund, projects have been adopted where it was recognized that the farmers simply could not reimburse the costs in full. Here, the question arises as to the extent of a subsidy that can be justified. For example, in the Columbia River Basin Project, it was estimated that farmers couldn't pay more than $85 per acre. But in other places it was estimated that they could pay considerably more. It is one thing to relate a revenue from a connected project to a subsidy for reclamation. It is quite another to get into the procedure proposed in the Hell's Canyon Dam. The Interior Department has now withdrawn from that, but earlier it had been proposed that the excess revenues from Hell's Canyon would go to finance the Mountain Home projects in Idaho. The construction cost was estimated at between $1,000 and $1,500 an acre. There is no relation between Hell's Canyon and Mountain Home. They merely contemplated using profits from Hell's Canyon in the area where that water originated.

The time-scale of repayment drew considerable attention, especially for its bearing on the nature and amount of federal subsidies.

SAMUEL B. MORRIS (Department of Water and Power, Los Angeles): I am in favor of repayment in 50 years as a basis for all projects financed by the federal government. The value of money beyond 50 years is low; these long-deferred payments do not represent much value as of now. It has been recognized, in the case of power, that revenue should repay in 50 years with 3 percent interest. For irrigation, which since 1902 has been exempt from paying any interest, we as federal taxpayers should know what interest we have to carry. I would not exempt nonreimbursable uses, but would allow for interest at about 3 percent in calculating costs of all projects. Then we should have a common denominator to show the federal taxpayer what he is contributing toward each of these undertakings. I don't think this method would destroy any irrigation or prevent its expansion because the people of the United States have gone along

with these nonreimbursable expenditures. We are in the habit of figuring local, or at most regional, benefits when we evaluate a project. I think there is a value to the federal taxpayer that should be related to the amount which he is going to pay—a value that could be figured out if we knew how. We know that the general taxpayer puts up the biggest amount of money, but we don't appraise the benefits he is receiving and use that as a means of determining the amount he should contribute toward a project.

MR. CHRISTY: I do not feel that you can set a limit of 50 years on a repayment contract. When we evaluate projects we have to take into consideration the political factors, as well as ability to pay, as there are still undeveloped areas in America which are vast storehouses of natural resources. For example, there are large undeveloped deposits of oil shale and coal in a number of areas.

It seems to me that we cannot set up an ironclad 50-year repayment plan, or anything approaching such a limit, unless we follow through with legislation that will provide for the protection and development of these natural resources that the coming generations are going to need.

MR. MORRIS: The diversion of some power revenues to pay for irrigation has not hitherto been mentioned here. It should be recognized by all that the use of the interest component on power revenues is not a payment by the power users. It is the payment by the federal taxpayers who hire the money. I think that the Collbran formula is even worse in that respect, for it defers repayment so long that the present value of later repayments is even less than the repayment under the diversion of the interest component.[6] Therefore

---

[6] The so-called "interest-component" formula for demonstrating the financial feasibility of irrigation projects uses power revenues in amounts corresponding to the interest costs of the power investment to help repay costs allocated to irrigation. A more recent innovation, the so-called Collbran formula, uses net power revenues collected after the power investment has been repaid to help repay irrigation costs. Both formulae have the effect of providing sizable subsidies to irrigation projects.

those factors tend to mislead the public and the Congress as to how fully self-liquidating these projects are.

MR. HARDING: The Collbran formula has some merit, depending upon its interpretation. It appears to me that its weakness is in not waiting until there is a net revenue. It makes possible expenditures to subsidize other types of development made today, interest free, so that by the time tomorrow's investment has been paid out, there has been a large accumulation of federal costs and deferred interest on the irrigation cost. If the cost of the irrigation units were deferred until the power profits are a reality, there would be much less cost to the Treasury.

MR. SCHEIDENHELM: The money is put up by the taxpayers at a given time, either in the form of actual tax money, or now, most unfortunately, the accumulation of additional debts and interest on those debts. Fifty years reaches well beyond the life expectancy of most of the contributing taxpayers. It is the longest period that should be allowed for repayment.

Comparing Costs of Public and Private Projects

In determining the relative economy of a public project and a private alternative, should the comparison be made on the basis of actual costs under each of the alternatives, or should differences between federal and private cost items be compensated for, particularly by putting interest and taxes on a uniform basis? Discussion, coming at the end of the subsection meeting, was brief; it stayed close to the immediate technical aspects of this problem rather than the broader associated issues. In general, the need for comparability was recognized.

CHAIRMAN'S SUMMARY

This section has examined the major problems of water use and control, has freely discussed the controversial issues of public policy, and has tried to indicate the questions deserving the most careful attention in the decades immediately ahead. Those decades will be a crucial time, not primarily because of prospective increases in the demand for water which do loom large, but because it will see the fixing of major outlines of water development over large areas of the United States.

We have had the wide and long experience of more than 200 persons representative of groups involved in water development. But we cannot offer a simple or even complicated answer to the question of whether or not there will be enough water of the right quality in the right place when it is needed. Do not be misled by easy or pat statements on water supply and demand for the nation as a whole. There is not enough evidence to say accurately how much dependable supply is available in many stream basins and underground aquifers. No one knows from the scattered statistics how much water actually is being used. Estimates of how much water we shall need are at best rough. We do think that large new demands are likely to be made, including heavy increases for irrigation in the humid East.

There is evidence of local areas where ground-water supplies have been "mined" so that they approach exhaustion, and of streams whose flow has been largely or wholly claimed. This does not mean that shortage threatens everywhere or even that the damage of overuse is irreparable in those areas. The one generalization we can safely make about water supply and demand is that each basin is unique with its own special conditions of rock, soil, vegetation, climate, and human use. Each has its own delicate balance of these factors.

At a time when great programs for the development of these streams are underway it is unfortunate that the elementary facts about water resources are still understood so incompletely. Too many project plans are based upon inadequate estimates of the quantity of water that may be expected. Present savings on a small scale in the cost of keeping the essential books on rainfall, stream flow, and ground water spell later waste on a large scale in construction costs.

Certain basic ideas in water development are well recognized: First, the concept of planning and development of water resources by drainage basins—ranging from small watersheds to our major river basins, covering large areas of the nation. Second, the concept of planning river basin developments for all valid multiple purposes. These may be some or all of the following: water supply, navigation, irrigation, drainage, flood control, recreation, pollution control, power, and fish and wildlife. Third, the concept of the interdependence of land and water resources in nature, which requires their consideration together in the process of planning and development.

As we look ahead we see the chief problems of wise water resource development as ones of using an expanded knowledge of the basic resource so as to meet human needs wisely at the suitable time and by methods that will promote healthy economic and political processes.

Some of our ideas of wise use are changing. Thus, the principle of riparian rights to water in the humid East is being challenged by emerging industrial and agricultural uses. Across the continent the concept of clean streams is in controversy: there are those who would in the national interest, fix quality standards by regulation; others would consider the national interest protected if control were applied only to the extent necessary to satisfy the uses required by the communities affected.

There is strong feeling that whatever new works for the development of water resources are undertaken in the future their planning and administration should involve larger participation by state and local agencies and by private interests. This is not to suggest that the federal government should withdraw from its responsibilities. The hope is that the nonfederal groups may enter into a more cooperative part in the job of multiple-purpose development of river basins.

Just how this can be done is not clear. There are no panaceas for the perplexing complexity of agencies, procedures, and coordinating devices by which water plans now are prepared and carried out. Most of the conflicts that plague us are rooted in conflicting federal legislation. Most of these differences in legislative policy grow out of early single-purpose programs under the care of different agencies to serve different interest groups in the nation. Our ideas of what a comprehensive river development in the interest of the people of the basin can be are ahead of our machinery for dealing with it. We need innovations in cooperative administrative arrangements, and while such possibilities as interstate compacts, interagency committees, and mixed federal-state corporations may be noted, other new, imaginative devices must be found. Definition of the public interest in new water undertakings is difficult at points and definition of federal responsibility under the Constitution is controversial.

With a resource that is fixed—unless rainmaking or sea water conversion become practicable—and with a need that is growing in a pattern that is increasingly inflexible, it behooves us to choose our new improvements carefully. We can no longer afford casual choices that commit a region's economic future. Economic evaluation is a tool to help select the most fruitful undertakings. It is an imperfect tool: it should be sharpened to cut finer measurements of benefits—national and local—and it should not be dulled to blur public understanding of benefits, costs, and subsidies involved.

The nation's base of water resources could be so diminished during the next 25 years as to precipitate a series of critical situations. Some ground-water reservoirs could be exhausted, pollution could creep farther along the streams, the land cover of watershed areas could deteriorate further. Major needs for electric power, for cultivable lands, for municipal supplies could go unmet.

There is little reason in the physical facts of the water resource to require that any of this happen. It will take place only as a result of human inadequacy in developing the available resource in advance of crisis need. Americans will have to find out more about the resource, make a better appraisal of needs, and do a more careful job of evaluating the effects of prospective work. Most so-called shortages of water are shortages in human vision and efficiency. Dedication to principle and ingenuity in organization can prevent much of the maladjustment that threatens in the next 25 years. Improvement will be gradual at best: local attitudes, state laws, federal bureaus, and scientific knowledge of stream flow are slow to change. The rate and quality of that change will determine whether a 1978 resources conference can say that the needs have been met at the right time by works that are sound and by methods that promote a healthy society.

GILBERT F. WHITE
December 4, 1953

Section IV

Chairman

EVAN JUST, Vice-President
Cyprus Mines Corporation

Co-Chairman

JOHN VANDERWILT, President
Colorado School of Mines

Steering Committee and Advisers

Steering Committee: CHRISTOPHER M. GRANGER, formerly Assistant Chief, U. S. Forest Service · ROBERT KOENIG, President, Cerro de Pasco Corporation · HAROLD F. MILLS, Manager, Iron King Branch of Shattuck Denn Mining Corporation · DONALD E. MONTGOMERY,* Chief of the Washington Office, United Auto Workers, CIO · W. M. PEIRCE, Technical Assistant, New Jersey Zinc Company · PHILIP J. SHENON, Consulting Geologist · LOUIS WARE, President, International Minerals and Chemical Corporation · NORMAN J. DUNBECK (Alternate for Mr. Ware), Vice-President, Industrial Minerals Division, International Minerals and Chemical Corporation · HOWARD I. YOUNG, President, American Zinc, Lead and Smelting Company · *Assistants to the Section Chairman:* S. G. LASKY, Technical Review Staff, Office of the Secretary, U. S. Department of the Interior; BRUCE C. NETSCHERT, Materials Office, Office of Defense Mobilization · *Section Rapporteurs:* ROBERT H. RAMSEY, Editor, *Engineering and Mining Journal;* HOWARD L. WALDRON, *Mining World*

Major Topics

1. THE CLAIM-PATENT SYSTEM

    Discussion Leaders: EVAN JUST and JOHN VANDERWILT

2. GOVERNMENT PROTECTION AND ASSISTANCE

    Discussion Leader: EVAN JUST

3. FEDERAL TAXES AS APPLIED TO MINING

    Discussion Leader: EVAN JUST

4. NEW TECHNOLOGY

    Discussion Leader: JOHN VANDERWILT

About 125 people participated in the section's work. The 120 who registered formally are listed on pages 394-97. Discussion followed the four main topics suggested by the steering committee. The Claim-Patent System was discussed by the full section on the afternoon of the opening day and by part of the group the following morning, concurrently with Government Protection and Assistance. Taxes and Technology were taken up simultaneously in separate groups the afternoon of the second day, and the full section met again on the morning of the final day to review the rapporteurs' digest of the proceedings.

* In a letter to the chairman, dated November 30, 1953, Mr. Montgomery said that under the time schedule followed he had not been able to review the steering committee paper and therefore wanted it made clear that he accepted no responsibility for it. He did not attend the meeting.

DOMESTIC PROBLEMS
OF NONFUEL MINERALS

PROBLEMS OF SUPPLY OF NONFUEL MINERALS from domestic sources were the chief concern of Section IV. Implicit in all the discussions was the knowledge that the United States cannot expect to supply its huge and still-increasing demands for metals and minerals solely from domestic sources. But there was a firm belief that given the proper incentives the American mining man can and will find and produce a large proportion of the nation's future requirements for metals and minerals, even though he has to go deeper into the earth to find them.

The section steering committee had put it this way: ". . . regardless of what may come our way from abroad, there is the possibility that it may not be enough or that it may not be available on terms that we consider reasonable . . . we should continue to rely on domestic production for a great part of our needs."

The mining industry was well represented and mining men taking part in the discussions expressed every confidence that this challenge can be met if adequate economic and legal provisions are made for working the deeper layers of the earth. Proposals to abolish the limitation on "expensing" of exploration costs received strong support; there were proposals for price subsidies, for tax exemptions during the first few years of operation. However, proposals for major overhauling of the mining laws and suggestions that many in the group felt might endanger the principle of percentage depletion encountered stiff opposition.

The group was in agreement that abuses of the mining laws should be stopped. Some of the participants believed this would require substantial changes in the mining laws; others believed it could be accomplished by better enforcement of the present laws. There was pretty general agreement that the annual $100 assessment work requirement per claim should not be changed, but all agreed that the work should actually be done each year.

Duplicate recording of mining claims was seen by some as a necessary next step in administration of the mining laws; others saw administrative difficulties and questioned whether anything worth while would be accomplished. A number of industry men urged that the burden of proof of the validity of a mining claim should be placed on the claimant.

There was strong support for changing the laws to provide for newer exploration methods, such as geophysical prospecting, and for multiple use of public lands before patenting of claims. But, again, there was little agreement on specific measures.

Because the larger subject of protection versus free trade came up in Section VI (see pages 266-74), this question was taken up only incidentally in the Section IV discussions. Likewise, since problems of research in their broader aspects were dealt with in Section VII (see pages 314-16), these were touched upon in Section IV only when they bore directly on mining matters.

At the concluding session, the criticism was made that the viewpoints of the mining industry had predominated in the section discussions and that other viewpoints had been represented inadequately or not at all. However, there was no quarrel with the fundamental concept of the section discussions, i.e., that the domestic mining industry should be encouraged to meet the ever-increasing demand for metals and minerals. The chairman and members of the steering committee pointed out that if other viewpoints were not represented, it was not because anyone had been barred or discouraged from participating but only because those with other viewpoints had not taken part in the discussions.

Discussion was focused on four main topics: The claim-patent system and whether it should be revised in order to eliminate present abuses and to stimulate use of the newer techniques of exploration; government protection and assistance and what form it should take; federal taxes and how changes might stimulate the mining industry to greater activity; technology and what steps should be taken to bring the newer techniques and scientific approaches into greater play in the mining industry.

Current problems of the industry—high costs, difficulties of finding the deeper deposits now that most of the outcroppings have been probed, the uncertainties of the market—came in for their share of attention. But it was evident from the discussion that the United States is still rich in opportunity for the mining man, even though in the process he becomes, of necessity, as much an earth scientist and an economist as a prospector.

The Claim-Patent System

Does the claim-patent system, as it exists in the laws governing mining activities on public lands, need revision because of present abuses and administrative difficulties or because of a need to encourage exploration, development, and the use of new techniques of discovery?

This general question was broken down by the chairman into the following specific ones: Should the discovery requirement be kept or abolished? Should there be duplicate recording of claims? Should there be multiple use of public lands? Should the assessment work requirement be increased? Should title to a claim be forfeited if no assessment work is done? Should there be dispossession if the use of the surface is not contributory to mineral activity? Should the mining laws be changed to cover new methods of exploration, such as geophysical prospecting? Should there be larger claims with vertical boundaries? Should leasing be optional with the miner?

Examination of these questions included discussion of the feasibility of an over-all review of the mining laws to bring them more nearly into line with the future needs of the industry.

There were frequent references to two bills to amend the mining laws which were before Congress—the Hope bill (H.R. 5358) and the D'Ewart bill (H.R. 4983). Discussion of these bills has been included in the excerpts that follow only where it seemed to bear directly and significantly on the questions before the section.

Comments on the claim-patent system, which was considered by the full section on the first afternoon of the conference and by part of the group on the following morning, have been fitted together as if there had been one continuous discussion. Mr. Just presided at the first meeting, Mr. Vanderwilt at the second.

FROM THE RECORD

Discovery and Recording

Should the discovery requirement be kept or abolished?

PHILIP J. SHENON (Consulting Geologist, Salt Lake City): I would suggest that some modifications be made in the discovery part of the Location Act. In the district that I am most familiar with, the Coeur d'Alene district of Idaho, the ore bodies are deep, and very often exploration work is based solely on structure and rock alteration. Millions of dollars are spent on those two criteria. Shafts are sunk 3,000 feet in some cases to prospect favorable-looking areas. I think alteration and indications of ore by geophysical methods should constitute a satisfactory discovery.

RICHARD W. SMITH (Chamber of Commerce of the United States): I think that the law as it now stands covers such things as hydrothermal alteration. It might not cover structural evidence or indications. Evidence of hydrothermal alteration is evidence of minerals, whereas the structural conditions might not be.

P. R. BRADLEY, JR. (California State Mining Board): I think the problem of definition of discovery is overemphasized. When is it important? The validity of discovery is the problem of adverse claimants in court, and, there, such matters as diligence and continuity of work, time of staking, and good faith have more effect on the decision, the way mining law has developed.

JOHN VANDERWILT (Colorado School of Mines): There are many situations where geologic evidence could be projected into an area, but according to the present definition and requirement of the law, you could not locate without a lode claim.

EVAN JUST (Cyprus Mines Corporation): In the eastern part of the Coeur d'Alene district you have a play going on for deep mineralization; nobody assumes that the ore bodies being sought reach the surface.

Claims are blocked out en masse, so to speak. If the government took a highly critical position it would be hard to justify all of those claims in terms of picture book discoveries, wouldn't it?

MR. SHENON: I dare say that half of them are not strictly legitimate claims. But the alteration is there. The alteration and the structure are the reasons they are spending a million dollars there to look at those claims.

ARTHUR NOTMAN (Magma Copper Company): It seems to me that if geophysical and geological evidence constitute proof of valuable mineral, the location law should be changed to cover that kind of evidence.

L. E. SHAFFER (University of California, Berkeley): With what limitation? Take an outcropping of uranium in the canyon wall.

How far back could you go? Or in tracing the horizon of a bedded deposit, how far back could you legally claim without a discovery? You could tie up a tremendous amount of ground there with no discovery at all. As it stands now 1,500 feet is as far as you can go.

GLOYD M. WILES (National Lead Company): A discovery by geophysics supported by structural alteration in adjacent canyons should support valid locations through a ridge.

MR. SHAFFER: In trying to establish valid claims on uranium outcrops in canyon walls, by the time you make your valid locations and undertake to move back 1,500 feet there are a thousand claims staked around you.

HAROLD F. MILLS (Iron King Branch, Shattuck Denn Mining Corporation): Will findings in a drill hole create a basis for a valid location?

E. D. GARDNER (U.S. Bureau of Mines): The law was passed in 1872, and they didn't have drill holes then.

MR. SHAFFER: According to an interpretation of the law in one of the cases you have to have a minimum-size shaft. The bore hole itself is not enough.

MR. JUST: If we accept the idea of a geological hypothesis as validating a discovery, this would inevitably include the kind of claimant Mr. Shaffer was talking about, would it not?

JAMES BOYD (Kennecott Copper Corporation): That is correct. It would mean changing the law.

Should there be duplicate recording of claims?

MR. JUST: We know, of course, that the Bureau of Land Management and the Forest Service favor double recording and that the traditional position of the mining industry has been against any change in the present law.

MR. SMITH: If duplicate recording required going in person to the nearest local land office or filing that claim in more detail than is required by the local courts, such as a legal description of the land, then it would be a hard-

ship, and I don't think the law should be changed to that extent.

JOHN PAYNE, JR. (American Metal Company Limited): Wouldn't double recording involve a tremendous amount of work, a duplication of work in the government? If the Bureau of Land Management were to do anything with this information it would have to keep it compiled and up to date, corrected and changed. That would be an enormous job. At the local level it is not so difficult.

JOHN H. SIEKER (U.S. Forest Service): The administrators of the public lands ought to know where claims are, and what areas are claimed. Speaking only for the national forests, we have something like 100,000 claims covering over 2 million acres of federal land. It seems to me that the United States, which has title to the land until the miner gets title, ought to know exactly what lands are claimed. As everyone knows, the failure to do assessment work does not void the claim against the United States.

MR. JUST: To what extent would your position be altered if it were made a requirement to have assessment work every year or forfeit a claim in the absence of such work?

MR. SIEKER: That would be very helpful, but I think that would be more of a hardship on some of the small miners than recording their claim.

MR. JUST: What is your view with respect to the administrative costs of double recording?

MR. SIEKER: It would be worth it to know what land was unencumbered in the national forest and what land was subject to a mining claim.

RAYMOND B. HOLBROOK (U.S. Smelting, Refining and Mining Company): I think we should keep in mind that many of these areas are unsurveyed. We can't expect a prospector to carry a transit around and tie these claims in with section corners. But even if you do know where the claim is located, you still don't know the status of the claim. You have to get on the claim to determine that. It would not be a great burden just to place a duplicate copy in the Federal Land Office, but I am very doubtful of its value. I have discussed this matter with people in Utah and Colorado and the impression I got from them is that the job could be handled cheaper and more efficiently by making microfilms of the records in the county offices than by filing duplicates in the Federal Land Office.

JOHN FRENCH (Wyoming Natural Resources Board): In Wyoming, a man will locate a bentonite claim one day, and the next day somebody goes down to Cheyenne and takes out an oil and gas lease on that same piece of property. We have had a number of law suits over that. I think it would be much easier if there were some central way to clear these things.

JOHN A. AMES (The Baltimore and Ohio Railroad Company): In Colorado, where the county seats maintain records in mining districts, there would be no difficulty in making duplicates of the records for about 95 percent of the claims, because the mining districts are old and are surveyed.

MR. BRADLEY: If there were any sort of a legal contest, I am rather sure that the written description would have no standing whatever. You have to remember that it is the actual location of the claim on the ground that counts. I certainly wouldn't recommend that the validity of a claim be subject to mailing a description to a federal office.

Should there be multiple use of the land until the land is patented, if the mineral claimant is first?

MR. FRENCH: I definitely am not in favor of multiple use of the land under the leasing act. We have a few coal mine operators in southern Wyoming. A lot of that coal is leased from the federal government. About the only thing an operator can do is sell his coal and meet his payroll. Somebody in the front office tells him how he is going to mine the coal and where he is going to mine it.

HORACE M. ALBRIGHT (U.S. Potash Company): Leases for oil, phosphate, and potash have been in use for 25 years without that kind of experience. Grazing takes place on top of the ground, and mining for minerals on top of mining for oil. That may be the solution in the long run.

MR. HOLBROOK: Public Law 250 provided that certain mining claims located after January 1, 1939 and before January 1, 1953 may be validated subject to the rights of claimants under the Mineral Leasing Act. It was merely stop-gap legislation. The principal claims involved were the uranium claims on the Colorado plateau.

LEWIS E. HOFFMAN (Bureau of Land Management): Those claims were declared invalid by our Department because they were made on lands covered by existing oil and gas leases.

However, the Atomic Energy Commission and the public generally want to see this uranium produced and the claims validated so that the discoverers can get the benefit of their discoveries and the country will get the benefit of the minerals.

But the bill itself went beyond merely atomic energy minerals. It went far in the direction of obtaining multiple use—mining of both leasable minerals and nonleasable minerals on the same ground.

MR. VANDERWILT: I favor multiple use. If we need uranium I favor permitting exploration for it wherever it can be found, even though the lands are covered by oil and gas leases. If we need petroleum, I favor permitting exploration for petroleum wherever it may be found, irrespective of the fact that the lands are covered by mining claims.

MR. HOLBROOK: Multiple use is a term that the mining industry has become quite shy of. Within limits, I think it is quite all right. There was a period of years when it had such a connotation that all you had to do was refer to multiple use and some mining people were terribly exercised.

MR. HOFFMAN: I think multiple use can be worked out. If it can, it will be a boon both to the miner and the lessee.

MR. HOLBROOK: As the law now stands, you can't make a valid location in any area that is under federal oil and gas leases, and in some states great areas have been blanketed with such leases. This problem is acute, because it is interfering with uranium production.

Assessment Work

Should the assessment work requirement be raised?

MR. JUST: One reason advanced for raising the requirement is that when it was enacted the dollar bought vastly more than it does today.

WILLIAM C. BROADGATE (Arizona State Department of Mineral Resources): We made quite a study of that about four or five years ago and came up with a figure that scared us to death. I think the proper economic figure turned out to be some 700-odd dollars per claim.

MR. HOLBROOK: Obviously the $100 requirement would have to be increased considerably to be comparable to what it was when the mining laws were established. But the amount of work is not the real principle involved. The work is only an evidence of good faith, which is the real test.

CHRISTOPHER M. GRANGER (formerly U.S. Forest Service): I think I would agree that it is not important whether a man spends $100 or $500 a year on his claim, if he can show that he has a real discovery of a mineral which a prudent man would feel justified in developing for commercial purposes.

MR. HOLBROOK: In 16 or 17 of the last 20 years Congress has suspended all requirements. The mining industry has opposed this; it has felt that the work should be done as a matter of good faith.

ALLEN L. HEARST (Philadelphia): In the interests of the mining industry, if we maintain the $100 limit per claim, it should be pointed out that there has been a terrific abuse in filing. I can show you many instances where

the actual work done was probably less than 10 percent of the amount reported.

MR. GARDNER: The responsible companies do the full amount of assessment work required by law each year, but many prospectors file an assessment certificate without doing the full $100 for each claim.

Should titles be forfeited if no assessment work is done?

MR. HOLBROOK: If you have automatic forfeiture, how are you going to determine who has the title to a claim? Suppose everything looks regular, but 10 years ago a fellow just did not do his work. There has not been any adverse location and there is no real question about the claim, but still one year the work wasn't done. If we change the law so that failure to do assessment work automatically forfeits the claim, we are certainly borrowing a lot of title problems.

MR. SHENON: On the other hand, I know of one case where a mining company bought a claim from three different parties because they were afraid of the title.

MR. GRANGER: A man may have allowed his assessment work to lapse for 15 years, but if the government—in the national forest, for example—wants to go in and grant surface rights to that land for any kind of development, to sell timber on it, allow its use for grazing, or build a road across it, the title is still held by the claimant as against the government and they cannot allow any of those uses without his consent.

W. M. PEIRCE (New Jersey Zinc Company, New York): I got the impression at the recent meeting of the Mining Congress in Seattle that if there were adequate administration of existing laws perhaps the majority of these claims which appear to interfere with the administration of the public domain could be cleared off the books.

MR. GRANGER: Theoretically, that is true. But in reality, it is a slow process to have a claim declared invalid—and an expensive one. In view of the some 100,000 unpatented claims on the national forests it would be quite a job, if we relied on that alone.

MR. HOFFMAN: Enforcement would mean the examination of every mining claim in existence by a competent engineer to determine whether it is being put to uses other than mining. That would be a task beyond the scope of any governmental agency at the present time. We have 11 mining engineers to cover the 11 western states. So we limit our activities to enforcement of the law where a patent is being applied for and to the investigation of claims where another governmental agency has other uses of the land. It took us five years to investigate claims on land needed for the Murock Bombing Range in California. But we saved the government possibly $50 million to $100 million, that otherwise would have had to be paid out on claims that our investigation showed to be invalid.

It would take a tremendous amount of money and a tremendous amount of personnel to see that everybody who makes a claim has done so validly and in good faith.

MR. GARDNER: If I locate a claim on a new discovery, I should also want to locate protection claims at the same time. I would then be protected during the time it took to make legal discoveries on the adjoining claims. I should think most decidedly that the mining industry does not want investigations of all mining claims, as long as they do not interfere with other rights.

MR. HOFFMAN: The courts have recognized in a good many decisions that a miner is entitled to a reasonable period to make a discovery or get off the land.

MR. JUST: What about a limitation on the number of years a man can hold an unpatented claim without doing any assessment work?

MR. NOTMAN: It is common practice for large mining companies to do the assessment work regularly. I don't know why the individual should escape from the same obligation.

NORMAN J. DUNBECK (International Minerals and Chemical Corporation): I would favor some limitation. If someone makes a contract with the government and fails to live up to it, why should he continue to have possessory rights? There are too many of these old filings cluttering up mining districts.

MR. PAYNE: In my opinion, if a man does not do his assessment work and does not record it, the government should not have to go to the expense and trouble of proving its case against him. Certainly there should be a limit on how long he can hold his claim if he does not do and record his assessment work—I would say three years at the outside.

MR. HOLBROOK: I am sure that the mining industry would be happy to explore this. I have discussed the question of automatic forfeiture with some of the best title attorneys in the intermountain area, and they have been quite concerned with the problems that may be involved.

MR. ALBRIGHT: I don't want anybody to think I am advocating abandoning the mining laws and going to leasing, but if you have an oil lease you have to do something with that lease within a certain length of time or lose it. It has worked for something over 20 or 25 years going along parallel with the mining laws. If we mining fellows don't work out this problem ourselves, it may be worked out for us in a way we don't like.

MR. BRADLEY: Is it easy to reclassify land —declare it to be nonmineral? If so, why isn't it done?

MR. SIEKER: It is not an easy process. It is easier to have the claim declared invalid if it is in fact invalid. You can't say simply because John Jones does not have a valid discovery that the land is nonmineral in character.

MR. JUST: It seems to me that we are asking for trouble in the mining industry if we are urging the Bureau of Land Management to go around declaring parcels of land to be nonmineral.

MR. BRADLEY: I am not urging that it be done as a general thing; I am urging that it be done when it should be done. Most of the present-day difficulties that we hear of are where people try to take timber and so on by staking mineral claims because they have no other way of getting it.

ROBERT KOENIG (Cerro de Pasco Corporation): I think this discussion raises very broad issues. The law on which the mining industry is based was passed in 1872. There have been great changes in mining technology, and great changes in our country as a whole in the intervening 81 years.

It is agreed that the original law was a very good one, because it resulted in a great mining industry in this country. That doesn't necessarily mean it is the sort of law under which the mining industry of the United States should operate in the future.

It seems to me that the advent of such tools in the finding of ore as geophysics and geochemistry changes the whole picture of prospecting and mine exploration and development work.

Perhaps the time has come to get to grips with the problem and perhaps make some changes in the mining laws in such a way that the concessionaire principle, or one more or less like the leasing of land which Mr. Albright mentioned, is adopted, so that affirmative evidence of having done a certain amount of work per unit of time, per unit of land, would be a condition precedent to the maintaining of whatever right may be granted under the law to do further exploration or to obtain patent.

MR. BOYD: I agree. We are trying to solve a tiny piece of the problem instead of looking at it broadly in all its effect. If you put in a geophysical claim, you still have the problem of how to maintain your rights to the claim that you have. I think it is time the whole thing be reviewed so that prospecting can be put on a sounder basis than it is today as far as public land is concerned.

MR. NOTMAN: I would like to endorse those views, too.

MR. PAYNE: We are dealing today with an entirely different situation than that which

existed in 1872 when we were looking for mineral which outcropped at the surface and could be identified. The problems in the future are going to be even more difficult.

MR. HOLBROOK: I think we should keep in mind that age alone should not be any criterion in determining whether the mining law is good or bad; on the other hand we must recognize the necessity of meeting changed conditions and keeping abreast of the times.

I think there are many features of our laws that have grown in stature with the years. If there is any place where you need the security and value of long precedence, it is in property law.

JULIAN D. CONOVER (American Mining Congress): What would be the nature of the basic changes that would be proposed?

MR. KOENIG: I was thinking in broad, general terms. I don't think this is the time to discuss the technique of how to do it. The general scheme that I have in mind, that I personally favor, is one that would make it considerably more interesting for private enterprise to engage in exploration and development work in the United States. We all know there are many areas in the mineralized districts of the United States that have been sat on for years by individual claimholders who are not doing any work on them and who, by one means or another, are able to retain title.

MR. CONOVER: I think there is no question that everybody is in full sympathy with those objectives. The question is whether it is necessary to replace our whole structure of laws, or whether the objective cannot be obtained by supplementing the laws which have become so well established. For instance, we already have been discussing some of the answers to the problem of the idle claims.

HOWARD L. WALDRON (*Mining World*): There are a number of problems that all seem to run to a common point, and they seem to deal with our mining laws as they stem, first, from the Mining Act of 1872 and the revisions and corrections of that law, and, second, from the vast, complex body of legal decisions that has been handed down over the period of these 81 or so years.

The best solution might be to rewrite the mining law in a modern sense. There are a number of serious weaknesses in this entire body of mining law. One of them is its extreme complexity. Another is that it is open to abuse, for instance, on this matter of surface rights. A third important weakness is that it in effect invites litigation, mainly because the burden of proof in the case of an invalid claim usually settles down to the Bureau of Land Management; I think the burden of proof belongs with the miner. Finally, another serious weakness of the law is that it doesn't take into account the modern and future aspects of mining, the encouragement of mining.

I don't mean that the old laws should be discarded. I suggest only that the whole body of law be brought up to date.

MR. PEIRCE: It seems to me that if we attempt to decide that the entire mining law ought to be rewritten then we might just as well adjourn because we are not in any position to discuss so broad a subject.

MR. GRANGER: There are one or two major points that might be further clarified. For example: Should there be any limitation on the time a man may hold a claim without applying for patent? Should the claimant be allowed automatically to acquire title to the timber on the claim which he doesn't need for its operation, without paying for it?

MR. CONOVER: I don't see that we have reached the point where we are prepared to say that the basic mining laws of the United States are obsolete. Let me say that if there is any great virtue in a property law it is the fact that it *is* old and has been construed and defined by many decisions. Any time you make any change in any law relating to property, particularly a major revision, it may be years and years before we know just how those laws are going to be construed. I don't want to imply that we can't approach these problems and work out a solution.

MR. SIEKER: Let me make clear that the Department of Agriculture wants to encourage the production of minerals and the discovery of minerals in this country. But the Department also recognizes that there are other values in these mountain areas. Water is one of them. Timber is another. Recreation is another. Wildlife is another. The Department believes that the public lands should be managed for all of those values, not for minerals only.

Under the present mining laws, mineral is the only thing covered; you can file a mining claim and get $25,000 or $30,000 worth of standing timber—timber worth much more perhaps than the minerals.

The Department of Agriculture does not believe that the mere discovery of minerals entitles a person to all the timber in addition to the minerals. It does believe that it entitles the claimant to possession of the minerals and the right to develop them and produce them.

MR. BOYD: I think we are all agreed, fundamentally, that the basic concepts of the mining laws, whereby a man, by location, can obtain the rights to that land, should not be tampered with. But you need to modernize those laws to bring you in tune with modern conditions. Perhaps we can get agreement on that philosophy. Then the details can fit into it.

MR. SHENON: I agree. I don't believe that any of us in the mining business want to give up the security of the basic mining law.

MR. BOYD: You are changing one concept of the law if you recognize that discovery is not necessarily the criterion for maintaining rights to the land; that doing the work on it is what maintains that right.

Should there be dispossession if the use of the surface is not contributory to mineral activity?

MR. SIEKER: We have a great number of mining claims on the national forests. Many are probably valid claims. A number of the claims have been in existence for 15 or 20 years. No mineral development has ever taken place, yet a cabin on the claim is used continuously as a summer home, or a residence for the miner and his friends. That is a very difficult case because the mining laws allow a miner to have a cabin for mining purposes. It is not a commercial use. Other people who do not use that device have to pay $25 or $30 a year and they cannot get a cabin exactly where they want it, perhaps right along a fishing stream, and keep other people from fishing on that stream.

Mr. HOLBROOK: As I get the picture, here is an unpatented claim; the man has an adequate discovery on it, but he doesn't intend to use it for mining purposes. If the D'Ewart bill were passed I think this fellow would lose a lot of interest in having that as a summer home; if he knew a road could be put right across his front yard and sheep or cattle may be grazed on the claim.

The difference between the D'Ewart and Hope bills, as I understand it, is this: Under the D'Ewart bill there is a definite reservation that the government or its permitees can't use the claim in a way that will interfere with mining. In the Hope bill all the control and regulation is left in the Department. I think that is the principal difference. In the D'Ewart bill, after patent the miner would get complete title, absolute title, which I think mining people feel is imperative. There would be a qualification with respect to the timber under the Hope bill.

Mr. SIEKER: Yes, but the mining claimant could purchase the timber upon patenting and have a fee simple title.

Mr. HOLBROOK: Of course, the mining industry wants to get away from these abuses. They are hurting the industry. Many of these phony claims do not have a valid discovery.

Mr. GRANGER: We have felt that authority should be vested in some administrative officer to determine that a particular claim contains such low mineral values that it would be against the public interest to develop it in the light of other and presumably higher values of the public lands in that particular location. For example, to prevent somebody going in and locating a low-value gold mine or some other mineral in a wilderness area, or in the heart of a very valuable recreational area, or in similar situations where the public values would seem to be much higher in other elements than in the mineral development of that particular site. I realize the problems involved, but it does seem an anomaly in this age and day that on the basis of a very low-value discovery the mining claim is given the complete right-of-way over any other values, no matter how high they may be.

Mr. CONOVER: The Hope bill is not a suitable answer. It provides discretionary authority to say whether the "deposits"—and it uses the word "deposits," which is a new term and has never been legally construed— are or are not sufficient to justify further development. That could very conceivably have been used to stop the development of the Utah Copper Mine, which is our greatest copper producer.

Mr. GRANGER: Of course a determination of the kind I speak about would have to be exercised with a great deal of prudence. I don't hold a brief for the specific language in the bill, but this problem, I think, needs recognition. You know there are placer mines that produce low-value gold, for example, but they skin hell out of the country.

Mr. HOLBROOK: The trouble is, if you make these things too expedient they become very arbitrary at times.

Mr. SIEKER: I think we all recognize that the mining law at present is favorable to mining. There are no real limitations. The miner may file a claim and if he has a valid discovery it sets up mining as the highest use for that land.

New Methods of Exploration

Should the mining laws be amended to cover new methods of exploration?

Mr. HOLBROOK: There are two problems here. Do you want to create a new type of claim, a geophysical claim or exploratory claim, or do you just want to enlarge by statutory definition what should constitute a sufficient discovery? We don't have in the law a definition of "discovery."

MR. HOFFMAN: Although the law itself doesn't define a discovery, the United States Supreme Court time and time again has said that the test of a valid discovery—which would mean a valid mining claim—is whether a reasonable person would be warranted to spend his time and money in further exploration work.

The courts have also upheld the validity of mining claims even where there wasn't actual discovery on the land itself, because the claim is in a mining district and there are operating and paying mines in adjoining lands.

If you amended the law so that an individual or group of individuals can explore an area by plane, say, and they find indications of valuable minerals, what would stop another person from recording a mining claim on the same land?

MR. BROADGATE: I happen to be the author of the proposed Geological and Geophysical Mining Claims Act of 1947. The general theory behind this bill was to lay out adequate tracts of land which could be temporarily located, after which the geophysical work could be done. If within a certain period of time a showing were made to the Department of the Interior that geophysical work actually warranted further physical work, such as core drilling, the life of the claim would be extended. Eventually, if the physical work showed a mineral discovery, the geophysical claims could be resolved into regular mining claims. That was the general principle of the bill. It does not disturb the ordinary and orderly process of the old mining law. It provides for an entirely new type and group of claims. However, hearings were never held.

MR. HOFFMAN: Where minerals are apt to be in the ground, the chances are that there already are a considerable number of mining locations of which we have no record but which are recorded in the county recorder's office.

I think modern science and modern methods ought to be recognized in exploration work.

But we have to work out these difficulties. Are you going to withdraw large areas for the use of exploration? What are you going to do with existing mining claims in those areas? What are you going to do with existing oil and gas leases, potassium and phosphate leases? What are you going to do with timber areas?

MR. BROADGATE: We felt that if a company were given the opportunity to stake this sort of claim, it would have to take the initiative in looking over the area ahead of time and in coming to some conclusion with respect to any existing rights within that area. It would be the company's problem. In other words, if you ran a 2,500-acre geophysical claim and you had not already ascertained that John Jones had two valid mining claims within that area, you would merely be doing work to his benefit.

But you may be able to come to some conclusion with John Jones, just as a railroad would have to do in setting forth a right-of-way. You could not eliminate those claims by any law.

MR. HOFFMAN: I realize the merits of the bill; I also realize what a headache it would be administratively.

MR. BROADGATE: Nevertheless, you can't let administrative troubles stand in the way of progress.

Should there be larger claims with vertical boundaries?

MR. HEARST: It is common practice for an individual, when he locates a claim, to locate at least one on either side and one on either end of his discovery for his own protection.

MR. HOLBROOK: The theory of extralateral rights is that if a fellow starts working down a vein, it is more practical for him to continue his operation than it is for the owner of another claim to sink a deep shaft and intercept the vein at the boundary and work it from there. For the most part, when such a situation occurs nowadays, people just get together and settle it.

MR. BROADGATE: We made a study of this situation in connection with the geophysical prospecting bill, and came to the conclusion that in general the extralateral rights should be undisturbed, at least until geophysical prospecting comes into greater vogue.

MR. GARDNER: In all the big mining camps the companies have vertical side line agreements, so the question has become more or less academic there. I do not believe it is of very much importance at the moment, one way or the other.

MR. HOFFMAN: If you enlarged the area of the claim from 20 to 40 acres, with vertical boundaries, there would still be the possibility that a vein might run outside the boundary. Moreover, there is no limitation on the number of claims a miner can locate.

MR. BROADGATE: I think nothing would be gained by changing the situation as regards extralateral rights when it comes to the present class of mining claim. But in setting up a new type of claim for the geophysical work, there might be an area for discussion regarding extralateral rights. I think the matter should be left open.

Leasing

Should leasing be optional with the claimant?

MR. DUNBECK: I think the word "optional" is extremely important. Leases have worked well in other areas. They have worked because there was no other choice. There was no other way of obtaining the property. If the miner had his choice he might prefer something other than leases.

MR. HOFFMAN: Whether you use the word "optional" or otherwise, the minute you change the mining law even in this limited way, you are destroying the very essence of what the mining law gives to the small miner.

The mining laws need certain reforms and changes to avoid abuses, but none of us wants to change the principle underlying the U.S. mining laws—that is, the right of a citizen to go on public domain and make a discovery and get title to the land. The minute you talk about leasing you destroy that principle.

MR. CONOVER: The mining industry is very leery of any proposals that undermine the basic principles.

Government Protection and Assistance

Various methods have been employed by the United States Government to assist the domestic mining industry—floor price contracts with purchase guarantees, subsidies in the form of premium prices, accelerated amortization of capital investment for tax purposes, loans. Proposed steps include a sliding-scale tariff and import quotas.

To date, government assistance to mining has been limited for the most part to periods of national emergency. What is the best system for the long pull? The chairman pointed out that this subject had been proposed by the steering committee "more or less on the assumption that some kind of protection would be extended to the domestic mining industry by the federal government."

The session dealt with means of assistance other than tax changes, which were treated as a separate subject by the section.

Discussion in the main concerned subsidies of various kinds and tariffs. One idea put forward was to combine the two, using revenue from the tariff as a subsidy. Another proposal involved government-guaranteed "economic prices" for specific metals and minerals and government stockpiling to take up any surplus that developed.

A recurring damper during the discussion was the idea that government assistance tends to lead to government regulation. Nobody was for that.

FROM THE RECORD

General Assistance

MR. JUST: We are not undertaking here to discuss protection versus free trade since that subject is being considered by Section VI [see pages 266-74]. What we are concerned with is trying to develop the best means of protecting the domestic industry. The alternatives would appear to be these: a sliding-scale tariff, direct subsidies, government purchase programs, and import quotas. I think maybe the first one to bring up is quotas. [There was no discussion of quotas.] I take it then, we can assume that quotas are not within the scope of interest of this group, at least.

SAMUEL H. WILLISTON (American Mining Congress): Is the purpose here to develop a policy based on no war, a hot war, or an intermediate condition?

MR. JUST: To lay a groundwork for discussion here, we have to try to design a peacetime program that is somewhat stiffer on the defense side than if we were just looking forward to the lion and the lamb lying down together.

———

Mr. Payne suggested a subsidy arrangement under which an "economic price" for various metals would be determined by industry-wide committees; if the market price fell below the economic price, the government would pay the domestic producer half the difference, and the government would stockpile a portion of the domestic production of the metal being subsidized. Mr. Payne emphasized that he was not advocating subsidies but was proposing what he considered to be the "lesser of two evils" if it were determined that the domestic mining industry needed assistance.

Mr. Williston proposed a tariff-financed subsidy. Under this arrangement there would be an ad valorem tariff of 10 percent for all imported metals and ores, and the proceeds from the tariff would be paid to the domestic producers of those ores in accordance with the amount of metal they produced. The more metal imported, the greater the total subsidy and vice versa.

———

MR. JUST: There are a lot of practical people who doubt that Congress would pass a nondiscriminatory or across-the-board subsidy.

STANLEY H. RUTTENBERG (Congress of Industrial Organizations): On the other hand, Congress has maintained both discriminatory and nondiscriminatory subsidies in the agricultural field for many years.

MR. BOYD: If you had a subsidy, you would have to have production controls, and that would mean as many planners in Washington as miners in the field.

MR. BRADLEY: I suggest that the problems of control are greater than the problems that would be created by stockpiling.

MR. RUTTENBERG: A tariff is a subsidy. Do those who believe in demand and supply as a good sound economic theory, believe in it only to the extent that it applies to the domestic market and not to the world market? Tariffs violate the basic concept of the law of supply and demand.

MR. NOTMAN: I certainly don't believe in that law merely for domestic production.

MR. RUTTENBERG: Then why have tariffs?

MR. NOTMAN: I am not for them.

JOHN D. MORGAN, JR. (Office of Defense Mobilization): In a peacetime economy the best way to increase the supply is to increase the demand. If prices are low the producers should stimulate new uses. Research on new applications has greatly expanded the use of some materials.

MR. SHENON: I am sure that as far as lead and zinc are concerned no one is going to look very hard for these metals at the present time. It seems to me that the environment must be improved. No mining company is going to spend a million or two to look for lead and zinc deposits at 10-cent zinc, which is equivalent to about 3⅓ cents a few years ago.

LEWIS W. DOUGLAS [who attended the meeting briefly]: What is the purpose of discussing all of these alternative methods of deceptively providing gratuities?

MR. JUST: To encourage production of domestic minerals, anticipating our expanding requirements.

MR. DOUGLAS: Isn't the price mechanism on the whole a fairly good device?

MR. WILLISTON: It certainly is. On the other hand, I know of no metals being produced from underground mines in the United States that can compete as far as cost is concerned with foreign production except molybdenum.

MR. DOUGLAS: Much of the copper production can compete with foreign copper production.

HOWARD I. YOUNG (American Zinc, Lead and Smelting Company): We should have a program so the industry can plan ahead. We have to plan 5 or 10 years ahead and it is a most difficult job to do. A year ago you were planning for certain things 5 years ahead. Today, you have probably reduced those estimates by 25 or 50 percent until you can see a little bit clearer what the government policy is going to be on the various things that we think the domestic industry needs if we are going to survive. I don't want to see a subsidy. I will tell you that frankly.

ROBERT B. McCORMICK (Department of Defense): Mr. Young, do you consider a tariff on metals of foreign origin a subsidy to domestic industry?

MR. YOUNG: No, sir, I do not. The reason that we got tariffs originally was to develop American industry. Now we have come down on the tariffs. Today we have a national debt we have got to meet, and the only way that is going to be met is by national production and national profits, and we have got to have an industry protected to an extent that they can still maintain the high wages that we are required to pay to compete with other industries.

Government-assisted Exploration

Discussion dealt in large part with the government's program of assistance in exploration for metals and minerals as administered by the Defense Minerals Exploration Administration.

MR. BOYD: At the time the DMEA program was started, exploration needed to be stimulated because of the world situation; we didn't see any opportunity of getting the tax question solved within a reasonable length of time, and we had to provide some artificial stimulus in the meantime.

We tried to establish that program in such a way that the government would be taking part of the risk in really risky exploration projects. But expenditure of government funds is of necessity conservative, and on at least one or two occasions the government has turned down the long chance that you or I, if we had a good position, would certainly take even on private money.

MR. WILLISTON: I think the bulk of the mining industry feels that permission to completely expense exploration and development costs [on tax returns] would be far more of an incentive to exploration than a government participation program.

MR. BRADLEY: I think there is a word to be said for the little fellow who is out in the hills trying to do prospecting. He can use government aid, has to have it, in fact, whereas many corporations may not need it so badly.

MR. YOUNG: I lean toward giving the little fellow help. This little fellow may go out and develop an important ore body.

MR. MILLS: As to stimulating exploration through tax reduction, in our part of the country the little fellow does need government help, and, conversely, he is in the position that he doesn't have to worry about taxes.

MR. NOTMAN: I would see no objection, Mr. Chairman, to allowing the training and experience and proven capacities of the Survey and the Bureau of Mines some leeway in conducting long-range exploration on things that they thought were worth while which private industry had not shown any disposition to explore. But so far as setting up any new, or continuing any existing, emergency organization for doing that sort of thing, I would be completely against it.

MR. WILLISTON: My feeling is that it should be done rarely and, if possible, not at all.

Tax Changes

Would there be more exploration for metals and minerals and consequently a greater production potential in the United States, if additional tax concessions were provided for mining enterprises? Would this be the incentive to bring out new investment capital and ultimately help the nation to meet more of its mineral requirements from domestic sources?

The answer of mining men participating in the discussion was a firm "yes." Discussion turned on what tax changes would do the most good or would stand the best chance of getting Congressional approval rather than on whether a tax arrangement more favorable to the industry is needed. A number of participants said that any immediate loss to the Treasury as a result of reduced taxes on the mining industry would be more than made up in the long run as the result of greater mining activity.

There was strong support for abolition of the $75,000 limitation on deductions for exploration expenses. Beyond that, there was no firm unanimity among the mining men. A number of participants warned against seeking changes in the tax laws that might endanger the system of percentage depletion under which mining enterprises are permitted to write off a portion of their profits to compensate for the depletion of mineral deposits. (See Section V, pages 214-15 and 243-45, for discussions of percentage depletion as applied to the oil and coal industries.)

There was considerable discussion of the way mining taxation is handled in Canada. Several contended that the Canadian system is much more favorable to mining than the United States system; others thought it would not work well in this country.

FROM THE RECORD

Deduction for Exploration Costs

MR. JUST: We have written our basic paper with the concept in mind that spurs should be given to domestic mineral exploration and development over the long term in view of what seems to many a tendency of exploration and development to lag in this country. At the same time, we anticipate gradually increasing requirements due to population growth and increased per capita consumption.

Many persons feel that we ought to develop the full use of tax benefits before resorting to other devices.

Does anybody here object to the principle of affording certain tax concessions to stimulate mineral exploration and development? Does anybody feel that they have already gone too far? Apparently not.

Should the present $75,000 limitation on the expensing of exploration costs be removed? As far as I know, the principle has broad industry endorsement, and the President's Materials Policy Commission came out flatly for removing the limitation. Where do we stand?

MR. NOTMAN: I can't see why there should be a limit. The idea is to pay no income taxes until you have some profits, and you can't have any profits until you get some money back. The limitation amounts to a definition of profits on the part of the Bureau of Internal Revenue, or the senators and representatives who framed the Act.

MR. BOYD: The principle is either correct or it isn't. If it is, it should not be limited.

MR. JUST: Doesn't the oil industry enjoy unlimited opportunity to expense this item?

WILLIAM I. POWELL (American Mining Congress, Washington, D.C.): It is not that simple. They have an option either to expense or to capitalize certain expenditures for drilling and development. You can't say that they have an open-end choice to expense their entire exploratory expenditures.

GEORGE MIXTER (United States Smelting, Refining and Mining Company): Also, the oil industry has the opportunity to expense so-called intangible costs, such as labor costs and other things that don't have a salvage value.

MR. YOUNG: Today the costs of developing ore reserves are much higher than they have ever been before. On the whole the outcrops are gone, and we have to spend a lot more money for drilling and going down to a greater depth. Looking forward to developing resources for the future, we must do the job and at the same time anticipate increasing costs as we go ahead. We should be permitted to deduct whatever it costs and not be limited by any given amount.

MR. BOYD: I agree.

MR. JUST: The industry position through many years has been that the attitude of the Treasury in limiting allowances of this type was to some extent self-defeating. There is a strong feeling of informed people in the mineral industry that the ultimate revenue would be much enhanced by encouraging development in the mineral industry.

MR. BOYD: I think it might be well to raise the question with the Treasury Department whether the cost of replacing reserves obtains full consideration in the calculation of the tax payments of any corporation or the mining industry as a whole.

Obviously, up to now, we have not charged off and haven't any way to charge off the cost of finding against the income received in the extraction of the ore itself. It is discrimination.

MR. NOTMAN: There are no profits until you get the capital back, and any taxation that pretends to be taxation of profits should be limited to what are profits.

I think the Treasury would get more money from the mining industry, if they gave us a chance to get our money back before they started taxing us. I am sure of it on the record of Canada; there has been no time in history and no place on the map where risk capital has had a better chance than it has had in Canada in the last 50 years, and the results are obvious.

I don't think there are many in Congress who really understand the unique position of a wasting-asset industry.

MR. JUST: You believe that we should extend this concept to the simple proposition that a mineral taxpayer should be permitted to recoup his investment before his income becomes taxable?

MR. NOTMAN: Absolutely. Under the Canadian system, the industry has profited tremendously and the country has profited. And they are in a far more favorable position from the standpoint of having places to look, because they still have a wide frontier that is unscratched, whereas we are constantly confronted with the increasing cost of looking.

Everything we do from here out is going to cost more until somebody comes along with something that you can see into the ground with.

MR. MIXTER: I would hate very much to see anything that we say here react unfavorably on the oil industry, but I think that their setup does have some logic.

MR. POWELL: It would be a great boon to the mining industry to have the $75,000 limitation and the 4-year limitation removed.

WILLIAM S. PALEY (Columbia Broadcasting System): It seems to be obvious that people exploring for oil and developing oil have a more attractive incentive than the people who explore for minerals and develop minerals. And more money and energy have gone into finding and developing oil than have gone into finding and developing ore. There might be a very close correlation between the incentive to find ore and the incentive to find oil, and the results in each field.

MR. JUST: If we should foster the concept that the industry should get its capital back before profits become taxable, wouldn't percentage depletion go out the window?

I think we can state as a principle that we all believe the mining industry should not be taxed on the recoupment of its investment as income, and we would all like to see Congress further that principle. It does not seem to me, however, that we are in position here to discuss details.

MR. BOYD: I am inclined to think that if the exploration expense limitations were removed, we probably would have achieved the incentive that we need as far as taxes are concerned, at least for the time being.

Depletion Allowance

MR. POWELL: We certainly wouldn't like to see anything disturb the concept of percentage depletion. It has been established in the law long enough to prove that it is worth while. It is a recognition of a well-established principle that capital should not be taxed as income.

Percentage depletion also helps create a fund for use in searching for another mine so that, as you deplete one mine and take your depletion allowance, you accumulate further capital and ready money to go out and look for another one. That is the only way mining can exist.

MR. PALEY: But if you ask for return of all capital investment before you pay any taxes, then you undermine the foundation on which your depletion allowance theory rests. I think it is a very dangerous concept.

There was further comment on the tax question when the full section met the morning of December 4 to review the rapporteurs' digest of discussions during the previous two days.

MR. RUTTENBERG [Who had not been present during the main discussion on taxes]: A subsidy is a subsidy by whatever name it may be called.

Depletion allowances, tax exemptions, or elimination of the $75,000 limitation on exploration and development cost the taxpayers money; they involve the whole principle of consumer costs and consumer involvement.

In the first place, a depletion allowance is something that is totally unseen and unknown to the consumer; he has no way of knowing what the cost will be because the actual amount allowed varies from year to year depending on the profits. But a premium price plan, for example, is direct, open, and aboveboard; it is known in advance what it is going to cost. Secondly, a depletion allowance reduces taxation, total revenue of the federal government, a loss that has to be supplanted by raising revenue from other sources to end up with the same amount of revenue. I am fully aware of the arguments that by granting greater depletion allowances and by giving tax exemption for the first three and a half years, as in Canada, or by doing certain other things to encourage investment expansion and exploration and research, there will be a greater industry expansion, greater profits, and consequently more tax income to the government.

But this argument can be made for any tax concession. I, as an individual and as a representative of a labor organization, am as much interested in the welfare of the domestic mining industry as those of you who represent the business side of the industry. Our unions have membership in some of your mines. Accordingly, if this industry needs aid and assistance —and I am convinced that it does—for exploration, research, and development, it ought to receive such aid directly, open and aboveboard, through such things as premium payment plans, price subsidies, stockpiles, discriminatory or nondiscriminatory subsidies. But whatever it is, it ought to be open so that all can see it, and it ought not to take the form of tariffs, depletion allowances, tax exemptions, or raising the limitations on exploration deductions.

Elimination of depletion allowance does not reduce by a single penny what you can deduct for the actual costs of exploration which you engage in, nor any actual amortization or depreciation of your normal plant and equipment. These are permitted under normal tax laws. Depletion allowances, as we all know, are over and above these normal deductions, the only limitation being the $75,000 on exploration costs.

MR. JUST [Comment submitted after the Conference]: Mr. Ruttenberg's remarks were made during a review period when rebuttal was not appropriate. I believe that the following points should be considered:

First, to state that depletion allowances are not open and aboveboard is somewhat prejudicial. They have not been obtained behind the scenes. At least twice during the Roosevelt Administration they were a highly publicized target for Administration attack. Also, they are sufficiently technical that the general public is hardly likely to take an interest under any circumstance, as would also be true of a direct subsidy involving as small a group as mining.

Second, the depletion allowance has a sound basis in recognized accounting procedure. It can hardly be disputed that a valuable mineral deposit is a capital asset and that revenue attributable to liquidation of this asset should not be taxed as income. A sound approach would be to consider no revenues as income until the investment has been recouped, and subsequently allow for liquidation of the capital asset in terms of capital gains. The depletion allowance is, in effect, a compromise, so that the Treasury will not be denied tax revenue during the period of amortization.

Third, as for subsidies, a nondiscriminatory subsidy is probably politically impossible, considering the wealth of some companies. Also, a discriminatory system would involve three serious handicaps: (a) an undesirable amount of bureaucratic control over industry, (b) transfer of much management attention to Washington from its proper job of efficient exploration and production, and (c) a tendency to make inefficiency profitable.

Should present depletion allowances be increased?

MR. MIXTER: I am afraid if you tried to increase the allowance much, you would immediately arouse a great deal of opposition which might react to the mining industry's detriment, and also to the detriment of the oil industry.

MR. POWELL: I wouldn't want to say that the need will never arise for a higher depletion allowance. Maybe some of the present allowances aren't high enough, maybe others are too high. I am not going into merits or demerits of the various allowances now in the law, but there might be an occasion to ask for increased depletion.

MR. NOTMAN: It seems to me that it all depends on how successful we are in developing methods for discovering the deeper ore bodies.

R. S. PALMER (State Mineral Resources Board, Colorado): It should be pointed out that the limitation on depletion allowance is curtailing the production of uranium in the Colorado plateau. There is a lot of exploration activity in that area, probably more than in any section of the country today, but I think it is a proven fact that this limitation on depletion allowance is curtailing production of materials that are highly essential to the national well-being at the present time.

MR. POWELL: Exactly. There may well be situations right now where an increase in the depletion allowance is needed. There may be other such situations in the future.

Exemptions for New Mines

MR. JUST: Do we want to take a step somewhat similar to the one Canada has taken? As many of us know, it has proved to be a very sound incentive for investment in new mines.

MR. BROADGATE: Two years ago I was instrumental in having introduced a bill to remit all federal taxes on new mining enterprises for five years. We got absolutely no reaction from the industry, favorable or otherwise, on that bill.

ROBERT H. RAMSEY (*Engineering and Mining Journal*): As I recall, in Canada, you get this benefit of no taxation for three and a half years after the start of production, and then in addition you can write off your investment, I think, over the next two years. It is a very substantial benefit.

MR. POWELL: Canada has a very complicated depreciation schedule, but, generally speaking, it is very much more liberal than the United States depreciation policy.

MR. PALEY: The President's Materials Policy Commission studies showed, as I recall, that there were certain administrative difficulties in the Canadian system; also by direct comparison the advantages didn't seem to be as real as commonly supposed. We found that in Canada these things were done on a very informal basis. A person who is going into mining operation talks to the people in the mining bureau and makes his own arrangements; each one is treated separately and differently. To try to handle it that way in this country would be much more difficult and certainly much more dangerous, because then you would have in the hands of government authorities the power to make separate and different deals with different people. That is what we had in mind when we talked about administrative difficulties.

MR. JUST: I thought it was a clear statute that was rather liberally interpreted by the tax authorities. To me the difference is that in the United States we have had an unsympathetic administrative attitude towards tax benefits, whereas Canada has a different philosophy in these matters. They try much harder to encourage the mineral industry. The spirit is one of encouragement rather than one of obstructionism by regulation.

MR. PALEY: Differences in spirit plus, I think, a certain degree of flexibility which is exercised in Canada, flexibility to a degree very seldom allowed in our tax laws. Our consensus was that the end result wouldn't be as good if we went the Canadian route as it would be if we modified the American route.

Exemption from Capital Gains Tax

MR. JUST: What about exemption of capital gains in the mining industry? It is a practice in Canada today. We know that it is a profound stimulus to investment in mining activities.

MR. MIXTER: I think that the principle is correct, and I think it would definitely be an incentive. Whether it would be expedient at this time is another matter.

MR. BOYD: Doesn't it apply, Mr. Chairman, to all kinds of investment? The capital gains tax, after all, is a capital tax. It is a philosophy of taxation, whether you apply it directly to mining or any other industry.

MR. JUST: Of course, we can't very well take up the whole question. It wouldn't be illogical, however, to say that the mining industry is a special case involving high risk and should be treated as a special case. It is true, of course, that in Canada the principle cuts across the board as I believe it does in all British countries.

MR. NOTMAN: What are the capital gains of an operating mining company?

MR. POWELL: None, unless it is sold.

MR. NOTMAN: Aren't we talking, then, about the investor rather than the mining company?

MR. JUST: That is right. You are talking about an investor in the mining company or a man who backs a prospector. Or a man who invests in the shares of a new mining venture.

MR. POWELL: All big mines were once little ones. And sometimes a man who finds a mine can't create enough capital to develop it. So if he sells it to a larger concern, or even to a corporation that he himself might be a part of, he has to pay this capital gains tax on it, and it hurts him considerably. There is no doubt but what the removal of the capital gains tax would be a great incentive for further exploration by small people.

MR. JUST: It certainly makes the financing of new mining ventures in Canada much easier.

MR. NOTMAN: My own feeling is that if we had an exemption from taxation for a period of years, plus the present depletion allowances, you would get all the risk capital you want.

Personally I am satisfied there are just as big fish in the sea as have ever been caught. But the problem is to know how to find them. The incentive is being pinched down all the time.

MR. JUST: In the last few years I have been up in Canada a good deal, and certainly there is a lot more willingness in Canada to take a chance, other things being equal.

I am not convinced that we should write off the United States as simply an aged nation with respect to minerals. A very serious attempt should be made by both big and small companies to bring back vim and vigor in the prospecting field.

MR. NOTMAN: I am sure the tax take would be bigger.

MR. JUST: And it seems to me that we must keep punching in this respect, trying to do what we can to improve the climate for aggressiveness in exploration and development.

MR. NOTMAN: You are getting up against a ceiling where there isn't any objective left to go out and do anything.

Wouldn't it be helpful to have some factual basis on which to determine how much stimulation you need? Should you just say you need all the stimulation you can get, or is there some way you can build up your cause, particularly if you are going before Congress, and say how much stimulating you need on some economic basis?

MR. JUST: Do you mean that we should attempt to quantitatively evaluate what each of these ideas would bring in?

MR. NOTMAN: Yes.

MR. JUST: I don't see how that can be done. All I can do is state my conviction that if we did all of these things we would not be going too far, we would not create a superabundance of energy in the prospecting field.

MR. PALEY: There is a danger in just throwing every good feature you hear about into the hopper. I agree with Mr. Notman. I think these things have to be worked out to make a sensible program, one that can be justified, particularly as you go to Congress to ask for the kind of relief you think is necessary. You might find upon examination —I am not a tax lawyer—that one idea contradicts another, or two ideas together are wrong fundamentally. I think you have to be qualitative about this.

MR. JUST: I think we could all agree there is no desire to be rash here or rush precipitately on to ground that might prove to be unwise when examined more closely.

MR. PALEY: That is one of the things I am afraid of. Some of these things might strike at the very root of the depletion allowance theory, which I think basically is one of the most important incentives to the mining industry. I think other things could be joined up with depletion allowance. But if you take other things which strike at the root of depletion allowance and endanger that, I think you are going backwards rather than forwards.

MR. NOTMAN: Of course, from an administrative standpoint, it would be a lot simpler to administer a tax law which recognized in principal that the extractive industries, those which are dealing with wasting assets, had a lower rate of taxation than others that were self-perpetuating. That is a simple device which would tend to attract risk capital.

MR. PALEY: Of course, such a theory could be translated immediately into higher depletion allowance. You would come to the same thing.

Loss Carry-Over and Dividends

MR. MIXTER: There are two other points. One is the unavailability, largely to the mining industry, of the operating loss carry-over features of the income tax law; if you attempt to carry back a loss, you must eliminate your percentage depletion. In most cases that means that if you use your percentage depletion you lose the benefit of the carry-back feature.

The other is another Canadian provision which I think means a good deal in the risk capital area, and that is the allowance of depletion on dividends to the stockholders which Canada permits. A mining company is rightfully allowed depletion in order that its return of capital is not taxed. A similar allowance should be made to a stockholder when he receives dividends, otherwise the portion of the dividends representing a return of capital is subject to tax.

MR. POWELL: Believe me, in several segments of the mining industry today the carry-over feature is becoming more and more important. But as it is now written it is hedged in with restrictions and "adjustments" and doesn't give the relief that it should.

New Technology

What new steps, if any, should be taken toward developing and applying new technology in the mineral industry?

The days of the mineral outcrop as a clue to hidden deposits are passing in the United States; they are already about over for some of the better known metals. The mining industry must turn more and more to the newer technology, the earth sciences, in its search for nonfuel minerals.

We must probe deeper and deeper into the earth's crust. Drilling alone, even if it were economically feasible, will not be enough. We must learn more about the relationships of wanted minerals to other phenomena in the earth: the chemical and physical nature of the earth, the minor elements, the structures, and alterations. Chemistry, biology, and nuclear physics as well as geology must be brought into play to point the way to the mineral raw materials that the nation will surely need.

The need for such new approaches was widely recognized; discussion turned on how to bring them about. Who should do the research? How can present and future knowledge best be made available to those who can use it? How can the necessary research scientists be developed? And, above all, where is the money coming from?

FROM THE RECORD

Problems and Approaches

MR. VANDERWILT: I think the statement of the President's Materials Policy Commission on this subject, as quoted in the Section IV steering committee paper, is significant. It states that abundant reserves of undiscovered minerals lie within economically accessible depths below the surface and that, with adequate research and development, exploration techniques capable of locating a large part of these reserves can be made available. The question, it seems to me, is how the development and use of technology in the field of mining may be accelerated.

MR. GARDNER: The fact that an ore deposit occurs in one particular place rather than another is for a particular reason; it is not by chance. I think there ought to be developed a new science and branch of geology; I would call the practitioners of this new science "clue hunters," specialists on clues leading to mineral deposits.

There is a "why" in each one of these cases. It seems to me that the subject is so broad and important for varied deposits that it is a matter for cooperative agreement in the whole industry, the universities, government agencies, and the appropriate departments of the individual mining companies.

EARL INGERSON (U.S. Geological Survey): The Survey has well-organized programs in both geophysical and geochemical prospecting. Several branches of geophysics, particularly airborne magnetometer and aerial radiometric surveys, are being used.

The geochemical work that is under way now is principally the defining of geochemical anomalies—halos around known deposits—and seeking similar patterns elsewhere. I believe that geochemistry can be extended to give some indications of hidden deposits at greater depths if we go into fundamentals of isotope geology and other branches of geochemistry that have not as yet been explored in relation to ore deposits.

A study of alterations is another possibility. The Survey has at least one extensive study under way on the relation of alteration to ore deposits.

One thing that the Survey has just barely scratched and that I believe should be undertaken either by the mining industry or by an endowed institution or an endowed laboratory is the study of conditions of formation of ore minerals. We ought to have a well-organized program on ore-forming fluids and ore minerals which would give fundamental information on what kind of physical and chemical

environments you would look for in exploring for a new ore deposit at depth.

Then, I think that a great deal of fundamental information can be obtained from an entirely new approach—the study of isotopes of oxygen and hydrogen in igneous rocks and the related ore-forming solutions. There is bound to be in the solution from an igneous rock an isotopic fractionation. It isn't possible to outline right now the differences that you would expect, but there almost certainly will be a difference in the isotopic composition of oxygen and hydrogen in an igneous rock and in the veins near an igneous rock, and progressive changes as you get farther away. Exploration of these gradients is an approach that hasn't been tried at all.

Another approach that has just barely been mentioned is the study of the ore elements. There ought to be a systematic difference in the minor element content of the igneous rock from which an ore deposit is derived and a similar rock that has no ore deposits associated with it. Recently two studies have been made that give very definite indication that the igneous rocks associated with certain types of ore deposits are lower in their content of these elements than similar rocks in other intrusions or in other parts of the same intrusion that do not have deposits of those elements associated with them.

One good example is the Iron Hill district in southern Utah where the igneous rock that has given rise to the iron ore deposits is almost entirely devoid of iron. The iron has been swept out of the igneous rock and included in the ore deposits. That is contrary to the ordinary concept. Ordinarily you would think of looking for an igneous rock that is high in copper if you want associated copper deposits. We may have to turn around and look at it from an entirely different point of view.

Another thing that we are starting in the Survey is looking for minor elements that do not occur as separate ore deposits where they can be worked; in other words, not geochemical prospecting as it is ordinarily understood but studying the chemical characteristics of the elements we are interested in such as niobium, germanium, and gallium. Where would they occur in common minerals in sufficient quantities so that they could be worked as a by-product? Niobium is very much in demand right now, but there are no known deposits of niobium occurring as such in the country.

Niobium in certain types of igneous intrusions and in certain veins is associated very definitely with titanium minerals such as rutile and brookite. A study of those minerals is likely to reveal significant sources of niobium where you wouldn't find any niobium deposits as such. That approach should be applied very much more widely to a study of minor elements.

To summarize, the new approaches that I have suggested are: (1) studies of artificial systems that would give the conditions of formations of the ore deposits; (2) isotope geology; (3) the study of trace elements; (4) studies of intrusions that have ore deposits associated with them and similar intrusions that do not; and (5) the crystal chemistry approach for minor elements.

EDWARD L. CLARK (State Geologist, Missouri): Approximately how many individuals are now involved in these studies—not in your geochemical studies, but your detailed trace element studies?

MR. INGERSON: About five people are involved in the niobium studies.

MR. CLARK: Here we are expecting five persons to carry this whole weight for the country at large, possibly for the world. I doubt very much that they are even full time. There are administrative duties that come in and interfere with them all the time.

I would like to have this group give consideration to the recommendation that all emphasis possible be given to such studies. They are basic and fundamental. I don't think geologists are going to do it alone. There will have to be physical chemists, physicists, and metallurgists.

We are going to have to give emphasis to such a program and see that it is not only set up but given some assurance that it will continue to be able to operate over a sufficiently long period of time to know whether or not we are going to get results.

MR. INGERSON: The niobium project is just one project. In the geochemical project we have 8 people, and the Mineral Deposits Branch has some field work in this area. So there are maybe 10 or 15 people altogether in geochemical prospecting. Geophysics is another branch. We have a half-dozen projects —isotope geology, crystal chemistry, and so on—that will have 2 to 5 people each. So instead of 5 people, on this whole geochemical-geophysical approach, we have more like 50.

MR. CLARK: That was understood. I merely used the niobium project to illustrate that we don't have enough people working on these problems.

MR. VANDERWILT: Mr. Ingerson, would you elaborate on your suggestion regarding work in geophysical and geochemical research that could be done by companies or endowed laboratories?

MR. INGERSON: The matter has been under discussion quite a while. Recently a conference was called by the National Research Council on research and publication in geochemistry. One of the recommendations of the group was that there ought to be somewhere a laboratory where systematic work could be done on the principles and processes of ore formation. I think the reason behind it is that it is very difficult for a small group working on one system or a small part of a system to get any over-all picture of it.

If we had a group of 15, 20, or 25 well-trained scientists working together all the time, I am convinced that they could do five times as much work over a five-year period as the same number of men working apart—say at California Tech, Columbia, the University of Chicago, the Survey, and the Bureau of Mines.

Who Should Conduct Research?

MR. CLARK: I can see this research work in mineral technology, and exploration right on through to the final product, as having many facets and conducted at various places. I don't think that all research work can be tied down to one individual laboratory, but we do need a central laboratory such as has been mentioned here, entirely independent of any group so that it can follow its own research into whatever ramifications it may lead. In other research, certainly the mining companies must continue not only what they have done in the past, but expand it.

I think that the U.S. Geological Survey and the Bureau of Mines should both be encouraged to go right on. Don't forget that we have state geological surveys. Some of them are not very active, but, among those that are, considerable basic research work is being conducted in the field not only on the metallics but the nonmetallics.

I would suggest that basic academic research be set up in a laboratory. You may want a staff of professors but you must give them assurance that they are there for a time sufficient to justify their taking leave or making a change.

We cannot ignore basic geologic mapping. Gentlemen, let us stop and think of the geological reports that have been published in the last 25 years on mining districts. How many of those were written before the mining district was open? How many after the mining district was closed?

Geology is not going to contribute to the mining field the way it can as long as we write reports after the camp is closed. If geology can find the clues that Mr. Gardner spoke of, let the geologists be the clue hounds and do the basic geologic mapping. Then, when you get ready to prospect an area, you know whether or not that environment has produced an ore body in the past. If you do the basic mapping first, your further exploration will be speeded up.

Then, too, how many of our geological reports on mining camps or mining districts are tied to a shaft, a series of shafts, or the immediate camp, as compared to those that go on out into the region and get the regional environment?

You won't find very many pieces of regional work in the literature. A company can't justify

such activity. Certainly the governmental agencies can do this without interfering with or duplicating the mining explorations and geological work of operating companies.

T. P. THAYER (U.S. Geological Survey): We have been aware, in our mapping work, of the problems mentioned by Mr. Clark. Formerly, all too often, work in mining districts was concentrated around the mines, where the geology was most complex and perhaps badly obscured by alteration. At the present time we are enlarging the scope of district mapping, and we have several large projects under way. The Boulder batholith in Montana, for example, is being mapped as a whole, to see how it and the related mineral deposits fit into the regional picture. Although several geologists are assigned to the project, it will take several years.

It is true that we have mapped some largely worked-out districts, but I think many people here, particularly Phil Shenon, will agree that the Coeur d'Alene district is far from worked out. We have had geologists mapping in the Coeur d'Alene district for several years, and as surface maps are completed we have been making them available to the local mining people. The Geological Survey does not have the man power to do comprehensive underground mapping and, moreover, we regard that as primarily a job for private industry. In the Coeur d'Alene district, our geologists have mapped selected mine workings to develop the district picture. As with surface maps, such information is made available as soon as possible through open file release, pending formal publication.

We have, I believe, largely overcome one of the criticisms of the past, namely, that all the Geological Survey did was perform an autopsy or write an epitaph for a district, telling where the ore was mined. Survey work has stimulated and contributed in a major way to revival of two metal-mining districts since World War II. Who can tell when a district should be abandoned?

A serious question that concerns us is the supply of geologists. The supply cannot meet the demand and will not, I would guess, for the next 20 years. It behooves us, therefore, to get the maximum efficiency from the men available. In an atom bomb, a certain critical size or mass is necessary to produce a chain reaction. The same principle applies to scientific research. The interaction of minds is fundamental; one fellow may have just the item to tie another fellow's story together. There is no substitute for the freest interchange of information.

Too many people are working in various corners, more or less ignored and ignorant of what others are doing; many are duplicating others' efforts. Take the matter of bibliography, for instance. When a man starts in on a new project, how much time does he take rounding up the literature? If a man is interested in the wall rock alteration associated with tin deposits, where can he find a comprehensive bibliography kept up to date? I believe the Geological Survey could serve as a clearinghouse for this type of information. Simply because the mechanics for making the information available are still inadequate, much indispensable information is lost to the individual researcher.

MR. INGERSON: I had no intention of proposing that all of the work even on systems be done in a central laboratory. To use the Geophysical Laboratory as an example, while they have done more than any one other institution on silicate research, they would be the last ones to try to corner it. When someone wants to undertake a problem in silicate chemistry, he is urged to go to the laboratory, talk to the men there, see what has been done, and get suggestions about what he can do to integrate his work with theirs so as to avoid too much overlapping.

I would picture the laboratory of ore formations as being the same sort of an organization, where someone from the University of Utah or the Geological Survey could go and find out what they have under way and start a project of his own that would tie in with what is being done there. And work could be done on parts of the systems or small systems in university laboratories and others all over the country.

But the whole effort should be integrated. It seems to me that the logical place for that integration is the National Science Foundation.

A panel of the Foundation has been considering these problems. I have been told that they are recommending the establishment of such a program under the general coordination of the National Science Foundation, but I think they are considering recommending that a major part of the work be done at the Geological Survey.

I would like to try to head that off at some level because we have more things than we can say grace over now. I would rather see that work go somewhere else. Perhaps one or two systems that our boys are interested in could be worked on at the Survey, but certainly no major part of the program. That ought to be in another laboratory. It ought not to be by government appropriation; it ought not to be by contributions from mining companies. There ought to be a fund. Where the money comes from originally, I don't know—perhaps from large single donations from the mining companies and a contribution from the National Science Foundation. But there either ought to be an endowment, or the program should be turned over to some research institution like the Carnegie Institution to administer so that it is assured that the program can continue.

I started on a program of hydrothermal research in 1935. It was five years before I even got the apparatus working. You can't turn out results in those fields in one year or two years. In some of the very difficult systems it will take 10 or 15 years to get any significant results.

MR. SHENON: First we have to know what the needs are. The Geological Survey does a good deal of mapping. I don't believe it does enough. The most valuable work the Survey does, from my standpoint at least, is the basic field mapping. You just can't put a money value, for example, on the professional paper that Mansfield wrote on the phosphate fields of southeastern Idaho. That report alone, I dare say, has pushed the development of that field ahead 10 years. It took a long time to do it, but the people who went out first to locate the phosphate deposits used his map. They plastered their leases over his map.

The same way with the Coeur d'Alene district. That old report of Calkins is still the bible up there. How he ever mapped that area in two years, I don't know. It's an area some 20 by 15 miles, and complicated as it can be, yet there are very few things on the scale he mapped it on that he overlooked. It is a wonderful piece of work. You just don't evaluate in dollars a work of that sort.

MR. WILLISTON: There is a vast amount of information that can be gotten from a diamond drill hole that the mining industry does not get at the present time—temperature surveys, electric logs, gravity surveys possibly, electromagnetic surveys, directional surveys, and so on. The information is there, but the mining industry has not been willing to pay for that type of instrumentation.

A. C. RICHARDSON (Battelle Memorial Institute): When a problem in prospecting or discovery gets down to the point where it is of specific interest to a given company, or a given small group, they will find ways and means to finance it. I think we are talking here about the broader basic fundamental ways and means of doing it, and I wonder if it would be so difficult to sell the industry on the idea of supporting research of this nature. I believe industry would support fundamental research, if the need were properly presented.

MR. VANDERWILT: I don't think it is an exaggeration to say that enormous amounts of industry money are going into research. But perhaps the results of that research aren't being used to the greatest advantage because there is no method of exchanging the information or getting it to other organizations.

MR. WILLISTON: The oil industry spends 50 percent of its income, before taxes, on exploration and research. I don't mean development; I mean exploration. The figure for exploration in the mining industry is more like 3, 4, or 5 percent. The oil industry found 35 years ago that they could no longer count on finding oil deposits by drilling seepages. They

had to spend their own money and they did. It is only within the last three or four years that the mining industry has recognized that it is now in the position the oil industry was in in 1918. You can no longer rely on finding mines from outcropping ores.

If you look at the mathematics of the explored areas of the United States, assuming that it is possible to mine down to 3,000 feet or so, and you calculate the amount of area that is covered and the amount of ore deposits minable which do not outcrop on the surface, you find that probably less than 15 percent of the mineral deposits of the country have been discovered.

MR. THAYER: The federal government, under the Mineral Leasing Act, turns all lease and royalty income over to the Treasury; there is no relation at all between the revenue from the mineral resources and the amount of money spent by the government. I wonder whether there isn't a possible source of income here.

MR. WILLISTON: You can go further than that. The government has a 75 percent carried interest in every mine in the United States. They take three-quarters of the profits and none of the losses.

MR. VANDERWILT: I agree with Mr. Richardson that with a well-presented program industry would show quite an interest in financing such projects.

MR. INGERSON: Should it not be pointed out to industry that with a central laboratory the results of the research will be available to all the companies? An individual company would put in only part of the cost but would have access to all the results.

MR. WALDRON: Several of the important mining companies in the United States, Canada, and other areas have spent a lot of money in developing new geophysical tools. I think that in many cases the tools are going to prove to be very similar. Yet each company is quite closely guarding its own findings.

MR. RICHARDSON: Quite frankly, if you have ten people contributing $10,000 to an over-all program, your $10,000 doesn't bring you ten times that in results, but it does multiply the investment by a modest five, at least. Frankly, a lot of basic information is pertinent to all, and if one company obtains it and keeps it to itself, they don't obtain much of an advantage over anyone else.

MR. WILLISTON: Not for very long.

Coordination of Research

EUGENE CALLAGHAN (New Mexico Bureau of Mines and Mineral Resources): Too much coordination can actually stifle the work. I think the coordination of a certain amount is certainly desirable, particularly in the matter of a clearinghouse to which information is voluntarily submitted, but involuntary coordination would be actually detrimental to the progress of research. Sometimes it is a very good thing for two or three people to be competing. Competition in research is as good as it is in business or any other phase of human activity.

MR. SHENON: Many of the new developments can be patented. I can see how some of the research or mining companies wouldn't want to let out information on their patentable processes until they were patented.

MR. INGERSON: Even if we take the problem of coordination as being mostly one of information, it is going to be very hard for any one office to have the details of all the different kinds of programs. But a central office might keep a record of where more detailed information was available.

MR. VANDERWILT: We generally agreed that you could have large numbers of organizations doing various types of research work. The question is, should there be a coordinating agency for all of those organizations?

MR. CLARK: I think we have to have coordination if we are going to come up with the result we are seeking.

MR. INGERSON: You will get more per unit of effort that way. But you are going to have to be very clear right from the start what the coordinating agency's role is to be so that you don't scare people away.

MR. RICHARDSON: Can you use the National Science Foundation as a starting point and, since we assume we are going to have contributing companies, can you not then have groups or committees that handle certain phases? Each one of these groups would probably have a hired man as liaison between the industrial group and the actual research group. He would be responsible to this control committee, or whatever you want to call it, from industry. You have to set up some kind of an organization to take any action at all, some group or organization with authority.

MR. McCORMICK: It seems to me the problem lies in the definition of the word "coordination." One type of coordination, as I see it, would be limited to periodic additions to a basic bibliography on published papers and perhaps a list of research projects by type and where they are being conducted, purely as a matter of information for all researchers. The other kind is trying to tell somebody he shouldn't do this because somebody else is doing it. Some people have that concept of the word "coordination" when it comes to something like this.

MR. RICHARDSON: You may have two men working on the same problem, but you may have different approaches to it. If they are identical problems, identical approaches, and the capacities of the two research men are equal, then you might have to flip a coin or something to decide, but how often does that occur?

MR. CLARK: You don't have to flip a coin unless you are subsidizing those men. Otherwise, let them go their own way.

MR. RICHARDSON: Usually they have separate approaches.

MR. INGERSON: It seems to me the whole program has to go a good deal further than mere coordination. Whatever group takes over the job of trying to sponsor or coordinate the work should have the power or function to suggest new projects that will fill voids in the present program, things that ought to be done that are not being done. We need an active group of people who know what can be done by newer techniques and who have the authority to suggest them.

MR. McCORMICK: I agree. What I am trying to get away from is the idea of finding two people working on the same thing and arbitrarily telling one of them to cease and desist.

MR. RICHARDSON: No matter how far apart you start, sometimes you come together as you approach a solution. I don't think deciding who has the best facilities, and so on, for going on and completing a project has ever been a serious problem where research is concerned.

MR. SHENON: Isn't the National Science Foundation supposed to sift out the projects and suggest the ones that should be done and maybe finance them? Why couldn't they be the medium also for suggesting new projects?

MR. INGERSON: I think they could. It would be a very good function for the Foundation. There are some agencies that actually foster an overlap or duplication of projects. The Atomic Energy Commission very often will let two almost identical contracts to see whether or not they get the same result.

MR. THAYER: It seems to me we should make a distinction between coordination and programing. We are not trying to set up a research program, we are trying to coordinate the efforts of people who have work underway.

MR. McCORMICK: The other facet of it is that you are going to define areas in which further research is desirable. It may never get done, but at least somebody has pointed it out.

Need for Research Workers

MR. INGERSON: No matter how much money we can get together or how efficient a coordinating organization we have, if you don't have well-trained people in earth sciences and related fields, you can't accelerate your research program very much.

The numbers of geology majors are dropping off at an alarming rate. There are very few schools equipped to train geologists or give them the kind of chemistry they ought to have.

We should start with the youngsters. We ought to appeal to the imagination of the really brilliant youngsters and get them interested in these problems when they are formulating their careers, instead of trying to pull them in when they are seniors in college or graduate students. If we can get the good youngsters interested in physics and chemistry, grounded in geology at the same time, we have a much stronger combination than having geologists working with chemists.

MR. CALLAGHAN: In our small organization we are hiring high school students to go out with field parties. We have had two or three years experience with that now. Every one of those youngsters now plans a career in geology or mining.

MR. KOENIG: I believe that finding ore deposits in the future, by new methods, new techniques, geophysical or geochemical or geological or what not, is the main job ahead. All the other problems will fall into place if we can find the ore.

I am not trying to belittle any of the work which the Bureau of Mines or other governmental agencies is doing on metallurgy. That is very valuable and is the sort of fundamental research which then becomes available for private enterprises to turn to account at the proper time. I think that should be continued.

MR. CLARK: Isn't part of our difficulty the fact that we can't get the personnel because we won't pay for it? Give us the money and we can get the personnel.

MR. INGERSON: That won't help the overall picture. You will just pull them away from somewhere else where the work ought to be done also. What you should do is increase the number of well-trained people available.

CHAIRMAN'S SUMMARY

Consideration of the problems of domestic nonfuel minerals was undertaken in general recognition that available domestic resources must be enlarged to meet the needs of our steadily expanding economy and to bolster the nation's security. To create this expansion, stimulation of domestic mineral exploration and development is necessary. Our discussion, therefore, largely concerned ways and means of stimulating domestic activity.

In describing the positions developed in our discussions, it would probably be unfair to infer that all points of view were adequately represented. Many people at this Conference, unable to be in two places at once, had to make a choice between groups in which they were interested. Beyond that, there were instances when the majority present seemed to be more inclined to observe than to participate. Therefore, this summary is not expressed as representing a true sample of national opinion; it is simply a report on the views of those who were in attendance.

Taxation

In the field of taxation, the following question was posed: "Should tax changes be made to stimulate the domestic mining industry to more exploration and more efficient extraction? If so, how and to what extent?"

Those present at the tax session seemed in general accord that new tax modifications to stimulate exploration and development are desirable. The whole theory of tax relief was attacked by one participant, however, at the section's final review session. As to specific measures, the following views received considerable support: (1) that the present limitation on the right to treat exploration expenditures as expense items should be removed; (2) that, because of the wasting-asset nature of mining, a new operation, with reserves of

uncertain extent, should not be conceived as achieving true profit until the initial investment has been recouped; (3) that a 3½ year exemption from income taxes, in view of its success in Canada, should be accorded to new mining operations, beginning with the production stage, provided that under United States conditions such a measure could be shown not to present important administrative difficulties; (4) that it would be unwise to seek special treatment exempting mining capital gains from taxation, despite acknowledgment that such action would profoundly stimulate investment in new mining ventures; (5) that, in general, it is not desirable to seek increased depletion allowances unless new justifications are created by changing conditions; however, it was evident that the preponderance of informed opinion on mining taxation insists that adequate depletion allowances are fundamental, in the light of the wasting-asset nature of the industry; (6) that adoption of such tax measures would result in increased ultimate revenues to the government, as well as rewards in the way of increased productive activity.

Technology

The section also undertook to discuss "What new steps, if any, should be taken toward developing and applying new technology in the mining industry?" In this category it was recognized that we are not beginning at zero but that very important work is under way under both private and government auspices. As to specific aspects, acceleration of the present program of geologic mapping was endorsed. The group seconded the recommendation of the President's Materials Policy Commission, urging a program under National Science Foundation guidance of making an inventory of knowledge, devising a course of action, and estimating the cost thereof.

It was also the preponderant view that research should not be done exclusively by selected parties, but should be an attack on all fronts, of sufficient breadth that probably both private and government financial support would be required.

Claim-Patent System

With regard to the system of acquiring title on public lands to mineral properties through the claim-patent system, the following question was asked: "Does the claim-patent system as it exists in the laws governing mining activities on public lands need revision because of present abuses and administrative difficulties or because of a need to encourage exploration, development, and the use of new techniques of discovery?"

This subject has been an area of sharp controversy between opposing groups for many years. The problems in this field are multitudinous and with respect to details there were many points of difference. I am pleased to report, however, that new areas of understanding seem to have been developed. Summarized very briefly, there was rather good concurrence on the following points: (1) that it is very desirable to protect the fundamental nature and intent of the claim-patent system, which encourages mineral development by private parties and affords an opportunity to acquire title through discovery and constructive development; (2) that cooperation should be given toward discouragement and disestablishment of "subterfuge" claimants who use the mining law to acquire rights apart from the acquisition and development of mineral deposits; (3) that provision should be made for a new type of temporary claim of broad extent and without the initial discovery requirements to encourage new methods of scientific projecting; (4) that sound multiple use of public lands prior to patenting claims is in the public interest; (5) that duplicate recording of claims and assessment work with federal

agencies is feasible if the process is kept simple and inexpensive; (6) that assessment work requirements should not be raised, nor should they be waived unless conditions cause genuine and widespread obstacles to performance; (7) that the present terms under which patents are obtained are sound if properly administered; (8) that no extension of the leasing system to new types of minerals is desirable; (9) that the present situation in regard to the size of lode claims and extralateral rights is reasonably satisfactory.

The view was expressed by several in the group that a restudy of the claim-patent system is warranted with a view to bringing it up to date, eliminating abuses, and clarifying title procedure.

In explanation of the gratifying degree of accord which was reached in this field, it seems only fair to state that the traditional mining industry resistance to change has been largely based on fears that the persons sponsoring change really intended to destroy the fundamental nature of the claim-patent system. New administrative attitudes and evidences of good faith on the government's side have done much to dispel these fears and I believe that further steps of a cooperative, progressive nature will be undertaken.

Government Protection and Assistance

The question under discussion here was "In what other ways, if any, should government further mineral exploration and development?"

Tariff was considered in our section in comparison with other ways of aiding domestic industry, not as a controversy between proponents of tariff and free trade.

In our group it was acknowledged that present conditions do not make it feasible to seek adequate assistance to domestic industry through conventional tariff alone. The section then discussed various alternatives to conventional tariff, including a sliding-scale tariff, quotas, direct subsidies, and government purchase of surpluses. Within the group there was no advocacy of quotas, which were dismissed as difficult to administer. However, although several advantages and disadvantages of the other alternatives were mentioned, no majority preference was developed.

Two new hybrid plans were suggested, a subsidy-plus-purchase arrangement, and a tariff-plus-subsidy plan. However, in these cases also no preponderant approval was established.

The section discussed continued government financial aid to exploration ventures, such as is currently being given under the Defense Minerals Exploration Administration. There was a lack of enthusiasm for this policy, with reservations in favor of aid to development of strategic minerals and to small operators.

With respect to the government engaging in direct exploration activity, the majority view was that this should be done circumspectly and only where justification is abundantly clear. In other words, government should, in general, avoid competing with private industry in mineral development.

Evan Just

December 4, 1953

Chairman
FARRINGTON DANIELS, Chairman
Department of Chemistry
University of Wisconsin

Co-Chairman
GEORGE M. GADSBY, President
Utah Power and Light Company

Steering Committee and Advisers

Steering Committee: AUSTIN CADLE, Economist, Standard Oil Company of California · JOHN M. CARMODY, former Administrator, Rural Electrification Administration · S. R. FINLEY, General Superintendent, Electric Power Board, Chattanooga · H. C. HOTTEL, Department of Chemical Engineering, Massachusetts Institute of Technology · R. L. IRELAND, Chairman of the Executive Committee, Pittsburgh Consolidated Coal Company · BERTRAND A. LANDRY, Battelle Memorial Institute · LEONARD F. MCCOLLUM, President, Continental Oil Company · C. PETRUS PETERSON, President, National Reclamation Association · J FRENCH ROBINSON, President, Consolidated Natural Gas Company · HENRY B. SARGENT, President, Arizona Public Service Company (alternate for Mr. Gadsby) · GLEN B. WALL, International Brotherhood of Electrical Workers · *Assistant to the Section Chairman:* GLENN E. MCLAUGHLIN, Economist, Export-Import Bank of Washington · *Section Rapporteurs:* F. G. FASSETT, Director of the Technology Press, Massachusetts Institute of Technology; CORNELIUS J. DWYER, Industrial Specialists Division, Foreign Operations Administration

Subsections

A. UNCONVENTIONAL SOURCES

Chairman: H. C. HOTTEL

Rapporteurs: HAROLD BARNETT, The Rand Corporation; PAUL W. MCGANN, Bureau of Mines, U. S. Department of the Interior; HERBERT E. STRINER, Bureau of Mines, U. S. Department of the Interior

B. ELECTRICITY AND SYNTHETIC FUELS

Chairman: B. R. TEARE, JR., Dean, College of Engineering and Science, Carnegie Institute of Technology

Rapporteurs: WILLIAM H. SNYDER, Bureau of the Budget; J. WARREN MCLAUGHLIN, Office of Defense Mobilization

C. CONSERVATION AND USE

Chairman: EUGENE AYRES, Consultant, Gulf Research and Development Company

Rapporteur: WILBERT G. FRITZ, Office of Defense Mobilization

About 225 people participated in the section's work. The 203 who registered formally are listed on pages 397-401. The full section met on the afternoon of the first day of the Conference to consider the broad question of the nation's total energy resources and needs. The following day, three subsections met concurrently for discussion of unconventional sources, electricity and synthetic fuels, and conservation and use. The morning of the final day of the Conference the full section reconvened to go over the rapporteurs' digest of the proceedings and the Chairman's report to the Conference.

ENERGY RESOURCE PROBLEMS

THAT THE UNITED STATES IS RICH IN ENERGY RE-SOURCES—both in materials and in the knowledge of how to find, produce, and use them—was never far below the surface in the discussions of the Section on Energy Resources and its three subsections. All participants agreed that the nation's energy bank balance is still in good shape despite the heavy and increasing drains upon it.

When it came to questions of how to make the best use of our energy resources from now on, there were a number of sharp differences of opinion. There was the question, for example, of whether the use of our oil and gas reserves should be governed entirely by the law of supply and demand or whether some of these materials should be set aside for future, possibly different, uses. There were clear-cut differences on the question of public versus private development of hydroelectric power and on what part private industry should play in the development of atomic energy.

Great as our energy potentialities are, future demands will far exceed anything we have known to date. It was pointed out that future generations will sit in judgment on how we use our energy resources during the next several decades. Not many in the group appeared to feel that the judgment would be a harsh one, but the knowledge that as demands mount for energy each generation of Americans will be held accountable by those that follow was clearly in the minds of several of the participants, and served to bring out aspects of the problem that otherwise might have been considered academic.

The section considered the effects of oil imports on the domestic petroleum industry but did not take up the larger subject of protection versus free trade, since this came up elsewhere in the Conference (Section VI, pages 269-72). The section dealt extensively with energy technology, leaving the broader aspects of research to the research section (Section VII, pages 312-14). But it was clearly indicated that vigorous programs of research, particularly those having to do with the development of energy from unconventional sources, should be maintained. Discussion of water resources similarly dealt primarily with matters of hydroelectric power; the over-all problems of water resources were dealt with by Section III (pages 126-75).

Total Energy Resources and Needs

Discussion in the first meeting of the full section dealt in the main with the best-known sources—oil, gas, coal. Consideration of such aspects of the total energy question as nuclear and solar energy, synthetic fuels, and hydroelectric power were largely left to the subsections. It was brought out, however, that techniques of finding and utilizing different energy resources are steadily improving.

At the same time, future demand for energy will be tremendous, especially for electricity. Regardless of how much coal, oil, and gas there is in the ground, the amounts that can be found and produced economically are what count. Reporting of reserves must take that factor into consideration. Oil and gas reserves are calculated in terms of oil and gas in proved reserves that can be recovered by present methods at present prices. The Bureau of Mines is now undertaking to calculate coal reserves on the same basis, whereas in the past the Bureau estimated the total amount of coal in the ground on the basis of geologic inference.

In general, the group appeared confident that requirements for at least the next half century can be met—taking full account of economic factors.

FROM THE RECORD

Appraisal of Resources and Needs

What are the likely limits to effective U.S. reserves of the major mineral fuels? How do U.S. reserves compare with world reserves?

A. C. FIELDNER (Bureau of Mines): On the basis of geological studies, the original inferred coal reserves of the United States totaled about 3 trillion tons. This estimate has recently been reduced by the U.S. Geological Survey to about 2 trillion tons, and the recoverable reserves to a little less than 1 trillion tons. Thus, it is seen that we are reducing our estimates of coal reserves to a more realistic basis and increasing our proved reserves of oil and natural gas by new discoveries and extension of deposits each year.

RUSSELL G. WAYLAND (U.S. Geological Survey): The re-evaluation of coal reserves now going on is a much more precise study than the one first presented 30 or 40 years ago. The objective is to get an ultimate figure and so break it down that it shows the depth of burial and the thickness, both factors in availability, and also the different types. The re-evaluation is about half finished.

GEORGE B. CRESSEY (Syracuse University): It seems to me the only way to estimate future reserves is in terms of human ingenuity and economic conditions. There are certain amounts of mineral resources in the earth. We don't know the total, but the amount of recoverable material will depend on both skill and the money we are willing to pay for it in the next 50 years.

MR. FIELDNER: The Bureau of Mines estimates 50 percent recovery. This figure is based largely on present prices and present mining practices in the Appalachian region. Actual recovery has been averaging about 50 percent but this, of course, is from the thicker seams; we have mined very little coal under 30 inches thick.

DANIEL PARSON (American Gas Association): To the extent that recovery techniques are improved the reserves of oil and gas will be increased even without the discovery of any additional supplies underground.

WILLIAM VAN ROYEN (University of Maryland): It seems to me that a discussion which relates to the future should not be limited to these effective reserves. There is no reason for us to assume that technical progress will stop today. Effective methods of underground gasification of coal, for example, might well change limits of seam thickness and depth used in present estimates.

JOHN A. WARING, JR. (New York): I recently put together figures on reserves from the most authoritative sources. These cover the entire world, which the Paley Commission report[1] did not, and include the countries behind the iron curtain.

———

Mr. Waring put U.S. reserves of crude petroleum at 26 percent of the world total, coal at 34.5 percent, and natural gas at 70 percent. Mr. Van Royen challenged these figures. He said the University of Maryland had been working on an atlas of world resources for about six years. Much more research would be needed, he said, "before we can adequately compare U.S. reserves in coal, for example, with reserves in coal in other parts of the world."

———

MR. VAN ROYEN: More than that, it seems to me that in trying to determine what is going to happen in the next 50 years in the world, any figures on petroleum are just so much eyewash. How many parts of the world are there where we may still discover other petroleum resources that we know nothing about now? It seems to me that techniques will move so far ahead that eventually we will be able to go up to a much higher figure than the present estimates of effective reserves.

J. E. SWEARINGEN (Standard Oil Company (Indiana)): As to oil reserves, they stand now at about 32 billion barrels for the United States. That figure represents the best opinion of competent geologists and engineers throughout the industry of the amount

[1] See The President's Materials Policy Commission, *Resources for Freedom*, June, 1952.

of oil that can be recovered from presently known fields by present methods at current prices.

Actually, the 32-billion-barrel reserve is more an underground inventory of petroleum than an ultimate reserve of any sort.

It is important to realize that we have been finding oil at nearly one and a half times the rate we have been using it up. There have been produced in the United States so far some 45 billion barrels of oil. I don't know what the average recovery of the oil in place has been, but I would guess it is probably not more than 25 to 30 percent. If we ever find out how to recover the oil remaining in the ground after depletion of oil fields by past and present practices, we could double or even triple the amount of reserves we now carry on our books.

MR. CRESSEY: It is clear that in fuel resources the United States is the richest country in the world. The second richest country appears to be the Soviet Union.

The U.S.S.R. has about 1 trillion 680 billion tons of coal. That is their figure, of course, but there is coal all across the country. And the Soviet Union certainly has very great reserves of petroleum as well as many other mineral resources.

MARY E. McDERMOTT (Atlantic Refining Company): In the last 27 years proven reserves of crude oil have increased at an average rate of 4.5 percent a year. In order to meet a demand for petroleum in 1975 of 5 billion barrels a year, allowing for approximately 2½ million barrels a day of imports, proved reserves would have to increase at a rate of only 2.4 percent.

SERGE B. JURENEV (Continental Oil Company): Aren't we attempting to do the impossible here in trying to estimate possible reserves? Our resources are dynamic, not static. Prices, technology, and other factors are all involved and affect the volume of reserves ultimately recoverable.

TELL ERTL (Ohio State University): We have talked about oil and coal and gas. I should like to talk about shale oil. I believe we are very close to commercial production of it; I feel there will be a production of oil from oil shale in 1975 of perhaps 1 billion barrels a year. One thousand square miles of the Piceance Creek basin of western Colorado will yield 100 billion barrels of shale oil from the high-grade Mahogany Ledge and perhaps 500 billion barrels from +15 gallon a ton oil shale. About 230,000 square miles of the eastern United States is underlain by oil shale. In fact, before the first oil well was discovered in Pennsylvania in 1859 there were 60 plants producing oil from oil shale in the central United States.

What energy sources will expand most rapidly in the next 25 years? How long will oil and gas gain in competition with coal?

ALFRED R. POWELL (Koppers Company, Inc.): The big thing in the increased use of oil and gas has been economics, not reserves. I was chairman of a Paley Commission group that studied the matter of chemicals and other things from coal. First we had to study the petroleum industry for the next 25 years. We reached a figure of 11 million barrels a day in 1975, as compared with approximately 6 million barrels a day at present—almost a doubling of petroleum use in the next 25 years. The Stanford Research Institute made a study a year or two later, and I think in a more scientific manner than we did; they also came out to 11 million barrels a day of liquid fuel demand in 1975. Published information on the increasing cost of producing oil from the deeper wells, plus the fact that we considered demand for coal would be much more stable over the coming years, led us to believe there would be a good deal of synthetic oil.

E. WAYLES BROWNE, JR. (Bethesda, Md.): Another study, which was not published but which was part of the working papers of the Paley Commission, suggested that gas may reach a peak consumption of 20 trillion cubic feet a year about 1970, dropping back to 15 trillion in 1975. Add up the consumption for the next 25 years, starting with 8.8 trillion cubic feet in 1952, and you will

find you have used up an awful chunk of the estimated ultimate reserves of gas. You may be producing oil in the East Texas field 50 years from now, but there will be no gas left in it.

What are the prospects for the unconventional sources of energy?

WILLIAM A. LOEB (Nuclear Development Associates, Inc.): If by "prospects" we mean "is there enough energy stored in the unconventional sources to be significant," I think the answer is certainly "Yes." Between nuclear energy and solar energy there is certainly enough to outweigh all of the energy we have been talking about so far. I would say that we can expect nuclear energy to provide on the order of 20 times the total energy in the more or less conventional fossil fuels.

In the early forties there was very little known uranium in this country. But people started looking, and the more they looked, the more they found. This seems to be continuing.

If the conventional fuels increase in cost, it will tend to make us change over to the so-called unconventional ones.

I think we must also think of other uses for our fossil fuels. Certainly if we are able, because of a new source of energy, to shift sources from energy into chemicals, it would have a marked effect on our total resources position.

What is the outlook for continued progress in technology of energy? Must we expect the rate of improvement to flatten out?

E. D. REEVES (Standard Oil Development Company): I think the extent of any resource is measured by the effective use that can be made of it.

Many of us in the oil industry, at least, have been quite disturbed by the tendency of the Paley Commission report to deprecate what has been done in technology on the useful application of our energy resources.

The report questioned the value from a crude oil conservation standpoint of improving the antiknock quality of gasoline. The Commission said that the efficiency gained from an increased compression ratio is at least in part illusory, because a great deal of energy is lost at the refinery in making the high-octane gasoline that must be used.

This impression is not correct. Technological developments applied to the refining of petroleum to improve the yield of more valuable products and to enhance their quality has been a tremendous force working toward conservation of crude oil. This is particularly true of improvement in the antiknock quality of gasoline.

Over the last two or three decades, the combined improvement in the antiknock quality of gasoline and engine efficiency has been such that two gallons of gasoline can now do the work formerly done by three gallons. It is true that some processes for improving the antiknock quality of gasoline do reduce gasoline yields from crude oil. In all such cases, however, the added antiknock quality imparts to the gasoline greater energy in automotive use than the energy of the raw material consumed.

I think that in converting products to higher octane gasoline the oil industry has used possibly the total production of an East Texas oil field, but this work, as a result, created maybe 30 East Texas oil fields.

What are the likely future improvements in transportation of energy?

HERSCHEL F. JONES (Bonneville Power Administration): I think we are all aware that the demand for electricity is increasing very much more rapidly than the demand for energy generally. This has some very interesting implications as far as the transportation of energy is concerned. Through government financing today, we are able to take power roughly 200 miles at a cost in the Pacific Northwest of about 1 mill a kilowatt-hour. That cost is going to drop appreciably, assuming the construction costs remain constant during the next three or four years, as we go to very much higher voltages. Our standard now is 230,000 volts. If we go up to 345,000 volts,

a single transmission circuit will carry approximately 500,000 kilowatts as compared with approximately 180,000 kilowatts over our standard circuit today.

This, I think, opens up the possibility that a great deal of fuel, instead of being hauled from the mine to a generating plant, will be used at the mine to generate power. The power will be moved then very much more cheaply over very much higher voltage circuits to the areas where it is being used.

There is already a tendency in this direction. I expect it to grow very rapidly.

What factors will determine when we resume heavy reliance on our large coal reserves? How can the use of coal be stimulated?

FARRINGTON DANIELS (University of Wisconsin): Research on the utilization of petroleum products has been very successful. Could more be done in research on coal to stimulate its use? Certainly such research will come in the future. Should it not come more vigorously now?

MR. POWELL: It is simply a matter of economics. When somebody finds that it is cheaper to burn gas than coal under his electric utility boiler he will burn natural gas. Yet from a conservation standpoint it is an awful thing to do.

I don't think research and technology will have nearly as much effect on the situation as economics and the time is coming when economics will take care of it. I feel sure there will be an increase in cost of both natural gas and petroleum. It is bound to come long before the reserves are exhausted.

R. K. LANE (Public Service Company of Oklahoma): It is not only a matter of economics but sound conservation to burn gas under a utility boiler in an oil country where gas would otherwise go into the air.

ROLAND A. KAMPMEIER (Tennessee Valley Authority): I wonder whether we are giving enough weight here to demand. Of course, you cannot determine demand without knowing something about supply. But likewise you can't determine what the supply is going to be without knowing a lot about the demand.

Demand has proven 99 times out of 100 to be underestimated. Estimates 5, 10, and 15 years in advance have been so pitifully low that I think it scared everybody out of making any more estimates. But I believe we need to do a lot more thinking about demand as well as supply.

RALPH A. MORGEN (National Science Foundation): I think we are all more or less in agreement that eventually petroleum will be less available and therefore the cost will go up. We will agree that sooner or later our natural gas will be used up. But until we know more about how to produce coal economically we will not have an answer to this question. So it comes back to this: When do we start to do more research?

Should supplies of high-grade resources be reserved for future users and for national defense? Can high-grade uses be encouraged?

That reliable, up-to-date information on all aspects of the energy situation is needed was implicit throughout the discussion, but several participants expressed belief that existing industry and governmental agencies in the energy field are fully competent to collect and analyze such information.

MR. JURENEV: Is this question to infer the desirability of end-use control? Are we talking about creating a special body which would determine who does what and when? To me there is an implication here of end-use control of fuels.

Use is determined by consumers' preference, the relative efficiency of fuels, and price. There is an automatic adjustment. Moreover, we are going to discover a lot more oil and a lot more gas than we can store. How could we store something we haven't yet discovered?

Should we not leave the answer to that question to be determined by economics rather than by government fiat?

MR. REEVES: I don't know how to define a high-grade resource. I think perhaps what

we should be talking about is high-cost and low-cost resources. Why take the lowest-cost and most readily available resources and lock them up and go out for the most expensive ones today? It seems to me we would be cutting off our nose to spite our face, because we can find out how to use the others more economically in the future.

E. S. PETTYJOHN (Institute of Gas Technology): Coal, we believe, can be converted into natural gas substitute at the ratio of 15,000 cubic feet per ton. One trillion cubic feet would take some 70 million tons of coal. There is no limit on the gas that could be produced from coal; conversion hinges entirely on economic factors, not upon scientific ones.

Exploration and Production of Mineral Fuels

Where are future reserves of oil and gas most likely to be found?

AUSTIN CADLE (Standard Oil Company of California): Since most of our oil has been found at moderate depths it may be inferred that future oil will be found at greater depths. Also, new areas open up as the search for oil goes on. I think it is extremely important to bear that in mind.

We know of the progress that is being made in the Canadian provinces, not only in Alberta, but in Manitoba and Saskatchewan as well. We know of the great activity which is beginning in the Williston Basin. And, of course, we have the more or less unexplored offshore lands.

Are the present rewards for exploration sufficient? Is further encouragement needed? Some aspects of these questions were later discussed in Subsection C, pages 243-45. See also Section IV, pages 191-97, for discussion of depletion allowances for minerals.

T. M. DAILEY, JR. (Humble Oil and Refining Company): In view of the fear expressed that we do not have adequate reserves, I think we might say that the incentive has not been too great. Certainly, it should not be reduced if we want to continue to meet the requirements for petroleum.

MR. BROWNE: What would the relative merits be if, instead of percentage depletion, oil people charged higher prices for their products and paid taxes like everybody else?

ROLAND V. RODMAN (Anderson-Prichard Oil Corporation): The question, "What would happen if you paid taxes like everybody else?" is illustrative of the great misunderstanding that many people in industry, in business, and in public life have of percentage depletion.

The oil business is not comparable to the normal manufacturing enterprise. It is based on prospecting and risk. We have to carry on our books a great many leases which result in a charge-out. We have to pay rentals on those leases for a great many years. We drill a great many dry holes from which we get no benefit. We carry on vast exploration programs, both geological and geophysical, that must be written off as failures.

These elements exist in a business of risk that do not exist in the ordinary manufacturing enterprise. Wherever you market a ton of coal or a barrel of oil you are converting your capital into income, and surely any business of that character must have some allowance for depletion. This was and is recognized by the Congress as sound business principle—never as a tax dodge.

Percentage depletion has worked. In 1926, when it went into effect, we had proven reserves of oil in this country of 8 billion barrels. Since that time we have produced 36 billion barrels, and we have in the ground today 28 billion barrels of crude oil and about 5 billion barrels of like products available for our use as the need requires. Under the percentage depletion system, the oil industry has kept up with public demand, has provided products at a fair price and, in the process, has profited less, on an average, than American manufacturers generally.

MR. BROWNE: We still do not have an answer to the immediate question: What would the price of the oil be if they did pay taxes?

MR. RODMAN: The question cannot be answered precisely, but without depletion allowances I know that the price of gasoline would be advanced sufficiently to offset it, because I know that the returns on invested capital in the oil industry are no more than adequate to attract sufficient capital into the industry to enable it to carry on.

How have improvements in production techniques affected output from old and new mines and wells? Should output be controlled on a comparable basis among the producing states?

MR. RODMAN: With repressuring and other modern secondary recovery methods, average recovery of oil in place has been increased to as much as 45 or 50 percent. Recovery in the East Texas field is perhaps as high as 85 percent. I think we can expect to see great expansion in the use of gas and water injection in the next 10 years.

MR. CADLE: As to production controls, on many past occasions Texas has borne the brunt of readjustments in supply. This burden should be shared more equitably by other states.

There is considerable need for a conservation law in California, and we hope in time to have one. I do not mean to imply we are wasting oil, but I think over the long run much would be saved by such a law.

MR. RODMAN: Only six states—Kansas, Oklahoma, Texas, Arkansas, Louisiana, and New Mexico—have the statutory right to regulate production of oil and gas. I think it is a fine thing for the individual states to have such a law, but I think it would be very impractical to have an over-all federal agency with that power.

MR. CADLE: I am not in favor of federal regulation; but I think cooperation, let us call it, between the individual producing states would promote conservation.

MR. DANIELS: We are interested in making the oil we have go as far as it will go.

Subsection A

UNCONVENTIONAL SOURCES

With many years' supply of the fossil fuels still at its disposal, the United States is at the threshold of being able to develop virtually unlimited amounts of power through nuclear fission at costs which may be nearly competitive with conventional methods. But there are many questions to be resolved, not the least of them the question of the respective roles of government and private enterprise in atomic development.

On the horizon are possibilities of economical use of the great but diffuse sources of solar energy, already a reality on a small scale in parts of the country. Over the horizon are other potentials. The flow of water changes from year to year but, in the words of one of the participants, "Nothing disturbs the flow of the wind; power can be gathered from it in commercial quantities and at a fairly steady average rate, one year with another, if we need it badly enough. Heat from the earth probably can become an economical source of power."

This subsection concerned itself principally with the most immediate possibilities among the unconventional sources—nuclear and solar energy. At the conclusion of the meeting the Chairman summed up the situation this way: "It is comforting to know that if we were never to learn more about our unconventional sources, and if all our fossil fuels were to disappear tomorrow, we should still be able to generate power for such a small number of times the present cost that our way of life, I believe, would not change significantly."

FROM THE RECORD

Atomic Energy

GEORGE L. WEIL (Washington, D.C.): When you fission an atom of Uranium 235 you get two major useful products: the kinetic energy of the fission products and neutrons. The energy can be used for useful work; the neutrons can, for example, produce plutonium.

Two types of power reactor plants have been considered. One is dual-purpose, producing plutonium and also useful power. The other is the so-called single-purpose or power-only reactor; this can include the breeder type reactor. Today, because plutonium is an atomic weapon material, there is a good deal of interest in the dual-purpose reactor. One can charge off a large fraction of the cost of the reactor's operation to the plutonium. However, in my opinion, one can't produce both power and plutonium efficiently. They are to some

extent incompatible.

The single-purpose reactor, in my opinion, is the more economical way to make power. It does not mean that you throw away the plutonium—quite the opposite. Here, one is interested in the plutonium as a fuel to take the place of the Uranium 235, which is being consumed in the reactor. It is a very important part of the economics of the single-purpose or power-only reactor.

The distinction is the value that is attached to the plutonium. If it has sufficient military value, then it is better to take it out of the reactor and sell it to the military. If it does not have military value then it is better to return it to your power plant and use it as a fuel.

HAROLD BARNETT (The Rand Corporation): Let us assume that the plutonium is not used to make bombs, but is just held. Let us assume further that the decay rate is very slow. That being the case, you eventually will be able to use *all* of the natural uranium and thorium, whichever method you use now.

H. C. HOTTEL (Massachusetts Institute of Technology): If we are examining the economic possibilities of nuclear power, I don't see how we can know the answer until the government agrees to an experiment which has power alone as its objective.

WILLIAM A. LOEB (Nuclear Development Associates, Inc.): It seems to me the first thing that needs to be determined is what the resources of uranium are. I understand that there are reputed to be something like 25 million tons of natural uranium in the world, not all of which by any means are in the United States.

The fissionable material in these 25 million tons, if we just burned it, would amount to about one-seventh of the total estimated energy reserves that are available to us in the fossil fuels, that is, the oil and coal fuels we know about today. However, if we went to the other extreme and converted all of the uranium into fissionable material, then we would have multiplied this one-seventh by 140.[2] Then there would be a supply of energy 20 times the total energy available in the fossil fuels we know about today.

In addition, there is thorium. The thorium reserve is very small, but people haven't been looking for thorium very hard.

FARRINGTON DANIELS (University of Wisconsin): Another way to increase reserves of fissionable material is to go to lower grade ores.

A tenth of a percent, or 2 pounds of uranium per ton of ore, is the lowest grade the United States Government will buy now, but if still lower grade ores can be used the reserves will be enormously larger.

Back of the economics lies technology; research can completely upset the present economic picture.

Can atomic reactors become a major source

of industrial power within the next two decades?

BERTRAND A. LANDRY (Battelle Memorial Institute): If by "major" we mean 50 percent, 30 percent, 20 percent, or even 10 percent, I do not believe that atomic energy can become a major source in the United States within the next 20 years; it may become a significant contributor.

MR. BARNETT: The aggregate U.S. requirement for electric power by 1975 will be in the neighborhood of 1,000-1,500 billion kilowatt-hours a year—three to five times the present level. What is to prevent atomic power from becoming a significant factor?

MR. LANDRY: The figure for 1975 is an extrapolation, really, of the present rate of expansion of the electric industry.

MR. BARNETT: It is the figure the Paley Commission and others arrived at on the basis of quite detailed estimates. But I grant you it is loose; that's the reason for the wide range. Certainly, with a reserve level many times the reserve of fuels such as gas and oil, which now provide 40 percent of our thermal power, there is a lot of room for atomic power.

MR. WEIL: Today we are at zero kilowatts of nuclear power. If we figure on nuclear energy for 30 percent of our requirements 20 years from now, it would mean developing it at a rate of about 2 million kilowatts of nuclear power a year.

The only power plant I know of that has been authorized to date will have a capacity of 60,000 kilowatts. The project is supposed to take three or four, and I have heard as much as five years. I think the important thing to remember is that this is only a competing method of producing power. The cost of nuclear energy will have to come down before it can be developed on a large scale.

HERSCHEL F. JONES (Bonneville Power Administration): Is it a foregone conclusion that construction of a 60,000 kilowatt plant will be the only activity in the next five years?

MR. WEIL: There may be others, but even this 60,000 kilowatt plant is estimated to cost

[2] It was explained that in uranium as found in the ground, only one part in 140 is naturally fissionable; the remainder must be converted to be useful.

many tens of millions of dollars. Once you have gotten the cost down to where it is competitive, then you can really start expanding.

L. E. GRINTER (University of Florida): Ten years ago people said electric welding was almost economic, but not quite. Now it has practically taken over the field. As soon as atomic energy develops a slight economic advantage over fossil fuels you will have geometric progression; it could take over almost completely in 10 years.

MR. WEIL: I think there is an important difference between the development of reactors and electric welding: that is the cost of a pilot plant experiment—the cost of getting information. But I heartily agree that once there is an economic advantage, even a slight one, ordinary industrial forces will make it grow.

DAL HITCHCOCK (Clark, Hitchcock and Associates, Washington, D.C.): Would not the utilization of radiant energy for purposes other than the generation of power have an important bearing on costs?

MR. LOEB: Nuclear power has a number of unusual aspects. Most of the people in the reactor business recognize that, but you can't assume that they can be turned to profit until some way is found to make use of them. At the moment, most of the fission products are detriments rather than attributes. You have to get rid of them and they are awfully expensive to get rid of.

I think the costs of reactors will be brought down within two decades, and that by then there will probably be plants which will be competitive. But they will not put all of the thermal plants out of business; they will be competing with new and replacement plants and hence will build up along with the electrical industry.

THOMAS P. COCKE (Bureau of Yards and Docks, USN): The impetus for further research and development may well be the transportation factor. There are plenty of places where the transportation cost of combustion fuels today is almost prohibitive, whereas nuclear fuels are essentially weightless.

MR. BARNETT: Atomic power does not have to compete with average power costs in the country. It has to compete with the incremental cost of power at the specific locations where power demand is increasing. Some of these locations are without much coal and with hydro power well utilized.

MR. WEIL: The fact remains, however, that new reactors cost at least twice as much as conventional plants.

MR. DANIELS: The situation, it seems to me, is optimistic. Before we even get started we are down to perhaps twice the cost. In nuclear energy we have a new technology; we haven't even begun to get at the practical shortcuts that always show up in actual operation. I think we should try several different types of reactors. I would like to see competing developments on a pilot plant scale.

I think it will be a long time in the United States before we are able to compete with cheap coal. But there are many countries where the situation is different. For example, Brazil or India, with lots of thorium and little coal or water power, and with industrial improvements greatly needed to raise the standard of living, could well consider nuclear energy now. We could be so conservative in the United States that foreign countries might forge ahead of us in the development of atomic power.

What are the possibilities of converting nuclear energy directly into electrical energy?

E. J. DRAKE (Australian Scientific Liaison Office): One thing that surprises me is the general assumption that we must necessarily degrade nuclear energy to heat. The laws of thermodynamics make it difficult to get the energy once we allow it to drop to a lower level in the form of heat. Is it conceivable, where fission first results in streams of neutrons and electrons moving with a very high velocity, that we might direct that energy into the useful channel of electrical energy?

MR. WEIL: To the best of my knowledge no process has been thought of that would provide more than a few percent of efficiency;

it would be a great step forward if somebody could develop such a process.

MR. DRAKE: When burning coal and oil under a boiler you get direct transfer by radiation on the tubes, which may account for about half of the total heat absorbed by a boiler. In a reactor you take the heat out at relatively low temperatures to start with.

MR. WEIL: And the ultimate temperature is more or less unlimited. You can go to much higher temperatures than with chemical processes.

Considerable discussion turned on the matter of government versus private development of atomic energy. Many participants believed that more information could be made public without endangering national security. Complicating the central question of private patents in the nuclear energy field are such matters as compulsory licensing, royalty arrangements, and what to do about patented inventions which originally had no relation to nuclear energy but which later became part of a nuclear operation. These and related matters were considered by some participants as slowing the industrial development of atomic energy.

ANTHONY W. SMITH (CIO Conservation Committee): We are opposed to the plans of the Atomic Energy Commission to turn facilities, patents, and further operations over to the large privately owned monopolistic corporations. The government itself, we are satisfied, could do a better job.

We hope that more attention will be given to the possibilities of peacetime uses for atomic energy, and the best way to guarantee that new peacetime ideas get into quick application is to keep the control in the hands of the Commission.

We are strongly opposed to granting restrictive private patent rights in atomic energy equipment and processes. If there is to be a monopoly of any kind, it should be a public monopoly, subject to control by the people through the government.

MR. HOTTEL: This is in a sense the big issue of the atomic energy development. Is there someone from the other side who wants to speak on this point?

C. B. ELLIS (Walter B. Kidde Nuclear Laboratories): We have been studying the matter of nuclear power reactors a long time and are engaged in official studies under Atomic Energy Commission auspices with the Duquesne Power and Light Company.

Our company believes it is possible right now to build a power reactor for less than a cent and a half per kilowatt-hour, which is less than twice the usual commercial rate for thermal power in this country. Also, we think this can be done by private industry and private capital without relying very heavily on government capital.

So, why don't we go out and do it today? To a very large extent the answer is patents. We believe we can find money privately for building nuclear power reactors, if people who make inventions from now on are permitted to have patents on those inventions. One cannot get any private capital into this business under the present rules of the game. We can go forward only if some more inventions are made. The people who pay the salaries of the folks who make the new discoveries ought to have the rights to those new discoveries.

EDWARD STONE (Institute of Life Insurance, New York): A patent does not give you a monopoly. The principle of patent rights is to induce you to disclose information that you are otherwise afraid of disclosing, and you then have exclusive right to dispose of the particular commodity that you make as a result of these patent rights.

Nobody is contending that the existing field of knowledge should be made a monopoly of any particular group. But I think we must bear in mind that one of the things that keeps industry from doing too much on this now is this problem of patent rights. You can't expect any industrial group to get the money together to attempt costly experimentation if it doesn't know whether it is going to have any of these rights permanently. We might be talking somewhat in a vacuum about costs and possibilities if we do not also realize the need for a favorable climate for industry action.

Mr. Hottel: If five different corporations spent their own money on five different ideas, I am perfectly convinced that some of them would lose a lot of money. I am equally sure that in the course of trying to keep from losing that money they are going to work very much harder than under some other system. I believe that the public will benefit, and that in the long run they themselves will retrieve their bad position.

It seems to me that the argument in favor of private initiative is that simple.

Frederick H. Warren (Consulting Engineer, Washington, D.C.): We need the incentive of patent rights but probably there needs to be a transition period in which those who want to get into this field can readily gain access to present knowledge. From that, they can start developing their own ideas in engineering improvements.

To enable only those who have been in possession of the majority of this information to start from scratch and develop their own patent position would, I think, a little restrict the field.

Maywood Boggs (International Brotherhood of Boilermakers, Iron Shipbuilders, Blacksmiths, Forgers and Helpers): [Mr. Boggs said he was speaking only for his union, not for the American Federation of Labor.] It is generally recognized that if a successful nuclear reactor is developed you will still have your turbines and generators, but the boiler as now known is out.

Nevertheless, we adopted a resolution in our convention last July endorsing the proposal of Chairman Gordon Dean of the Atomic Energy Commission, before the Joint Congressional Committee on Atomic Energy, to license certain patents that the government holds and permit developments by private industry and private capital to be patented under certain restrictions by the particular group making the discovery or making the product.

Personally, I have held the belief for a long time that public monopolies can be just as bad as private monopolies, and vice versa. Many things have happened in the history of the world which, at the time they happened, were just as important as the discovery of and the ability to use an atomic bomb. We didn't have to put all of these things under complete government control in years gone by, and I see no reason why in our country we have to do it now.

Ralph A. Morgen (National Science Foundation): If we are going to talk about atomic power competing with power from fossil fuels we must start from the same beginning points. We believe in private enterprise in this country; that is the system under which we work. Therefore, within the limits of security, if we can put the atomic power industry on the same basis as the oil business or the coal business, with proper protection for the public benefit, then I think we can begin to get somewhere; we will be starting from the same basis.

The potentialities that may lie in other unknown sources of atomic energy were considered.

Mr. Hitchcock: What is the outlook for sources of atomic energy other than uranium and thorium?

Mr. Ellis: This is a fascinating question. I earnestly hope that research in this field will be pushed forward. Technically, it is not forever an impossibility to get atomic energy from things other than uranium and thorium. You cannot say, for instance, that it is impossible to get atomic energy some day from hydrogen out of the ocean—and there is plenty of that. We certainly should be trying. I personally expect to see nuclear power on an enormous scale from other things.

Mr. Hottel: In any appraisal of the prospects of atomic power in the next 20 years we should remember that further research in the fossil fuels can also greatly enhance the availability and efficiency of these sources. Shale oil added to petroleum resources would greatly change the picture of the time in which we need to become concerned about petroleum; the energy in our fossil fuels has a thermodynamic availability that is substantially 100 percent, and we are now using about 25 to 30 percent.

MR. LOEB: There are still other possibilities. We speak of fossil fuels, but they are fuels only because we use them as fuels. They have chemical properties which uranium and thorium do not. Some day we might consider ourselves profligate in burning them up.

Another part of the story is transportation of energy. Should atomic energy some day prove both feasible and economical, you will be able to carry in your hand a quantity of fuel equal in energy to 100 carloads of coal.

Solar Energy

MR. HOTTEL: Boston receives 390,000 B.T.U. of sunlight per square foot per year on a horizontal surface. That is fairly typical, I believe, of the solar energy potential of American cities. The other extreme in our hemisphere is San Juan, Puerto Rico, which receives 710,000 B.T.U. These two numbers substantially bracket the field.

In terms of fuel oil equivalent, the sunlight per square foot per year amounts to 2.8 gallons for Boston and 5 gallons for San Juan—that is, if the fuel oil were burned with 100 percent efficiency. So we have in solar energy a source of high potential but very dilute.

The story of solar energy is very different from that of atomic energy. Presently proposed uses of solar energy can be understood or visualized by the layman, whereas advanced knowledge is needed to understand atomic energy. But there is no dodging the fact that solar energy is so thinly spread over the earth as not to be "free" just for the taking.

At what stage is the development of solar energy?

MARIA TELKES (New York University): There is a tendency to evaluate what has been done in terms of research spending. It has been estimated that for each $100 spent on atomic energy development only a fraction of a cent has been spent on solar energy development.

Yet the small amounts spent have produced some results.

It is obvious that solar energy has many commercial applications. For example, there are about 50,000 solar water heaters in operation in Florida right now. The efficiency of these devices, in converting solar heat into hot water, is 40 to 60 percent. The initial cost has been rather high, but fuel savings and conveniences are offsetting factors.

Solar steam engines have been pioneered in this country by Erickson. He was followed by Schuman's development in Africa, where an efficiency of $4\frac{1}{2}$ percent was attained in converting solar energy into steam with parabolic reflectors. The cost was debatable, but it was generally agreed that for Egypt, where the tests were made, power could have been generated at about the cost of fuel in Egypt at that time. This was in 1913.

Dr. Abbot at the Smithsonian Institution has done a considerable amount of work on solar steam engines, as you know. He has given a figure, based on calculation, which is around 12 percent. The solar steam engine by Schuman in Egypt covered one-third of an acre, whereas Dr. Abbot's device was a smaller model.

Recent experiments with solar house heating, using water as the heat storage medium, were carried out at the Massachusetts Institute of Technology by Professor Hottel's group. These solar collectors can be built for moderate-level temperature collections with an efficiency which conservatively is around 35 percent during the winter. This, however, could be increased to an annual average of possibly 50 percent.

You have to store solar heat from clear days for the night and for cloudy days. Several heat storage systems have been proposed. One of the latest is using phase change, or heat of fusion. This involves changing a solid crystalline material to a liquid, or partially liquid material, by using solar heat. A great deal of heat can be accumulated in a small space with this form of storage.

There are several materials which have moderate melting temperatures or phase change temperatures, so that the combination of these phase changes with solar collectors can produce suitable means of storing heat. About 10,000 B.T.U. can be stored per cubic foot of material. The cost of such a solar heating system may be approximately the same as that of conventional house heating, with further development. This method has been proposed by myself and was used in a test house at Dover, Mass.

Solar evaporation is another application. Efficiency of this method could be as high as 60 percent. Experiments are in progress.

GEORGE O. G. LÖF (Chemical Engineer and Research Consultant, Denver): There are two devices for collecting solar energy and converting it to heat that have been experimentally used. One is a black flat surface which is overlaid by one or more pieces of glass through which the sun shines and heats the black surface. The escape of heat from the black surface is prevented by the glass cover plates because they are opaque to the type of long-wave radiation coming back. Heat is then obtained from the black surface by circulating a fluid around it.

The other system involves focusing the sunlight by means of large mirrors onto smaller surfaces; the heat is actually transferred to the working fluid at those smaller surfaces. The amount of surface that must be exposed to the sun to collect a certain number of B.T.U.'s is the same in both of these systems.

Taking the efficiency of collecting the solar energy and converting it to heat as 40 percent to 60 percent of the incident radiation, and employing this and the efficiency of conventional heat engines which convert heat to electric power, we can compute some over-all efficiencies of sunlight to electric power. Then we can calculate how many square feet of collecting surface are needed to supply a kilowatt-hour of electric energy, after which we can get an approximate idea of the costs.

For the flat-plate collector, with a conventional heat engine operating at a maximum temperature of, say, 240 degrees Fahrenheit, we might expect an over-all conversion efficiency from sunlight to electric power of $4\frac{1}{2}$

percent to $5\frac{1}{2}$ percent. That does not look very good, but even in fuel-burning power plants, 25 percent is a good efficiency in getting the heat out of the fuel into electric energy. So we have perhaps a fivefold difference.

With the focusing type of parabolic mirror concentrated on a small spot or on a tube in which steam is generated, and with a heat engine operating at a top temperature of about 480 degrees Fahrenheit, an over-all efficiency of sunlight to electric energy of 12 to 15 percent can be obtained. Of course, the mirror type collector is more expensive to build than the flat-plate type because of its greater fabrication expense and the requirement that it must follow the movement of the sun.

Take Queensland, Australia, as an example for solar power plant economic comparison. If we can build a flat-plate collector for $7.50 per square meter, the supplementary, non-firm electric power that we could produce from solar energy would be competitive with the power that is now produced by thermal plants at a present fuel cost of 0.85 cent per kilowatt-hour.

In Japan, the average fuel cost per kilowatt-hour generated in existing thermal plants is 1.4 cents. If we can build a collector for about $14.50 per square meter we can produce supplementary solar power as cheaply as thermal power in central Japan.

The situation is not nearly so promising in the United States. The average fuel cost in this country for thermal electric power plants is 0.34 cent per kilowatt-hour. We would have to be able to build a solar collector for $3 per square meter in order to match that fuel cost and sell power at the same price. Building a collector for $3 per square meter appears impossible. The minimum cost would be more like $10 to $20 per square meter, or $1 to $2 per square foot.

But electricity from solar energy is a borderline proposition in some of the areas of the world where fuel is very expensive.

MR. HOTTEL: Calculations have been made, based on solar data for El Paso, Texas, from which it was concluded that if four glass plates were used, air spaced and treated for low reflection, this would constitute the optimum number of glass plates for power production in the El Paso area; and an annual over-all efficiency in conversion of sunlight to power of slightly over 8 percent, instead of the 4½ to 5½ percent just stated, could be realized. That's a little better, but it is still not good.

El Paso would yield 0.04 of a kilowatt-hour per square foot per day from such a plant, or 15 kilowatt-hours in one year from each square foot of the plant. So the capitalization of the value of 15 kilowatt-hours is what one is permitted to spend on this square foot. If the collector is going to cost $1 to $2 a square foot, then this power will cost from 0.75 cent to 1.5 cents a kilowatt-hour.

MR. LANDRY: The cost of the collectors is the principal item, but the load factor on the plant may also be important. Was that included in the calculations?

MR. LÖF: In my study it was assumed that the solar plant would be part of an integrated system in which thermal or hydro would carry the load when the sun was not shining. So the only saving made possible by the solar plant would be in fuel. Storage is not considered, only the replacement of fuel that would ordinarily be used during the daylight period.

Mention was made of the uses of solar energy in connection with the photoelectric cell and with the photosynthesis work being done on single-celled animals and plants.

MR. HOTTEL: There have been some developments with the photoelectric cell that present some interesting possibilities. General Electric presented a paper some time ago before the American Physical Society on the performance of the germanium photocell, which looked quite promising.

Then, quite recently I had a preview of a Bell Telephone Laboratory effort. They have attained a conversion of incident sunlight to useful electrical energy that is 6 percent efficient, a rather remarkable advance over the conventional photoelectric cell. This is an-

other kind of flat-plate gadget using silicon. It is not a heat engine. It takes energy from the sun and converts it directly to electricity.

If we knew how to build silicon blocking layer photocells by the acre at low cost, 6 percent would begin to be an interesting number. The blocking layer is only one-ten thousandth of an inch thick, so there is not much silicon in that part of the device. However, large quantities of copper, presumably, would be required to collect this low-voltage energy from large areas.

MR. LOEB: One of the many methods of using solar energy that is receiving a great deal of attention at this time is photosynthesis other than in normal agriculture, which is certainly one of our biggest solar energy industries. What I have in mind here is the work being done on single-celled animals and plants, like algae. The conversion from solar energy into energy which can then be used, let us say, in a power plant or for people to eat—not electrical energy, but another form of thermal energy—has been found to be rather high in laboratory experiments. There is an argument as to whether it is 25 percent or 75 percent. Even 25 percent is higher than the ones we have been talking about. The first approach is probably to use this energy as a food source. While the amount of energy used as a food is only about 1 percent of the energy we use in the United States, the price we pay for this type of energy is very, very high.

Solar energy is coming to this earth all the time. It seems to me we should use as much of it as we can to replace the energy that otherwise must come from coal and oil and thorium and uranium. Then we can use these resources for things that solar energy is not suited for. It seems to me solar energy is important from the conservation point of view.

Several participants expressed their views on the prospects for solar heating and cooling of houses on an economic basis, and as a means of conserving conventional fuels. In response to a question, Mr. Hottel estimated that about 20 percent of the energy consumed in the United States goes for space heating.

MR. LÖF: Several houses have been built and tested and occupied, which have been heated almost entirely by solar energy. I think those working in the solar field feel that house heating will be the first sizable use for solar energy because we can get efficiencies of about 50 percent, and we can employ simple, relatively cheap solar collectors to operate at the moderate temperatures required. A house does not need expensive, high-temperature heat, or expensive converted heat in the form of electrical energy.

It appears from most of the rough economic analyses that in areas of the United States where there is plentiful solar energy and where fuel may be higher than average in cost, solar heating is almost competitive with fuel heat. Of course, it has to be supplemented by some auxiliary heating to take care of periods of severe weather.

In addition, studies are going on in the other direction—cooling—which indicate that this can be incorporated with a heating system. And the probabilities are that the system can be made competitive with conventional house-cooling equipment.

MR. HOTTEL: We have been, perhaps, a little too casual about the 40 to 60 percent efficiency of the flat-plate collector. It makes all the difference in the world which of these numbers you use in any economic study. A plot of incident sunlight, plotted against the time of day, is a sort of bell-shaped curve. The performance of flat-plate collectors is extraordinarily sensitive to the absolute height of this curve; so the difference between Boston and Bluehill is a profound one in terms of the possibilities of solar heating. Much balancing of economic factors will be needed to arrive at optimum combinations.

I personally think that in due course we shall see solar house heating on an economic basis in parts of this country.

MR. MORGEN: Another factor is the number of cloudy days. The more cloudy days you have, the more storage you have to provide, and this affects your costs.

MR. LANDRY: The fact is that all of us who live in houses use solar heating. We cannot escape it. In the summer it is obvious, of course, because of its discomforts. But we get it in the wintertime also. On a clear day, when the sun is shining brightly, our furnaces shut down more of the time. It seems to me that more exploration is needed toward development of materials for walls and roofs of our houses that will accept heat better when we need heat and reject it when we don't want it.

MR. HOTTEL: We experimented at MIT with the idea that the south wall of a house might be the place to install a combined collector and storage unit and that this might reduce the cost of the over-all system. The wall was insulated by two glass plates, with an air space, plus an aluminized shade which came down in response to a thermostat at night. A fan in a beaverboard partition separating the collector wall and living area brought heat stored in the wall into the main house as needed. It didn't work; night losses were excessive.

MR. LANDRY: I would not hope for complete solar heating, but only that you could stretch out the resources by better utilizing the solar energy that is there.

MR. HOTTEL: I agree. At MIT we have been encouraging our Architecture Department to use what the engineers know about the sun to influence the design of houses.

MISS TELKES: The President's Materials Policy Commission estimated that by 1975 there may be 13 million solar-heated homes in the United States. Frankly, I do not believe it will happen quite that fast.

Obviously, you need to know much more about both the technology and the economics. You need a wall structure which will transmit solar energy quite freely but also has excellent heat-insulating properties. You need to know at what level the heat should be stored. Possibly a combination of both solar heating and cooling is needed, storing heat during the winter, at say 75 degrees Fahrenheit, and during the summer accumulating night cooling at the same level.

Another question is whether such a system should be connected with a heat pump. We just don't know enough about the collector, the heat storage, or heat distribution, and their connection with summer cooling.

MR. DANIELS: Our descendents 1,000 years hence may curse us for using coal, oil, and gas to heat our houses, when we might as well have used the sun.

It seems to me that even though we do not need solar energy in the United States now, we should use it to conserve our fuel for future generations and to raise the standard of living in other parts of the world.

Should government assist research? What is the relative importance of supporting long-term research and of supporting engineering developments of pilot operations?

MR. CADLE: It seems to me that government assistance should be concentrated in the field which is most likely to contribute the most in the shortest possible time. I can't help feeling that is probably atomic energy. Moreover, I gather that it is well within the capacity of private industries, rather small private industries, to develop such items as solar home heating.

MR. MORGEN: If people planning to build homes could get some sort of tax reduction on solar heaters or solar refrigerating systems, the building of such homes might increase greatly. Maybe that is the way for the government to help.

MR. LANDRY: Everyone agrees that the irreplaceable resources are just that. Some day they will be gone forever. Whereas, as long as life can exist we will have sunshine and heat; this is something we must eventually fall back on. The question is when we should start. Now? A hundred years from now? A thousand years from now?

Everyone agrees that solar energy is costly. But with the passage of time fossil fuel costs will increase. The cost of engineering materials thereby will increase, including the cost

of solar energy installations. I say now is the time to get started. We should put in pilot plants and then go on to larger and larger installations. This is the time when we can afford to do it; as time goes on we will be able to afford it less and less.

MR. CADLE: A great deal could be done simply through education of our architects, and more particularly the general public, as to the possibilities of solar energy in home heating. People still think of solar energy as being in a far-off age. It was only 10 or 12 years ago that they thought of atomic energy in the same way.

If the possibilities were better publicized, that in itself would stimulate private industry as well as the government to go ahead with more extensive research and possibly pilot plants.

MR. HOTTEL: As long as the oil companies can maintain a 12-year inventory in the ground, we are not going to shift very fast to solar energy. We are at the stage where research is infinitely more important than pilot plant work.

I feel very strongly that government money in solar energy should go into research as against pilot plant operations. The government might support the construction of a number of experimental houses. But so far as a solar power plant is concerned, I do not see any present scheme interesting enough to warrant a pilot plant operation. The elements of solar power plants can be studied as individual pieces of the problem at a very much lower cost.

MR. LANDRY: I feel we should go beyond the pilot plant stage to the final plant. This is the time we can afford to start building solar energy plants of all types. When we begin to need it badly we won't be able to afford it.

We know enough right now to make a start. You can store solar energy indirectly by letting water build up behind a dam while you are feeding power from your solar plant into the lines that normally originate at that dam. While your solar plant is operating, the turbines are stopped and the water level behind the dam is rising. That is 100 percent efficiency.

MISS TELKES: Solar energy is not like other energy forms. The amount is proportionate to the surface. Whether you use a small-scale or a very large-scale solar energy collector it makes very little difference. A commercial-size plant would not be necessary until you use a solar energy device in combination with something else. I dread the time the government builds, say, a 10,000-kilowatt solar generator, only to discover that the whole construction of the individual focusing collectors is all wrong and you have to throw them all away.

It would be very advantageous to build experimental houses of various sizes, or at least room-sized units. With practically everything else the size factor is irrelevant, because all solar energy collection is a function of the surface. For instance, I have built a solar cooker which could be manufactured and sold for $5.00. You could bake and roast with it in Manhattan as of last month. Developments of this type do not need large pilot plants. Yet you can learn more from such a device than you could from a pilot plant covering "tremendous" areas.

MR. LÖF: I am an "anti-pilot-plant man" as far as power and water production studies are concerned, perhaps because of background in the chemical industry. The chemical industry builds pilot plants only when it is sure the idea will be an economic success. I don't think we should plunge into solar pilot plant work when we can definitely calculate that the idea can't be economically successful.

However, I don't call solar-heated houses pilot plants. They are full-scale plants. There isn't any true pilot plant stage for a solar-heated house. You do your research and then go directly into full scale. But there has been so little full-scale work that we don't even know how to keep the rain out of these collectors or how to keep the air from leaking in and out; there's a dirt problem, and things of that sort. They are just plain, simple, every-day mechanical construction difficulties. If we had a substantial number of houses built

in various parts of the country with various solar heating systems, these problems could be worked on and solved, and we should advance the date of solar heating by several years.

MR. BARNETT: Our starting point in every case, it seems to me, has to be the costs and the valuation which society places on the service. You can't just disregard the higher costs by saying we won't be able to do it later. I would argue the other way around—that you will do it later if the pressure on fuel reserves makes their costs go up.

MR. HOTTEL: The main question is: Does solar energy research merit some kind of governmental support? The people who spend the money will have to decide whether to spend it on pilot plants or on fundamental research.

HAROLD TURNER (The Ohio Power Company): The large expenditures for atomic research do not prove we should spend a lot more on solar energy research. But it seems to me it would be prudent to spend more than the extremely small amount we are spending. I don't feel that it is a thing for the government to underwrite and build up, but I think the government can lend some research assistance. And I think it is much more important to support long-term research than engineering developments or pilot operations.

BRADLEY COZZENS: (Department of Water and Power, Los Angeles): The costs of oil and gas have been going up, and they will continue to go up. My suggestion is that we look not only into solar energy but into other continuous sources. Water, of course, can be a continuous source. Year after year it saves our basic resources.

MR. ELLIS: I favor more money being put on solar housing research and on solar electric power research. But I don't see why we should assume that we definitely are going to have to use solar energy.

Nuclear physics is now in a stage of very rapid advance. In another 100 years we may well have found a way to get the enormous amounts of nuclear power that are locked up in ordinary substances. Things are moving pretty fast. If that door is unlocked, mankind will not exhaust this energy source, no matter what.

MISS TELKES: I think we should remember how solar energy has been developed so far. Was it a logical effort supported by a logical thinking group of men? Not at all. It was a haphazard exploration dating back to almost prehistoric times.

We should not try to ponder all the technicalities. Frankly, I am very skeptical about anything but individual effort and brains. I think the greatest drawback to the utilization of solar energy is just human stupidity.

MR. DANIELS: As I see it, we probably will have nuclear energy on a considerable scale. It will be centralized power, with large capital investment. In the case of solar energy—and I expect this to come also—it will be spread over a large area, weak and diffused. It can be used in small units like house heating units. The capital investment would be quite small compared with that of nuclear energy. The nuclear energy research program is secret and centralized. If we can get many people interested in many different ideas, and if there is no secrecy involved and comparatively little expense, solar energy research and development can go on simultaneously with that of atomic energy.

MR. HOTTEL: Typical of the kinds of things that could change the solar picture would be some technique of producing multiple layers of glass treated for low reflection cheaply. Dr. Vannevar Bush has some ideas about laying down glass in little curved cusps that overlie one another to form a multiple layer of quite thin pieces of glass, so that the total cost of a four-layer system overlying a black plate would be markedly less than four sheets of glass suspended on their edges in conventional ways.

That kind of a development, chemical etching of glass for low reflection, so that the reflectance would be zero at one wave length and have a low average value, appears to me to be well worth pursuing.

———

Other ideas advanced included: Development of simple solar energy devices for use in times of national disaster when people are cut off from normal energy sources; storing off-peak electricity in the form of materials, such as aluminum, which require large amounts of electricity to produce; installing supplementary solar energy facilities to help take care of intermittent but sharp daytime load increases in industrial plants; using water and other materials to store house heat during off-peak periods for use in times of peak demand.

———

Energy from the Wind

For more than a decade research has been conducted in Vermont at Grandfather's Knob upon a 1,000-kilowatt windmill. A more ambitious project is that of Percy Thomas, whose projected windmill was designed to achieve 7,500-kilowatt capacity and would cost around $1.5 million.

W. A. LYONS (New York Gas and Electric Company): The main difficulty in the earlier Grandfather's Knob experiment seemed to be the standard upon which the windmill was elevated. That broke down. The experiment itself seemed to prove a good deal of utility. The standard has been very greatly improved and now goes up to 550 feet, where there is a great deal more wind.

The possibilities seem to be very great. There has been a considerable refinement of the theories of aerodynamics, and what has been learned in the wind tunnels for airplane propellers has been put into effect in these new models.

C. E. BENNETT (Federal Power Commission): I had considerable contact with the Percy Thomas studies in years gone by. There were several things that Mr. Thomas advocated very strongly. He felt that some of the theories of aerodynamics have been improperly applied as between taking power from a propeller and putting power into a propeller. Most of the theoretical and experimental work has been directed to putting the maximum amount of power into a propeller. His problem was to get it out. Mr. Thomas advocated the construction of at least a 7,500-kilowatt wind generator.

One important point developed in connection with the Thomas work is that while the wind is highly intermittent in strength over short periods, if you consider the total wind power of any one year and compare it with the total for another year, there is no such thing as an adverse wind year comparable to an adverse water year. That is because the amount of solar energy falling on the earth is pretty constant and there is little to disturb the pattern of the wind currents. At any particular place, the total wind in a year and the amount of kilowatt hours you can depend on is relatively constant.

It was Mr. Thomas' belief that the capital cost of a wind generator of the size and general design that he contemplated would be comparable with that of a steam plant. Even if this estimate were 100 percent wrong, it is still an attractive proposition because of fuel saving, and is something I believe to be a proper project for the government. That is a type of pilot plant I would advocate for the reason that there are so many practical details of development that must be worked out.

From the very nature of the thing, the wind turbine cannot be protected effectively by patents. So the only way in which the development expense can be pooled between the interested parties is through the medium of government spending.

Earth Heat

MR. HOTTEL: If one considers extraction of heat from the deep earth with some kind of a grid system, it is easy to see that temperature defects will be established rapidly, the earth becoming depleted of its high temperature and coming to an equilibrium which is extremely unfavorable; or that extended heat transfer surfaces will have to be provided in the ground. That is not the way to take heat out of the earth.

On the other hand, if there are faults in the earth's structure, some of which occasionally show up at the surface and give us hot springs, and if we knew enough about the earth's structure so that we had some guidance as to where to drill holes to hit these faults so as to use nature's heat transfer surfaces, then a huge amount of heat becomes available.

For example, if one could tap into a fault at two places, send water into one and extract steam at the other and not have to invest in heat transfer surfaces, the returns might be interesting. This calls for a kind of geophysical prospecting that we haven't gone in for yet. I am sure there are spots on the earth where this can be done. The problem is what it may cost to find where they are.

Subsection B

ELECTRICITY AND SYNTHETIC FUELS

During the next quarter-century the demand for electricity is expected to increase much more rapidly than the demand for energy in any other form, with liquid fuels running a not-too-close second.

With its water power potential not yet fully developed but, more especially, with its large stores of coal, the United States can expect to meet its needs for electric energy with no great difficulty. What proportion of the future development should be done by public and private interests, however, will not be decided easily. There are three principal agencies—private utilities, local public agencies, and the federal government. A number of the participants voiced the belief that the problem will not be satisfactorily solved without full cooperation among all three interests.

Research on production of synthetic fuels, particularly from oil shale, has reached the point where there is no longer any question that large supplies can be made available from such sources. But when should we go ahead with large-scale experiments? Several representatives of the oil industry felt that enough more would be known about production of synthetic fuels in the next decade or two to warrant postponement of large pilot plants. Basic research, they agreed, should be continued.

Underlying the discussions on both electricity and synthetic fuels was the knowledge that the nation still has enormous stores of energy materials and has developed the technical skills to make them available as needed. The question of public versus private development of electricity was, as might be expected, the most warmly debated of all the questions before the subsection.

FROM THE RECORD

Electricity

B. R. TEARE, JR. (Carnegie Institute of Technology): In the last 25 years electric power production and use increased 400 percent, and the Paley Commission projections indicate an increase of 250 percent in the next 25 years, whereas an increase of a mere 100 percent is predicted for energy as a whole. An increase of 170 percent is expected for liquid fuels, electricity's nearest competitor. It is likely that more of the increase will come from mineral fuels than from water power.

How can we best develop electric power supply from various energy sources to meet rising demands?

CLARENCE W. MAYOTT (Consultant, retired from Hartford Electric Light Company): According to estimates published in *Electric Power Survey* in October, from the end of 1952 to the end of 1956 a total of 42,463,923 kilowatts of new capacity will have been put in. Of this, 37,128,440 kilowatts will be thermal and 5,335,483, will be hydro.

ROLAND A. KAMPMEIER (Tennessee Valley Authority): These figures point up the changing proportion of steam to hydro. For about a generation the proportion has been fairly constant, roughly one part hydro to three parts steam. That proportion is changing

rapidly now and will change considerably over the next several years.

Whether for the long pull we should try to encourage more hydro development may be one of the questions this group will want to consider.

R. K. LANE (Public Service Company of Oklahoma): The development of our power facilities should be based on engineering studies in which we evaluate each area and region. The past 75 years show that America knows how to meet sharply rising power demands.

The period of sharply rising demands has somewhat passed, at least for the present. At the same time, the ability of the manufacturing industry and of the power supply agencies to meet increased demands is now much higher than at any time in our history. We always figure that our demands will double on an average of once every eight years.

Of course, there should be coordination between all types of power, wherever that is feasible and economical, so that all regions are adequately supplied.

It should be remembered that the cost of purchased power in a finished manufactured article is relatively low. Currently, it is estimated to be about 0.6 percent of the value of the finished product for the average industry.

FRANCIS L. ADAMS (Federal Power Commission): The Bureau of Power of the Federal Power Commission estimates that the remaining undeveloped water power, not all of it necessarily economic, is on the order of 400 billion kilowatt-hours average annual production.

Assuming this is all developed and adding the approximately 100 billion kilowatt-hours already developed, it appears that the water power proportion of our total electric energy production would never reach more than about 30 percent.

Advance of the art in design of steam plants is making it more and more difficult to justify some hydroelectric plants which previously may have looked pretty good. The efforts to cut the cost of steam plants by such things as outdoor-type construction or going to considerably larger generating units, and the very force of load growth itself, are all tending to lower the cost of thermal power. The competition with water power is becoming keener, but as time goes on I think we will eventually find it feasible to develop most of our water power resources.

MR. MAYOTT: There are other factors beside those of straight economics. It is becoming more and more difficult to obtain land for reservoirs. The competition for water for municipal and other purposes is increasing, and will continue to increase. Real estate developments for camps and cottages are more and more forcing limitations on reservoir drawdowns, particularly during the vacation seasons. These factors are all tending to restrict reservoir construction, making it more expensive to build and less valuable in operation.

ALEX RADIN (American Public Power Association): There are still many excellent undeveloped hydro sites, particularly in the northeastern region. Those present a very favorable picture in relation to present steam costs.

MR. ADAMS: There are very few steam plants in the Northwest, so the cost of constructing hydroelectric power in that region can't be measured by steam electric plants yet. Someday we think it will.

S. R. FINLEY (Electric Power Board of Chattanooga): Down in our area we have a great many hydro developments. We have a reasonable rise and fall in them, but that has not been too much of a handicap. People realize that the levels are going to fall at certain times of year. I don't think we should preclude hydro developments on account of that factor.

MR. LANE: In our part of the country, the drawdown can get to be a very serious matter. Right now in the Pensacola Reservoir on the Grand River the drawdown is something like 30 feet. It has caused a great debate as to whether the project was built for power or for multiple purposes. People point out that the value of the recreation around the lake is on the order of $20 million a year, while the value of the power is only about $1½ million.

The Authority finds itself in financial straits because of the low flow in the stream, and is claiming, and perhaps rightly so, that by the act of the Legislature the project was intended primarily for power. This problem of low flow is very serious in all of the projects in the area.

MR. KAMPMEIER: I think we should take the large view of any projected development and consider what all its benefits may be.

ALBERT LEPAWSKY (University of California): Where does atomic power fit into this whole problem? Does it argue for more hydro development now and delayed steam development, or the other way around?

MR. MAYOTT: Atomic energy is just using another type of fuel. If the price becomes low enough, of course it will affect the economic balance of some of these hydros. It isn't going to supersede hydro and it isn't going to supersede steam.

What additional coordination is needed to improve the utilization of power from all private and public suppliers?

MR. ADAMS: There are many problems in determining what would be economic interconnections between electric power systems, but I feel that there are good remaining possibilities in virtually every part of the country.

We know, from studies around the country, that there are many situations where two or more systems can be tied together to take advantage of load diversity.

For example, there are areas in the Southwest where peak loads occur in the summer months due to refrigeration and air conditioning, while not very far to the north are other systems whose peaks occur in the winter months. There are large periodic surpluses of energy in the Columbia River area. Energy comes in the spring months in such quantities that it can't be used locally, but California could use it and save fuel. Such an interconnection would also have reciprocal benefits to the Northwest during the winter period when the energy available on the Columbia River is relatively low.

MR. RADIN: Some of the difficulty in the the Pacific Northwest arises from the lack of storage reservoirs. The operation of the Northwest Power Pool is an indication, however, of the benefits that can accrue from integration. I think it has added about 400,000 kilowatts to the total capacity.

MR. MAYOTT: The United States is very effectively covered by an interconnected network. The area from Maine to Washington, D.C., has a relatively strong system covering that section, operating as a unit whenever justified. The country from the tip of Florida to Chicago, Pittsburgh to Oklahoma, and all between, is operated practically as one large system, although composed of a large number of financially independent utilities. The Pacific Northwest operates as a unit, as does the area covered by the states of California and Arizona. Texas has its system which is interconnected with the central region. There are very few areas that are not as effectively interconnected as economics justify. Growth of load and capacity has been, and will be, well taken care of by the utilities.

THOMAS W. DELZELL (Portland General Electric Company): Our Northwest Power Pool embraces five states and British Columbia. We have one of the greatest power potentials in the United States; nevertheless, we have had some power shortages.

I have no objections to interconnections with California. The difficulty is due to contractual situations brought about, I think, by erroneous federal power policies. Last year several utilities out there had to put up about $10 million to cover a power shortage. The operation of the steam plants benefited all who were in the Power Pool, but the costs were not distributed equally.

R. L. SCHACHT (Consumers Public Power District, Columbus, Nebraska): Anyone who has operated on his own water power in conjunction with steam knows that you have a great deal more flexibility than where you have rather rigid contractual requirements in the integration of water power and steam. That has been one of the snags, although I am quite sure there has been a lot of prejudice.

MR. LANE: One of the things wrong is that we don't start coordinating before projects are built. After all, the power supply of the United States is fundamentally from the free enterprise, taxpaying companies. Those companies recognize that certain areas and functions are government's in the development of streams and preservation of natural resources. When it is economical and practical to develop and produce hydroelectric power, and that is the proper thing to do, the companies are agreed that it should be done.

If the companies and the government could sit down together and determine, all things considered, what would really be best for the country and for the people at large, then I think the coordination would be much better carried out than it was when projects were built by one or other side without consultation.

How should electric power from federal projects be made available to consumers? Through federal transmission and preferential allocations? Through nonfederal transmission and sale at the bus bar[3] to preference custom-

---

[3] The bus bar of an electric plant is the "carry-all" mechanism from which all power generated by the plant is transmitted to the lines. A bus-bar sale is the sale of power at the generating plant to the highest bidder.

ers and private concerns? Or through some other arrangement? Should major water power cites be developed by the federal government, or by state and local governments, or by private agencies?

MR. KAMPMEIER: Before we get into sharp discussion of pros and cons on these questions, it seems to me we should remind ourselves that the strength of this country arises in no small part from the diversity of ideas, methods, and techniques that result from freedom of thought in approaching the problems that face us all. Whatever else we should conclude in the field of power supply, which from the beginning has involved both private and public systems of various types, this one thing we ought to retain—the opportunity for different methods, different approaches. I believe that, in the long run, if we try various ways of doing a job we will all be better off than if we try to determine in advance dogmatically that one particular way is the best.

HAROLD J. STRAUB (Utility Workers Union of America, CIO): Our union has adopted the following policy: This government was not built to become a business organization, manufacturing and distributing products of any kind. It moves beyond its scope when it undertakes to distribute electric power to the people. Our union calls for curtailment of government encroachment into private enterprise and a return of the electric power business to regulated, taxpaying, privately owned companies.

We look with alarm upon government power projects that seem to be unnecessary and are in direct competition with light and power companies with whom we hold contracts. We want to see the resources of our country developed and used for the benefit of our nation. We believe that the water resources properly belong to the nation and that water development programs in most cases can only successfully be accomplished by the government. Our union is in favor of these developments and urges the government to use our resources to overcome floods, to aid navigation, to prevent soil erosion, to supply

water for irrigation and other purposes, and to make use of power that comes from our rivers, lakes, and oceans. These worthy projects should not, however, be the means of destroying taxpaying utility companies which, under proper regulation, are furnishing adequate service.

MR. RADIN: As to the marketing of federal power, it seems to me we have developed over a period of years a policy which has been successful and which has strong roots in our nation's history. Ever since 1906, we have had a policy of giving preference to public agencies in the disposition of federal power. That policy has proven to be fair and equitable and has brought about great benefits to consumers. And it has not meant any monopolization of power by the preference customers; the fact is that the nonpreference customers are obtaining more federal power under this policy than the preference customers. The privately owned power companies and the industrial consumers together are getting about two-thirds of the federal power at the present time.

MR. DELZELL: It seems pretty sound policy for each community in the United States of America to be free to decide for itself whether it prefers municipal utilities or so-called private ownership. That decision should be made without coercion one way or the other. It also seems pretty sound policy that the federal government should do those things that it can do better. That applies, of course, in the multipurpose projects, and particularly with reference to the flood control and navigation features.

As for transmission, I think it would be sound economics and sound policy to have such nonfederal agencies as the people prefer, private or public, build as many of the transmission lines as they like—or all of them—and deliver the power to the ultimate consumer, if they can. The federal government should come in only when the local agencies, public or private, are unable or unwilling to do the job.

Distribution should be handled in a fair and equitable manner, so that we have no first-

and second-class citizens but sort of an FEPC in the distribution of power.

MR. MAYOTT: Most certainly the preference clause is what it says; it is a discriminatory clause. Why should a customer in Area A escape paying his share of the taxes that a customer in Area B has to pay? It is not fair in any way, shape, or manner. That is one of the things I very strongly disagree on with these public power boys.

WILLIAM C. WISE (Wise and Potamkin, Washington, D.C.): There should be only one issue: What is best for the whole country?

I don't see how one can recognize the international menace and not realize that if it had not been for the dams built by the federal government, we today would not be in a position to stand up against Russia and certainly could not have won the last war within the time we did.

On treating all customers alike, if you can show me one bus-bar sale where the public has benefited to the same extent as under the preference clause, I will be greatly surprised.

MR. LANE: Private power companies have always been ready and willing to develop water resources that were economical and feasible and from which power could be supplied on the same cost basis as from steam plants within the area.

And as for getting along with government hydro, we made a satisfactory contract with Southwest Power Administration and a satisfactory contract with Grand River Dam Authority. We think they are fair and equitable; they seem to think that they are fair and equitable. We are getting along happily together.

———

Mr. Lane said the private power companies believe that: government should encourage development by private capital; existing programs of local suppliers should be included in federal reports dealing with power demand and supply; much of the river basin development can be accomplished by nonfederal capital; local agencies, not the federal government, should be responsible for the adequacy of power supply for nonfederal needs; all projects should be economically justifiable; benefits should be required to exceed costs by substantial margin; power developments should be truly self-liquidating; there should be no subsidies for power development; power should be sold at market value; federal power projects should pay taxes or tax equivalents; licensing under Federal Water Power Act should be encouraged; existence of Congressional authorization of a project should not preclude nonfederal construction; disposition of power should be nonfederal marketing, federal power should be sold without discrimination; some water use should have precedence over use for power.

Anthony W. Smith (Congress of Industrial Organizations) said that the CIO is solidly behind TVA; that hydroelectric potentials should be developed by public agencies, mainly federal; that publicly produced power should be transmitted by public agencies. The CIO, he said, endorses the preference clause and favors enough publicly owned and operated generation, transmission, and distribution in the country to serve as a measure of the performance of the private utilities.

Mr. Straub introduced a document entitled "Statement of Policy of the Utility Workers Union in Regard to the Issues Connected with Public Power as adopted at the Sixth Convention held in Detroit, Michigan, on April 24, 25, 26, 1953."

Mr. Finley introduced a statement of the American Public Power Association's position. It embraced the following points: To conserve fuel supplies, hydroelectric power should be developed to the extent that is economically feasible; public agencies should have preference in such development; Congress should set standards of economic feasibility, and these should apply to all projects; the government should build and own fuel-burning plants and transmission lines where they are economically feasible and necessary to the efficient operation of federal projects or to supply public agencies and cooperatives accorded preference by Congress; the government should not engage in distribution of electricity to ultimate consumers if they can be properly served by local public agencies or cooperatives; state rights and local interests should be recognized in plans for water power development; further electrification of rural areas should be accomplished as soon as possible.

———

W. W. Bayfield (American Coal Sales Association): It has been pointed out that water power comes and goes; therefore, we must have standby steam plants. I think it is time everyone realizes that we are rapidly reaching the point where the coal industry cannot afford to maintain standby mines just to produce coal when water power or some other fuel is not available. You cannot economically turn a coal mine on and off like a spigot.

C. Petrus Peterson (National Reclamation Association): I serve at the moment as president of the National Reclamation Association. Over the years, our association has had a good deal to do with the development of irrigation and incidental power.

It seems to me that we ought to agree, all of us, that the task before us in the next 25 years of increasing the available electric energy by something like 250 percent is one that cannot possibly be shouldered off on the federal budget. Any such appropriation would be so large as to be rejected immediately. If we then say, "Let's get it all done the other way," we fail equally.

The fact is that the American people for this 25-year period are going to need private capital, which in my judgment will carry the major portion of the load; we will need the local public agencies, and there are many of them; and we are going to need the federal government.

I should like to see these contending groups sit down as reasonable people and make this three-horse team work. It has been done in some of the areas. You have a fine example of it down in Arizona where federal agencies, local public agencies, and private utilities are doing teamwork. There is no reason in the world why that can't be done elsewhere. But

we must deal objectively with this thing we call "the preference clause," transmission lines, and all of the other problems.

Mr. Lepawsky: In my opinion the energy problem is primarily a technological not an ideological problem, although ideologies cut across the problem continually. I wonder whether it might not be feasible to establish, say, an American energy institute or foundation, with sections devoted to engineering, accounting, legal problems, and possibly a section in which administrative or managerial skills would be represented.

Such an institute would not by any means displace the Edison Electric Institute, but it could gather statistics and carry on discussions on a relatively high technical plane on all phases of our energy problem in this country. I believe it would serve a very useful purpose.

Herschel F. Jones (Bonneville Power Administration): In the Northwest, because our power supplies have not been adequate to meet all the demands, public, private, federal, and nonfederal agencies have had to cooperate very closely. At the operating level, at least, no one pays any attention to whether it is public or private or federal or nonfederal.

I am hopeful that some of the heat in this controversy will die down and that we will find that the federal government, private companies, and public agencies all have specific places in resources development and that we learn to live together.

What more can be done to utilize off-peak supply? Is there evidence of technological advances that may lower the cost of long-distance power transmission? (Further discussion of these questions, as they apply to space heating, took place later, see page 251.)

Mr. Jones: Very rapid improvement has occurred in techniques of long-distance transmission of power in the last 10 years, and we are on the brink of even greater technical advances.

In 1940, the Bonneville Power Administration, using 230,000-volt lines, was carrying about 90,000 kilowatts a circuit. Our average transmission distance at that time was somewhat less than 200 miles. By 1950 we had doubled this to about 180,000 kilowatts a circuit, still on the same 230-kv lines.

We have under construction lines that will operate 340,000 volts and will carry about 500,000 kilowatts per circuit. With a single circuit on a set of towers, these lines will represent a decrease in costs of about 30 percent. If we put two circuits on a single right-of-way and carry as much as a million kilowatts, we will do somewhat better than that.

In our part of the country, hydroelectric plants generally cannot be located close to the population centers. Consequently, we have to carry power long distances in order to bring it from the plant to the market. In the East the pattern has been to locate fuel generating plants at the market or as close to the market as possible.

I think the increasing cost of moving coal, particularly by railroad, plus the lowering cost of transmitting electrical energy will enable the electric industry in the East to develop very large plants near the coal sources, perhaps at the mouth of the mine, and take the power to the cities at lower cost than the cost of transporting the coal from the mines to the urban centers.

H. S. FITCH (West Penn Power Company): It is a practice in the bituminous coal fields to locate the power stations at the mine mouths, eliminating all of the cost of transporting fuel. We can transmit a million B.T.U.'s of energy at 132 kv about 10 miles for one cent. By rail, the equivalent cost is six cents. Another factor has come into our situation, that is river transportation—100 miles for one cent. Consequently, power sites are not now rigidly confined to the coal mine mouths, and there is much more flexibility in locating the plants along other sites on the river.

BRADLEY COZZENS (Department of Water and Power, Los Angeles): We know that large-capacity lines are possible, but what happens if one of these lines goes out of commission? With today's customers, you have to have 99.999 percent continuity of service and,

therefore, you must have at the receiving end other sources capable of picking up the load.

MR. JONES: A few years ago we would never have dared to put a million kilowatts on a single right-of-way because that would have represented better than 50 percent of our total power supply. It is only when you get into a very much larger system and one that is interconnected so that power can flow over alternate routes if you lose a circuit, that it is possible to do this and still maintain reliability of power supply.

Also, the high-speed reclosing breakers that we have now have greatly increased transmission line reliability.

R. E. MORRIS (Allis-Chalmers Manufacturing Company): The question implies that you will use transmission lines to take care of peaks that differ in various areas. But I wonder if our problem first isn't to try to utilize the load in the area in which it is generated, that is, when it is generated close to the urban areas. For example, with the air conditioning load here in Washington in summer it would be a great help to our local power company if more homes here were heated electrically.

The utility industry is faced with the problem of selling its capacity in the same way that the manufacturers in the early days were faced with the problem of selling their excess plant capacity.

MR. KAMPMEIER: One of the concerns that power systems have had about taking on an electric heating load is that it might create peak problems which would be difficult and expensive to meet. Now, instead of that, many systems are finding that the air conditioning load is creating peaks for them in the other half of the year that are difficult for them to meet. This may take some of the edge off the argument against electric heating.

MR. LANE: In the Southwest, our peak is June 15-September 15. It comes from refrigeration and air conditioning and summer increase in industrial activity. In that part of the country there is going to be a great demand for peaking power in the next 10 years.

MR. FINLEY: I believe the American public is going to demand more and more electric heat. I hope it will take the form of the heat pump. I believe our customers would pay more for electric heat than we ask them, because it has been so satisfactory.

MR. JONES: It has been the experience of some of our distributors in the Northwest that the electric heating of homes complements their summer irrigation load.

Synthetic Fuels

W. C. SCHROEDER (University of Maryland): We have vast resources of materials that might be used to make liquid fuels instead of petroleum.

Oil shale is one. Coal is another. Agricultural products are possibilities, and while we don't have large reserves of tar sands here in the United States, there are extensive deposits in Canada that might be considered as sources of oil.

There is oil shale in Colorado, Utah, and Wyoming; some in Nevada. By far the greatest reserves are in Colorado.

It is possible to mine oil shale for relatively low cost. Beds are about 70 feet thick and the shale contains 30 gallons of oil per ton. You need no roof support, and production rates in excess of 150 tons per man-day underground are possible. It is generally agreed that mining costs will run around 50 cents a ton.

With that as a starting point, both the Bureau of Mines and industry have done a respectable job of developing methods of retorting or heating the shale to produce oil, and retorts are now available which will handle shale on a continuous basis at very low cost.

The refining of shale oil presents problems considerably different from those of refining petroleum, but good progress has been made in that direction as well, and it is now certain that we can produce any grade of motor fuel, diesel oil, heating oils, and the normal range of petroleum products from shale. The investment cost per barrel of production would not be high, and is comparable with petroleum operations.

As we see it today, there are two processes for converting coal to a liquid product. Both of them hinge on German developments. One is coal hydrogenation in which hydrogen gas is used to liquefy the coal. Plant investment for this process is high, probably two or three times the investment in normal petroleum operations. There has been much disagreement as to how much it would cost to produce gasoline from coal by hydrogenation. If credits are taken for chemicals, gasoline comes out at a reasonable price; otherwise it is expensive.

My own guess is that many of the questions on coal hydrogenation will be answered by the chemical industry. Union Carbide has built a plant at Institute, West Virginia, which will produce some two or three hundred barrels of product a day, principally chemicals.

The second process, the Fischer-Tropsch process, can use coal, natural gas, or any other material that will produce carbon monoxide and hydrogen. A plant built at Brownsville, Texas, to produce liquid fuels and chemicals from natural gas, has had a rather unsatisfactory history and is now shut down, but I understand that there is a possibility that it may be operated later. Here again, the initial investment in the plant is fairly high compared with normal petroleum operations.

E. D. REEVES (Standard Oil Development Company): I think that technically today we can make synthetic fuels from shale, natural gas, coal, and probably tar sands. These processes, though, certainly have not been developed to the same extent as those for making similar fuels from petroleum.

There is a chance the plants you might install 10 or 15 years from now might be a great deal more effective or more economical than the ones we would have to put in if we started off today on a synthetic fuels program. Considering that we do know technically a great deal about synthetic fuels, that we have already made a start on the commercial and semicommercial exploitation of these various processes, that we will have ample warning of a real shortage of oil, it seems to me it is best for industry and for the country to postpone the installation of synthetical fuels until they can be justified economically. That is the basis on which we try to do most things in this country, and it seems to me in the long run we are going to wind up with a better synthetic fuel program by that approach.

I think also that the oil industry is perfectly willing to accept the responsibility for carrying through the development. We are in the business of marketing what we call liquid energy. We don't intend to go out of business, and I am sure that all of us in the industry would want to do everything we could do to bring in the synthetic fuels if we really thought that to do otherwise would threaten our industry.

What further technological developments in making synthetic fuels are needed? To what extent should additional research be undertaken?

H. H. STORCH (Bureau of Mines): There is one rather important problem in synthetic liquid fuels to which industry, I think, should give a great deal more attention. That is the problem of making either hydrogen or synthesis[4] gas from coal. The cost of synthetic liquid fuels from coal, by whatever route, is greatly dependent upon the cost of mining coal and the cost of converting the coal to either hydrogen or a mixture of hydrogen and carbon monoxide.

In the Fischer-Tropsch process the cost of the synthesis gas is approximately 60 to 70 percent of the total cost of producing gasoline. In the case of coal hydrogenation the cost of compressed hydrogen will vary from 35 to 45 percent of the total cost of producing gasoline from coal hydrogenation. In making high B.T.U. gas from coal the situation is even worse.

More economic processes for making hydrogen or mixtures of hydrogen and carbon monoxide from coal are needed. The production of high B.T.U. gas from coal, which may be classified as a synthetic fuel process, is perhaps of more immediate importance economically than the production of liquefied fuels, and here the problem of cheap synthesis gas is extremely critical.

The Bureau of Mines has spent an increasing share of its allotment during the past 10 years on this problem of gasification of coal and underground gasification. Unfortunately our work on underground gasification at the moment has been discontinued. The data have not yet been thoroughly analyzed and, when they are, the question as to whether that should be continued and on a larger scale may possibly be answerable.

My own feeling is that it should be continued, and on a very much larger scale, to get definitive answers as to whether there is any chance of making hydrogen-carbon monoxide more cheaply in that fashion than by controlled gasification in specially constructed gas fires above ground.

MR. SCHROEDER: The question of hydrogen enters into everything we do because the coal molecule is short of hydrogen. In order to produce gasoline you must put in about two or three times as much hydrogen as the coal originally contains. It is one of the basic problems that has to be solved.

The new Pelipetz process will produce a much higher proportion of aromatics.[5] Dr. Pelipetz works for the Bureau of Mines in Bruceton, Pennsylvania. His work has shown that it is possible to make a highly aromatic gasoline from coal in one step by hydrogenation. The preliminary cost figures indicate that this development would save about 15 to 20 percent on the installation and operating costs. Pelipetz is convinced that the process can be further improved.

MR. REEVES: I think we all agree that what the Bureau of Mines is doing is what we all like to see done. When we are talking about conservation, however, we ought to recognize that the Fischer-Tropsch process uses up half the energy in the fuel, and some of these other processes do the same thing. We are all agreed that the Bureau of Mines should do exploratory work on a continuing basis on the bench and continue to find new ways to approach the problem. The processes we have today look as though they are opera-

---

[4] A combination of carbon monoxide and hydrogen.

[5] Aromatics—a component of liquid fuel high in antiknock qualities.

ble, but they don't look to us like very good things to do with your money now.

On what scale should present processes be tested? What further encouragement is needed in the field of synthetic fuels, including the development of shales and oil sands?

MR. SCHROEDER: If we had decided to do our oil shale research in the laboratory on a chemical engineering basis, let us say, I think we would have missed the entire point of the research. If it costs $2.00 to mine a ton of shale and there is three-quarters of a barrel of oil in that ton of shale, then you are spending $2.00 for the raw material to produce oil which, at the most, is not worth more than a $1.50. So obviously, you are defeated before you start.

What was done was to set up an experimental mine. The result was that, instead of 5, 10, or 15 tons of shale mined per man-day, a production of 150 tons per man-day was obtained. I don't think anybody has ever mined hard rock at that rate before. This established a raw-material cost which was low enough to make the whole shale operation possible.

MR. STORCH: In the last Congress 90 percent of the synthetic liquid fuels program was eliminated. I believe we need more effective and impartial evaluation by bodies such as the National Academy of Sciences of what is going on, particularly in government research on synthetic liquid fuels.

MR. SCHROEDER: Frankly, I don't care whether the government does this research or whether industry does it or whether it is done by combined effort. However, the government has now spent something over 70 million dollars on this work. It has been going on on a large scale since 1944. During that time the government has built up a very fine organization to carry out the program. Regardless of who does the job, this organization should be preserved. If it is torn down now, I doubt if it will ever be put back together again.

MR. COZZENS: Laboratory and economic answers are often very far apart. Are the present appropriations so low that you would not be able to get any economic answers out of laboratory studies?

MR. STORCH: It is possible—and industry does this every day—to take the laboratory experiments and make assumptions as to what a new procedure will produce. That is possible even on test-tube results, obviously. But when the process comes up through various stages, you refine your original estimates on the basis of new knowledge and new engineering experience. There is no general rule as to how far you have to go before you can get a realistic and critical appraisal of a process. In some cases, you don't have to go much beyond the laboratory stage. In other processes, you have to go virtually to a full-scale unit before you can get such answers.

MR. REEVES: There is a difference between government research and research by private industry. The purpose of government research generally, as I understand it, is to do basic work that is of common interest to all the people. The purpose of private industry is to do research specifically of interest to the particular company doing the research.

With that in mind, it seems to me that the work done by the Bureau of Mines on synthetic fuels ought to be of the exploratory basic type. It ought to give the leads that are going to be required as time goes on to develop new approaches to the synthetic fuels problem.

I think that the industry approach to this thing is going to be along somewhat different lines. Many of us in industry have done what we consider to be enough work on this problem, so that we have a good understanding of just what the problem is. We know how to make synthetic fuels from various raw materials. We know what the technical difficulties are. We know in general what the economic difficulties are.

If we had to go ahead today, there are certain lines that we would have to pursue, but we don't like to pursue those lines. As always happens in these things, research work carried out on a broad front and examined in the light of a particular problem will before long give solutions to that problem. That is the approach that we are taking today—at least, that my company is taking today—on synthetic fuels. What we are looking for now are leads from our whole research program as to how those problems can be solved more effectively than is possible with the tools of today. Once new ways of attacking these problems are found, it will then be our purpose to carry them through the small and large pilot plants that are necessary.

MR. TEARE: Would you say that industry research on synthetic fuels is going on at a slower pace than formerly?

MR. REEVES: I think it is in some respects. All of these things have their ups and downs. We did a great deal of work in the late twenties and early thirties in synthetic fuels because we were concerned at that time about possible shortages. We don't see the need today from an economic standpoint for pushing minor changes to a large pilot plant scale. We think that the interests of our company, the interests of our stockholders and the interests of everybody are best served by doing the kind of research that is needed to develop a much more economic synthetic fuels industry, one that can compete on an economic basis with crude oil. Once that happens, why then we expect to go ahead full tilt.

MR. TEARE: Do you think that more work has been done by industry collectively than the Bureau of Mines has done?

MR. REEVES: I don't know, except in a general way, what other people have done. But over a 20-year period my own company has spent over 40 million dollars. Now, that includes such things as the purchase of know-how, the purchase of patent rights on hydrogenation, work on synthesis from natural gas. I would guess we have spent almost half as much as the Bureau of Mines. Other companies I know have spent a great deal. Industry in the aggregate probably has spent more money than the Bureau of Mines has on synthetic fuels. Add the Brownsville plant, and it is a great deal more.

Subsection C

CONSERVATION AND USE

The United States still has enormous reserves of conventional energy materials. In the foreseeable future, will the way they are used be determined by technology, costs, and customer preference, or by end-use control? Many participants in the subsection discussions definitely preferred the former course, but some questioned whether this would achieve the best use of our resources in the long run.

Representatives of the coal industry said that it was harmful not only to their industry but to the country to use gas and oil for industrial purposes to which coal is well suited. Oil industry spokesmen responded that they were following sound business practice in seeking markets for their products and that any interference with this would do more harm than good. Gas industry people pointed out that their industry is regulated by the Federal Power Commission and state regulatory bodies and that they couldn't over-expand if they wanted to.

A lot of oil could be saved, it was pointed out, if people would buy smaller cars or would use public transportation instead of driving to work; but as long as people want it that way that is the way it is going to be—as long as gasoline is available at prices they can afford. Meanwhile, automobiles and the gasoline they burn have become more efficient than they used to be. But getting around in them in the city is becoming more and more difficult. (In its discussion of Urban Land, pages 38-40, Section I also dealt with this growing problem.)

But if we were to set aside reserves of oil and gas now, how do we know they would be needed later on? Oil from shale—and we have a great deal of oil shale—is already a near-commercial possibility. Underground gasification of coal looks promising. Atomic energy is just around the corner and, if need be, we could get much more energy than we do from the sun and the wind.

Nevertheless, much can be done to utilize our conventional energy resources more efficiently. The majority of the participants appeared to believe that optimum efficiency can be reached through the continuing play of competitive forces.

FROM THE RECORD

*Oil, Coal, and Gas—Some
Conservation Problems*

How much fuel can be saved through better mechanical efficiency in automobile engines and through improvements in fuel processing?

EUGENE AYRES (Consultant, Gulf Research and Development Company): We know that efficiency in conversion of coal or fuel to electric power is far better in the United States than in any country in the world. We know that, in general, our use of coal is more efficient in this country: we use fewer open fireplaces, have more central heating; our heating appliances are usually superior. On the other hand, it can be argued that our use of motor fuel is less efficient by one definition, for the simple reason that we demand more from the motor fuel and the motor car. We may not be less efficient, because we get more out of the motor car; but we do consume more fuel per mile or per ton-mile.

SERGE B. JURENEV (Continental Oil Company): One thing we have is too high octanes for the compression ratios in the cars we have on the road today. We also have too heavy cars, not enough aluminum in the cars, as they have in Europe; too much horsepower, too many gadgets. In this country, where gasoline is being sold at such reasonable prices, the people don't care.

W. J. SPARKS (National Research Council): Only about 20 percent of the total cost of driving a car goes for gasoline.

BRADLEY COZZENS (Department of Water and Power, Los Angeles): The fact that we use cars weighing 3,000 or 4,000 pounds rather than 1,000 and 2,000 is part of our high standard of living. Any time we have to, I think we can go back to the light-weight car, but I don't think any of us wants to.

MR. AYRES: I believe that even those who are most pessimistic about supplies of petroleum would feel that the ceiling on gasoline costs would be determined by the cost of synthetic fuels, and there is no particular reason for those costs to skyrocket. So I suspect that the only thing that could bring very high prices would be high taxation.

J. E. SWEARINGEN (Standard Oil Company (Indiana)): The best way to improve the efficiency of the automobile and save gasoline is to make every car haul six passengers every time it pulls out of the garage.

MR. COZZENS: An increasing problem in our cities is simply getting the car off the road when you get where you want to go. We take it for granted that a terminal must be provided for rail facilities, but we have done very little about providing terminal facilities for automobiles.

MR. AYRES: We used to have good electric car facilities, high-speed interurban vehicles. Now, we have all the motor cars driving into town, and there is nothing to do with them. We could save an enormous amount of energy if we could make greater use of high-grade electric transportation. Of course, they do that in New York City with their subways. The number of B.T.U.'s required per passenger is very tiny on the subway compared with the B.T.U.'s per passenger in an automobile. Unfortunately, our electric commuter systems have been going down in quality. People are using them less. Most of them are bankrupt. The services are not so good as they were. The schedules are slower. There are fewer streetcars in our cities. The whole thing has deteriorated.

Mr. JURENEV: I wonder whether urban electric transportation is really cheap. In New York we started out with a nickel fare. The IRT System went bankrupt. Then, the city took it over. They jacked the fare up to 15 cents and, I think, are still running in the red. And there has been no improvement in the service.

WILBUR F. FAIRLAMB (Federal Power Commission, Fort Worth): You can get into a vicious circle. Your revenues go down, you ask for a rate increase; you get a rate increase, it drives away your passengers. I don't know the answer.

K. W. SPENCER (H. Zinder and Associates, Inc., Washington, D.C.): The decline in mass transportation in any urban area is continually going on without any relationship to fares. You have a decline of anywhere from 3 to 11 percent a year, some of that being, of course, a fall-off from war years' transportation in the larger cities. People are choosing to drive their own automobiles. If it becomes sufficiently difficult to use individual transportation, they may return to mass transportation.

JOHN BAUER (League for Industrial Democracy): For regular travel from home to downtown business, it is crazy to use automobiles. The great majority of people ought to be riding mass-transportation vehicles. It is an abuse of the streets to use your automobiles. But if you are living out 8 or 10 miles you just can't take the kind of service that is provided by practically all the transportation systems—the frequent stops, the overloading.

If you had free-moving bus operation, with express schedules for the outlying districts properly adjusted to traffic flow, everybody could have a seat and you would get fast service; you would get convenience far beyond that of the automobile. But if a person has to crowd and jam in, with frequent stops slowing up service, he is going to use his automobile.

Express service would cost more, but I think people would be very glad to pay higher fares if they got fast service and seats, without the responsibility and the nuisance of car operation. I think you can work these things out and get masses of automobiles off the streets.

MR. SPENCER: Express service has been tried a number of times. You are selling distance in transportation, and people will not pay enough for that distance, even in express service, to compensate for it in most instances. If you are going to have private investors putting up their money for that type of service, they will expect some return on their investment. They are not altruistic. Municipal operation is a different matter, but I don't know that this has been completely successful. I don't think the revenue bond is the answer, either.

MR. AYRES: I think the job can be done through private company organization, company management, and cooperation, if only the psychology is a little different.

MR. BAUER: I think companies and cities should get together on a financial program that will provide a return to investors, and then work together to get people to ride mass-transportation vehicles.

MR. AYRES: I figured up one time that if a taxicab in New York City, at the time of greatest congestion, could travel as fast as a horse and buggy, a free-moving horse and buggy, the taxi operator could afford to pay 80 cents more per gallon of gasoline than he does now.

This subject of mass transportation should be studied in specific applications; it has a decided bearing on consumption of motor fuel.

WILBERT G. FRITZ (Office of Defense Mobilization): It seems to me that this subject of conservation divides pretty clearly into two categories: conservation within the equipment itself, and what might be termed external conservation.

When you get into the matter of external efficiency or external conservation, it is very hard to know what might be accomplished. However, when you consider the matter of efficiency within the equipment itself, you can get some idea of the limits that you are working with. There we can set some standards. I don't know just what the efficiency would average in an automobile, but I suppose it would be not more than 8 or 10 percent.

E. D. REEVES (Standard Oil Development Company): I understand that over the last 30 years not only the ton-miles but the actual miles per gallon in cars of comparable quality have greatly increased.

MR. AYRES: That is true. But there is an offsetting factor. Mileage has improved not only because the motor has been improved but because the fuel has been improved, and it has cost a lot from the standpoint of conservation to improve the fuel.

MR. REEVES: I don't think I would agree with that. Our studies clearly indicate—to us at least—that the energy required to improve the quality of gasoline is much more than compensated for by the added benefit you get out of improved gasoline. Over the entire range of driving conditions, improvements in the efficiency of the engine in effect add to your potential resources because the resources are so much more useful. Studies indicate that these improvements have already increased engine efficiency by about 50 percent, and by continuing research I think we can certainly get another 50 percent, at least.

E. O. JONES (Ethyl Corporation): The Paley Report states, "We blow thousands of tons of lead into the atmosphere each year from the high octane gas burned up in our cars because we like quick pick-up on the road and enjoy beating the other driver at the stop light."[6] In 1950, the use of tetraethyl lead in

motor fuels is conservatively estimated to have contributed an otherwise unattainable 10 percent to the efficiency of motor vehicle engines. This is the equivalent of 270,000 barrels per day of gasoline, or 642,000 barrels per day of crude oil. Thus, in 1950, the use of 105,000 tons of lead in antiknock compounds made possible the conservation of 865,000 tons of steel in refining equipment, plus the material for 44,000 average oil wells.

MR. AYRES: Counting the gas, counting all the products, the residual, all the fuels, is the over-all thermal yield of a refinery as good with catalytic cracking as it was with thermal cracking?

MR. REEVES: It is better. The change from thermal cracking to catalytic cracking was really a radical change in processing, and that in itself made a tremendous difference in the yields and octane levels that we were able to obtain. I think the processes themselves have resulted in an over-all general energy credit.

MR. COZZENS: We are in the vicinity of 28 or 30 percent efficiency in steam generation of electricity, which is pretty close to the theoretical limit. However, it is highly desirable that we develop water power as rapidly as possible to save for future generations the oil and gas that is being consumed for electric generation. There is a possibility of saving upwards of 3 trillion cubic feet of gas or on the order of 600 million barrels of fuel oil a year.

R. L. IRELAND (Pittsburgh Consolidation Coal Company): Isn't the residual oil you use for electric generation the last squeal of the pig that has no other use?

MR. REEVES: The oil industry has recently developed a number of processes for the conversion of residuals to other products, but the price of residuals hasn't come up. Residual production has been going down each year.

MR. AYERS: Conversion of residual fuel oil to distillate is not conservation, because you have to do work to make that conversion and you will have fewer B.T.U.'s out of the barrel of petroleum when you do that.

MR. REEVES: Railroads have been using

---

[6] The President's Materials Policy Commission, *Resources for Freedom*, 1952, I, 11.

residual fuel in competition with coal for steam engines; they also use diesel engines on distillate fuels. When they operate on residual fuels, I think their over-all efficiency is on the order of 5 percent; on distillate fuels I believe it goes up to about 20 percent. That is a fourfold improvement in the efficiency, and you certainly don't lose 75 percent of the residual when you try to convert to products. The industry is trying to produce products which will be more efficient in the equipment that uses it. I think that is sound from the conservation standpoint.

ROLLA D. CAMPBELL (Island Creek Coal Company): There is such a thing as desirability of use, too. Your automobile engine is not as efficient as some of your modern steam plants. Gasoline is considered as a high use because it contributes to our modern way of living.

What steps can consumers take toward more efficient use of primary and converted energy?

MR. AYRES: It seems to me the answer to that question is: they will take steps that are profitable and agreeable to them, and no others.

MR. JURENEV: I agree. For instance, we have considerable improvement in insulation in new houses, so that consumption of No. 2 distillate fuel is gradually going down. We also have the trend towards smaller houses. That, again, conserves energy.

Distillate fuel is selling at a low price, so people are very careless with it and will be so long as the price is low. If the price should go up, the consumer will become more conservation conscious.

MR. AYRES: Nothing would conserve more than high prices.

This led to discussion of the price effects of percentage depletion. (See also pages 214-15, Section V, and 191-97, Section IV.)

E. WAYLES BROWNE, JR. (Bethesda, Md.): What would the price of oil be if the oil producers paid taxes instead of having a depletion allowance? This might turn out to be a better conservation measure than some of the other things we have been talking about; let the customer actually pay the price directly rather than in a tax subsidy.

MR. JURENEV: It has been estimated that to compensate the industry for the depletion allowance of 27½ percent, the price of crude should go up about 50 cents a barrel or more. Probably the brunt of this increase would be borne by gasoline; so let's assume the price of gaoline goes up 2 cents a gallon. Everybody is happy because the industry is getting the same income and the consumer pays a little more, but not much more.

But suppose the price didn't go up. Remember, the market for refined products is highly competitive. If price didn't go up, it would mean that capital wouldn't flow into the oil industry for exploration effort. It would mean that our cash inflow wouldn't be sufficient to maintain the exploration effort at the present rate. Things would be all right for a while, but then three or four years later you wouldn't have any geological or geophysical crews in operation; they would be selling apples or something. The industry's exploratory staffs would be completely disrupted.

Look at the record. The demand for petroleum products has gone up about 6½ percent a year for the past 25 years and the production has kept up with it pretty closely. The 27½ percent depletion provided exploratory effort which was sufficient to keep up with the demand and not much more than that. If you cut out the depletion allowance, exploratory effort will decline to a point where we won't be able to keep up with the increase in demand from year to year.

Of course, this country could import more crude oil, but is that what we want to do?

MR. SWEARINGEN: Most wildcat wells are drilled by individual promoters and small companies or syndicates. One of the major reasons why individuals outside the industry put money into exploration is the depletion allowance. That is where you would be seriously hurt if prices were raised and depletion allowances per se were done away with.

DONALD W. JEFFRIES (Arthur D. Little, Inc.): Would increasing the depletion allowance on coal make much difference in the amount of research that goes into new production methods?

MR. CAMPBELL: I don't think so. What we need is a higher price. Many companies are having to do selective mining now, because the prices they are getting don't pay for the cost of recovery in their higher cost sections. Many of the higher cost mines today are closed down. Depletion is important to us, but maybe not to the same extent as it is to the oil industry because we don't have the exploration expenses.

MR. COZZENS: Do I understand correctly that a higher price would make for greater conservation of the ultimate fuel supplies?

MR. CAMPBELL: Very definitely. A great deal of coal has been permanently lost through the shutting down of developed capacity. You can't store coal economically and, therefore, you can only produce it as it is required. With the loss of so much of our market to oil and gas, we have had to cut prices to hold what we still have left, and that has had its effect on the mining of high-cost coal.

KIRTLEY F. MATHER (Harvard University): To what extent is the price of coal determined by the price of crude oil?

MR. CAMPBELL: The price of crude on the Eastern Seaboard is very definitely a limiting factor. We have to meet the price of residual or we don't sell to the big steam plants. The same thing is true with natural gas. Natural gas is a cheaper fuel now than either coal or oil in many places.

MR. SWEARINGEN: When you produce oil, you have to produce gas. It has been the practice in the industry to allocate all the costs against oil and take whatever one can get for gas. That has been one reason for low gas prices.

DANIEL PARSON (American Gas Association): At the present time, approximately one-third of all net production of natural gas comes in association with oil, and two-thirds from dry gas formation.

MR. AYRES: One thing that the government could very well do to help conserve fuel would be to let prices go where they please; not regulate the price of gas, let it go sky high if it wants to; let any prices take care of themselves on the market. I believe that would do much for conservation.

MR. BAUER: Doesn't that come right back to the depletion allowance? Why not treat the federal taxing of oil on the same basis as federal taxes for other kinds of industry—depreciation allowances on the basis of capital costs of the plant and the construction and development put in? Then just let the industries compete for markets on the basis of price. Doesn't the special treatment of the oil industry really fog the atmosphere and bring a lot of criticism on the oil industry that with competitive marketing would be absent?

MR. SPENCER: That presupposes that the value of natural resources amounts only to the cost of their recovery.

MR. BAUER: There is a national policy in regard to depreciation that applies to all industries. The question is whether there is justification in singling out a particular industry and treating its depreciation provisions on a radically different basis from industry in general.

MR. AYRES: It seems to me the petroleum industry is unique in that the finding of petroleum is a great gamble. It is in the national interest to encourage that gamble.

MR. JURENEV: What are we complaining about? The power plants and industrial establishments are getting cheap energy fuel. What is wrong with that?

MR. BAUER: I am not complaining as a consumer. I think the industry has done a good job. But the problem isn't quite that simple. On the basis of low prices, for example, an enormous amount of residential gas heating has been put in. But wait 5 years, 10 years, and double or triple that price, and it is going to be awfully ruinous to a very heavy social investment throughout the country.

MR. JURENEV: If you cut out the depletion allowances there won't be any gas; you won't have to worry about it. You can't sustain present levels of consumption on stationary reserves. You have to keep on adding to them.

E. S. PETTYJOHN (Institute of Gas Technology): The question of future price of gas is entirely in the hands of the Federal Power Commission, because they regulate the interstate pipeline trade. If we are going to have free competition and charge the customer whatever price we think the traffic will bear, we have to set aside the whole system of regulation which is now in existence. I don't believe this group wants to advocate that.

We are concerned with conservation, and the extension of pipelines is a conservation measure. The pipelines have picked up what had been flare gas and transported it for domestic use.

I don't think the gas companies have in any way sought to mislead their customers or prospective customers. The price has been set by the state commissions and the Federal Power Commission, and the customers have had the advantage. In fact, the companies have not been able to supply the demand at present prices. They are not permitted to accumulate funds with which to build new pipelines. At the same time, prices on the producing end are higher, and construction costs are three times what they were in the thirties. So any new gas brought in would naturally have to be at a higher price. Without the ability to accumulate funds, the companies cannot take care of the additional demand at the present price level.

MR. FRITZ: Percentage depletion isn't related necessarily to any expenditure on exploration. Would expensing of exploration costs provide a greater incentive for exploration? Expensing would permit quick recovery of any expenditure for exploration and would relate such expenditures more specifically to actual operations, would it not?

MR. CAMPBELL: The rates were not just grabbed out of the air; they were based on a study of the over-all depletion represented as a percentage of gross income. The rates are fixed upon historical charges, on average performance of the industry up to the time the rates were set.

MR. MATHER: It would seem to me that the depletion principle is perfectly valid. I would suggest that our only question is whether or not the present rates for depletion allowances are optimum from the point of view of conservation and day-by-day profits in a competitive market. The principle, it seems to me, is firmly established and here to stay.

MR. AYRES: There is probably nothing sacred about $27\frac{1}{2}$; but I think the thing has been so thoroughly thrashed out by all those concerned that it would be rather hard to improve on it.

Conservation of Gas

Views were expressed on ways to conserve gas through extending the markets for coal and through underground storage.

MR. CAMPBELL: There are some changes which we think should be made in governmental policy which would conserve gas and possibly permit coal to supply markets for which it is peculiarly adapted. One would be to forbid the granting of licenses for new pipelines to carry gas for industrial purposes into markets already served by coal.

Another source of conservation could be the storage of gas in the summertime to supply the wintertime demand, instead of gearing the supply to peak demand and selling the seasonal surplus for use under boilers.

Further, we think it would be helpful to allow the pipeline companies the field price of gas in setting up their rate structure.

MR. PARSON: The gas industry is anticipating spending a minimum of 20 million dollars over the next few years in the development of underground storage facilities.

As to preventing the sale of gas to industrial users, I think no pipeline company would undertake to construct a pipeline which was based largely upon industrial use, because industrial requirements for gas are subject to radical cyclical fluctuation. But frequently it is necessary to maintain some substantial amount of industrial sales in order to maintain high load factors for those pipelines and make them economically feasible.

MR. AYRES: Sometimes the coal people don't see the advantage of underground storage and oppose it vigorously on the ground of safety.

MR. IRELAND: The coal people do favor the creation of gas storage, but there is the very serious problem of the uncharted abandoned wells. I would hate to take you into a coal mine with me and have us cut into an uncharted abandoned well overlying a pressurized gas storage. The coal industry as such is very much in favor of the creation of gas storage if we can only find a way to do it without subjecting our employees and ourselves to sudden death.

I think the reassuring thing that has been brought out here is the fact that the energy industries—oil, gas, and coal—have more than anticipated the current need. The fact that they are continuing to maintain reserves for the future indicates that we are in a pretty healthy condition in this country.

MR. REEVES: I agree. I think there is too great a tendency to evaluate our natural resources in terms of present demands projected into the future. I suggest that one of our greatest energy resources, as we look ahead, is a flexible and expanding technology, and that this can integrate all of our resources with our expanding needs in all fields.

What Does Technology Promise?

What new technological developments are likely to increase efficiency in the use of fuel sources—in particular, coal and oil?

MR. CAMPBELL: The Carbide and Chemicals Corporation has developed a new machine to mine the coal that it is going to use in its hydrogenation process. They spent $3\frac{1}{2}$ million dollars, I understand, on developing

this automatic mining machine, which works with controls all from the exterior of the mine. It has not yet been put to commercial use, but there is considerable promise that they have hit on a line of development that ought to be highly productive.

MR. AYRES: Certainly, when demands for coal are high, as they may be within the next few decades, it will be necessary to mechanize mining far more than it is mechanized today, to substitute engineers for miners and mine coal at a reliable rate without interruption.

MR. MATHER: What is the situation concerning the gasification of coal underground without mining it?

MR. AYRES: There are a lot of problems connected with it, the low B.T.U. of the gas, the tendency to cave in on combustion, cracks in the earth. But there is considerable belief that something will come of it in the long run. Those who know most about it are enthusiastic. Probably it won't be competitive for a good while; but when we are scraping the bottom of the jar we will be very glad to have some technology of that sort worked out.

MR. BROWNE: Will the room-and-pillar mining system permit subsequent underground gasification?

MR. CAMPBELL: Yes; probably the first application of a commercial adaptation would be to try to burn up the unmined coal left in old mines.

MR. BROWNE: To what extent would the surface be disturbed?

MR. MATHER: That is a geological problem. In a few mines there probably would be no collapse of the earth above. But probably in the majority of the coal mines the pillars are holding up more than the immediate roof and it would mean a settling of everything above, clear to the surface, with consequent possibilities of great damage at the surface.

MR. AYRES: There also is work being done on underground gasification of shale oil and petroleum. The shale oil work doesn't seem to be quite competitive with the mining of shale in conventional mining. If you had a geological situation where you couldn't mine cheaply it might be a solution. Work that has been done on petroleum gasification underground has been more with the idea of increasing the percentage of oil recovery by the application of heat where the petroleum is imbedded.

MR. FRITZ: I believe that in the experiments with oil shale it has been possible to get almost 100 percent combustion. With coal it is more difficult.

MR. MATHER: I think that probably your 100 percent combustion applies only to the kerogen[7] in the shale, and the total percentage of the kerogen to noncombustible mineral matter is relatively very low. My own impression is that economic gasification of oil shale is many times as difficult as the economic gasification of thin coal seams.

MR. BROWNE: Is any progress being made on moving coal by pipeline?

MR. IRELAND: We have had in operation for some time a three-mile long pilot pipeline of commercial size, with all the angles and turns that might be found in normal construction. We have determined the rate of wear on the pipe from the abrasion of the coal and the effect on the coal itself. We have got figures on the costs and are now looking for a customer at the other end of the pipeline. Coal that would pass through an eighth-inch, round-hole screen is the best size to put through a pipe. It is carried in a solution of 50 percent water.

The big problem is the removal and clarification of the transporting water and the control of the dust created in the process of drying. It is competitive with railroad freight rates, but you not only have to figure out what the saving would be under present rates, but also the margin of profit that the railroad has in its existing rate in order to figure out where you will be after they cut their rate to meet your competition.

MR. AYRES: You may have to use oil instead of water.

[7] Shale oil in its natural state before being extracted from shale.

MR. IRELAND: There has been quite a bit of work done in trying to make an oil-coal emulsion which could be used, but so far they have found no way of keeping the coal from settling out of the oil. They apparently don't have very much affinity for one another.

Should "High-Grade" Uses Be Encouraged?

Would the national interest be served by having some form of encouragement of "high-grade" uses of fuel?

MR. AYRES: I think what is generally meant by this question is that when a fuel is exceptionally good for one purpose it seems unfortunate to use it for something else where it isn't exceptionally good but just competitive.

MR. CAMPBELL: There is another factor. No matter how you figure your coal reserves, they are so much greater than the reserves of oil and gas that where two fuels have equal efficiency for a given use and one is four or five times as plentiful as the other there is an element of conservation involved.

MARY E. McDERMOTT (Atlantic Refining Company): On the other hand, we might refuse to burn gas under boilers to save it for home heating, a "superior" use, and then find that home heating was being taken care of by electricity energy from coal. We might save it and have no use for it.

MR. CAMPBELL: Natural gas can be used for making gasoline; it can be used to make ammonia fertilizers and help improve the productivity of our soil. There won't be any lack of use for natural gas, don't worry about that.

MR. BROWNE: I would suggest, also, that it is not smart to expect too much of inventive genius before it has produced. I think we would be better advised to save some of the high-grade fuels for high-grade uses that may not develop than to run short by using them up too fast.

CORNELIUS J. DWYER (Foreign Operations Administration): There is a theory that if, 15 or 20 years from now, the value of the fuel you are thinking of "saving" would not be equal to the cost of getting it out of the ground now, plus interest of 2 or 3 percent compounded semi-annually, then it is more economic to "waste" it by leaving it in the ground. If you "save," at considerable cost, something, the future value of which won't be much higher than the present, you have crossed the line between "conservation" and "hoarding."

Take coal, for example. If you go into a seam and take out all the coal by the longwall system as against leaving one quarter of it underground as in the case of the room-and-pillar method, don't you have to justify the increased present cost by assuming that the future value of coal will be substantially greater than now?

Mr. IRELAND: Longwall is much more expensive than room-and-pillar. How you look upon the value of a ton of coal in the ground depends upon the value of the acre, the extent that you can expand your reserves, roof conditions, seam conditions—all those things. To try to drill it and evaluate it in advance is too expensive; so you may start in with the idea that you are going to get maximum recovery but find, because of the cost factor as you go along, that you have to retreat to a room-and-pillar system. A lot of factors enter into the economic operation of a given coal mine, or one coal mine versus another one, and the uses to which the coal from one mine is put as compared to the uses of the coal from another mine. You can't generalize.

Mr. CAMPBELL: However, high extraction can be had at a higher price, and the price level today is based upon the lower percentage of extraction inherent in the room-and-pillar system as against the longwall system of mining.

The experience during the war, when we had higher prices, was that a great many operators recovered coal they formerly considered irrecoverable.

Mr. DWYER: I think, however, that when you say you are going to "save" so-called

"high-grade" fuel, such as natural gas, for use in the indefinite future, you are really advocating "hoarding."

What significant types of nonfuel products are likely to be made from energy resources? Will the use of energy resources for the production of chemicals and other nonenergy purposes make serious inroads into our fuel supplies?

JOHN R. SUMAN (Standard Oil Company (New Jersey)): The petroleum industry is engaged in making chemicals in a very large way now—I think about 400 different products. All the market we can see now for chemicals that can be made from oil would represent two days' production in the United States. So it is going to be a long time before we put 365 days in the chemical business. You can make so much of it with so little.

Mr. IRELAND: It takes an awful lot of nylon stockings to keep a coal mine going, too.

Mr. AYRES: The thing I am afraid of is that by the time we need the raw materials we will have used them up as fuel.

Mr. SUMAN: What about ammoniated fertilizer made from petroleum? You put it on the soil and you grow some food; you eat the food, and that produces energy. It is all an energy proposition.

Mr. AYRES: As a matter of fact, the production of certain things from fuels has meant a great saving of wood and of agricultural products in general. That liberates land for production of food. The fact that food can be grown in surplus now doesn't mean that we may not be short of food some day, the rate our population is growing. So I think conservation of land through use of these fossil fuels for chemicals is very important.

Mr. SPARKS: I think the best example of such conservation is detergents. The consumption of land is very high in making soap from soybeans. But the crude oil used in making detergents is an insignificant percentage of petroleum production.

Petroleum Imports

Are imports of crude oil desirable to supplement domestic production, and to permit reservation of some domestic supplies? (This question was approached from a somewhat different angle in Section VI, see pages 269-72.)

MR. SUMAN: We have been asked by the Army and the Petroleum Administration for Defense to build up more than a million barrels a day of excess productive capacity in the United States as an emergency measure, and we have built it up and are carrying it. At the same time we are importing about 600,000 barrels a day of crude and 300,000 to 400,000 barrels of products, principally residual fuel oil.

Now, there is a lot of heat being generated here and there by various factions in industry over whether there is too much coming in, but, by and large, I think it is a supplementation that is highly desirable during this emergency period when the government has asked us to carry this excess potential. There is no shortage of oil in the United States. We have the oil, and the excess capacity is being carried at a considerable cost to the producers of the United States.

MR. AYRES: The question here is conservation. Clearly, we are not importing to conserve. We are importing so we will have that margin of capacity in case we need it. Whether that conserves in the long run is a question.

MR. SUMAN: Well, we have imported oil for many, many years. I don't think any elements in the industry particularly object to the supplementation of our domestic production. It is the amount that seems to bother from time to time.

MR. JEFFRIES: When does the supplementing end and the supplanting begin?

MR. CAMPBELL: As I understand it, the position of the importers is that they, not the government, should be the ones to decide how much oil to bring in. Yet they are in a position where they cannot agree among themselves.

MR. SUMAN: Secretary McKay has said that the amount of the supplementation through imports should move up and down with the domestic demands and that it should be accomplished by business statesmanship amongst the importers.

MR. CAMPBELL: But not by agreement. That is a wee bit illegal.

MR. SUMAN: Exactly. If importers got together to effectuate this suggestion, they would all be in the penitentiary in about six months, maybe a year. Yet it seems very, very sensible, to work this out by what they call business statesmanship. Now, here you see elements of the independence that is exercised by our great competing companies in the petroleum industry. One fellow may think one way and one may think another, and the business statesmanship factor sort of zigzags back and forth.

MR. CAMPBELL: It increases every month, I notice. We are very much upset by the constantly increasing quantities of imported residuals. They have devastated our markets for steam coal on the Eastern Seaboard and have affected prices all the way inland. The oil companies tell us that they will regulate the matter properly and for us not to worry—that they will take care of it; but they take care of it by taking, each month, a little more of the market.

ABRAHAM GERBER (American Gas and Electric Co.): Have any estimates been made as to the quantity of coal that could be sold on the East Coast if all residual were kept out?

MR. CAMPBELL: The direct loss which we claim due to increases in residual imports since 1947, is approximately 30 million tons a year, all told. The indirect loss may be another 20 million tons. We are not laying to imports of residuals any loss in the railroad fuel markets or any loss which we have sustained in the domestic markets. We are talking about direct losses that we can pin on the utilities, particularly on the Eastern Seaboard.

MR. AYRES: I think the situation is quite temporary as far as residual competition with coal is concerned. It has been growing in the past and will continue to grow perhaps for another year or so. But I think it is bound to reverse itself, in part because residual fuel oil will be more attractive economically when converted to distillate fuel.

MR. IRELAND: One of the problems that is facing the coal industry today is the fact that at the beginning of World War II, your excess gas reserves were not available, because there were no pipelines. Oil was being refined to the nth degree for military use and so they had to fall back on Old Man Coal to pick up the slack. We had to increase our production from 400 million tons a year to 600 plus, and it hurts to have to go back to normal.

MR. CAMPBELL: There seems to be some feeling among some protagonists of the oil industry that it is entitled to a steady percentage of the increase in the energy market. Our industry has not only had a decline in production, but we have had a constantly declining percentage of the energy market. We are not breaking even; we are going backwards.

Now that, we think, has a rather important effect on the country's stability, because our coal mines today are highly complex affairs; they are very expensive. We aren't talking simply in terms of wanting to make more money. True, we would like a better return on our investment. But we think there are social and economic consequences of considerable magnitude as well.

FORD K. EDWARDS (National Coal Association): Most of the oil imports fall on the East Coast. Of course, the major coal markets are in the East. When you bring oil in and drop it into that highly concentrated coal market, it seems to me that you get what amounts to extreme supplanting, rather than supplementation.

MR. SUMAN: After we have sold all the domestic residual that is economically available to us, we import residual fuel oil on the Atlantic Seaboard for our customers' use. It is a highly competitive situation, and we just sell what we can. Under the free enterprise system and laws of competition, we can't think we are doing anything that is particularly bad. To the best of my knowledge, our customers prefer this type of fuel, and we sell it to them.

MR. EDWARDS: Of course, we realize that this residual oil is a joint-cost product and that you can go as low as you need to to undercut coal.

MR. SUMAN: We have some very ardent salesmen and we try to fill their orders. I think that is the American system of free enterprise; if you ever start deviating from it, I think you are going to change this country from what we want it to be.

MR. EDWARDS: From a defense standpoint we still feel that you need coal around. Maybe oil can't get here. We feel that coal is very, very essential to the economy in an emergency. You can't dry it up in peacetime and have it on tap in wartime.

JOHN A. WARING, JR. (New York): Eventually, neither oil nor coal will be used in the United States and Canada predominantly as fuel. Coal will be used chiefly for chemicals, and oil will be used mainly for lubrication and chemicals. Most of our energy will come from renewable sources, such as hydro power, wind, tides, and sunlight. And I mean within our lifetime.

MR. AYRES: I would put it off a little further than that.

MR. MATHER: I have heard many complaints from independent oil producers that if their market is seriously curtailed by the large volume of importation, they won't have the money to plow back into exploration.

MR. SUMAN: The production of oil in the United States has been on the increase since 1950. It has never decreased. Your operations aren't being curtailed when you are doing more than you did the year before. The independents find a lot of this oil.

Electricity—As an End-Use Energy

To what extent can electricity, through improvements in utilization, become more impor-

tant as an end-use energy? (Much of the discussion here supplements the discussion on pages 234-36.)

MR. AYRES: I suppose that takes into account air conditioning, the heat pump, radiant heating, electrical heating, uses of electricity to produce aluminum, titanium, and so forth. Every time we substitute one metal for another, we have to use more power to produce it. Aluminum takes almost 10 times as much power to make as iron; magnesium takes more than aluminum, and titanium takes more than magnesium. So as we progress, our energy needs increase by leaps and bounds. Everything about our industrial civilization tends to higher and higher consumption of energy. All we can do in the way of conservation is to see that that energy is used as efficiently as can be to accomplish the results that we are after.

THOMAS W. HUNTER (Bureau of Mines): Is much being done by the power producers or the equipment manufacturers toward the advancement of electricity for heating homes? Then coal would get back into the picture in those markets that have been lost to competing fuels.

MR. PARSON: I think you would find that in most areas of the country where the consumer is left to his free economic choice, the cost differential between electric heating and other fuels is so great that any distinctive trend towards electric heating for all of your houses is quite distant.

MR. AYRES: I think there will be a trend toward electric space heating, but as it is, the power companies can sell all the power they can make, and more, with a relatively favorable load factor and they don't want this kind of business. The load factor may have to be worked out in conjunction, perhaps, with heat storage.

What are the prospects of development in the direction of more industry-produced electric power in order more efficiently to integrate power and process-heat needs? Or more use of waste heat in industry or power production?

MR. AYRES: It seems to me that one of the very fundamental problems for future technologists to work out is the utilization of low-level heat. That is where the enormous losses are in the manufacture of atomic bombs—all this hot water that flows into the river. If there were some good way of utilizing that low-level heat, we would do more to conserve energy than anything I know of.

MR. BROWNE: Not only is the heat wasted, but in evaporating water to get rid of the heat there is also a water loss. The water resources people consider this one of their problems. The water conservation people and the low-heat conservation people should try to work out a solution.

MR. AYRES: It is a very fundamental problem—an area in which research work should be pressed. It is where most of the loss goes in a motor car. You have to blow a stream of air through the radiator in order to take away a lot of heat. The heat doesn't accomplish anything except in the wintertime to warm us up in the car. If there were some way to make use of the heat that is lost in a motor car, it would accomplish more than all the engine changes and octane numbers put together and more than changing from large to small cars.

MR. FRITZ: We can use energy only where we have a fairly steep heat gradient; if it is dissipated slowly, we can't use it effectively as a general rule.

MR. AYRES: That is right. But there is a theoretical efficiency, low though it may be, for conversion of low-temperature heat into work; if we could just come somewhere near that point, we would be doing a great deal.

ALFRED R. POWELL (Koppers Company, Inc.): The chemical industry today is probably in the forefront on this problem. In a chemical plant, the prime mover, whether a reciprocating engine or turbine, is designed in such a way that the exhaust steam comes out at a temperature that makes it useful for process heating.

CHAIRMAN'S SUMMARY

An ample supply of electrical and mechanical energy is vital to a high standard of living in any country. The increase in energy production in the United States during the past few decades has been phenomenal. The increase in the future will be still greater.

This rapid increase in energy production, as seen by the Section on Energy Resource Problems, involves both economics and advances in technology. The situation is never static. As soon as economic stability is approached with a given technology, new advances based on scientific research create new economic factors. This dynamic character of the development of energy sources was evident over and over again, as the section or its subsections considered such problems as the mining of coal seams less than 30 inches thick or the use of thorium in nuclear breeder reactors. It was clear that there is an inescapable tension between existing economic situations and the possibility of technological advance which will bring into use hitherto inaccessible reserves or new methods worked out in the laboratory or on the drawing board. These changes may greatly alter the relationship of supply and demand and thus affect the price structure.

There was thought to be an ample supply of coal, oil, and gas for the next 25 years, at least; but there was continuing emphasis on the difference between "ultimate" resources, calculated as coal has been calculated from geological inference, and "inventory" figures such as those used in petroleum practice. These resources have been discovered, developed, and operated by private enterprise.

Prominent in our energy resources is hydroelectric power which has been developed by private enterprise, local government, and federal government. The section heard the opinion expressed that in the development of hydroelectric power closer collaboration between these three is important. A suggestion was made that a center be established for the exchange of ideas and the consideration of joint action. In the ideal solution, it was pointed out, each of the three groups in this common enterprise would handle those tasks for which it has the chief competence, and local power policy problems would be settled freely at the local level.

Atomic energy has been developed entirely by the federal government and there was discussion of possible ways to expand this potent new source of energy through private enterprise, while at the same time insuring the public interest.

There was clear consensus that between now and 1975 power from nuclear energy will not constitute a large fraction of the total installed capacity and none of our present energy-generating equipment will be rendered obsolete. By 1975, however, nuclear energy may supply a considerable portion of new construction. It was equally clear that eventually the contribution of nuclear energy to the nation's power store will be of major significance. Firm predictions of the time and extent of these developments were considered to be next to impossible in view of the influence of military policies and problems of technology such as those involved in the breeder reactor.

The possible contributions to the economy that may be expected from other unconventional sources of power—such as solar energy —similarly depend in great measure upon the counterbalance existing between economics and new technology. The sun now heats water for residents of Florida on a thrifty basis. Though one may not yet blithely extrapolate that the sun—unaided—will heat his house for him if he elects to live in the North, it was seen that before long solar heating of houses may be of marked importance in the nation's way of life. Further application of solar energy to operate engines and produce electricity directly, depends on further research.

In the subsection discussions concerned with conservation and wise use of our energy resources, the theme of technological advance, then economic fixity, then new technological advance, then new economic fixity was heard repeatedly. There was consideration of ways to encourage exploration and greater production of mineral fuels. The economic theme underlay the discussion of the depletion allowance, which, under occasional attack, was strongly defended by representatives of the oil industry and actively supported by representatives of the coal industry. Research directed toward the development of additional fossil fuels, oil shales especially, and the chemical conversion of coal into gasoline was seen as warranting support from federal government.

Thankful for the abundant resources of fuel and water power that nature has given us; proud of the achievements of science and technology which have used these resources for cheap power, vigorous industry, and a high standard of living; aware of the fact that private enterprise and government have both shared in these developments and believing that a continuation of this relationship is desirable—we face the future with confidence. We realize that we have abundant energy resources for far more than the next 25 years, that those types of fuels which become exhausted first can be replaced by other types, that nuclear energy can be brought in when needed, and that still other sources of energy (notably solar energy) lie ahead if we maintain a vigorous program of research.

FARRINGTON DANIELS
December 4, 1953

Section VI

Chairman
EDWARD S. MASON
Dean of the Graduate School of
Public Administration
Harvard University

Co-Chairman
E. G. COLLADO
Assistant Treasurer
Standard Oil Company (New
Jersey), New York

Steering Committee and Advisers

Steering Committee: DENNIS A. FITZGERALD, Deputy Director for Operations, Foreign Operations Administration · STACY MAY, Economist, International Basic Economy Corporation · MORRIS S. ROSENTHAL, Foreign Trade Consultant, New York · STANLEY H. RUTTENBERG, Director, Department of Education and Research, Congress of Industrial Organizations · H. DEWITT SMITH, Consulting Engineer, New York · SIMON D. STRAUSS, Vice-President, American Smelting and Refining Company · *Assistant to the Section Chairman:* ROBERT BLUM, Consultant, Foreign Operations Administration · *Section Rapporteur:* JOHN W. EVANS, Director, Office of International Materials Policy, U. S. Department of State.

Subsections

A. COMMERCIAL POLICY

Chairman: STACY MAY

Rapporteurs: JOHN LINDEMAN, Economist, Washington, D.C.; MARY JANE HEYL, Office of Industrial Resources, Foreign Operations Administration

B. INVESTMENT AND DEVELOPMENT

Chairman: H. DEWITT SMITH

Rapporteurs: WILLIAM B. GATES, JR., Economist, Export-Import Bank; E. EDWARD SCOLL, Investment and Economic Development Staff, U. S. Department of State

C. MARKET STABILIZATION

Chairman: SIMON D. STRAUSS

Rapporteurs: WILLIAM T. PHILLIPS, Professor of International Economics, School of Advanced International Studies, Johns Hopkins University; RICHARD WEBER, Foreign Operations Administration

About 200 people participated in the work of Section VI. The 180 who registered formally are listed on pages 401-4. The full section met together the afternoon of December 2 to consider general aspects of its problems, divided into subsections for morning and afternoon meetings December 3, and met again together the morning of December 4.

U.S. CONCERN
WITH WORLD RESOURCES

THE MAJOR FOCUS OF THE MID-CENTURY CONFERENCE
was domestic: How can we best develop and conserve the natural resources within
our own borders? However, the nation's industry draws its raw materials requirements from a world-wide resource base, and many raw materials that the United
States produces find world-wide markets; our whole resources position can be
affected by what happens abroad in response to what we do or do not do at home.
In examining the raw materials part of the resources problem, therefore, we must
look beyond our frontiers and think in world-wide terms. This was the task of
Section VI. As the section chairman put it: "The emphasis here is on United
States concern with world resources. We are looking at world-resource problems,
but through the eyes of an American citizen."

The materials considered here are industrial raw materials, excluding foodstuffs; and the approach is primarily from the point of view of the United States
interest in assuring future availability of these materials in sufficient quantity for
continued economic growth and national security.

What are the prospects for adequate supplies to meet the needs of the
American economy over the longer term—particularly supplies of those commodities
entering largely into world trade? On this question there were wide differences of
opinion in detail. But the area of agreement was sufficient to make it possible to
discuss most issues on common grounds. There was general acceptance of the Paley
Commission's forecasts, although its specific projections were challenged in certain
respects. Discussion was based on the assumption that, over the longer run, American
industrial production will continue to grow, our consumption of raw materials will
grow comparably though at a somewhat lesser rate than the gross national product,
and our dependence on imports of most extractive raw materials will increase, despite
the fact that the United States will still be the most important raw materials
producer.

While the principal task of the section was to explore alternative policies for
the longer term, the short term could not be ignored. Whatever the outlook of the
United States may be for raw material supplies 50 years from now, more or less
violent oscillations between surplus and shortage will occur in the interim. They

can seriously affect the strength of American industry; they can affect both the volume and the direction of American and foreign investment in natural resources; and they can very directly affect our foreign relations. In consequence, they can have an immediate bearing on our national security. It was pointed out that a policy best designed to meet the problems of the next 5 or 10 years might be quite the wrong one if our sights are raised to a more distant objective. Conflict between short- and long-term objectives was not believed to be inevitable, however, provided that the long-term policy is so devised as to avoid intensifying the short-term problems known to exist.

As for the national security, there was no dissent from the view that our calculations must take into account the possibility of war. The need for taking prudent precautions against this possibility must enter into the determination of all our policies but is particularly pertinent to the international area. On the other hand, there was no disposition to suggest that national security in this narrow sense should be our only concern. The economic strength of the United States and of friendly countries, the importance of our role of world leadership, the objective of avoiding unnecessary hardship to American producers, to American consuming industries, or to foreign producers and consumers, all must be weighed in the scale.

Security and Other Basic Considerations

Certain basic aspects of the problem, including the broader aspects of national security, cut directly across the group's three separate areas of discussion. Is it wise to consider world resources from a purely domestic viewpoint? If so, how broad or narrow should the approach be? What, really, should be our chief long-range goals, and how can they be related to short-term problems? These, and the issue of security, were considered in the opening general session of Section VI in their relation to the issues of commercial policy, development of resources abroad, and stabilization of raw materials prices subsequently examined by the three subsections.

Discussion centered largely on the stockpile approach to the problem of materials availability in the event of war. Is it an adequate answer to the question of security requirements? How does the concept of atomic warfare affect determinations of what materials should be stockpiled, where they should be stockpiled, and in what forms and quantities? And, in the light of these considerations, what action on commercial policy, foreign resources development, and price stabilization is in the U.S. interest?

The possibility that the stockpiling function should be extended beyond its present security objective to that of economic stabilization was proposed, but this question was referred to Subsection C for more detailed examination (pages 294-95, 299-300). Brief consideration was also given to the relationship between economic development in the producing countries and U.S. security interests, a subject that was later discussed more fully in Subsection B (pages 276-85).

FROM THE RECORD

U.S. Interests in Foreign Resources

EDWARD S. MASON (Harvard University): Perhaps the first interest of the United States in foreign resources is to meet its requirements for materials involved in prospective growth. To what extent should our rapidly increasing materials requirements be satisfied from domestic sources of supply? To what extent from foreign sources? The extent that we depend, and want to depend, more on foreign sources of supply is likely to affect our commercial policy; the question of how best to develop those foreign sources also comes squarely into the picture, and the question of whether one does something about the instability of raw material prices, whether that will facilitate this development.

A second primary concern of the United States in world resources is tied in with our security problem. The possibility that war may come changes markedly the way one has to look at this raw materials problem. The problem of war and the preparation for war involve in the first place a consideration of how the composition of the requirements for materials may change and how we may prepare ourselves for that change. Secondly, of course, there is the possibility that we may be cut off from certain customary sources of supply. In view of those possibilities, is any change implied in our attitude toward foreign sources of raw materials?

How Domestic a Viewpoint?

WILFRED MALENBAUM (Massachusetts Institute of Technology): A definition of security interests which is narrowly limited to the United States and our industrial allies in Western Europe and perhaps Japan is in itself inconsistent with what I assume to be the program or policy of our own government, which has defined our security problem to encompass progress and development in the underdeveloped areas. I would like to see our approach include the need for this development. Such an approach to the security problem has many important aspects in addition to our desire for increased accessibility to raw materials in the underdeveloped areas.

MAURICE E. H. ROTIVAL (New York): I object to the principle of studying resources development only from the point of view of the American citizen. We are the leaders of the Free World; therefore, we must look at it from the point of view of leadership. When we take raw resources from an underdeveloped country we do not give it much, from an economic point of view. The only way we can raise the standards of these people is to give them industrial development. That conflicts with the principle that the raw materials from these countries must be brought in here to be processed if we want to maintain the high standard of life which we want in the United States. The increase of the standard of life here is going at such a pace that, even with all our efforts in technical assistance to any country I go to, the comparative curves are getting wider and wider apart from year to year. What are we going to do to develop resources for the benefit of the underdeveloped countries? What kind of economic supports are we going to establish? What industries can be established abroad without preventing our own here from selling their goods? It is certainly not by taking raw materials only that we are going to establish the economic circuit that will raise the existing low "equilibrium." Our studies have to go much further.

SAMUEL W. ANDERSON (U. S. Department of Commerce): It seems to me that there has been very great preoccupation with the fact that the United States needs huge quantities of materials for the next 50 years or so, probably beyond that as well. But there is a determined drive on the part of most of the raw materials countries to become industrialized and to use their own raw materials. What consideration should this conference give to the inevitable industrial development of Latin America, for example, which is a considerable source of our raw materials? Where will that development, by the year 2000, leave our determined drive for overseas sources to supplement our dwindling domestic sources of raw materials?

The Long-Term Versus the Short-Term View

W. S. WOYTINSKY (Twentieth Century Fund): The old concepts of commercial policy, of investment and development, and of stabilization of markets cannot be used in the discussion of problems this country will be facing, let us say, 50 years from now. The trends in the world economy should be taken into account.

For instance, consider the functions of private investment and public investment in the development of foreign countries. If we are talking only about the immediate future, I would be inclined to agree that the problem of providing raw materials can be solved very successfully by private industry. But as soon as we begin to consider the general economic trends in the world, and put the question of what will happen to direct investments abroad in 10, 15, 20 years from now and what will be the political conditions in which they work, we must conclude that certain problems cannot be solved by development of private investment abroad. And we must conclude also that this long-range view must affect our requirements and our action for the immediate future.

So my contention is that, in discussion of commercial policy, of development and investment, and of stabilization, we must at least put to ourselves these two questions: What is our goal for the next 10 years? And, what is our goal for a much longer time?

MR. MASON: I take it that this conference is not exclusively concerned with the raw materials problem of the next year or of the next decade. An essential part of our problem is: What is the natural resource situation faced by this country and by the Free World likely to be over a longer period of time?

If you look at that problem, it does seem to me that the critical questions turn around the rate of economic growth and the impact of that growth on the magnitude of our materials requirements. Even though you look forward to a persistent, rapid rate of growth in the United States and elsewhere, there will, of course, in this raw materials field, be a continuous oscillation between surplus and scarcity around that long-run trend, so that we can by no means exclusively devote our attention to this projection of long-running trends and their sequences; we have to take account, also, of periodic surpluses, periodic scarcities of raw materials, and how we deal with that kind of problem.

We also have to superimpose on this picture the kind of security consideration we have been talking about. When all three of these elements are taken together, there arise some interesting and important questions as to what the role of government and the role of private enterprise should be in handling these problems.

Security Implications of Raw Materials Policy

MR. MASON: In the event of war, we must have available supplies of raw materials from safe sources. We cannot take the general attitude that, if the United States supplies its requirements from lowest-cost sources, that answers the problem. We have to be prepared to supply our requirements from safe sources, in the event of war, whether they are high-cost or low-cost. How does that security consideration affect the United States interest in foreign resource development?

Some people say that, as a large number of our most important raw materials are exhaustible, we ought, in time of peace, to rely as heavily as possible on foreign sources and conserve our supplies for wartime use. There are, however, certain difficulties with this approach. One is that, as we increasingly rely on foreign sources, we may, in the event of war, be cut off suddenly from our supplies. Others say that, since we have to have safe sources of supply, we should make the United States as self-sufficient as possible. But, in the first place, the more rapidly we exhaust our sources of certain materials, the worse our eventual position is going to be. In the second place, depending exclusively on domestic supplies will, in many cases, markedly increase the cost at which we are going to meet our requirements; and that cost would, of course, affect peacetime as well as wartime production. Both of these views are, I believe, oversimple views. There is a tremendously difficult problem as to how U.S. security considerations affect this choice between domestic and foreign sources of supply.

There is, furthermore, another and highly important security aspect to this natural resource problem. We are, by now, pretty firmly committed to what amounts to a system of alliances in the event of war. The question as to how our allies are going to meet their requirements for raw materials then becomes, to some extent, a security concern of the United States.

WALTER J. LEVY (New York): I am wondering whether we are looking at the security problem continually in terms of the past rather than in terms of the future. First of all, in view of the nature of atomic warfare, I believe one can reasonably assume that a major war might well be won or lost in 30 to 60 days. The estimate for all resources which are needed to sustain the civilian economy as well as the war economy of our country would then be very different from that based on any concept we had had before.

Will it really be as important as in previous wars, then, to have domestic productive capacity sufficient to satisfy requirements on what we traditionally consider a full-fledged war level? Or will it be necessary to have only a strong domestic industry in general, the stockpile being, in fact, the material basis on which the first 30 to 60 days will be fought? In view of these new concepts of atomic and long-distance war, will it still be necessary to grant protection on any substantial scale to our domestic mining and other industries to the extent, at least, that the need for such protection is based exclusively on security considerations? As far as I am aware, there is practically no industry claiming continuous protection, quotas, or any kind of subsidy on the basis that its profits would be affected. The major reason given is security. I think that range of problems needs the most challenging investigation under present conditions and present military planning.

MR. MASON: I cannot help wondering

whether the whole stockpile concept is not based on an outworn set of assumptions. The commodities that are stockpiled are largely commodities coming from areas which are considered to be vulnerable; and the areas considered vulnerable are largely areas producing commodities for shipment to the United States which might be intercepted at sea. That was, of course, a concept which was of tremendous importance in World War I, and which still had a great deal of weight in World War II. But with the development of intercontinental bombing possibilities, and with the development of the atomic and hydrogen bombs, is that concept any longer of great significance?

May it not be that the domestic sources of supply in the United States are at least as vulnerable to attack as the supplies from foreign sources are vulnerable to interception at sea? If that is so, doesn't it profoundly change the nature of this whole vulnerability issue, certain assumptions of which underlie our stockpiling program? Here is a range of pretty important considerations as to how this security issue really affects, and should affect, our commercial policy, our foreign resource development, and the other aspects which are under scrutiny in this section.

MR. ANDERSON: There is a large stockpile goal for aluminum. I think the two most important justifications are these: First, we have discovered from experience that the demand for aluminum in war spirals up very fast and to very high figures. In the absence of a stockpile, if we are confronted again with the problem which faced us in the last war, we would have to build rapidly new aluminum plants after M-Day, including power plants. The first justification, therefore, is to avoid placing this strain on the economy during wartime.

The second justification is, I think, of equal importance. Aluminum is a stockpile of power: every pound of aluminum is a stockpile of 10 kilowatt-hours. If you had an enormous stockpile of aluminum, and if enemy damage should be concentrated (as I suspect it might be) on power plants, you could even shut down aluminum plants after M-Day and use that power for something else of greater priority at the moment.

I cite these two reasons over and beyond the ordinary garden variety reasons for a stockpile of a metal like aluminum to illustrate how reasoning in connection with a stockpile ought to fan out in all kinds of directions, and should be examined in each case to see what its ramifications are.

MR. MALENBAUM: Wouldn't Mr. Levy's point on the prospects of a very short war lead to the conclusion that you must stockpile, and presumably deploy throughout the world, the *finished* products necessary for conducting war? It would seem to me that this is an obvious stockpile implication for a one-thrust, short-period hot war.

WAYNE C. TAYLOR (Foreign Operations Administration): I think you have to define the area—what kind of security you are talking about. Are we stockpiling what we consider to be our own needs? Are we carrying the inventory for what we consider to be our defense group? Does that inventory have to be carried in this country? Can it be carried somewhere else?

MR. MASON: As soon as you extend the concept of requirements of materials availability in the event of war beyond the borders of the United States to the group of countries which presumably are going to be fighting with us in the war, the whole question of what materials you stockpile, where you stockpile them, and in what quantities, takes on a rather different kind of significance.

EDWARD SYMONDS (International Bank for Reconstruction and Development): There are a number of commodities that cannot be stockpiled, either because they are perishable—such as agricultural products—or because, from their nature, they present physical difficulties—petroleum, for example. So no program can hope to be completely comprehensive. Among those commodities that *can* be stockpiled in the United States—and obviously among those that cannot—the answer to the question whether to stockpile, and how much to stockpile, cannot be settled in isolation. The answer must be heavily weighted by consideration drawn from other subjects—price stabilization, development of source countries, and, indeed, U.S. commercial policy.

R. J. LUND (Batelle Memorial Institute): We have talked this afternoon a little about possible damage to raw material production capacity in this country—to mines and so on. But can't we just as well expect damage to our fabricating capacity? Therefore, shouldn't this factor be one to consider in setting stockpiling goals? Are we going to be able to fabricate these tremendous sums of metals and minerals that we are stockpiling at the present time?

STACY MAY (International Basic Economy Corporation): I wonder whether the changed nature of the security problem does not have real relevance to thinking through a position not only on the development of primary materials in certain outlying areas, but conceivably on the initial stages of fabrication also, in certain instances—whether dispersion of facilities, let us say, should be a major item of a new strategy of safety against vulnerability in terms of atomic considerations. This question applies to tariffs, because we are somewhat more lenient on the primary materials than we are on the processed materials.

ANDREW FLETCHER (St. Joseph Lead Company): In my opinion, the best stockpile is a prosperous mining industry. When the Army decided the tonnages that should be stockpiled, they were based on the assumption that we would have a mining industry in the United States. However, unless there is a basic change in the attitude of the Administration toward the mining industry, we are not going to have one. If we do not have one, the Army's stockpiling requirement will probably be greatly increased.

Should the Stockpile Objective Be Extended to Include Economic Functions?

RICHARD M. BISSELL, JR. (Washington, D.C.): I feel that, if you are going into the stockpiling policy further, it is necessary also to go beyond the purely security standard. As long as we have a stockpile and are adding to it, whatever its purpose, the temptation will exist to use that stockpile and to vary the rate of additions to it in ways intended to have beneficial economic effects. Under the pressure of circumstances, most of the variations in the rate of stockpile purchase in the last five years could scarcely, even by design, have been more destabilizing; generally speaking, we seem to have followed the rule of accelerating purchases when markets were strong and tight and cutting back our purchases when markets were soft and the rest of the world urgently needed foreign exchange resources. If the stockpile should continue to grow, even though at a modest rate, are there ways in which that operation can be carried on which will contribute to other objectives at the same time?

Mr. Mason: Whether stockpile purchases should be used for economic stabilization is a very difficult question. With a $9 billion stockpile, there are already sizable opportunities for stabilizing operations. If that stockpile were to be increased to include a lot of domestically produced materials, those opportunities would be even greater. On the other hand, of course, as soon as you attempt to use a stockpile for stabilizing purposes, you are introducing a very dangerous principle into the whole stockpiling program, in the sense that

any vested interest group which finds it difficult to sell its output at prices it considers reasonable will go then to the government and say: "How about accumulating some of this material for the stockpile?" There are arguments both ways.

William B. Mather (Southwest Research Institute): There is another angle to the stockpile question. Many of these raw materials we are unable to produce in this country. For example, we were dependent on Malaya for tin, and now we are dependent on Bolivia. We know that many foreign countries are handicapped by internal unrest; the spirit of nationalism is rising. For example, unless we have a stockpile of tin in this country, industry will not get any tin. I think this same thing could be true of other resources. The stockpile is merely an assurance that industry would have the material available, in time of need, whether the situation is created by war or internal trouble within the country of supply.

Mr. Mason: Insofar as accumulating stockpiles for other than military purposes is concerned, you are relying on a different kind of argument, an argument which has to do with the over-all stability of the American economy, in the sense that you are talking about the continued access of processing facilities to available flow of materials.

Subsection A

COMMERCIAL POLICY

The United States has built its prosperity on a wealth of raw materials largely within its own borders. In relation to our unprecedented production of goods and services, that raw materials wealth is now declining. To conserve our resources and yet assure continued economic growth and security, we must in the future depend increasingly upon foreign raw materials supplies. This situation brings with it pressing questions of commercial policy as it relates to long-range U.S. interests. Has our commercial policy kept pace with these broad developments? How well are our present policies designed to serve our future national interest?

The subsection recognized at the outset the complexity of the national interest that commercial policy must serve—the political and strategic, as well as economic, aspects of this interest; the pull of sometimes conflicting interests as between various economic and geographic groups within the country; the reconciliations that must often be made between short-term and long-term interests.

All these complexities were kept constantly in mind in discussing the main issue: What should U.S. commercial policy be with respect to imports of raw materials? The approach to this question was almost entirely in terms of government action on tariffs and other impediments to imports; some of the more positive methods of encouraging beneficial trade, and production in other countries were discussed by Subsections B and C. The main question was dealt with in three major stages: (1) Materials outlook as it bears on commercial policy; (2) Current commercial policy: how well does it fit the situation? (3) Appraisal of current policy on specific materials. The commodities discussed most fully by way of example were petroleum, lead and zinc, and copper.

Materials Outlook

Discussion of current and future commercial policy as it relates to raw materials called for a broad, if hasty, review of the general situation and outlook on natural resources. About how great are our needs likely to be, and what proportion of them might be supplied advantageously from domestic sources? What, if any, considerations of military and political security should be borne in mind?

Some basic assumptions were needed here. The subsection chairman suggested three: That, if the nation's economy continues to follow its historic growth trend, the needs for raw materials will increase greatly in the years ahead; that dependence on imports of raw materials will increase; and that the major sources of the increased imports will be the areas of the world that are now relatively undeveloped.

The subsection members seemed willing to work on these assumptions, at least as general guidelines. A number of participants had reservations, such as the uncertainty of any long-term projections and the need for considering short- as well as long-range situations. It was suggested also that even if the long-term expansion in total demand is as great as the President's Materials Policy Commission anticipated, changes in the pattern of usage and new domestic mineral discoveries might affect future import requirements for some materials. There were wide differences, too, on the effect that a drop in the proportion of military requirements might have on materials consumption.

The supply problem, for the most part, was seen as one of efficiency and costs rather than of absolute materials shortages. Questions of how much might be available from other countries brought up the general problem of encouraging foreign production, an issue that was examined only for its immediate relation to U.S. import policy since the broader meaning was discussed in Subsection B (see pages 275-88).

Confidence appeared widespread that, if U.S. commercial policies are such as to assure an economic basis for raw materials production, the supplies available will be sufficient to support continued economic expansion.

Discussion of the factor of national security hinged largely on the relative importance of keeping domestic producing industries in readiness for emergencies and of encouraging trade with friendly nations, and on the extent to which the two objectives are compatible.

FROM THE RECORD

How Sure Is the Long-Term View?

ROBERT G. PAGE (Phelps Dodge Corporation): I do not think anything was established by the President's Materials Policy Commission. I would regard their views as, first, assumptions and, second, hopes. I would agree that they are entirely valid hopes. The only thing I really know about 1975 is that I do not know what the situation is going to be then. I do not know of any other field in which a group of men sit down and say: "Let's formulate a policy which is valid for 25 years." I do not think this group should attempt it either, except subject to the recognition that policy has to be changed almost day by day, and certainly year by year.

DAVID A. SHEPARD (Standard Oil Company (New Jersey)): I want to speak in favor of flexibility as an important constituent in whatever commercial policy is deemed right for the United States. I feel strongly about this because of my convictions about the fallibility of human prophesies and the impossibility of predicting what are the depths and shoals which are going to be met. I think it is time to emphasize the need for quite a lot of room to move in over the fairly short-term future.

STACY MAY (International Basic Economy Corporation): I agree that it is very foolish to have a policy which takes no cognizance of where you are immediately, or which gives no hedges against the possibility, or probability even, that your prognosis may be wrong.

I think all you can do is to say: "Look, we have had a kind of pattern in the past; we have liked it; we would like to extend this pattern into the future. Therefore, we ought to be thinking in policy terms which would give us the kind of picture we want; and we ought to have a policy which looks toward our aims."

Possible Modifications in Domestic Supply

JEAN VUILLEQUEZ (American Metal Company, Ltd.): We have been told that we will be dependent increasingly on raw materials from foreign sources. I wonder to what extent consideration was given, in arriving at this premise, to the possibilities of new geological methods which may, from a long-range point of view, change the position of the United States in relation to the rest of the world. I am not one who thinks that this country's mineral resources have been exhausted. I think the question is to find them.

MR. PAGE: Every company I know about is spending quite large sums on attempting to develop for hidden mine deposits what the oil people have long since accomplished on hidden oil deposits. Most of the geologists I know believe that there are, in this country, ore deposits which have not been found. Almost all of the ore deposits that have been found have outcropped or have been traced from surface indications. It seems a reasonable assumption that additional ore deposits exist, the presence of which is not apparent from the surface indications, and that methods will be developed to find them.

WILLIAM T. THOM, JR. (Princeton, N.J.): Although you can never count upon making a discovery until after you have made it, I think the next 3 to 25 years will see very extensive and important discoveries of concealed ore deposits in the United States. The general geological picture is such as to warrant that expectation.

Beyond 25 or 50 years, the presumption is that, since we have such a small part of the world's total area, and since we exploit it much more extensively than the others do theirs, eventually we may need to go to other parts of the world in increasing degree, and in terms of price aspects. Naturally, I think it is going to be highly advantageous to make barter arrangements, or the more usual arrangements, to get substitutes from abroad and allow each area to produce according to its qualifications.

EDWARD M. BERNSTEIN (International Monetary Fund): The central point that must be kept in mind when discussing the aggregate supply of raw materials is that there is room for successive substitution of one material for another. We are not faced with a breakdown of our economy for lack of materials, but with the problem of increased costs attached to adjusting output to a collection of raw materials involving different degrees of scarcity.

RICHARD A. GRIFFITH (General Electric Company): Where you have material substitutions in any degree—as of aluminum for copper, for example—it will be based upon the fact that the consumer will be able to foresee a long-range price differential between the two metals.

Then, too, there will be the difficulty of adjusting the machines to take the new metal, because there is not a complete correlation between one metal and another; technological changes will be necessary. You have to make your design engineers, and even the people on the drafting board, aware of new materials which will do the same job as the traditional ones. You have to break up the traditional habit of using a given metal for a certain particular job.

Can Increased Foreign Supplies Be Assumed?

BENJAMIN GREENSPAN (New School for Social Research): Assuming dependence on foreign sources for raw materials, we should, I think, bear in mind that, at some time in the future, the foreign materials may not be available, whether it will be for economic reasons or for political or security reasons. We should take into consideration the possibility of a stimulated use of those materials by the so-called underdeveloped countries in a new process of economic development that may take place during the next 25 or 50 years. The stuff may not be available to us.

MR. GRIFFITH: Steady growth of industrial activity in this country depends a great deal upon how much we can sell and export, since we will not consume everything which we produce; and a lot of that depends upon how much those underdeveloped countries can sell to us in the form of raw materials. I think our whole policy should be, in the long-range point of view, to help the underdeveloped countries have the means by which they can achieve their own industrial expansion; and that is that we should buy from them the materials we need.

CHARLES INCE (St. Joseph Lead Company): As these countries become more industrialized, they will be using more of their raw materials themselves. What you are saying is, buy their raw materials so they can become industrialized. If we buy their raw materials, we become more dependent on them for these materials. In other words, you are setting up a means by which you start losing your raw materials.

The widespread fears of exploitation and the intense desire of the underdeveloped countries to gain greater economic independence were recognized as factors that complicate the question of future raw materials supplies from foreign sources. What account should our commercial policy take of these factors?

MR. MAY: I think that we have done far too much to encourage the general supposition that developing raw materials abroad is a dirty trick on the area concerned and that it is exploitative in some way. This idea is very widely spread in some of the relatively underdeveloped areas.

This is another field where research is

needed. Before we do much more talking about development, somebody had better examine, first, with some care, relative costs of various kinds of development in various kinds of areas, along with the hazards.

But, second and directly on this point, we had better find out more about what net advantage there is to a country from various kinds of activities. I have tried to look at oil in Venezuela in these terms, and as nearly as I could find out, 87 percent of the gross selling price of the oil which has been produced in Venezuela has stayed in Venezuela in one form or another.

I am not trying to apply this as a generalization everywhere, to all extractive industry. But I do not know of any systematic study that has been made to measure the accruals to date, per dollar of investment, to the economies of countries in which foreign investments have been made. I think it ought to be done.

JOSEPH PINCUS (Arlington, Va.): I still think we are confronted with a very strong psychological viewpoint on the part of the underdeveloped areas. They do not want so-called holes in the ground after whatever deposit they have had has been exploited. Most of them now are emerging from a strictly raw materials stage. They feel, moreover, that the wide fluctuations in the prices of raw materials require them, for balance-of-payment reasons, as well as reasons of general economic growth, to diversify their economies.

Consequently, I do not believe they are as anxious or willing now to permit intensive exploitation of raw materials resources without a balanced development along other lines; industrialization, for example.

MR. SHEPARD: The human-relations problem must be faced; it is tremendously important. But it is an area in which generalization is extremely difficult, if not impossible. Let me give just one example of what divergent circumstances can arise.

In South America, that startling and fascinating country of Brazil has a slogan which says: "The petroleum is ours!"—a very vigorous nationalistic attitude which tells anyone who

is willing to listen, in effect: "We do not want anyone not a native Brazilian to have a hole in our ground." On the other hand, on the same continent, there is another extremely interesting country—Colombia—with a completely different attitude, one which is very full of free-enterprise ideas (now, anyway), and which gives every sign of welcoming foreign investment and partnerships of all sorts and kinds which look to be promising.

Speculations on Future Military Requirements

MR. MAY: I want to raise a fourth premise for you as a question. First, a little of the background on the question: United States manufacturing capacity has increased 30 percent in durable goods since June, 1950; the minerals output—that is to September, 1953—has increased just about 10 percent. There is an obvious disparity there, even when we recognize the long-range tendency to do more fabrication on a given amount of raw materials. How much of that is due to the fact that our very high level of manufacturing output, not only in the United States but in Western Europe, has a great component of military output in it? I think it is something like 25 percent of durable goods in the United States at the present time. Dollar for dollar, military things have a tremendous amount of fabrication in them as compared with weight of metal. Therefore, our indices go up on that.

The implications of this, as you see, are that, if we were moving out of the present state in which a very large volume of our durable goods production is devoted to military, and if Western Europe were doing the same, and we were able to hold our over-all levels of production and go ahead on the gross trend, it might be that our present surpluses of minerals, but particularly of metals, would be turned into deficits again.

MR. INCE: If the impact of military expenditures should be lessened or removed, it is quite possible that we could become practically self-sufficient in some of these minerals; we do not know. In 1935, the figures in the section working paper show, we produced 86 percent of the copper we needed, 97 percent of the lead, and 90 percent of the zinc. It is the period 1940-50, in which military expenditures were heavy, that gives a basis for seeing a long-term trend toward more dependence on foreign sources. My point is that, if this military production were removed or lessened, the trend might be reversed. I am not saying that it would be reversed to the point where we were in 1935 because, obviously, there is a per capita consumption that is independent of military expenditures.

If we were to protect what mineral industry we have today, our dependence on foreign supplies might decrease, instead of growing continuously in this period up to 1975.

Is it a valid assumption that, in terms of dollar value, military production uses less material than civilian durable goods production?

MR. INCE: I would very much question that $1000 worth of military production requires much less material than $1000 worth of civilian production. Take an item like brass cartridge cases—the amount of material going in, per $1000, is far greater than on a fabricated item like a carburetor for a car, for example. I think the suggested premise is entirely erroneous, in the case of metals.

MR. BERNSTEIN: There is a long-term trend in which the use of raw materials falls relative to the value of output; and I believe that this is true of practically every raw material.

You can see evidence of that if you take automobiles in the United States. If you set up a table, taking automobile by automobile, you will find that the greater the value of the automobile, the more the fabrication per unit of raw materials; or, put in another way, the more the dollar value for each point of weight which goes into that automobile. That trend is a steady trend, and it is not confined to one industry; it is true of industry in general.

If you can do the job with less metal, you have not merely saved the metal—that, in itself, might not be a strong enough incentive —you have improved the end product by getting out the weight of nonfunctional metal. And this is a job that is going on all the time.

Current Commercial Policy: An Appraisal

In general, current U.S. commercial policy on primary raw materials imports was felt to be in line with the needs of the anticipated demand situation. Some changes were suggested, however. Those who favored giving more positive encouragement to new raw materials production abroad saw need for one or both of the following revisions: (1) reduction of tariffs on materials that have gone through a secondary processing; (2) reduction or removal of tariffs which benefit the producers of substitute materials, rather than domestic producers of materials to which the tariffs apply.

A number of participants, on the other hand, favored further import restrictions. Special attention was called to possibilities of increasing domestic production by these means and to the need for general tightening of protective measures with respect to critical strategic materials which the United States does, or can, produce in substantial quantities.

FROM THE RECORD

Present U.S. Commercial Policy

Mr. May: We have had a generally liberal policy toward raw materials in the primary state; it could be denominated this way: There is a large free list; the tariffs are generally low and, for the most part, far from insurmountable; quota policies are not generally applicable to this field or, at least, they have not generally been applied to this field of primary raw materials, except in the case of long-staple cotton. Remember, we have ruled out our foods from consideration.

It is stated in the summary prepared for us by the steering committee that "Buy American" legislation is not too important in this field; but I have a query as to whether it does not have some importance through its applicability in the Defense Appropriations Act of 1953 and in the Stockpiling Act also—it applies to both on the books at least.

I think we might discuss also the claimed deterrent effect of the injury and escape clause and the peril point provisions, which apply to this field as well as to all others; and I think we should discuss the difference, generally, between our tariff climate, our tariff provisions, for primary raw materials and raw materials which have some degree of fabrication.

Mr. Bernstein: Our tariff rates are, with few exceptions, quite low on the minerals and metals. This has been brought about in general by two things: Because we have specific duties, the rise in the price level has reduced the tariff substantially—say on an average, by half; and we have negotiated tariff reductions for many of the minerals and metals.

While that is the general rule, there are three exceptions to it: (1) On certain minor metals (and I am excluding here the three basic nonferrous metals—copper, lead, and zinc), tariffs are, on occasion, exceptionally high and not always meaningful. (2) On metals which have gone through any degree of processing, there is often a penalty rate that works against the import of the first processed form of the material. You cannot take out the complete waste, for example, without paying an extra high duty in order to sell the processed material to the United States. (3) On a material which is combined in its ore form with even minor quantities of one or more other metals, an unreasonably high rate of duty occasionally arises; this is especially true in iron ore.

In the field of the fibers, the tariff on wool has remained fairly high, by any tests, even though its objective has completely changed. At one time its purpose must have been to exclude foreign wool. But today it is impossible for the United States to get along without foreign wool. Therefore, the real purpose of the present wool tariff is simply to set a new level of prices for the U.S. producer and to help carry out the provisions of the general agricultural policy.

On long-staple cotton, there is the quota limitation; and that has, in effect, kept out long-staple cotton, or kept the amount which comes in far below what would be reasonable requirements for the United States.

Mr. Pincus: I think many of the short-term problems which are giving rise to agitation for changes in our commercial policy are due primarily to the carry-over of stocks from the peak periods. We must take into account the fact that there will be fluctuations about the general trend. If we are to decide on a commercial policy, therefore, I think we have to decide first whether we are going to talk about policy in the light of a secular trend or of just an immediate period. My feeling is that some of these problems are of a very temporary nature; and, as we are sitting here, they are probably in process of solution.

General Problems for Commercial Policy

Mr. May: The real question for commercial policy, as I see it, is whether our pressures are going to be now on the demand side instead of the supply side, and whether we have gotten into a situation in which the incentives for materials production have become less, to a degree, than the incentives—I am thinking of the incentives for putting capital funds into the facilities necessary for production of materials—for turning out fabrication.

If that is true, I think your commercial policy will have to be looked at in terms of whether it is one which is promoting the necessary flow of raw materials to prevent price distortions between these lines, differentials between the two.

I think we have done far too little work in terms of attempting to estimate the amount of capital accretions which are needed in the raw materials field to produce raw materials, whether of the types we have traditionally used or substitute types, in sufficient volume to meet the needs as they occur.

MR. BERNSTEIN: The real question is one of costs. We must bear that in mind because, inevitably, when talking about a particular metal, for example, someone is going to tell us that, if only we will pay 50 percent more, or 100 percent more, for that metal, we can get all we want, say, from the United States. The paying of twice as much to get a metal produced here is not the answer to the question of adequate supply of raw materials. We can get, at much less than double the price, by successive substitution, an economic equivalent of a scarce metal.

We are likely to hear that we can reduce our future dependence upon foreign supplies by utilizing inferior ores to increase our domestic supply. In my opinion, this would be undesirable from the point of view of the American economy. What are substandard resources now may later become economic resources if certain technological changes occur, either in the method of treating the ores or in the uses to which they can be put. It would be a mistake, it seems to me, to force-draft the expansion of such resources prior to the right technological time, at the high cost which would be paid by the users of these raw materials, when other material resources of a cheaper and better character are available.

MR. PAGE: It has been said that it would be a mistake to have a forced draft on uneconomic deposits which would not otherwise

have been developed at this time. If that is a mistake, it has already been made.

RICHARD A. YOUNG (American Zinc, Lead and Smelting Company): How are you going to handle the wide fluctuations in metals imports? That is the problem. In time of boom (1951), we were virtually cut off from foreign countries which normally shipped zinc metal into this country; the stocks were accumulated. And the only two periods of extremely heavy imports into this country have been in 1949 and in 1952-53, at both of which times they caused a tremendous drop in the market. Foreign producing areas send it here when they do not need it on their markets; when they do need it on their markets, it is withheld from this market.

Mr. Young attributed these fluctuations to "unrealistic price ceilings" in this country and to faulty decisions of the International Materials Conference in allocating metals.

MR. THOM: We might be justified in expecting supplies to be available to continue our growth pattern if the policies we develop are such as to establish a clear mutuality of our interests and the interests of the countries to which we look for these supplies.

But the fact that we admit products duty free will not greatly encourage the supplying countries if they feel that they are greatly dependent on us. There are instances where we have materials other than agricultural which can be sent abroad to great advantage. I think we should encourage that export arrangement under private auspices, in such a way that the mutuality of our interests and theirs can be clearly understood.

As one illustration of what I have in mind, at the present moment we are having considerable difficulty in the coal industry. At the same time, Brazil has wonderful iron-ore reserves but very small supplies of metallurgical coal. Our dependence on foreign iron ore is real, and is going to grow. The boats which carry ore to us are admirably adapted to carrying coal in the other direction. We could stimulate the development of a steel industry in Brazil that would be dependent upon our metallurgical coal. That development would greatly accelerate the industrialization of Brazil and greatly accelerate the opening of markets for all sorts of goods.

MR. BERNSTEIN: It is not always true that the principal effect of a tariff or a quota is to protect the producers of that commodity. For example, the exclusion of long-staple cotton is probably of small consequence to the producer of ordinary American cotton. The chief beneficiary is the producer of other fibers or other materials—silk, nylon, and rayon—because they will be substituted for the long-staple cotton, not necessarily short-staple cotton. Similarly, in the case of wool, the American farmer gets very little market protection (exclusive of price) from the high tariff. The producers of synthetic fibers are the big beneficiaries.

To a lesser extent, I believe, that is equally true of minerals and metals. In the case of petroleum, the principal objectors to the entry of residual oil on fairly generous terms are the soft-coal miners. To what extent is it sound to let a tariff intended to protect an industry be imposed for the benefit of producers of goods which would be substituted for that industry's goods?

J. W. FOLEY (The Texas Company): We are studying resources for the future; and

certainly that involves questions of defense and security. We are talking specifically about minerals, oil, copper, lead and zinc—questions concerning deficiencies in these materials on the North American Continent and imports from overseas to supply these deficiencies.

We have also made some assumptions, based on the supposition of our being cut off in the event of an emergency. But how can we expect to arrive at any reliable conclusions as to how secure we are on any of the materials that must come from overseas? That is an entirely military question.

ELMER W. PEHRSON (U.S. Department of the Interior): I think there is considerable opinion here that our commercial policy with respect to critical and strategic minerals needs pretty drastic revision. We have discussed only a relatively few commodities here. There have been major developments in manganese in this country; and some people now feel that we could get self-sufficiency in manganese at 100 percent ad valorem protection.

MR. YOUNG: I think Mr. Pehrson is absolutely right that there is a very strong feeling on critical and strategic materials, that they should be separated from all other foreign policy, because they are different from so many other goods.

Specific Materials

The subsection examined in some detail problems of petroleum, lead, zinc, and copper, on all of which commercial policy issues appeared likely to come up for action. Brief consideration was given to long-staple cotton and apparel wool.

FROM THE RECORD

Petroleum

MR. SHEPARD: We who believe that crude oil imports should not be curtailed by some drastic change in the present tariff arrangements feel strongly that the domestic industry has not been seriously damaged by the amount which has come into the country to this point.

All of those elements in the industry which do import are also heavy investors in the domestic industry; it certainly seems to me they would be very stupid to acquiese in a situation which would bring severe damage to the domestic industry. They have a different attitude from those whose interests are limited to activities in the industry in the United States.

So long as the domestic industry is not seriously injured, it is highly desirable, from the standpoint of the United States general interest, to have as wide a variety of sources as possible in a variety of places in the world —sources of petroleum and its products available for peacetime as well as for emergency utilization by the United States and its friends; and it is important to have United States investment in those sources.

WALDO E. STEPHENS (Oklahoma City): I am connected with a very small oil company in the Southwest. My statement is directed to the question before us: namely, the security position of the United States.

Whether or not the domestic oil industry is being damaged by imports of foreign oil is not the whole story. What I am concerned about is the growing public opinion, rooted in resentment, of a large, active, and determined group, which can have very serious repercussions when it comes to a matter, say, of our State Department going before Congress to ask for an appropriation for some foreign project.

Thousands of little independent oil companies, with tens of thousands of employees and their families depending upon them for their living, are in desperate straits today because of the cutbacks they must make in production with foreign imports being increased. There is a cutback of 30 percent in the daily allowables of our domestic producers.

It appears to most persons connected with the thousands of little independent oil companies in the United States that there is a very serious conflict between the policies supported by two departments of our government, namely the Department of the Interior, which has urged the oil industry here at home to drill more and more wells each year, and the State Department, which many oilfield workers feel is responsible for the expansion of oil production in the Middle East that is resulting in a larger volume of imports to compete with domestic oil. I am not contending that this evaluation of the situation is correct, but there is one fact we cannot ignore: there is a growing resentment and opposition produced by this situation.

I am not advocating a change in the tariff policy as this discussion is not dealing with that issue. It is evident, however, that the situation confronting us calls for some adjustment on the part of major and independent oil companies, rather than a revision of the economic policy of our government. Perhaps the solution rests more with the large oil companies operating in the Middle East and in Venezuela. They could assist in the stabilization of the oil industry in the United States by a voluntary cutback in their imports of oil to enable the small companies to make the necessary changes and adjustments which are imperative.

MR. SHEPARD: Two or three of the big importing companies have reduced their imports through a voluntary exercise of industrial statesmanship, and the imports of crude oil now occurring and planned are materially below earlier levels. This solution, I believe, is greatly to be preferred over so inflexible a device as a more restrictive tariff.

The chairman then asked for comment on residual fuel oil imports, particularly as they relate to the coal industry.

Mr. SHEPARD: All the imported residual fuel which enters this country (I think, literally all) comes into the Eastern Seaboard, where there is, as all of you know, a very, very high concentration of industrial activity and, accordingly, a very high consumption of fuels.

Over recent years, the bituminous coal industry has lost a lot of outlet. These losses, according to us, have resulted mainly from the following influences: (1) the dieselization of railroads, which has caused a large fraction of the coal industry's total loss of outlet, and (2) a striking growth in the utilization of natural gas. Over-all, coal has lost, over the last five years, something like 150 million tons of output. During that period, the importation of residual fuel oil (and its consumption) has increased by something like the coal equivalent of 18 million tons. We do not see how such an increase in residual fuel oil imports can account for the reduction in bituminous output.

MR. PEHRSON: I feel that one of the most anti-conservational practices in this country today is this invasion of petroleum products into fields formerly supplied by coal, of which we have much more abundant resources. If we are here considering policy problems in the resources field, we cannot overlook the fact that we do not see our petroleum security very far ahead. And we do not want to overlook the position of coal, which would be the primary replacement for residual fuel oil in an emergency. I do feel that the coal industry has a vital stake in this important petroleum problem. Anthracite production, for example, has declined in the past quarter-century from 100 million tons to 60 million tons, and will probably not go beyond 30 million tons this year. It would be extremely difficult to expand production rapidly if an emergency arose. We have a distressed industry here, which everybody is trying to do something about; but it is a very difficult problem to deal with.

MR. SHEPARD: The anthracite industry's loss of markets has been mainly to natural gas and to distillate petroleum fuels, of which substantially none is imported.

MR. BERNSTEIN: My observation is that there would be practically no net gain to the domestic industry by excluding imports of oil.

Suppose that we kept out residual fuel oil completely. Before you can provide a barrel of residual fuel oil to the New England consumer, you have to be prepared to market very large amounts of the other products which precede it, the refined products, the lighter distillants which go with it. It is very doubtful if it would be found worth while to undertake a wide readjustment in prices and techniques of production in order to secure as a residual the extra 300,000-odd barrels a day which are imported as residual fuel oil. In short, there is no reasonable basis for assuming that the exclusion of residual fuel oil would induce the American oil industry to expand aggregate production of refined products.

The other import which we are considering is crude oil, but we are large exporters of refined products. If we did not import the crude oil, that crude oil would have to pass through the refineries abroad. The crude oil which we import is just about (or was, a year ago, at the peak) equivalent to what would yield the amounts of refined products which we send out. In short, a reduction in our imports of crude oil would cause readjustment in the international supply and distribution of oil which would cut off our market for refined products.

My conclusion is that insignificantly increased amounts of domestically produced oil would come into the regular stream of commerce if we excluded imports, because it is reasonable to assume that we would simultaneously lose our oil exports.

I do believe the coal industry would benefit. But that raises the very big question: To what extent are we justified in excluding a product which the customer prefers in order to enable another product to be sold in its place? If we push this far enough, since every product is to some extent a substitute for another in consumer expenditure, nothing would be imported.

MR. PEHRSON: In the event of an emergency, with the seas blockaded, can we meet our requirements? In terms of emergency needs, who is going to take care of the consumers in the Eastern Seaboard who are now using petroleum products, if we have our coal industry pared down to a decidedly small capacity?

MR. SHEPARD: I do not know what the emergency requirements are, in case of global war. That is a matter partly of military estimate, and the figures are not available to me. We do have about a million barrels a day of stand-by crude-oil producing capacity in the United States, ready to be brought into operation in an emergency. Whether that is enough for wartime, I do not know. It is a little less than twice the present daily importation of crude oil.

MR. STEPHENS: It is true that the oil industry, in response to the request of the Interior Department, did achieve an additional capacity to produce a million barrels of oil a day. I believe the engineers will point out to us that, if an attempt is made to produce this amount of oil daily over a period of time in case of an emergency, damage will be done to the wells due to the dissipation of reservoir energy. This could mean that the ultimate recovery of oil reserves, which is a vital factor, would be much less than the present estimate of reserves will show. This means, as I view it, that we will need to hold the foreign sources of oil to meet the future needs of the Free World. Some leaders in the oil industry would no doubt take exception to my position. They contend that the nation should have high tariffs on foreign oil to prohibit imports in such volume that the domestic oil situation is seriously weakened.

Lead, Zinc, and Copper

MR. INCE: There is, undoubtedly, a growing dependence on lead and zinc imports. The question, it seems to us is: Should we not minimize that growing dependence? It really comes back to the question whether it is more important to have maximum production within our own borders.

In recent years, we have assumed that, in the case of lead and zinc, one-third has been supplied from outside this country and two-thirds from within the country. But, owing to large imports at prices which domestic mines cannot compete with, we are beginning to lose the approximately two-thirds of our own mine production which was formerly supplied as that portion of our requirements.

That is the reason the mining industry recently has asked for relief under the escape clause. It comes back to the question of to what extent we should maintain a domestic mining industry, what effect the loss of that mining industry might have on our security position; also, what effect a growing dependence on imports will have on our domestic economy.

This more liberal policy we have had under the two previous administrations has now reached the point where it is affecting our own self-sufficiency of that two-thirds. I wonder whether that is not a dangerous policy to pursue further. When we lose that two-thirds we are putting our reliance on a very uncertain source. When we needed it, the metal was not there; and, for what metal foreign

suppliers did ship here, they charged premiums over our domestic market. When we did not need it, they shipped substantially more than that third. This has been mainly responsible for the wide fluctuations in price we have had in this country, which our domestic consumers so violently resent.

MR. YOUNG: The North American Continent (the United States, Canada, and Mexico) is more than self-sufficient in zinc-smelting capacity, but it is not quite self-sufficient in ores. It needs imports of something like 100,000 tons per year, which have come in the form of concentrates from South America.

The United States takes a large part of Canada's ore production and has taken all of Mexico's since the first days of World War II. And we can continue to take them—we need them, those raw materials from Canada and Mexico, and a certain amount from South America. That is not the problem in the domestic zinc industry. The problem is that when the rest of the world gets an oversupply of zinc, the surplus comes into our market. World production has held fairly constant; but because of a drop in consumption, Europe has accumulated large stocks; and European countries, which are not normally exporters of zinc to the United States, have been putting these stocks into the U.S. market. Our tariff is so low that it is a very easy barrier to jump.

In 1930, when we were self-sufficient in zinc, we had a tariff of 1.75 cents. That tariff has been cut, on metal, to 0.7 cent. The industry's application now before the Tariff Commission is for a restoration of the tariff to 50 percent over the January 1, 1945, rate, which means increasing the rate by 1.4 cents. The purpose in requesting the increase is not to exclude our normal suppliers; it is, frankly, to make the tariff barrier harder to jump in sending here excess supplies over and above our requirements.

There is debate in the industry that this rate may not be adequate; that, even if we go to 2.1 cents per pound in zinc, it still may not result in a price which is high enough to *maintain*, not increase, the domestic mining industry on a basis that gives us some sort of security in the case of a national emergency.

A healthy domestic mining industry is necessary to our security. The best way to maintain it, probably, is to increase the tariff. The increase proposed here is not one that will make a tremendous difference in our economy as a whole or impose a great cost on consumers.

MR. PAGE: It looks to me as if, basically, the situation on copper is, in one respect, very much the same as that on lead and zinc. All three industries, for years, have had a perfectly economic production which could satisfy a very substantial part of the demands of this country. All three now are in a position where some imports are needed.

Copper has not yet attained the unenviable position that lead and zinc have reached in the last six months, where imports have been so great as to force serious curtailment of domestic production. But it looks pretty much as if, in copper, there is an excess of world production capacity. I might say right here that I do not know that the existence of a world excess of capacity for producing a metal is abnormal. If you go back prewar, I think probably most metals had it; I think it is probably desirable.

One thing which has not been said by Mr. Ince seems to me to have importance; that is, in copper, as in lead and zinc, I think, the average cost of production abroad is lower than the cost of production here. It is due to a variety of factors but, certainly, one of the most important is the fact that our wages, when you include fringe benefits and whatnot, are, I should suppose, 150 percent of those of Canada and up to 10, 15, or 20 times the wages in most of the other mining districts. If I could pay the wages which the average of our foreign competitors pay, I would not worry at all about foreign competition.

I think the copper producers—and I do not see why the lead and zinc producers are not in the same position—should be entitled to a tariff which reasonably equalizes the difference between foreign and domestic costs of production. It seems to me that a tariff arrangement should be effective which, in the event that world consumption drops for a while to, say, 85 percent of world mine ca-

pacity, will prevent the curtailment in mine production from being thrown wholly upon the domestic industry, as is happening now in the case of lead and zinc.

A. FORD HINRICHS (Committee for a National Trade Policy): In this matter of the impact on the American mining industry, isn't it important to take into account the nature of some of our marginal production, particularly in connection with zinc? Don't we, in fact, have the high-cost area of the world in our marginal production, while a substantial block of the production is going to vary more or less along with world production? Under those conditions, you are almost bound to find the fluctuations being taken up, in the first instance, in any sort of a free market, by American marginal producers.

If your problem is to keep these people in production for some kind of security reason which is not completely clear, with Canada and Mexico as the primary alternative sources, is it not much more effective and substantially more economical to pay them whatever may be needed by way of the price at the high-cost mine to keep the mine either in a stand-by condition or to bring the production out?

But the tariff would seem to be one of the most dangerous things from the point of view of our security, because you would then be transferring the full impact of the swings in the American consumer market across our borders, expecting stand-by capacity to be maintained either in Mexico or in Canada. Under those circumstances, we might find that in time of emergency the productive capacity simply would not be there.

Mr. Young replied that it is not a marginal situation—that over 85 percent of the mining industry in the United States today is operating at a loss.

MR. VUILLEQUEZ: Mr. Page said that the average cost of production of copper abroad is lower than the average cost in the United States. I am quite willing to accept that statement, but I would like to point out that some of the big copper mines in Africa and in

Chile have higher costs of production than some of the big mines in the United States.

Going to lead and zinc, Mr. Ince made a comment to the effect that we cannot depend on imports of lead and zinc when we need them; and he referred to 1948 and 1951. In 1948, we had an absolutely free market for lead and zinc, and the reason the imports to the United States were reduced was a price question. People in Europe were willing to pay a higher price than the American consumer. In 1951 and part of 1952 the United States imposed a unilateral ceiling price on lead and zinc which was substantially lower than world market prices; and I believe—as was stated by the International Materials Conference—that there was no shortage of lead, since they decided not to make international allocations. However, with regard to zinc, we got our share at ceiling prices.

Regarding the question of tariffs, our company's position has been that, since we need these metals badly from import sources, the tariff will not help. I do not agree with Mr. Young, for example, that the higher tariff, to the extent he mentioned, would maintain the flow of imports of lead and zinc to the United States. I disagree with that particularly with regard to the mining properties our company has in Mexico, which today are losing money, and certainly would not come in on a higher tariff.

I disagree also with Mr. Young's statement that marginal properties are not involved. They definitely are involved. Furthermore, with regard to lead and zinc, the large mines in the United States can compete with foreign properties. They are today, and they are making money—not so much as they would like to, but some.

Our position has been that tariffs are not the answer—that tariffs would injure our foreign sources of these materials, particularly in the Western Hemisphere, much more than they would help here. If, for security reasons or for any other reasons, we feel that we need to maintain certain mines in operation, we think that subsidies would be the answer, rather than higher tariffs.

As to the security point of view, I think that about 70 percent of our imports of lead and zinc have come from the Western Hemisphere, the bulk of it available by rail from Canada and Mexico.

STANLEY H. RUTTENBERG (CIO Department of Education and Research): We are interested, as a labor organization, not only in the welfare of the workers, but in the welfare of the companies which employ them and, certainly, in the national welfare, which depends upon our trade relations with other countries throughout the world.

I question the proposition that the way to help the United States lead and zinc industry is to increase the tariff. By imposing a duty here, we affect the economy of Canada and Mexico—countries which are very close to us—and to some extent do damage to our international relations. At the same time, the imposition of that duty will not necessarily benefit workers or industry in the United States.

The moment we put a duty on lead and zinc we reduce the ability of Mexico, for example, to buy on the United States market many of the products which workers and industries in the United States depend upon for their incomes.

Long-Staple Cotton and Wool

Neither long-staple cotton nor wool—two other commodities suggested by the steering committee as presenting immediate problems of commercial policy—was discussed at length, but a brief comment was made on each. The comment on wool was strongly critical of present protection policy, but there was no debate.

READ P. DUNN, JR. (National Cotton Council of America): Cotton is in quite a different situation from the metals and minerals you have been discussing so far in that the United States produces cotton in excess of domestic requirements. What we call extra-long-staple cotton is covered both by tariff and quota controls at the present time. The tariff is not particularly meaningful; it is about 3½ cents a pound. The quota is meaningful.

During the last war, efforts were made to

expand production of extra-long-staple cotton in the United States by means of a minimum-price guarantee to the farmer. That support was taken off just after the war, and production dropped. When the Korean war broke out the Department of Agriculture, at the behest of the military, instituted another program to support prices and to stockpile extra-long-staple cotton to induce production.

Total requirements for cotton of this character have been going down steadily for a number of reasons, including the competition of other fibers, primarily nylon and some rayon. Also extra-long-staple cotton in this country has lost more ground to shorter-staple cotton by virtue of improved technology that permits use of shorter cottons and less expensive cottons. There is considerable question as to whether the present quota will be filled over the next few years, assuming that there is no war. Neither the tariff nor quota problem is of very real importance in considering adequate resources for the future.

There is, as you will also note, a very high quota restriction, which almost amounts to an embargo, on what we call ordinary-staple cotton. At the present time, with agricultural price support on cotton, you cannot maintain solvency without controlling the production; and controlling production means controlling imports as well as domestic production.

In the main, our import policy on cotton is tied up with the whole question of agricultural price policy. That is what makes it important, not the question of providing adequate resources of fiber for the future. I do not think anybody questions the ability of the United States to produce the cotton which may be required a decade from now, two decades from now, or in 1975.

MR. BERNSTEIN: Wool represents one of the less intelligent applications of commercial policy to the needs of the country. Historically, we have had a policy of protecting domestic production of wool, but we are no longer capable of producing any very large proportion of our needs for wool. In order to enable domestic producers of a very small portion of our total consumption to stay in business, we are raising the price of wool very considerably through a tariff and an import fee.

The question is whether it is sensible for a country to put a penalty upon acquiring from abroad, raw materials of a type which it cannot provide at home, and for which its supply capacity is steadily decreasing.

For the first time this year, the woolen manufacturers have taken cognizance of the penalty they suffer from this tariff on wool.

Subsection B

INVESTMENT AND DEVELOPMENT

While the other two subsections were examining import restrictions and market instability as aspects of the raw materials problem, Subsection B considered the materials themselves. Will the imports be available? Attention was given to the steps required to expand foreign raw materials resources, the relation of resources development to general economic development, and technical assistance on geological exploration.

Petroleum and nonfuel minerals were the materials discussed here, with particular emphasis on minerals as presenting the most critical supply outlook and requiring the largest investment to assure future requirements from foreign sources.

Certain background facts were assumed: Not only United States import requirements, but the requirements of other industrial countries, will increase in the years ahead; at the same time, the underdeveloped areas that provide these imports are likely to use more of their production for their own industrial activities. If our needs are to be met, therefore, world production will have to increase by much more than the projected increase in United States requirements.

Discussion brought out general agreement on two basic points: (1) The necessary expansion in production will not occur without foreign assistance to the underdeveloped countries on resources development. (2) Most of this assistance can best be provided by private investment. The principal question at issue was whether the United States Government should take steps to assist private enterprise in developing foreign resources, and, if so, what should be the nature and extent of this assistance.

Foreign Raw Materials Resources

Will the increased demand for raw materials imports automatically call forth the necessary volume of production abroad? Expansions now being undertaken abroad in petroleum, iron ore, and lead and zinc were reported to be in line with the projected requirements trend. It was pointed out, however, that these examples were given by participants whose companies operate in areas that are relatively favorable to foreign development of their resources. In contrast, present governmental policies in many of the mineral-producing countries were described as almost prohibitive obstacles to foreign investment. Unless these obstacles are removed, it was regarded as certain that capital will not enter these countries to expand existing developments or begin new ones.

There were wide differences of opinion over what part the government should play in this situation. Some members advocated a strong policy of protection to investment interests abroad. Others believed that the only possible government course is patient negotiation, based on a broad understanding of the viewpoints of foreign countries.

Consideration was also given to the possibility of creating a better investment climate in the producing areas through reciprocal treaties guaranteeing against abuses or through long-term contracts between United States mining interests and foreign governments, providing similar guarantees. In addition, revision of present United States tax laws applying to dividends on foreign investments was suggested as a means of stimulating the flow of capital to resources development abroad.

FROM THE RECORD

Need for Supplementary Action

The importance of special measures to assure an adequate flow of needed imports was implicit throughout the discussion. One participant put it into words.

JACK BENNETT (Chevy Chase, Md.): Some people may feel it would take too much capital for us to try to make sure now of tying up certain basic resources that we may need in the future. But we should remember that a large part of the area where we now say that we can go and get the minerals when we need them may not be so ready to admit us. Especially in the African area, they are nearly all captive territories and they are not our captives. If we sit by and wait until some distant day in the future, somebody else may have gotten there before us, or political and economic circumstances may have so changed that we may not be able to get where we want to go.

How Much Can Private Enterprise Do?

Reports on past and present performance indicated a belief by several industries that they can meet future requirements without financial aid.

E. G. COLLADO (Standard Oil Company (New Jersey)): On the question whether private enterprise abroad has done the job necessary to provide an adequate flow of raw materials, both for United States and foreign requirements, I think the facts in terms of the petroleum industry are pretty simple. There is an adequate flow of petroleum; and there is every reason to believe that the increased requirements anticipated for the future will be met.

The petroleum industry is not only probably the largest single postwar foreign investor, but it is also the largest segment, I think, that has had no direct government or public lending participation. Such participation has not been required nor has it been sought. In fact, it would be preferred by the industry that there were no public lending in this field.

FRANCIS CAMERON (St. Joseph Lead Company): Private industry, at least in the field of lead and zinc, has done a fairly good job. There have been new discoveries of great promise, which will, I think, affect our overall import position in this country.

I think that the United States Government can give very little direct aid to the industry's mining operations abroad. In the North African development, the United States Government made a loan to the French companies with which we were associated in order to bring these properties into production rapidly.

If it had been left entirely to private financing, production probably would not have come in quite so rapidly, largely because we were uncertain what the demand would be. In Latin America, certainly, we haven't required and do not anticipate requiring direct government aid.

Speaking only for my own group, I cannot see where we need any government assistance in carrying out the program that we have in mind at this time. If, in the interests of defense or other purposes, it should become necessary to accelerate what we consider normal development, and if this should require large financing, then we might ask for government assistance, but otherwise not.

EARL M. RICHARDS (Republic Steel Corporation): Prior to World War II, the United States imported only 2 or 3 million tons of iron ore annually, but the situation is changing. The rich ores in this country are now nearing exhaustion, thereby making a marked change in our national picture. So iron ore imports are on the increase, amounting now to about 10 million tons per year. By 1975 we probably will be importing from Canada and abroad 65 to 70 million tons, and that is a tremendous change.

The steel industry is meeting the situation in two ways: (1) *Low-grade ore*. For example, my own company and Armco Steel Corporation are now spending over $160 million to develop techniques of using low-grade domestic deposits. Low-grade ore developments by other steel companies are in progress. (2) *Foreign ores*. We are a part owner in the Labrador development in Canada where over $200 million is being spent to bring iron ore into this country, starting in 1954. United States Steel Corporation and Bethlehem are doing the same sort of thing in Venezuela. Republic is interested in a company developing iron mines in Liberia. So the trend is considerably toward iron ore developments outside our country.

The steel industry does not want any aid in this development. We have been handling it on our own. We would like to continue handling it ourselves, and I think we can.

ALAN M. BATEMAN (Yale University): In the case of ordinary development and financing to take care of our peacetime needs in the 25 years to come, it seems to me that private industry can continue to do an excellent job in developing foreign resources. From the standpoint of defense, I think we have to look at it a little bit differently. For example, the government, with a jet plane program, couldn't see enough nickel ahead to take of the defense effort and the civilian effort together. The financing that took place there was, in large part, to speed up what might have come along normally over a period of many years. In such situations, I think there is quite a justification for the government's aiding development of resources in foreign areas.

Some others felt that the larger peacetime developments might on occasion need supplemental government financing.

ROBERT KOENIG (Cerro de Pasco Corporation): At present there is a surplus of many of the nonferrous metals and there is talk about there being a surplus of copper in the near future, so that whatever I have to say is going to be colored not by the immediate economic climate, but by the longer-term view.

You may not approve of the Paley Report in detail, but in general its conclusions are not too bad. The principal conclusion is that the increase in world population and increased standards of living are going to draw more minerals per year out of the ground during the next 25 years than were drawn out in 1950.

Assuming, further, that a substantial portion of such additional production will come from mineral deposits located outside the United States, the problem of how to finance such work is immediately generated. The new mines being developed are, generally speaking, large and low-grade deposits and require an investment of capital far beyond that of many existing mines. It is apparent that funds will come from two principal avenues. One of them is such profits as a company can plow

back into its own business. But that isn't enough to do the sort of job which I have in mind. Where is the other source? In the past we could depend upon equity financing of one kind or another. But the nature of savings in the United States has changed in the past generation, and there isn't the sort of risk capital available that there was a generation or more ago. As savings in the United States increase, they take the form of life insurance policies, deposits in savings banks and investment trusts and things of that nature. The people who control these funds have to act in a sort of trustee relationship and are not in a position to make risk investments in mining enterprises, particularly offshore.

The only other source of capital is United States Government financing. I don't like that any better than a great many of you people do, but there it is. That financing is going to have to take the form of loans by such entities as the Export-Import Bank. You can eliminate the World Bank, for its charter states that any loan made to a private industry in any country must be guaranteed by the government of that country. If a government—any government —guarantees a loan made to a mining company, it will try to run your business for you. We have enough trouble trying to run our business ourselves.

I feel convinced that as demands for increased consumption and production of metals come—and they come in waves—there will have to be government financing in order to assure United States industry the increased amounts of metals and minerals it will need to keep going.

W. S. WOYTINSKY (Twentieth Century Fund): I think that if public loans appear necessary, maybe the best way of providing such loans would be not through the United States Government, or any other single government, but through the International Bank for Reconstruction and Development, which can act indirectly as an agent for American and other private investors. The International Bank can expand its operations only if it can sell on the open market the bonds for the respective operations.

Obstacles in the Producing Areas

H. DEWITT SMITH (Consulting Engineer, New York): How can foreign investment in raw material production be made more attractive to industry if we are going to have private industry continuing the development? This concerns both the elimination of obstacles in the foreign countries to investment and the question of taxation by the United States Government. Particularly, just how are we going to meet the problems that arise when private industry, from past performance of a country, has no confidence in its ability to carry out contracts? How are you going to have developments done in those countries, no matter how rich they are?

There are certainly very great difficulties in inducing new capital to come into some countries. For example, I think there are very few companies, with what they see at the moment, aside from those that are already in those operations, that will wish to take a chance on losing their funds in a number of the countries in South America. As far as Argentina is concerned, there is an embargo on any foreign dollar export. In Bolivia you have a recent example of galloping expropriation. How are we going to meet that problem in the great belt of South America, which sooner or later should provide large stocks of materials we need?

MR. CAMERON: When we talk about private enterprise abroad, we are not talking necessarily about American companies. We are talking about private industry representing nationals of that country, other nationals and ourselves. We are subject to all the laws and regulations of those countries in which we operate, and we lean over backwards to be sure that we are well within the law and the spirit of the law; and when we ask for government aid, we ask the government of the country in which we are operating.

Those are the points that lead us in the raw materials industry to pick and choose with great care. We wouldn't, for instance, attempt to develop operations in certain countries, even though we may have had reconnaissance and explorations. When it comes to spending our shareholders' money, we are very cautious as to which political climate we press those investments in. We have no right, except as shareholders, to appeal to our State Department for help, nor would we get a very sympathetic hearing in most cases. They would politely say, "Well, you are just an investor in a foreign country."

WALTER J. LEVY (New York): I believe difficulties will always confront foreign investments, particularly in a basic industry. The more a country develops, the more it may resent the fact that a basic resource is controlled by foreign investors. It is essential to face this problem realistically by pursuing an enlightened policy.

One participant questioned whether obstacles in the producing countries, however real and obvious, were the root of the trouble, and suggested ways to make foreign investment more attractive in relation to domestic investment.

WILFRED MALENBAUM (Massachusetts Institute of Technology): I would like to suggest that this is a field in which very much attention has, quite appropriately, been paid to obstacles and their elimination. Perhaps more attention might also be focused upon the more general question of whether the overseas countries, and particularly the underdeveloped countries, are, from an economic point of view, a very attractive area for the investment of capital. Compared with the very broad horizons for new investment in the United States, the opportunities for investment in many of the underdeveloped areas are much less attractive. I wonder whether a really significant outflow of American private capital would occur even if the obstacles were removed.

It has been my impression that where it serves the clear interest of private industry to make foreign investment, such investment takes place despite the obstacles. The shortage of private investment may thus really be a reflection of the relative lack of attractive investment opportunities. If there is some merit to this view, I think there are certain implications for United States action in those countries in which we have a broad security interest. We might help create conditions under which private investment is more likely to pay off from an economic point of view.

For example, if certain types of government investment were made in basic utilities —roads, power and so on—this might help create an economic environment in which more private capital (whatever luck we had with the elimination of obstacles) would be tempted to go in, as against going into the safe and rather hopeful fields that the United States economy offers. [For more extended discussion of the role of general development, see pages 283-85.]

What is the best response to general difficulties in political and economic climate for investment in some foreign countries? Is the responsibility largely up to the U.S. Government, or does private industry, too, have a big contribution to make?

WILLIAM B. MATHER (Southwest Research Institute): So-called nationalism in some Latin-American countries can be particularly irritating. Extreme nationalism has resulted in expropriation of American property. It seems to me there is but one way to stop expropriation: The American Government should handle these people with an iron fist, rather than a gloved hand. It is high time American industry got support from its government. Each time there is expropriation, our State Department makes some inane statement to the effect that it is all right. The trouble is going to continue unless Americans abroad get support from the American Government. We have tried friendship. We have tried buying them off. Neither has been effective.

CHARLES K. LEITH (Washington, D.C.): I grew up on the theory that all men are created free and equal and with the power of sweet reason. I want to say bluntly that I have become quite a convert to power politics.

By that I mean economics and everything else that comes into it in order to keep a little order in the situation.

Now, under certain episodes in our power politics, as applied to minerals around the world, we made selfish bargains. We must, of course, go the limit in seeing that the other fellow is being taken care of. That is being done now under practically every new contract that is made. But at a certain stage in the game, I believe that a firm word from our State Deparment would help in carrying through things that are necessary and desirable from the standpoint of just giving us natural resources, and that firm word has been lacking several times. The support we are looking for hasn't been coming forward quite as fast as we want it.

HERMAN W. STEINKRAUS (Bridgeport Brass Company): I think it would be a most unfortunate situation if power politics were to become the key of our American foreign policy. I think the problem with us Americans is twofold. First, we are very impatient. We want to remake the world in a period of one administration's term of office (even though it may be 20 years). In the second place, we are very ignorant. I think, as far as our relationships with foreign governments are concerned, we have only a grammar-school or a lower-grade understanding of the other fellow's viewpoint, and I think the basic thing we have got to look forward to is education and understanding, and we have got to have patience while we are doing it. I don't think we ought to be racing all over the world butting in on everybody else's business in order to get their raw materials, badly as we need them. I think they ought to have something to say about what conditions we come in under.

We handle things from the standpoint of what's good for our business. I am a businessman, mind you, but I think some things are much more vital than that. We do silly things. For example, recently we increased the U.S. tariff on ping-pong balls from Canada 800 percent and we classified them as ammunition —ordnance. When asked how we could figure that ping-pong balls were ordnance, we said that ping-pong balls take the place of corks, in pop guns, and so the tariff was raised 800 percent. Now, just how much respect do we build when we do these selfish, little, mean things?

I think the last thing we should do is to use our power in respect to other countries. I think we should use our Christianity. I think, after all, the very basis of all industry, to which I have devoted my entire life, is service to others. If you serve well, your business will grow. But if you try to hop on anything that comes along, you will be in trouble all over the world, as we are today.

MR. SMITH: Mr. Steinkraus, I think your views are echoed by every forward-looking industrialist. I don't see how you can help this country unless you make friends and not just try to do the easiest thing. We make plenty of enemies just through ignorance. One of our greatest problems, not only in industrial relations on mineral resources, is lack of understanding. From this point on, we should try to do a more decent job with our friends to the north and our friends to the south. We are going to need them some day.

Private industry has a large responsibility. In many of the most promising areas for development, I don't think the United States Government can take any step without incurring the ill will of the countries concerned. On the other hand, if private companies will do a decent job, and operate as citizens of the country they are working in, they can do more than a group of government officials going in there trying to establish good will.

More specific suggestions for overcoming present obstacles included treaties of friendship, commerce, and navigation, and less formal bilateral arrangements.

MR. BATEMAN: As I see it, if we are to have a large source of copper in the future, relations between Chile and the United States must be maintained in a friendly position. And the only way I can see that that might come about is through government aid—not financial aid, because I think it would be a very bad situation indeed if the United States Government should ever be a partner, as a government, owning properties in other countries, particularly Latin-American countries. But I do believe that bilateral arrangements could be worked out that would overcome some of the obstacles and make Chile a more favorable climate than it is. I don't think any company wants to go in with new investments under existing conditions.

There are reports that in connection with the proposed sale of copper to the United States the Chileans, in turn, might agree to elimination of the export tax, which is the most vicious of all taxes, and substitute instead an income tax; that they might cut out the dual exchange; that they would turn back the selling of the copper to the American companies there. If something of that type could be worked out, a favorable climate might be created in those southern countries.

CHARLES WILL WRIGHT (Washington, D.C.): When the Peruvian Government took up the question of encouraging American capital, it did so by modifying its mining code. The Mines Department, the Minister of Finance, and mining companies all worked together on the new code which was published in 1951. With that code in mind, our Bureau of Mines prepared and submitted to the Latin-American countries a series of questions, to which private enterprise wished the answers. We now have answers to most of these questions from several of the countries. They have not been published, but may be eventually.

In the meantime I have prepared a plan by which an independent group would be engaged to make a study of the mining codes in the principal mineral-producing republics. To carry out this plan there should be, in each country, an advisory committee, as was established in Peru, with representatives of its department of mines, the ministry of finance, and the mining companies. These local committees would cooperate fully with the field engineers engaged by the organization sponsoring the general survey. Two or three consulting engineers with wide experience in Latin America would be sufficient, and a representative of the U.S. Bureau of Mines might well be included. This group would examine and compare the existing code, taxes, and tariffs of the country under study with those of Peru, Canada, and other countries and together with the local committee help prepare recommendations for a new mining code with changes in taxes and exchange controls necessary to attract American venture capital. Until this is done, I don't believe we will get very far in encouraging mine investment in many of the potential sources of mineral supply south of the Rio Grande.

If a foundation or some other group would supply the funds for such a survey and engage a firm with competent mining consultants for the job, it would be a big help in establishing a better and bigger field for mining activity in which U.S. as well as local capital would take part in building up the production of needed mineral products for the future.

P. T. HITCHENS (National Foreign Trade Council): The National Foreign Trade Council and National Foreign Trade Conventions that it sponsors have been very much concerned with the question of developing a proper climate for foreign investment. One of the chief things that they have been working on is the establishment of reciprocal treaties of friendship, commerce, and navigation and tax treaties in this field of economic development. These treaties embrace a great many principles that we would like to see established. Among them are guarantees against expropriation, with provision for prompt, adequate, and effective compensation if a country wants to take over foreign property; guarantees against discrimination in the granting of exchange; and guarantees against tax discrimination—all kinds of tax discrimination and unduly burdensome and unfair taxes. But we place more stress on the general attitude of the underdeveloped countries. If they really want foreign capital, they must treat it fairly; otherwise they won't get it.

Our people have felt that one of the greatest obstacles to getting underdeveloped countries to enter such treaties has been their expectation that they are going to get United States Government or United Nations funds for economic development. We feel that as long as they expect that they can depend on those funds, they will not take the necessary steps to create the conditions necessary to attract capital. Technical assistance has its place, but, so far as economic development is concerned, the most effective way the United States can provide knowledge is through the example and work of American industries located and operated in the underdeveloped countries.

U.S. Tax Laws and Foreign Investment

MR. SMITH: Private enterprise realizes who its major partners are every time it goes into business in foreign countries. One is the government of that foreign country, with a take of the profits, and beyond that the United States Government, with a further take for which, sometimes, it hasn't done much of anything. When the dividends come in, a total of 52 percent of them has been paid in the form of taxes; and the United States Government steps in further when those dividends are passed on to private investors.

If the United States Government is really interested in private American funds going into foreign investment, a little freedom from taxes could be given for a period of a few years. The Canadian Government gives freedom from taxes for the first three and a half years of operation. You might think that is a little thing, but it helps when you are overextended and owe a lot of money to the banks. It is a very handsome return you get in the first three or four years before you are paying 30, 40, or 50 percent out in taxes.

WAYNE C. TAYLOR (Foreign Operations Administration): The consensus of most of the groups that have worked with the question of taxation in the two countries is that incentive taxation or more favorable taxation on the part of our government would probably be the most effective single thing that could be done, more importantly because it would give an incentive to the other government to give an incentive. I don't know what the answers on this 52 percent are going to be, but I can assure you that the Treasury seems to be somewhat reluctantly conscious of it.

General Economic Development

Are loans of public funds to foreign governments for purposes of general economic development required to assist private enterprise in expanding raw materials sources abroad? Sharply conflicting positions were taken on this question.

Some participants said that general economic development will automatically follow upon the increase in national income created by private investment in the development of a country's resources and that public funds should not be used for this purpose. Others maintained that many underdeveloped areas with rich mineral resources lack the facilities necessary to their development—such as roads, ports, power, transport, and communications—and that public funds might have to meet at least part of the cost of constructing such facilities before private capital would undertake resources development in these areas. The possibility that some support would have to be given to the establishment of secondary industries and to the provision of health and educational services was also discussed.

Still others felt that neither of these approaches is broad enough—that progress and opportunity in the producing areas, as well as benefits to ourselves, should be an objective of resources development, and that the use of public funds may be necessary to assure this objective.

The desire of the underdeveloped countries to industrialize was briefly touched upon in terms of the effect that it may have on future United States supplies from these areas.

FROM THE RECORD

Is General Economic Development a Cause or an Effect of Resources Development?

MR. HITCHENS: No country provided the United States with capital to develop us, as such. They provided capital to develop certain products and industries that they wanted because it was of interest to them. And I think the same considerations, whether we like it or not, will probably determine the extent to which the United States is going to help develop other countries. If American private investors could see a chance to make a profit by the development of some product, they would go in there. If they saw a chance to make a profit in the development of a public utility, they would go in there. But I doubt very much that they will go in unless there is some chance of making a profit or of producing something they want. And the people of the underdeveloped country profit from such private investments. They get income; they get both primary and secondary industries, and that is the way the country gets developed.

The National Foreign Trade Council regards economic development as primarily the province of private enterprise, because it believes that the provision of capital alone will not guarantee development of production. It has to be accompanied by the managerial and technical skills essential to its effective application. Unless you have that, making the funds available will not get the development you want.

MR. SMITH: Southwest Africa is a case where the development, in the first place, of the diamond industry and the copper-lead-zinc properties has changed the entire economic outlook of the country. Often we can tremendously help the economic development of the country, and at the same time help our country, by developing resources which were not available before.

MR. CAMERON: In the postwar years the developments with which I am personally familiar in North Africa have practically changed the whole economy of that part of the world. They freed the French from importation of lead and zinc, to a very great extent, and therefore relieved the French Government of the need of dollars for that purpose. In Latin America, also, the economies of Peru and Argentina are significantly expanding on the basis of their metal industries.

R. J. LUND (Battelle Memorial Institute): Perhaps to start with, the development of ore reserves is certainly a very important factor in the initial stage of general economic development of a country. As the country develops economically, it is going to need more of its own ore for its own industrial uses. Therefore, the question is: How much of that additional production can we depend on, as opposed to how much will be needed for the further economic development of those underdeveloped countries?

MR. MALENBAUM: With respect to how much aid materials development by private enterprise can give to the general development of underdeveloped areas, we really do not know what the potential is in a lot of underdeveloped areas. I think it is safe to observe that Venezuela, to which reference is frequently made in this context, is probably not a typical underdeveloped area. I think there are relatively few underdeveloped areas where the by-product of raw materials development is significant stimulation of the over-all economy. There are many underdeveloped areas where the best efforts at raw materials development could only make a relatively small contribution to the general economy. They simply don't happen to be very rich in the type of resources that private industry would be interested in developing.

It seems to me that the United States should attempt to create a generally more attractive economic development situation in these countries, to attempt to assure for us an attitude that is both receptive to future resources development by American private enterprise and also sympathetic to our broad security interests.

MR. WOYTINSKY: There is truly a correlation between the utilization of mineral resources and the welfare of the country, but this correlation is a very complicated one. The economic growth and welfare of the country is by no means a direct function of the extent of utilization of its mineral resources. The growing export of raw materials is not an indication of the economic progress of the country. There are countries in which the value of exports is 150 percent of the national income. (Such, for example, was the situation in Thailand.) You can export a lot of materials from a country without contributing much to its economic growth and the welfare of its population.

Government Aid on Facilities

MR. TAYLOR: The most important question we have to consider is how you finance the utilities because there is no indication that the private market here can take on that load. It's all very well to say that American enterprise, if it is given an attractive enough deal, will finance the utilities, like power and transport. Our experience has indicated that, in recent years, that just isn't so. It is unfortunate, but true, that, by and large, American utilities operating abroad cannot finance themselves in that market. Without export facilities, transportation, power, schools, medical facilities, to mention just a few of them—you are going to be terribly disappointed after you find the product which you are capable of finding. It will just stay there until it is possible to get it out, and in order to get it out you have to have the facilities.

SAMUEL J. GORLITZ (U.S. Department of State): On the general question of the government's role in this kind of development, the Export-Import Bank made a loan in the Northern Rhodesia copper and cobalt development for power facilities for which private financing was not available. In the steel development in Liberia, the U.S. Government helped the Liberian Government build a magnificent port and railroad bridge, without which there would have been no access to the ore. In the Belgian Congo, the ECA, through a counterpart loan, was able to expedite the development of transportation, communication, and other things. Without that sort of assistance, the very fine developments which you gentlemen are talking about would not have come in so quickly as they did.

THOROLD F. FIELD (Consulting Mining Engineer, Washington, D.C.): I have been connected with some of the copper mining in Northern Rhodesia, where the government is right now aiding development of resources by helping corollary industries. For instance, it is advancing about $14 million toward rehabilitation of the Northern Rhodesian industries, and a little over $22 million for hydroelectric power. If you think the United States should go in the lending business, they are very good loans from a banker's point of view.

Two Longer Views

WILLIAM VOGT (Planned Parenthood Federation of America): There has been talk here today about cooperating governments, but in many of these countries the governments simply do not represent the people. In Venezuela we have a working arrangement with the government, but among the masses of the people, the Yankee is often personified as the devil.

It seems to me this is a very practical matter. Somehow the benefits of what we do must be passed on to the people of these countries. There has been a very encouraging trend among some of the petroleum companies in South America who have not only fairly shared their income—at least we think it is fairly shared—but who have carried on remarkably sound programs in agriculture, health, and interpretation. We are just waking up to the fact that public relations are important in some of these overseas areas just as they are at home. And it seems to me that looking at this problem as an economic one, or as a resource one, is so lopsided that we cannot come out with the right answer. It is also a political problem, a cultural problem, and even a religious problem.

MR. MALENBAUM: I feel that at least as fundamental as the need of the United States to acquire resources is the fact that throughout the world are people who have certain rights to hope for a new kind of life—a life which the rather recent growth of technology has given them a window to see. They can see what life can be like, and though very few of them, perhaps, in their lifetime can attain it, they all have some right to expect some improvement in their condition.

We have had ample testimony to the fact that private enterprise has been able to do very important jobs abroad. It seems to me that we must recognize also how important it is to put real effort, consistent effort, into raising the level of living for people in the underdeveloped areas. With that, I think, we will have a better chance of creating the kind of world in which a lot of things we like can happen, including continued access to the raw materials we are going to need increasingly from these areas.

Technical Assistance on Geological Exploration

Where are the desired imports coming from? More accurate determination of the extent and location of the world's mineral resources would be a significant aid to private enterprise in developing additional sources of supply. The difficulties that often deter private capital from undertaking the costs and risks of extensive preliminary exploration to establish long-range reserves were discussed. A need was seen for encouraging the underdeveloped countries themselves to make initial surveys of their minerals potential as a basis for further exploration and development by private enterprise.

Here, many persons felt, was a field for government action to help the underdeveloped countries make initial geological surveys. The work of the United States Geological Survey and the Bureau of Mines in this field was reviewed and the possibility of expanding their services was considered. The Technical Assistance program was proposed as a means. Some objections were raised, however, partly because of possible misinterpretation by people of other countries, partly because of a feeling that minerals development might not be the best way of helping the underdeveloped countries raise their standards of living.

FROM THE RECORD

Problems of Locating Ore Reserves

MR. RICHARDS: There must be enormous bodies of ore all over the world of which we know little. If we are to make a plan for the future, the first thing we ought to do is to encourage the countries to make surveys of their areas to find out what is there. After we obtain the facts, then I think the next job is to determine how to develop these bodies.

MR. SMITH: Geological exploration is under way in many countries. In some countries, it is being undertaken with the cooperation of the United States Government. In Angola, the United States and Portuguese Governments have joined in a geological survey of the entire country. In other areas, like the Belgian Congo—which is doing a gorgeous job from the economic point of view—they are going to run their country to suit themselves. They do not request government aid, but they are rapidly learning what their own resources are. I think Bethlehem Steel has five major concessions in Southwest Africa. They have probably about 40 or 50 geologists, and they are making a tremendously careful survey in that area. It is difficult to get the necessary exploratory work on reserves done except either through huge governmental organization, which God forbid, or through governmental pressure on private companies to do a more adequate job than at present.

MR. CAMERON: A great deal of cooperative work has been done by Latin-American governments and the United States Geological Survey. The survey has supplied on loan, on some mutual financing basis, people for investigation of raw materials all over Latin America and all over Africa. It is, basically, reconnaissance investigation. We in private industry generally do not do that type of work, but we follow up the leads which the Survey has developed, and I think that they have been quite successful.

In the lead and zinc industry, we are not accustomed to projecting requirements 25 years ahead; most well-regulated companies seldom have known reserves of more than four or five years in advance of actual mining. If we attempted to enlarge our reserve picture, we would be tying up unnecessarily a great deal of capital.

MR. FIELD: When it comes to finding mines and developing industry, don't you think it is important to differentiate between an exploring company and a company studying a particular mine and developing it? For instance, to go out and find mines, it is important to eliminate some of the risk. It is important to go to a country where there is good hunting, as far as finding mines is concerned, and then get a large enough concession so that you have a chance to find several good things. That is more in the province of private financing or company financing, rather than government, because there is a great chance of wasting money in ordinary exploratory work. Some of the private companies have done very well in finding mines in Africa, and also in Canada.

MR. BENNETT: Government-to-government cooperation in minerals exploration is necessary, I believe, and without any commitments as to what will be done with the minerals should they be found. Exploratory companies that go into a completely undeveloped area face quite an expensive undertaking, hundreds of thousands of dollars, before they can even begin to say there is lead, zinc, copper, silver, and so forth. In Ethiopia, for example, virtually nothing has been done because it seems to be an almost insurmountable problem to get some exploration company to go and spend that amount of money in order to look for the minerals. Now, if a company comes into such a country on a limited scale and says, "Well, we think maybe there are certain minerals here, and we will look for them, but you will have to give us a concession," that company must get a very fine concession. The government itself would be selling a pig-in-a-poke, and the exploring companies buying a pig-in-a-poke. Both the companies and the country are reluctant to engage in such a transaction.

Attitudes in Recipient Countries

Several persons pointed out inherent limitations of technical assistance as a method of quickly developing particular minerals. Efforts may be ill-received, they said, unless they are clearly in the long-range interest of the host country.

WILLIAM D. JOHNSTON, JR. (U.S. Geological Survey): The Geological Survey has been engaged in geological assistance abroad since 1941. In the years since then, about 250 U.S.G.S. geologists have spent some time abroad and at present about 50 are working in some other country in cooperation with the geological survey or equivalent organization of that country. Most of the current foreign geological work is financed by the Foreign Operations Administration.

One of our major problems is that of maintaining continuity of plan under the ever-changing foreign aid organizations of the U.S. Government. Another problem is maintaining continuity of personnel, for we have found that our geologists are most effective after they have been in a country long enough to

learn the language and to acquire the confidence and respect of their technical counterparts in the host country. Still another problem is to maintain a judicious balance between studies of resources needed for the industrial economy of the country and resources for export. That balance is not the same for every country and it is influenced by political factors.

Our geologists working on problems of mineral reserves abroad might be regarded as certified public accountants who map the geology, estimate the ore reserves and then prepare a report with maps that might be regarded as a "certificate of assets" that can serve as a basis for discussion and negotiation by mining companies, banks, and governments. We have seen many of our geological reports serve to bring together the elements necessary to develop new mines abroad.

Complementary to our geological assistance abroad is the training of young foreign geologists in the United States. We select our candidates carefully, send them to American universities or train them with our own field parties. We are rather proud of our geological graduates who have gone back home. They bring some understanding of America and American mineral industry into the councils of their own country.

MR. LEITH: I just want to interpose a little question about Point IV. When Point IV was established, many of us were hopeful that we would begin to get immediate aid, in many parts of the world, on mineral developments. This program has done perhaps more than any other individual item on the list to develop countries generally. But my own impression is that the people in charge of it have given our mineral industry very little attention. We have had to hang around the edges to get any help.

MR. GORLITZ: I know from my personal experience that Point IV and ECA have tried hard to get technical help. ECA did some mineral surveys, but only after meeting with tremendous difficulties in trying to get geologists from the companies that you represent. They were almost totally unsuccessful in getting anyone. The response was that you people, rightly so, couldn't let them go. So Point IV necessarily had to turn its interest away from the minerals field to agriculture, health, etc. In any case, the need was greater in those fields because Point IV was, after all, not primarily interested in obtaining resources for the United States, but in helping develop the resources of friendly governments.

MR. BENNETT: I think the Point IV administration might be excused somewhat for not having done more in the beginning, at least, on minerals development. As a representative of an underdeveloped area—Ethiopia —I tried to get our government and the Ethiopian Government to combine in a project to explore the almost completely unexplored mineral resources of that country. I found that there was a suspicion on the part of the Ethiopians that the whole objective of Point IV was not to give them broad technical assistance, but to come in and find what mineral resources we could take away.

MR. BATEMAN: A lot can be done through the Point IV Program toward developing reserves by geological studies in cooperation with foreign areas, and the training of persons in these areas in methods of making geological investigations. I don't feel that those reserves have to be developed by the United States. If we are short of nickel, for example, and new supplies can be developed in one country, that is going to aid the entire Free World. We must realize that the rest of the Free World has got to have a share of these minerals, and perhaps in greater proportion than we in the future, because of the tendency of so many countries to increase their standards of living

and to develop their own manufacturing and their own resources.

As more is known of resources, I think our private industry is sufficiently strong to step in and bring about the development.

MR. WOYTINSKY: The Point IV Program is operating along the same lines as the Technical Assistance Program of the United Nations. The principles of both programs are very similar. According to the general agreement, the United States cannot initiate any project. It waits until a project is initiated by the host government and then it comes in with the technical assistance. There is a definite political philosophy behind this attitude. There must not be the slightest suspicion that assistance is given from the point of view of the immediate direct interest of the United States.

So the question is not: Why did not the Point IV and the U.N. Technical Assistance Programs go into the problems of mineral resources? The question is: Why did not the host countries ask for more help in developing their mineral resources?

The Point IV Program must not be dominated by the desires and the interests of the United States, or even of all the groups of industrial countries. The principle of the Point IV Program and the Extended Technical Assistance Program is completely unselfish aid to underdeveloped countries in raising their standards of living. I am convinced that, without these programs, we would be building our raw materials policy on sand, and there would be a danger of eventual collapse of our foreign investment in a not too remote future.

Subsection C

MARKET STABILIZATION

What is the relation of market instability to world production and trade in raw materials, and, consequently, to the resource position of the United States? The pros and cons of government action to stabilize the international market were considered from this angle, rather than as a world problem for its own sake.

Some general background points suggested by the section steering committee were used as the starting point of discussion: Raw materials prices tend to rise and fall farther and faster than other prices in response to changes in demand. This is because of the relative inelasticity of raw materials production; farmers and miners cannot change their volume of output as rapidly as can most other producers. In producing areas, many of which are almost wholly dependent on one or two raw materials, extreme declines in prices of these commodities cause serious economic hardship which may have disturbing political consequences. In consuming countries, sudden upswings in price distort the cost structure and create problems of supply. To the extent that price uncertainties discourage resources development, they also operate to reduce the volume of future supplies.

The relation of these wide price fluctuations on the international market to the satisfaction of increased U. S. requirements for raw materials and to Free World security was recognized in the questions considered here. Although discussion ranged over considerable territory, two central issues stood out: First, should special stabilization measures be adopted? Second, if such measures are considered desirable, now or in the future, what methods appear most promising? This part of the discussion consisted largely of examples of tested or proposed techniques and analysis of their strong and weak points. Most of the possibilities considered called for some type of intergovernmental action.

Special Price Stabilization Devices

The premise that violent fluctuations in raw materials prices are undesirable was accepted without challenge. But members differed widely as to whether stabilizing devices are a desirable or a feasible remedy.

Some regarded the proposed cure as worse than the disease. They believed that estimates of future supply and demand made by governments would be no more accurate than those arrived at through individual action on the open market, while the flexibility of the market to correct erroneous judgments would be destroyed. Detailed objections were raised, also, to the far-reaching economic and political complications that might result from international commodity agreements and to difficulties and costs involved in negotiating and carrying them out.

Other members pointed out the extent to which governments now intervene in raw materials markets through price supports, tariffs, quotas, and similar measures designed to protect their own producers. They believed that, since disruptive unilateral action is the alternative, some form of coordinated international attack on the violent price fluctuations in these materials should be attempted.

Regardless of which course they favored, most participants agreed that the United States should approach the problem from a broader viewpoint than its interest as a consumer of raw materials. Discussion of this point touched upon the effect that completion of United States stockpiling objectives will have on those producing countries that have greatly increased their production in response to our stockpile requirements. The implications of this situation for the nondollar consuming countries and the impact upon United States exports were also noted.

A number of participants emphasized the importance of keeping our economic activity at a high level so as to maintain the best possible demand for raw materials imports. Some believed this to be the contribution that the United States can make to solution of the problem. Others thought that, in addition, it is in the United States interest to undertake commodity agreements as a means of assuring the producing countries some measure of protection against production cutbacks that would depress their standards of living and endanger their political security as free nations.

FROM THE RECORD

Is Government Action Desirable?

ADAM K. STRICKER, JR. (General Motors Corporation): If you begin to have administered decisions take the place of market decisions, you raise more problems than you can possibly solve. You have to decide who is going to stabilize prices and at what levels. If it is going to be done by governments, then you have to decide whether it is to be done on a unilateral basis by the United States or on an international basis. If it is to be done unilaterally, then you have the next problem. Are we going to favor consumers or producers of these materials? If it is to be done internationally, are we going to favor consuming countries as against producing countries?

I think that we ought to do what we can to make the market work more perfectly. We ought to have more information on market conditions in the world. I think our government and other governments have done a lot to mitigate the business cycle through fiscal and other matters, which will probably dampen out these more violent swings that have been talked about.

ANDREW FLETCHER (St. Joseph Lead Company): My opinion on multilateral government contracts, international stockpiles, quotas, cartels, and all devices of that type, is that they are impractical and inadvisable.

With an international commodity agreement, all governments would work together, decide how much each country was to produce, and how much each country was to consume. Under such a condition, it would not be necessary to worry about tariffs, devaluation of currencies, or anything else, because the standard of living in every country would be controlled through the allocation of the raw materials.

In view of the difficulties that the so-called tin cartel has had—and there are only about three countries in the world where tin is produced—I would hesitate to try to stabilize lead, zinc, or any other commodity that is produced in many parts of the world through such a device as a cartel.

EARL A. GRAHAM (Federal Trade Commission): Are we going to go on with crutches for the next 50 years or are we going to get back eventually to a relatively free market—with such protection as we may really need? It seems to me that the question here is one of principle much more than of detail—whether or not in the long future we do better to operate as a free enterprise system in the world, making the markets as free and open as possible and letting prices find their own level. I am talking about substituting the judgment of millions of buyers for the judgment of a few people. Of course, you can't do that in a time of war when you have to have artificial props.

MAX GIDEONSE (Rutgers University): Actually governments, through stockpiling, tariffs, and quotas, do exercise a major influence over the market, over prices; and under those conditions the logic of Free World solidarity would seem to suggest that national government action should either be coordinated through commodity agreements of some sort or another, or you should move to a genuine free trade policy. It won't do to appeal to the beauties of the free market when actually every time you have a downturn in business activity the large governments, such as the United States, save their own producers and leave the burden of adjustment entirely to the outside producer. You have to face that problem, it seems to me.

STEPHEN RAUSHENBUSH (American Academy of Political and Social Science): The people who keep talking about the danger of governmental intervention ought to say in the same breath that the tariff is a governmental intervention. It is a one-nation intervention. And while it doesn't help other nations very much, it might hurt them very badly. That is a distinction of some importance. The intervention of various governments acting together might turn out to be of a different character than proclaiming, "You cut down your production and we won't cut down ours," which is the essence of the ordinary high-tariff argument.

LESLIE A. WHEELER (International Federation of Agricultural Producers): I am in favor of international commodity agreements, but for reasons that may be applicable only to agriculture. The main reason is that there does exist in the world today widespread government intervention in respect to agricultural price supports which in my view is bound to continue.

All the strictures that can be leveled against international commodity agreements can also be leveled against national price supports in agriculture. And there is one stricture against national price supports, I think, that cannot be leveled against commodity agreements —that is, the commodity agreements do not cause a tremendous amount of friction in international relations. Rather, the attempt is to bring a little more order out of a prevailing system of national measures in respect to agriculture. This may not apply to most of the things that you are discussing here. But I simply want to point out that there is at least one good argument for international commodity agreements.

FRANCOIS P. CORBASSON (Organization for European Economic Co-operation, Washington): In the long run we all know that we shall need more and more raw materials. In that case it might be worth while to stabilize prices so that production of raw materials should go along even though at times there may be a slight recession.

Can Enough of the Factors Be Foreseen?

Members opposing stabilization questioned the soundness of government judgments on outlook. On balance, are stabilization programs based on imperfect foresight helpful or harmful?

MR. STRICKER: The International Materials Conference in its report on its first year of operations, which came out in April of 1952, indicated that we were going to have a fairly stringent situation in zinc for most of the year. Now here is a case where we had a world review of availabilities and requirements. In April of 1952 the zinc picture was still tight and allocations were continued. Yet, within two months the zinc market collapsed. I think the IMC was as well equipped to make an estimate of availabilities and market conditions as any organization which could be established. Their complete failure to forecast market conditions should cast grave doubts on the feasibility of such an approach.

RICHARD A. YOUNG (American Lead, Zinc and Smelting Company): Isn't our present price situation on raw materials due largely to the recent international materials control efforts where countries made honest estimates as to what they thought they were going to need, and during a time of great shortage built up tremendous stocks over and above their needs? If we hadn't had that, one can speculate that we might not have had the runaway prices that we did have, and we might not have stimulated the production that we did, and therefore we might not have this violent fluctuation in the price on the downside. The one experience we have had with stabilization has been one of the most unstabilizing factors that we have ever run into in our markets.

MR. RAUSHENBUSH: The alternative to some kind of international commodity agreement is a high tariff. Shouldn't you also ask the mining companies and the oil companies and the others who are favoring this unilateral government intervention in their behalf whether they also have figures on whether international private price and production controls have worked or not?

It isn't enough to ask, has this international commodity arrangement worked so far? The alternatives have to be considered at the same time. I wonder whether there aren't some very real questions there—whether the tariff will work best for our international strength and security, whether the decisions of the purely domestic producers as to the proper level are not just as questionable as the levels which might be considered for the international stockpile by our producers with both foreign and domestic interests.

WILLIS C. ARMSTRONG (U.S. Department of State): Are governments smart enough to make sound judgements either collectively or individually? They make mistakes, of course. Would it be better, as an alternative, to have a lot of people making individual judgments, the result of which is the market? Then you get into a psychological problem— the tendency in a great many of these situations for people to make individual judgments which all run in exactly the same direction and which produce a violent swing in price; and they may all be just as wrong as wrong can be. Mass psychology gets hold of people and they all go roaring off in a particular direction, and that is the thing that makes their governments go roaring off in a particular direction. We all talked very differently in 1951 from the way we do now, and I think we might as well recognize it.

SIMON D. STRAUSS (American Smelting and Refining Company): The difference between the individual estimate of the businessman and the estimate of the International Materials Conference or some international stabilization committee is that when an estimate has been made by the international group, action is predicated on it and the direction of that action cannot be changed rapidly, whereas when the individual business-

man makes his estimate he is in a position to change his decision within the day, or even within the hour. An international stabilization committee must act on a consensus of opinion. A businessman can act on his own views.

MR. STRICKER: I don't know how you can set quotas and decide that somebody is going to absorb so much or use so much—or be allowed to use only so much if it is a question of a shortage—unless you allocate production among the fabricators and decide how they are going to fabricate.

I think that you get into a process of control which you didn't intend to get into. All of these things start on a very simple basis, but each problem solved opens up three that nobody ever imagined would arise. And that requires further control.

MR. STRAUSS: Assuming that it were possible to stabilize the prices of lead and zinc, for example, at 18 or 20 cents a pound, I am sure that the domestic producers would feel no need for tariff protection and we could thereafter dispense with that. Furthermore, the price would be at such an attractive level that the problem of domestic investment in these resources would also be solved.

But at this point, with stabilization at a level sufficiently high from the producer's standpoint, a third factor enters. If we stabilize the prices of lead or zinc or any other material at a level so high as to be attractive to producers both within and outside the United States, what then happens to the consumer's interest?

MR. FLETCHER: If we start trying to control the domestic economy, it won't be long before we are pushed into the position where we are trying to control the economy of other countries. If you set up import or production quotas for the United States, we will force other countries to set them up. This is absolutely and totally inadvisable. If we can't do it with wool, which is relatively simple, how are we going to do it with other commodities? We are trying to build up friendship in the world, but if we start to try to control the economies of other countries, we will make enemies. The further we keep away from any international contracts, quotas, buffer stocks, and so forth, the better off we and the rest of the world are going to be.

Mr. WHEELER: The United States is not making a great many friends in the world at the moment with its unilateral price support policy on agricultural products, including cotton.

B. N. DARBEYSHIRE (Graduate Institute of International Studies, Geneva, Switzerland): I look at this question from a European and perhaps also an African viewpoint. It seems to me that insofar as you have price supports and also promote international commodity agreements, you will come across the trouble which you have experienced already in the International Wheat Agreement with the United Kingdom—while you have price supports, the prices you wish to obtain under such an international agreement are in excess of those which the great consuming nations are prepared to pay.

My own thinking is quite to the contrary of subsidies. A high price economy should be protected by tariffs rather than by subsidies. Tariffs don't affect the international price structure in the same way as a subsidy, particularly if you are setting the price for your international commodity. When one of your programs is to raise living standards and at the same time you are raising international prices so that consumption cannot rise, you can cause a great deal of dissatisfaction abroad.

How Broad a Viewpoint?

WILLIAM H. WYNNE (U.S. Treasury): First, I would like to state that my views are purely personal. Our interest as a consumer, of course, is in low prices of the commodities we import. But I don't think we can approach the question of these agreements from the point of view of our narrow consumer interest. We have world-wide interests now in the welfare of the economy at large, and when we are considering whether an international agreement for a raw commodity is desirable or not,

I think we have to look at our United States interest as very broad.

Taking that point of view, we have got the question whether it would be to the interest of the United States to participate in international agreements, even if the net result might be to keep the price up against us. First of all, the difficulty of the raw materials producing countries is not so much in the price of the commodity as in having stable levels of income; it is not at all certain that if you keep the prices somewhat higher than they would otherwise be, all producers would have a generally higher range of income. I think we in the United States can make a very real contribution by maintaining our own economy at a decent level. Our demand for raw materials in this country depends much more on the general level of business than it does on prices. To the extent to which we adopt policies that will not permit us to get into the kind of slump that we had in 1933, we already are making a very substantial contribution to a greater degree of stability on raw materials.

ROBERT GOLDSMITH (British Embassy, Washington): In the United Kingdom itself our interest is a consumer interest, and therefore on the whole low prices suit us better than high prices. But we can't look at these problems purely from the point of view of the United Kingdom because we act as bankers for the sterling area. And the sterling area is a very important producer of raw materials. Some of the important ones are rubber and tin in Malaya, jute in Pakistan and India, copper in Rhodesia, bauxite in Central America. Any reduction in United States demand for these commodities can reduce the standard of living in those countries, which increases the danger of political unrest.

Over and above that, our main dollar earners are exports of these raw materials to the dollar area. And insofar as dollar earnings are reduced by reductions in U. S. purchases, we are at once faced with a very difficult position in the United Kingdom. The only thing we can do to prevent our gold and dollar balances from draining away is to impose rigid import controls in the United Kingdom and ask our sterling area collaborators to do the same sort of thing. That, of course, reduces world trade almost at once.

Mr. Corbasson: From the point of view of the foreign producing countries, I would agree with Mr. Wynne that the most important contribution the United States could make to solving our problem is to keep up a high level of domestic activity.

Mr. Goldsmith's remark with reference to the sterling area is important also for the rest of Europe because sterling has been for a long time one of the means for Europe to earn dollars, and if the United Kingdom is in difficulty with regard to the dollar area, it reflects immediately on the rest of Europe. Then import restrictions have to be clamped down on the rest of the European countries, which in turn tends to depress again the level of activity in the United States because the United States cannot export its goods. United States citizens on the whole are more aware now of the importance of their export trade with regard to the level of activity in their country. This is quite a new development in the last 10 or 15 years, which I feel is very important.

Mr. Stricker: It has been my feeling that if we can maintain a high level of demand here, we will make our maximum contribution toward maintaining the incomes of the people in producing countries. I think we can do this without attempting to establish prices and marketing arrangements through international agreements.

The very marked price swings have accompanied wars or a period of deep depression. No agreement we could negotiate would cover wartime conditions or would be able to stand up through a period of very deep depression. We can help other countries by maintaining our own economy, and we certainly can time our stockpile purchases more intelligently than we have in the past.

The question was raised whether, from the standpoint of assuring maximum supplies at some future period of anticipated scarcity, the outlook for low prices might not be a good thing.

Mr. Strauss: In the case of minerals which are today being produced largely from low-grade sources, the development of new production is a matter not of months or even of 2 or 3 years, but of 5 to 10 years. A period of low prices which inhibits exploration and development of new sources of supply at low prices might leave you five years from now, let us say, in a position where the industry was inadequately developed to meet a sudden increased demand, and you would then be faced with a period of very high prices again simply because production cannot be expanded quickly.

It is true, of course, that a low price is helpful in developing consumption, and, for certain materials, a broad field of consumption may encourage expansion of productive capacity. Perhaps the best example would be aluminum, of which much raw material is available, and for which there has been a policy of stable and fairly low prices. But in the mineral field generally it is not true that a period of low prices is helpful with respect to future supplies.

The effect that cessation of U.S. stockpile purchases will have on the producing areas was suggested as an argument for international action.

Mr. Armstrong: We have stockpiled a great many materials, some of which are the sole or the most important product of individual countries. Now we are reaching the point where we don't need any more, and yet world production is to some extent adjusted to take care of this demand of ours. In some countries the adjustments to the cutbacks can't be made fast enough to avoid a major social or political problem. So when you buy for stockpile to insure against a future political crisis, you are at the same time, by going in and out of the market, creating a number of other political crises of smaller scope. And I think that is a problem that ought to be examined because, by being a major market factor, whether you want to be or not, you have got yourself some responsibility. The question is, does your responsibility extend to the transition back to a more normal type of production and trade?

MR. GOLDSMITH: United States stockpiling, which seemed very necessary to us all, has had the incidental effect of increasing output of these materials in the sterling area and of perhaps leading the producing countries to expect a higher level of continued demand than can in fact be the case over the longer term. When the stockpiling ends, it is all the more important, therefore, that full normal consumption be maintained. There are many difficulties in working out international agree-ments on such matters, but insofar as commodity agreements enable producers to continue to produce steadily over a long period, we tend to favor them.

MR. CORBASSON: It is important to keep in mind those people, particularly in the underdeveloped countries, who may be a prey to Communism very easily if they cannot provide a decent level of living for themselves. In the underdeveloped countries, to start the production of raw materials, it is desirable to have a sort of long-term possibility of markets. Unless raw materials production does start, there is very little chance of seeing the standard of living of these people improve.

Some Stabilization Devices

Two types of stabilization schemes were examined in some detail by the subsection: (1) the multilateral contract, as a means of stabilizing price within a narrow range for a substantial period of time; and (2) the buffer stock, as a means of simply mitigating extreme price fluctuations.

Because no multilateral contract exists on minerals, the International Wheat Agreement was used as an example of this type of commodity action. Discussion concerned principally the difficulties and delays encountered in negotiating the agreement and the heavy costs which the United States has borne in connection with it. Although these costs were explained as arising in large part from our internal price support policy on wheat, considerable doubt was expressed that this type of international agreement could or should be widely extended in the commodity field.

On the buffer stock type of stabilization device, discussion centered on the costs of carrying stocks for the long periods of time contemplated and on the risks involved, including the risk of endlessly accumulating if no break in price occurred and the risk that new patterns of usage or discoveries of new materials sources in the future might largely reduce the value of the accumulated stock.

The subsection also discussed whether U. S. stockpiling should be extended beyond its present purely security objective, to function as a sort of unilateral buffer stock for price stabilization purposes. Several participants questioned the wisdom of any such extension of the stockpiling function.

FROM THE RECORD

Multilateral Contracts

EARL TURNER (Texas Independent Producers and Royalty Owners Association):
Isn't it more or less at the expense of the United States that we have undertaken this particular stabilization effort on wheat? Could not part of the enthusiasm on the part of other

governments, or most governments, for such an agreement be accounted for by this fact?

Assuming this method did work, is it conceivable that we can undertake such a thing for all of our products on an international basis if we are to underwrite it as a nation?

It was noted that the cost of the first Wheat Agreement to the United States was $600 million, and the continuation of it will cost us about another $400 million.

D. A. FITZGERALD (Foreign Operations Administration): That cost was not due to external policies or interests of the United States, but to internal policies. The United States felt it desirable to maintain a certain level of internal prices for wheat. In order at the same time to continue to export some of our wheat supplies, we had to pay what amounted to an export subsidy of $600 million. It is still a cost, but I think we should be clear as to why.

ROBERT B. SCHWENGER (U.S. Department of Agriculture): The problems of negotiating the Wheat Agreement were tremendous. One lesson we have learned is that negotiation of an agreement is extremely difficult for even a single commodity; and the more complicated the commodity, the more difficult it is. Even if it were to be agreed that the way to solve the sort of problems we are discussing is through international commodity agreements, the question whether it would be possible to achieve working arrangements would still loom very large. But if the method proved successful, belief in the technique might grow, and therefore the technique might work better. I think it is fair to say that in the course of the Wheat Agreement, there developed among the countries participating a feeling that it was better to have an agreement than not to, all things considered.

When the Wheat Agreement was negotiated, there had been a very substantial fall in the world price of wheat, and it was thought that we were entering a period of recurrent, if not continual, surplus. The price that was

incorporated in the Agreement was a guess as to an average over the next four years, roughly; and as far as the negotiations revealed, the margin of difference in guessing wasn't very great. What we didn't foresee was Korea. The Agreement had a lower level as well as an upper level, and if prices had gone down, the net advantage would have been with the exporters. The way it worked out, the price of wheat was above the Agreement range throughout the life of the Agreement. In looking at the new agreement, some of those considerations undoubtedly will be taken up.

MR. STRICKER: There were, as I understand it, four wheat-exporting countries. All the rest were importing countries, and as far as I can tell we were the only exporters who were actually supporting an internal price at a level different from the world price. If we had not had this difference in price, I don't think the Agreement would have been particularly important because we would have been back to a free market world price.

MR. WHEELER: I think that the Wheat Agreement has worked reasonably well. I would like to see a cotton agreement, but I can't see any possibility of a multilateral contract. I don't think any governments of cotton-importing countries are likely to take the responsibility and risks involved in the guaranteed purchase of cotton, while obviously many countries are prepared to take those risks in respect to wheat.

I think what is really necessary is to get back to some kind of combination of buffer stocks and quota agreements. It might be only something to bring some sort of international consideration into the operation of existing national buffer stocks, of which the conspicuous examples are the United States and Brazil.

MR. STRICKER: There is, of course, competition between fibers and synthetic materials. I don't see how you can make a multilateral contract for cotton or for wool or for any of these products for which you have a possible industrial substitute unless you are going to allocate production of the industrial substitute and control the rate of invention and of capital flow into those industries.

Buffer Stocks

As an example of the international buffer stock, the subsection chairman briefly described pre-World War II operations of the International Tin Agreement, an intergovernmental organization of producing countries which superimposed a buffer stock (varying in amount between 5 and 10 percent of world production) upon a production quota plan.

MR. STRAUSS: From the producers' standpoint, the International Tin Agreement was a highly successful operation. They felt the price was satisfactory. Many of the consumers in the United States were very much opposed to it, but there was no consumer representation at meetings of the committee. It was purely a producer venture, handled through the governments of the countries involved. In my opinion the experiment worked only because practically all tin enters the export trade. No large-consuming nations are significant producers.

MARION W. WORTHING (U.S. Department of State): It was not a plan though that worked smoothly over a long period. Every once in a while it would sort of break down. Also, while just after 1932 the resulting price rises were much greater than if there had been no control, over the whole period the difference from lead and copper and zinc was not so great; the others just climbed more slowly.

MR. GIDEONSE: The idea of a genuine buffer stock, just a buying and selling operation without quotas on either trade or production, used to be discussed in the middle forties, and the United Nations reports speak very highly of the theoretical soundness of an international buffer stocks scheme. I know of no examples of its actual operation. The idea arouses a good deal of skepticism as to whether it is not a way to lose an awful lot of money. The answer to that depends on how you operate a genuine buffer stock. If you fix rigid prices

at which you buy and sell, it is perfectly possible that you can lose a powerful lot of money if you have made the wrong estimate in fixing the basic price.

On the other hand, you can say, "We will try to determine what the basic price is and then we will have a buying price at 20 or 25 percent below the basic price and a selling price 20 to 25 percent above." In that case it would seem relatively riskless and might do something to give confidence to the Free World community as to the outer limits of price ranges. But of course, when you set the buying and selling prices that far apart, you don't get nearly as much stability as some people demand.

MR. STRAUSS: Of course, it is a little bit like a system that they use at Monte Carlo. You do have to have an awful lot of chips because whatever level you set, whether it is 20 percent below or 25 percent below, presumably you have to stand willing to accumulate indefinitely if price weakness persists. That is one of the aspects of this situation, of course, that is so difficult to define. Also, there is interest to be considered, and the cost of carrying these commodities over long periods. You may show profit on the books, but have you really made a profit if you have issued government bonds, run into debt, and so forth?

MR. CORBASSON: I wonder if the buffer stock is not in the position of the Casino, rather than the consumer. Since the consumption of raw materials is going to increase with the increase in population and the improvement of living standards in most countries and in the United States, how can the buffer stock lose money in the long run? The Casino at Monte Carlo makes money; whether you lose or I lose, the Casino makes money.

Perhaps we are thinking in terms of much too short a period, and not in the long-run period, in terms of around 30 years. It seems to me that no raw material has in fact been in surplus over the last 30 years.

MR. RAUSHENBUSH: If you are talking about the pure buffer stock, without production restrictions, I think we might drop that idea rather rapidly. Even with any reasonable growth in demand, you would get too much money tied up there in no time. With everybody running free and opening new mines, you would just cut your throat before you started. I think that this whole concept of stabilization carries with it some common responsibility for slowing down a little on production. I think the producers, in order to get prices and employment out of it, might be glad to make some temporary restrictions in production in emergency periods.

The objections raised to international buffer stocks, and some additional objections, were believed to apply also to unilateral buffer stocks.

MR. STRAUSS: There would be nothing to prevent a unilateral buffer stock by any one country that was willing to do that. A recent operation by the U.S. Government, for instance, is perhaps in a sense a small buffer stock, although it is tied up with the stockpile.

In view of the Korean situation, this government decided to set minimum prices for domestic production of certain minor materials for which we are heavily dependent on imports. Some of the commodities covered are mica, columbium and tantalum, domestic manganese ore, tungsten, and cobalt and chrome. Our government has agreed to pay a certain fixed price for any domestic production delivered prior to June, 1958.

This sort of thing, of course, is relatively effective. It certainly gives promise of price stability. In these instances the tonnages involved are not so great as to tie up any large amounts of capital. But had similar floor prices been adopted for zinc or lead, then the quantities of money involved by now would have been very large. The big question is this: Is price stability, desirable though it is, worth a price as great as that?

MR. STRICKER: If prices are set by markets, they are impersonal and we don't get into the international complications that we have

when government representatives set prices that other countries don't like. The action of private citizens, operating in a free market, is something that nobody can resent. While there can be no doubt that over the next 25 years we will need increasing quantities of many materials, we cannot afford to build large civilian stockpiles for the future. Interest on the funds involved is a cost which must be considered. There is also the problem of a changing pattern of consumption—the "product mix." Nobody knows what the product mix is going to be 25 years from now and what relative prices for various materials would result in free markets at that time. I can see possibilities of fantastic losses in such an operation. The presence of these losses, in turn, would be used to suggest various controls over the economy so as to use the stocks of those commodities which are excessive rather than those which would be demanded in an otherwise free market.

MR. FLETCHER: One of the reasons why we have today such a depressed condition in both lead and zinc is because of the liquidation of the British stockpile. The imports of lead are today greater than the domestic production, and more than we are talking about for buffer stocks. The liquidation of individuals holdings on the part of speculators in other countries has also been very detrimental. They were fooled into thinking that there was a shortage of lead and zinc in the world because of our government's statements, whereas there never was any shortage.

MR. GOLDSMITH: When the British Government decided to return responsibility for importing to the trade, it had to come to some reasonable arrangement for getting rid of the stocks it had on hand, which were trading stocks and not a stockpile. [Here Mr. Goldsmith outlined the procedure for zinc stocks.] When you compare releases of 4,000 tons a month for seven months and 2,000 a month thereafter with consumption in the United States, which I think Mr. Young said is about a million tons per annum, it is a little difficult to see why the British Government should be blamed for the reduction in the price of zinc on world markets.

GEORGE W. ROTHSCHILD (Foreign Operations Administration): I wonder if, in the sliding-scale tariff arrangement proposed for lead, there isn't something of a unilateral buffer stock of domestic production of lead, putting the real onus, the prime burden to the extent that the United States is a major consumer of lead, on the foreign producers for the extreme swings, the low swing in this case?

Stockpiling and Price Stabilization

MR. STRICKER: Our stockpiling program is a matter of security. I don't think that the stockpile ought to be used as a stabilizing device; as a matter of fact, it can't be used as a stabilizing device without legislation, because under existing law the act very clearly provides that material can't be taken out of the stockpile and used for market purposes.

MR. TURNER: We need to be prepared for short emergencies, and military stockpiling is a means of doing so. As contrasted with military stockpiling, economic stockpiling is unsound. I couldn't accept even the statement that within 25 years we are going to need these buffer stocks that we have accumulated. The statement has been made that we are running out of things—that ultimately instead of buying we are going to be needing all of these things we are accumulating. I don't accept that at all. We will never run out of anything if we are a free virile economy; we never have. We have always found substitutes that are improved long before any scarcity or complete diminution of the resource occurs. Stockpiling for economic reasons is not related to stability of the entire economy, which in my view must be approached from another angle rather than that of price fixing and production controls.

Some means must be had, if we are to have price stability, of having a stable over-all economy, which comes back to some type of do-mestic monetary policy by which we can assure adequate purchasing power to balance maximum efficient production. In my view, the discussion so far has dealt with price-fixing, not price stability.

MR. STRAUSS: There have been times when some of our stockpile negotiations have been a little colored by other than purely military considerations. Whatever the theory of stockpiling, we are in practice occasionally departing from the hard and fast rule of simply buying materials when we need them for military purposes. For example, we are now seriously considering buying copper from the Chileans in order to help them out. The Chileans tried to sell it at 35½ cents at a time when copper was freely available at 30 cents, and this is rather difficult to do. They have come to the United States and suggested that they would like to sell it to our stockpile.

I think that this particular deal is in effect a sort of one-shot buffer stock negotiation; let's call it that—the buffer stock unwittingly accumulated by the Chileans and now about to be tenderly transferred to the U.S. Government.

MR. FLETCHER: As soon as our government gets into a situation, they certainly confuse it. The Chilean copper situation is a good example; the large unsold tonnage would not be facing us if the U.S. Government had not set ceiling prices on copper, as on lead and zinc. Chilean copper was being sold normally in the world markets, but when we set ceilings below the world markets, Chile naturally objected to selling to us, and we were forced to buy at over the ceiling price.

Another point: our government couldn't have done worse in its buying for the stockpile. They bought in periods of scarcity, on the apparent assumption that if a commodity was in surplus, it wasn't needed. The result was the government forced the price up way beyond that which would have prevailed if they hadn't bought at just the wrong time. There is plenty of lead and zinc lying around the world now, but do you think the government would buy it? Not a ton.

MR. ROTHSCHILD: The vagaries of the stockpile purchasing may show the problems of getting government into the business, as Mr. Fletcher has said, but I think part of it is attributable to the appropriations factor. When prices were low, it was pretty hard to get appropriations for the stockpile, and in the Korean scare they got about what they wanted, plus the DMPA purchases. I suppose some of those have been shifted into stockpile.

MR. ARMSTRONG: We start out with the purest of motives to buy a stockpile of metals and other materials because we may need it for security purposes. The law gives all sorts of protection to make sure that this is a fact. We say we are not going to interfere with markets. Well, you can't buy 9 billion dollars' worth of stuff without doing something to markets. The place you get into difficulty is in not admitting that the stockpile is in effect a market force and is liable to be a market force. Your main point there has to be to keep it from being a major market force and to be sure it is not used intentionally as a market manipulating device, either upwards or downwards.

CHAIRMAN'S SUMMARY

The section on United States Concern with World Resources defined the principal issues for discussion as follows: (1) What should the United States commercial policy be with respect to imports of raw materials? (2) What are the most effective means by which the development of resources abroad can be assured? (3) Is it desirable to use special devices to stabilize raw material prices? If so, how should this be done?

This definition of these issues admittedly excluded certain international questions of current importance in the raw materials area, in particular the problem of disposing of U.S. agricultural surpluses. This exclusion was at least partially justified on the ground that the surpluses in question are mainly foods while the concern of the Conference is principally with industrial raw materials.

The issues presented for discussion clearly overlap but it was agreed that the advantage of discussion in small groups outweighed the disadvantages of a partial approach to the whole problem and that no subsection was debarred from considering the relation of its own subject to that of the other subsections. The emphasis in the assignment given to the section on United States interests, together with lack of time, compelled a neglect of many problems of economic development of great interest to resource countries. The problems of general development were considered only so far as they bore directly on resource development.

Security Considerations

It was obvious from the outset that security questions impinged directly on all the issues considered by the section. The necessity of materials availability in the event of war clearly affects the extent to which we should depend on foreign as against domestic sources of supply. The development of resources abroad likewise requires a consideration of security interests. And the repercussions on stabilization policy of stockpile acquisitions are an important part of the problem. Discussion of the security question raised in the minds of some a doubt whether materials security is not too frequently considered in terms of the situation confronted by this country in previous wars, and the suggestion was made that stockpile goals and commercial policy measures designed to promote national security might be reviewed in the light of more current concepts of vulnerability.

Commercial Policy

The discussion of commercial policy started with a recognition of the fact that tariffs in the raw material area are generally low, that there is a large free list, and that existing quotas are relatively unimportant. Furthermore, the "Buy American" acts are not of much significance in this area and customs simplification is of less importance than in the field of manufactures. Consequently, while the "peril point" provision and the escape clause in existing legislation have potential importance, U.S. commercial policy with respect to raw material imports can be accurately described as already a liberal policy. This is not so true of higher stages of processing or fabrication.

Given this situation, the realistic alternatives appeared to the section to be: (1) the retention of this liberal policy, pressing here and there for further tariff reductions which must be recognized, however, as not being of overwhelming importance; (2) the retention of a liberal policy with, however, increased tariff protection in a limited number of cases; and (3) a fairly widespread increase in tariff rates.

The consensus of the section is that, broadly speaking, the kind of liberal tariff and quota policy which we now have with respect to

raw materials is appropriate to the conditions that we now foresee. Some of the participants, however, would interpret this statement as allowing few or no exceptions; others are inclined to believe that there may have to be several exceptions. The discussion of the permissible range of exceptions brought out divergences between the economic, political, and strategic interests of the United States, between minority and majority interests, between short-term and long-term interests, and the interests of domestic producers as against the interests of producers in friendly foreign countries.

Discussion of commercial policy with respect to particular materials centered around oil, lead, zinc, and copper. Those who believed that exceptions to a liberal commercial policy should be made in the case of these materials emphasized security considerations, including the necessity of having a healthy mining industry in the event of war, and the hardships involved in shutting down domestic operations in favor of foreign sources of supply. Those opposed to exceptions for these materials noted that for most of them alternative low-cost sources of supply are available in relatively safe areas already and offered the opinion that hardship cases might be handled better in some other way than by raising the price to all consumers in the United States through tariff increases.

Investment and Development

The discussion of problems of foreign resource development centered around the respective roles to be assigned to private versus public action in this area. At one extreme the view was expressed that foreign private investment could do the whole job with the possible exception of government financing of technical assistance for geological surveys and government loans to private U.S. and foreign enterprises in cases where it was clearly established that our strategic interests require a considerably more rapid rate of development than could be expected with private financing alone.

At the other extreme the view was advanced that unless the United States Government undertakes a leading role in the promotion of the general development of resource and potential resource countries, it is doubtful whether these countries will long be available as sources of U.S. materials imports. A middle view might be stated as follows: Private investment and enterprise must be considered the primary agent of foreign materials development; nevertheless, government has an important role to play not only in financing technical assistance and the production of certain strategic materials but, through public financial arrangement or such lending agencies as the International Bank and the Export-Import Bank, in financing installations such as port facilities, public utilities, roads, and irrigation projects which may, in large part, serve as auxiliary facilities to resource development.

Despite substantial disagreement on the relative roles of private and public action, there was a consensus not only that foreign private investment must be relied on for a major part of the job, but that private development of resources could make and has made a substantial contribution to the general economic development of resource countries. It was generally agreed, therefore, that the removal of obstacles to foreign private investment had an important contribution to make both to the resources development and the general development of underdeveloped areas. While interest was expressed in the continuation of the current trade and investment treaty program, some skepticism was expressed by representatives of the mineral industry concerning the effectiveness of the program. Some of these representatives were inclined to believe that revision of U.S. tax laws was the most important contribution that could be made to foreign private investment.

Market Stabilization

The discussion of stabilization policy started from the fact that raw material prices are substantially more volatile than most other prices and that for many raw material producers the lack of alternative employment opportunities involved special hardship under conditions of falling output. There was general agreement that while the raw material outlook may promise a substantially greater stability than had been possible in a period characterized by two wars and a severe depression, even a continuation of high levels of industrial activity could not be expected to eliminate a serious degree of raw material instability.

While agreeing on the nature of the problem, discussion in the section evidenced little agreement on what needs to be done. Among the stabilization devices discussed were international commodity agreements, buffer stocks, and the use of a military stockpile for purposes of economic stabilization. There was a consensus that the latter device had little merit since in the accumulation of a stockpile, security is the overriding consideration and consequently sales from the stockpile should not be permitted except in emergencies. There was general agreement, however, that purchases for the stockpile could be accomplished with much less market dislocation than has in fact characterized U.S. purchases since the end of World War II.

With respect to intergovernmental commodity arrangements there was general agreement that price and quantity regulation is a complex and difficult task. Some doubted that it could be done effectively, if at all. Others felt that the United States had become heavily involved in market regulation domestically, particularly in agricultural commodities, and that we should be willing at least to attempt to work out multilateral arrangements recognizing the complexities and difficulties involved.

The discussion of international buffer stocks, which are arrangements for supporting falling prices and holding down price advances, indicated no marked enthusiasm. It was pointed out that such a sales and purchases program involved the determination of a long-run equilibrium price and that in the face of structural cost and demand changes this was a difficult job. It was also indicated that political pressures either to buy or to sell might be intense and that the costs of holding stocks large enough to exert a stabilizing effect would be large.

In general it was felt that although raw material price instability presents a serious problem both to exporting and importing countries, the difficulties of dealing adequately with the problem are most serious. In the view of some of the participants, however, these difficulties were not considered to be insuperable, and the seriousness of the problem was felt by them to require that this matter should be kept under continuous review.

EDWARD S. MASON
December 4, 1953

Section *VII*

Chairman
EARL P. STEVENSON, President
Arthur D. Little, Inc.

Co-Chairman
R. E. GIBSON, Director
Johns Hopkins University
Applied Physics Laboratory

Steering Committee and Advisers

Steering Committee: ELI GINZBERG, Professor of Economics, Graduate School of Business, Columbia University · COLUMBUS O'D. ISELIN, Senior Physical Oceanographer, Woods Hole Oceanographic Institution · VINCENT SAUCHELLI, Director of Agricultural Research, Davison Chemical Corporation · THEODORE W. SCHULTZ, Chairman, Department of Economics, University of Chicago · PAUL B. SEARS, Chairman, Yale University Conservation Program · WILLIAM H. STEAD, Resource Management Consultant, Washington · *Discussion Leader:* EMIL OTT, Director of Research, Hercules Powder Company · *Rapporteur:* HOWARD MEYERHOFF, Executive Director, Scientific Manpower Commission · *Assistant to the Chairman:* ROBERT G. SNIDER, Vice-President-Director of Research, The Conservation Foundation.

Major Topics

1. THE BASIC CHALLENGE TO RESEARCH IN THE RESOURCES FIELD
    Introductory Speaker: PAUL B. SEARS

2. THE WAY AHEAD FOR RESEARCH IN—

    RENEWABLE RESOURCES
        Introductory Speaker: STANLEY A. CAIN, Chairman, Department of Conservation, University of Michigan

    ENERGY RESOURCES
        Introductory Speaker: PHILIP SPORN, President, American Gas and Electric Service Corporation

    NONRENEWABLE RESOURCES
        Introductory Speaker: THOMAS B. NOLAN, Assistant Director, U. S. Geological Survey

    SEA AND AIR RESOURCES
        Introductory Speaker: ATHELSTAN SPILHAUS, Dean, Institute of Technology, University of Minnesota

3. FUNDAMENTAL RESEARCH AS A RESOURCE
    Introductory Speaker: R. E. GIBSON

4. PEOPLE AND ORGANIZATION
        Introductory Speaker: PAUL WEISS, Professor of Zoology, University of Chicago

5. AN ANALYSIS OF COMMON PROBLEMS
    Discussion Leader: EMIL OTT

Approximately 175 persons attended the Research Section. The 151 who registered formally are listed on pages 404-7. The section did not divide into subsections, but met as a single group for each of its four half-day sessions. Discussion was built around the five major topics listed above. The final topic—An Analysis of Common Problems—was essentially a pulling-together of previous discussions; accordingly, the main points from the record of that session have been incorporated in the earlier material.

PROBLEMS IN
RESOURCES RESEARCH

THE ENTIRE MID-CENTURY CONFERENCE took a deep interest in research. Each of the other seven sections gave a large share of its attention to the needs and possibilities in its own particular resource area. But in Section VII discussion of research ranged across the entire resource field. Viewing research as a resource in itself, this section considered means of developing and utilizing that resource and explored fundamental problems that require long-range action.

Emphasis was on future requirements rather than on present needs. The section chairman made this clear in his introductory remarks: "Our job is essentially one of looking ahead in terms of the research that should be undertaken now, in order that the next generation will not be handicapped in attempting to solve the problems which we may unwittingly pass on to them. Our purpose, consequently, is to take inventory of where we are, to study the problems in their perspective, to gain some sense of priorities and some understanding of the interrelations of these problems."

This approach focused attention on those problems that involve long-range economic and social considerations. As a by-product of such a comprehensive review, some light was shed on broad issues that went beyond the narrowed approach of other sections—conservation of nonrenewable resources, for instance, or possible changes in the total patterns of requirements for resources.

The steering committee working paper had suggested several questions as bases for discussion: What are apt to be the critical problems of the next generation? What is the role of fundamental research in their solution? How should we go about these urgent tasks? How are we to enhance our capacity for research?

In response, Dr. Sears, the initial speaker, broached the underlying problem of whether or not there is a top limit to expansion prescribed by a finite resource base. It was evident that even those participants who described themselves as optimists felt the technological requirements to be immense. If we are to provide an adequate foundation for meeting tomorrow's demands, research, both basic and applied, cannot be permitted to lose momentum.

Projecting itself 25 years into the future, the section asked: What research should have been started by the middle 1950's to meet the needs of 1975-80? The road ahead was explored for research along four specific lines—renewable and nonrenewable resources, energy resources, and resources of the sea and air. Leading problems and possible approaches towards solution in each area were discussed. The common threads that ran through these separate lines of inquiry were drawn together later in the discussions of Fundamental Research and People and Organization.

Little attempt was made to set up a strict differentiation between basic and applied research, although there was strong evidence of need for more attention to the former. Problems connected with a better evaluation of research results were actively discussed.

The training and utilization of scientific manpower deeply concerned the section as a whole. Participants disagreed only as to the relative emphasis that should be placed upon financial or social incentives. The group also considered—with wide differences of opinion—the types of organizations best suited to fostering research.

Much importance was attached to the need for increasing public and Congressional awareness of the value of research as a national resource.

The Basic Challenge to Research
in the Resources Field

FROM THE RECORD

PAUL B. SEARS (Yale University): At the outset we must make the assumption that rational and humane individuals want to see the human adventure continue without being throttled by a lack of the materials and energy. But beyond this point there arises a serious difference of opinion. On the one hand there are biologists, geographers, demographers, and doubtless some historians who take it for granted that the present increase in world population and rise in the standard of living with consequent pressure upon natural resources cannot continue without disaster. On the other hand, there is an impressive group which holds that we have, in human resourcefulness itself, an unlimited resource which, by exploration, invention, and organization, will be able to meet any emergency that may arise.

As between the two groups of opinion, the odds at present are heavily in favor of support for the kind of research and action the optimists advocate.

The process whereby man and resources are interrelated involves three complex and dynamic patterns, all functionally interrelated. These are (a) the resources themselves, (b) the human cultures sustained by them, and (c) the numerical pressure of population upon them. If something like this is correct, the basic problem becomes one of trends, rates, and limits.

The surface area of our planet, though vast, is finite, and the same may be said of the energy impinging upon it. Populations, however, tend to increase geometrically. And, so far as we know, the limiting factors, when they do operate, are harsh. Had Malthus never lived, his formulation would have been suggested by the weight of biological observation and experiment. Yet clearly it carries little weight with an influential sector of scientific and lay opinion, or the results would be obvious in the present emphasis on research.

Where is the present burden of proof for the assertion that a finite planet cannot support an infinitely expanding population of a single species—Man—and the economy which goes with it? The answer, it seems to me, is clear from the kind of scientific activity that gets the bulk of encouragement and support. One has only to compare the amount and quality of research devoted to the conversion of materials and energy for consumption with that devoted to the problem of human fertility and its consequences.

To get the evidence, whichever way it may lead, seems to me the fundamental problem for mankind at this juncture.

The present encouragement for study of this type of biological process is not impressive. The best young minds are being drawn into the exciting fields opened up by the application of physics and chemistry to the activity of the individual organism, neglecting the great pattern of which the organism is a part. It is this pattern and its laws that cry for attention. Much may be done by judicious financial encouragement. A great deal more can be accomplished, it seems to me, by teaching science in context with the rest of human knowledge and experience.

This is something not now done in a great many cases. It is a curious paradox that we strain the principles of physical science to their limits in our study of what goes on within the living cell, leaving untouched the operations of those principles upon the world community of living organisms.

The use and care of natural resources is in the end a problem of human values and behavior. The importance of the social sciences, particularly as they are concerned with normal cultural processes, cannot be overemphasized. But I have gone on the assumption that values and behavior shape themselves in the long run in accordance with ideas. Every great religious and ethical system bears witness that men tend to govern their actions to fit their ideas of the kind of universe in which they believe themselves to be living.

I would not for a moment discourage the continuing search for new sources and new processes, for substitutes, and substitutes for substitutes if need be. But I would urge the clearest understanding of the difference between research that is fundamental and that which is merely palliative, designed to meet emergencies as they arise in the hope of eating cake and having it, too. Only when this distinction is clear can we undertake research of a third type, truly remedial research designed to fit our activities to the universe of reality and make the very best of it throughout a continuing future.

It is unlikely that the central problem I have outlined will be solved at a stroke. It is much more likely to clear up gradually through the accretion of evidence of many kinds.

At this point, I want to offer some concrete suggestions: The rate of increased urbanization, waterproofing the earth's surface while it increases astronomically the demand for water, needs careful examination. The possibility that a continent, despite rainfall, may undergo slow desiccation at human hands, deserves inquiry by a variety of disciplines, including that of the historiographer. So, too, does the long record of climate change, now opening up to investigation through the fossil pollen analysis of deep lake sediments. Finally, there is the problem of human fertility and its consequences. The whole process of human reproduction, physiological, psychological, and social, should have continuing study. Cheap and efficient means of contraception should be sought for and made available by those who believe in voluntary parenthood to great groups of mankind, who, like the Islamic world and apparently the Hindu, can readily incorporate it into their ethical systems.

Meanwhile, we may hope that biologists and ethnographers and historians will continue their researches with skill and open minds to find out whether any species, including our own, can transcend the physical limitations of its environment.

In the final summing-up session of the Research Section, Mr. Sears made these further points:

MR. SEARS: The central problem is to understand that man is no exception to certain great biological laws, and that he increases his numbers indefinitely at his own peril, particularly if he fails to look ahead and make the necessary adjustments. So instead of lying down and letting the juggernaut of population and technology run over us, we have an obligation to know what is happening.

Obviously, there is great need for a better mutual understanding between the people who are back of the two basic differences of approach I mentioned earlier. Few engineers have any opportunity for valid experiences in the field of biology; and conversely, too many of the people who go into biological studies have an emotional block against the exact sciences.

The need for population research was stressed by several participants.

RICHARD H. GOODWIN (Connecticut College): Man has one unique capacity over all other animals, namely, he has developed tools by which he can voluntarily limit his own population. Sociologically, perhaps, we are not ready for this, but it is an area where we should not neglect careful research.

ELI GINZBERG (Columbia University): I would throw back at the conservationist that the question of population is not quite as obscure as it has been made out to be. Even if it were, one of our major recommendations should be to push population research work further than it has been pushed because many things begin to fall into line if one really gets a clearer perspective about population movements throughout the world.

The rate of utilization depends not only on the number of people requiring or using material resources, but also upon their habits of utilization. Can we afford unlimited use of materials, energies, and services?

MR. GINZBERG: Can the people who are working in conservation research come up with evidence pointing to the necessity of introducing specific social controls against the normal drift toward free use of resources? Until they do so, there is really going to be no good reason to interfere with the expansionary influence in our economy.

EDGAR McINNIS (Canadian Institute of International Affairs): The use of resources depends to a very large extent on the structure of the society and the habits that society has developed.

The great barrier to successful conservation programs is not the lack of knowledge, but the resistance through social and economic habits of a wide variety of groups within the community.

STANLEY A. CAIN (University of Michigan): The physical level of living that we enjoy is an extremely recent phenomenon and even today it applies to a relatively small percentage of the world's people. I hate to be a gloomy prophet, but I can see signs that even within my own economy, I may find it necessary to revise what I really need of a biological origin.

FAITH M. WILLIAMS (Bureau of Labor Statistics): The factors affecting consumption levels and patterns haven't been studied for the United States as a whole since the middle 1930's. If we are to make an adequate plan for use of resources in the future, we must study these factors and trends. We do not know at the present time, for example, the extent of dietary inadequacy in this country or enough about the reasons for it.

ROBERT L. LOFTNESS (North American Aviation, Inc., California): President Roosevelt said before the last war that one-third of the nation was ill-fed, ill-clothed, and ill-housed. I do not know whether he meant that the other two-thirds was overfed, overclothed, and overhoused, but in general I think so.

Although most of us are overfed, we are still poorly fed. Proper nutrition and diet standards have been established, but few of us bother to regard them—and we pay for our disregard in a heavy toll of stomach ailments.

Without a doubt we are often oversheltered. Certainly we overheat our homes and offices. And, generally, the men, at least, are overclothed.

MR. CAIN: Many American demands are not set by American biological needs. They are set by keeping up with the neighbors or by those who set the styles.

RICHARD MEIER (University of Chicago): How much of this energy is actually necessary? By applying present scientific knowledge it looks as though one could set up a civilization as comfortable and convenient as that of the United States, which would consume only 8 million Calories of fuel per person per year, instead of the 80 million used today by Americans.

PHILIP SPORN (American Gas and Electric Service Corporation): Can we, and if we can, should we, turn the clock back? In essence, that is what you are saying. I don't think we can. We cannot continue the improvement of the lot of the average person, except by more and more displacing him as an energy producer.

I don't think there is any kind of solution along the road of going back to the kind of thing that I have seen within the last year in the Near East, where you can travel along the road and see a human being, a fine-looking specimen of humanity, on a wheel, pumping water. And after 12 hours of work, you find that he has generated exactly 1 kilowatt-hour of energy, which we produce in one of our fine plants at a production cost, exclusive of capital cost, of about 3 mills.

WILLIAM C. DUCKWORTH (Tennessee Corporation): Our standard of living would not be decreased if the horsepower of an automobile were 50 instead of 200.

EMIL OTT (Hercules Powder Company): There you have touched on a definition of values. There is a difference between high horsepower and small horsepower in an auto-

mobile. But whether that difference is a true value or an artificial value remains to be seen and is, perhaps, a region for research.

JOHN R. MENKE (Nuclear Development Associates): I don't think Dr. Meier was proposing that we take a step backward, or that this country try to confine its expansion in the use of its natural resources. I am sure that he was addressing himself to the first goal that a different society might set up as it got started; such a less fortunate society might set a very useful, profitable goal, entirely different from ours.

In that sense it is valuable to talk of what you can do with more limited resources. We have been very much oriented on the natural resources and the economic situation of our own country, which I think is a little bit too narrow a viewpoint.

MISS WILLIAMS: Going from social to physical research, we have almost no emphasis on research on measures for the durability and the utility of consumers' goods. Consumers now go into the market and buy, in many cases, very blindly.

MR. SEARS: Many corporations, which thrive by encouraging the most reckless extravagance on the part of the public, practice the most rigorous economy in their organizations, or they couldn't stay in business five months.

MR. GINZBERG: In our concern about the great rate at which this rich economy is consuming goods, it may be pointed out that more and more of our total national effort is moving over into the service area.

The Way Ahead for Research in Renewable Resources

FROM THE RECORD

MR. CAIN: Our central problem in renewable resources is that of maintaining and, where possible, increasing the natural capital

and its yield of useful and desirable products and services. Our frame of reference should therefore include not only the problems of material products and market economics, but also the services and benefits that are less easily measured.

American history has been an extremely favorable and fortuitous one, but we do not know whether or not the American dream of an ever-expanding economy can for long be supported by the resource base or whether there is a limit to growth.

Our success in pushing back the frontiers and in raising the level of living has depended in part on our utilization of this resource capital, as well as on our utilization of other people's resource capital. We have not balanced our natural resource budget and, to a certain extent, our ever-rising level of living has been at the expense of the potentialities of the future.

I want to emphasize what I think is the ecological nature of the problem we face in the renewable resources. The renewable resources are interrelated. We know that water affects vegetation and vegetation affects water. We know that both affect soil and soil affects both, and so on through the whole gamut of renewable resources. It is like an elastic web, and this elastic web extends beyond the interrelations among the resources to the interrelations among all the aspects of man's culture which produces, processes, distributes, and uses these resources.

Because man is the creator of culture and is at the same time its creature, the problems of resource use are only partially scientific and technological. They are also—perhaps largely—social, economic, and political problems. We cannot definitely realize particular research problems in the absence of the situation in which these problems are created and the answers that are obtained will be applied. Only a deeper and wider understanding of the nature of human ecological problems can bring about the necessary social and financial support for their prosecution and the needed wedding of physical and social fields of research. Here I find the greatest underdeveloped area in the national research program.

One of the very greatest difficulties behind any work with interrelated resources, despite our wealth and despite the diffusion of knowl-

edge throughout our society, is to get adequate, widespread, and at the same time effective surveying, inventory, and analysis. When the budgetary ax falls, whether in Congress, in state legislatures, or in universities, it falls first on that kind of activity. Furthermore, these are not always activities that we can reasonably ask industry and business to support.

Research must be continually pushed, for tomorrow's technology has to rest on today's basic knowledge. Consequently, planning, activating, and facilitating research must have both short- and long-range aspects. In a healthy situation the two are closely integrated. In actual situations short- and long-range investigations often lose their coordination and become increasingly separated with the result that both are piecemeal, inadequate, and belated.

In fields subject to rapid technological change and with a comparatively large and quick return on investments, research and development are being carried on by industry itself. In such fast-moving industries 3 to 10 percent of sales are regularly allotted to research. In slow-moving industries, however, the figure is more likely to be 1 percent or less. Expenditures for research and development by government, industry, educational institutions, and foundations have for a decade exceeded a billion dollars annually. But what is spent for basic research in the renewable resources is "peanuts," and we don't even know how many peanuts.

If one takes into account the human resources—in relation to which the other resources take their sole meaning for man—expenditures for research on human biology, ecology, sociology, psychology, etc., are likewise relatively small. For example, with growing populations at home and abroad making more difficult the struggle toward a favorable relationship between people's needs and the resource base that supplies them, American expenditures on human reproduction, including sterility and fertility, conception and contraception, are estimated at not more than half a million dollars a year.

In summing up, I want to reiterate the need for support of long-range problems, in spite of the strong trend toward diversion of investigators to the solution of short-range problems. We need also a more adequate financial foundation for basic research in all of the fields. What I think we need to study —and this is a problem in itself—is an equitable division of responsibilities for the various types of research that need to be carried on.

Turning to the renewable resources, and to man himself, the problems are largely ecological. They are difficult problems of interrelations among the various resources and problems of interrelations between resource-use patterns and resource-use processes and what goes on among people in government, in politics, and in economics. The central problems lie in interrelations and call for cooperative efforts and research teams.

This, in turn, raises the question of finding, training, and employing those generalists who can help us coordinate the invaluable efforts of the specialists.

The need for surveying, inventory, and analysis raised some questions and led to a discussion of the undeveloped resource that lies in data which have already been accumulated.

JOE W. PEOPLES (Wesleyan University): The oil companies have done a magnificent work in research in geology, but one of the national problems is that only about 11 percent of the United States is mapped geologically on published maps. The oil companies undoubtedly have in their files maps of large areas. If it would be possible for some of this mapping to be released it would help greatly in broad studies of basic materials of all kinds.

PHILIP NEFF (University of California, Los Angeles): We are pouring too much of our resources into the mass collection of data, without devoting sufficient resources to the development of hypotheses essential to the selection of the data to be collected and the use of data presently available.

R. E. GIBSON (Johns Hopkins University Applied Physics Laboratory): We have a woeful burden of ignorance, and an almost intolerable burden of knowledge. We have got to handle our data and our knowledge with less expenditure of manpower, and the only way I see of doing it is to combine the knowledge that is coming out of our study of the brain and nervous system, with our knowledge of implementation by machines. It may be quite a while before it is done, but it will be a very fascinating problem.

Work in forest genetics was offered as an example of the need for fundamental coordinated research.

SCOTT S. PAULEY (Cabot Foundation, Harvard University): I was very pleased that Dr. Cain defined ecology in such a broad manner, because many of our forest practices developed when ecologists had a much more restricted definition of their field. There was a tendency to place primary emphasis upon environment while almost entirely neglecting the genetic characteristics of the tree and other organisms.

Much of the publicity given to forest genetics has emphasized the breeding aspects, which is a direct application of forest genetics. But fundamental to that is the research for variations in heredity which will eventually lead to improved races in forest trees.

I would like to emphasize that the fundamental research in forest genetics that has been going on is so closely tied in with numerous ecological, physiological, and other related factors, that team research is needed.

ALBERT G. SNOW (U.S. Forest Service): I agree with Dr. Pauley that fundamental research in forest genetics is important. At the same time, I would like to make a plea for concomitant research in applied forest genetics. Every year there is increasing interest in renewing our forest resources by artificial means. To do that, we have to be able to apply the small amount of knowledge we now have. There are specific places from which we can get better seed to plant in given locations.

The Way Ahead for Research
in Energy Resources

FROM THE RECORD

MR. SPORN: One of the obvious areas of spectacular growth during the next quarter century will unquestionably be in the demand for and utilization of energy resources. A two-fold growth in the total energy demand is predicted during this period, accompanied by an increase in the utilization of energy in the electrical form from 440 billion kilowatt-hours in 1953 to an estimated 1,600 billion kilowatt-hours in 1978. The development of this energy demand is essential to the continuing rise in the welfare level of the mass of our population.

This increased demand can be brought about and it can be met, but there are a great number of technological problems which must be solved in the process. Successful solutions to these problems will depend on: (a) continued availability of power in substantially any quantity needed by an area in order to encourage the development of instruments and media for the use of energy; (b) a continuation of the development of electrical utilization devices and methods; and (c) a continuation of the historically favorable cost relationship of energy vis-à-vis other items in the socio-economic scheme of things.

The problems that will be presented in any effort to supply this much power 25 years hence will fall roughly into three classes: (a) problems in growth in size and concentration of power facilities, (b) problems of maintaining and improving efficiency, and (c) problems of the better utilization of resources to keep the whole system in balance. Looked at in this light, it becomes clear that our electric generators will continue to be powered by steam. The contributions of tidal, wind, and solar power to the power supply are likely to be only negligible. Hydro power is unlikely to supply more than 20 percent of the total power supply. It is still too early to evaluate the position of nuclear power as a competitive source, but over the next quarter century its contribution will probably not be very great. Yet it is quite important to continue to carry on the fundamental work at the various national laboratories and to provide the foundation for a rapid rise in momentum, which may be expected as soon as a point is reached when economic gain incentive can be visualized by private enterprise.

Conventional fuels are clearly the major source of electrical energy which will be available and, of the fuels, coal will have to pick up more and more of the burden dropped by gas and oil. The fuel to produce this energy by 1978 may reach a figure equivalent to some 445 million tons of coal, with coal itself accounting for some 360 million tons of the above. This represents an increase of some 400 percent over the energy coal produced in 1953.

Despite a relatively large coal reserve, economy of utilization is highly desirable; it can be achieved through improvement of coal technology and the solution of many problems involved in the energy conversion process. Further research is clearly needed on the combustion of coal and disposal of resultant by-products. For example, the problems arising out of the discharge into the atmosphere of finely divided particulate matter and of gases resulting from that much coal burned, may become difficult— perhaps even acutely so. Studies in meteorology will be particularly pertinent to such atmospheric pollution. Over the next decade or two, exploration of our available coal resources and analysis of their chemical composition would appear highly profitable. Underground gasification needs to be explored further if we are to be able to utilize otherwise uneconomical coal resources. One other problem facing us in fuel is that the coal industry may be subject to very difficult economic competitive forces over the next decade and then, after a protracted condition of relative starvation, will be asked to pick up and do a giant's job in a national emergency.

A major potential opportunity for economy in the use of our fuel resources over the next 25 years and beyond is in the field of residential and industrial heating through further development of the heat pump, possibly in connection with heat storage and utilization of solar energy. The development of the fuel cell, involving direct conversion of heat energy into electrical energy, may not reach the point of commercial application within the next quarter century, but it is possible that important advances will be made with this interesting and potentially highly efficient conversion process.

In bringing about and meeting this tremendous growth in energy demand, we are faced with the necessity of creating some $4 billion to $5 billion of new productive capital facilities in power each year, as well as large additional amounts of new capital facilities in other related industries. No authentic answer has yet been given to the question of whether our economic system is creating new capital at a rate fast enough to make possible a balanced socio-economic system of the kind visualized.

Beyond the question of adequate capital resources, we must devote attention to the question of assuring adequate human resources. There is serious question as to whether or not the supply of engineers is adequate to meet our needs with regard to both numbers and breadth of training.

Who should undertake the necessary research and how should it be stimulated?

WILLIAM V. DOERING (Yale University): Mr. Sporn, how many of the problems you mentioned would not be advanced at a pretty rapid rate just as the normal response of industry today?

MR. SPORN: The problems that I am fearful will not be advanced in natural response of industry to opportunity are those that are either too far removed from a point of economic return or cover too wide a segment of the spectrum. It is when questions either lack immediate impact or apply across the entire spectrum and need to be covered on a broader range that we need to be concerned. In many cases we go on to a certain point, and then, finding the financial incentives to go beyond that to be for the present rather small, we stop. Yet, if we look far enough ahead we can see that we ought not to lose momentum. Research can lose momentum very quickly.

WILLIAM J. COPPOC (The Texas Company): It seems to me that the primary thing we are talking about is the interchange of ideas, keeping these problems in the scientific press or in scientific discussions to a point where people are aware of them. I think the solution comes along naturally if those involved with different fields of activity are aware of the problems existing in related fields.

PAUL E. KLOPSTEG (National Science Foundation): Does Mr. Sporn have some suggestion as to how the responsibility may be divided or shared, particularly when there seems to be some uneasiness in industry that government is moving into research areas where industry should be doing the work?

MR. SPORN: That is the matter that I would think needs exhaustive get-together and discussion. I don't believe there is as much conflict between industry and government as would appear on the surface. The minute there is any real incentive of economic gain, development will spring up in the necessary activities to carry the project forward.

Mr. Sporn was unable to be present at the final summing-up session of the Research Section. In his place, Mr. Menke made the following remarks:

MR. MENKE: Mr. Sporn considers himself limited to the provision of electrical energy, which is not altogether a necessary limitation. He has addressed himself to the advancement of the present systems through higher pressures and temperatures, and through development of different systems, especially away from the evaporation of water and steam, to the use of gas turbines.

These are not, in my mind, areas which require new investment in research or that should concern this Conference. They are, in the very large sense, adequately supported by government and private industry for business and military purposes.

There are other important new technologies for energy, perhaps less well-supported. The fuel cell, which Dr. Sporn mentioned, is just beginning to come near the threshold of utility, although it has been a subject of research for a great many years. The problems are those of economics, of geography, and of physics, especially in the solid state area of physics.

Solar energy is a large resource which is not being adequately attacked. But I would direct attention not to the direct use of solar energy through house heating and that kind of thing, but especially to photosynthesis and the use of

solar energy to provide another salable form of energy, food.

Furthermore, carbon dioxide is a major product of a power plant, and now no more than a waste. But, come a photosynthetic economy, one would be keeping the carbon dioxide balance more even, since one of the major concerns in a photosynthetic industry will be the provision of carbon dioxide.

EARL P. STEVENSON (Arthur D. Little, Inc.): Algae are a very useful tool for the study of solar energy, and raise the question: "How do single-celled organisms like algae absorb solar energy, and by what cycle do they convert that energy into carbohydrates, proteins, and fats?"

We can't design a factory to grow algae, because we don't know the mechanism of the conversion of solar energy, but if we could, we should be able to convert algae into useful food products at a rate five times that of the best conversion by conventional agriculture.

The Way Ahead for Research in Nonrenewable Resources

FROM THE RECORD

THOMAS B. NOLAN (U.S. Geological Survey): If we view our assignment as an attempt to point out means of reaching a solution that is good for only a finite and relatively small number of future generations, and if we also neglect the troublesome matters of trade barriers and related political questions, I think that research (both basic and applied) may be expected to yield some positive and helpful means of meeting requirements for the nonrenewable resources.

There are three broad fields of research that seem to be especially promising.

The first field has to do with research on the origin of mineral deposits and related applied research aimed at the development of tools by which we can detect such deposits. This is the most attractive for immediate ap-

plicability of results, and one for which we have a larger base of past accomplishments on which to build.

Each of the general classes of mineral deposits, three insofar as exploration is concerned, presents a somewhat different research requirement.

The first class includes such materials as coal, limestone, and gravel, which occur in extensive layers close to the surface of the earth and which are generally uniform in composition. As such, they pose few problems in exploration for the research geologist.

A second class of commodity normally occurs as concentrations within such sedimentary layers. Oil, potash, and some iron ore deposits are examples. For petroleum, particularly, there have been comprehensive and very well supported research programs over the past 30 years directed toward the origin of the substance, and toward the development of tools by which the concentrations can be determined beneath the earth's surface.

Research on the origin of the third class of deposits may be just well under way. These have formed as a result of processes related to the emplacement of bodies of igneous rock, and are relatively small and erratically distributed. The commodities obtained from them include copper, lead, zinc, tungsten, and talc. This research, which will include work on the factors that localized the deposits, will be difficult and wide-ranging. Similarly, the development of tools to locate concealed deposits of this kind will be a difficult task as the targets to be looked for are much smaller than those of the petroleum geophysicists.

It is probable that such researches will be stimulated by an increasing realization that most of the outcropping domestic deposits have been discovered and that foreign exploration has been made relatively unattractive because of trade barriers. Moreover, there seem to be sound geologic reasons to believe that within 1,000 feet of the present surface, there may be something on the order of five times the presently known supply. The past few years have seen the development of such new and effective tools as the airborne magnetometer and scintillometer and such new techniques as those of geophysical and geochemical prospecting. I suspect the future will require, and produce, devices that will permit the measurement of increasingly minute differences in the physical and chemical properties of rocks at increasingly great distances below the surface, and that these will be the tools by which we may discover buried or concealed ore bodies.

The second broad field of research will be directed towards a better knowledge of the distribution of elements in the earth's crust in concentrations too small to be presently workable. Two sorts of problems will have to be solved. One will be the development of suitable methods of exploration for these low-grade deposits; the other, the development of practical methods for beneficiating such material.

Research on exploration may well take two related paths. One will be a systematic collection of analytical data to show the distribution of one or more elements or commodities in various types of geologic environments. The other will be to determine the principles that control the distribution of the elements in nature and the factors that cause their relative concentration in one environment and relative absence in another.

Emphasis will probably be given to recovery methods which will permit successive reductions in the amount of ore to be treated, as well as to processes that will allow regeneration of reagents required by the process. I personally expect much wider application of one or another of the relatively new chromatography techniques.

By such methods it is conceivable that a whole rock formation may be mined and treated for a number of elements, few or none of which are individually present in commercial amounts. The phosphorea formation of the Rocky Mountain region is such a unit; it is thought to contain more than a half-dozen commodities which have a combined gross value of around $5 a ton.

The third broad field of research is likely to be concerned with the basic physical and chemical properties of the nonrenewable resources, with the objective of developing synthetic or substitute materials from either renewable resources or from more abundant and more accessible nonrenewable resources. It is possible that future scientists and engineers may actually invent or create out of abundant materials new substances that have predictable and specific desired properties.

Better utilization is another appropriate field for research, but, like substitution, it should be very largely controlled by a better knowledge of the physical and chemical properties of materials. I suspect that utilization, as such, will be most likely improved by better education of the consumer, and this is a research problem for the social scientist rather than the technologist.

I am convinced that through one or another of the methods of improved exploration techniques, exploration of presently unavailable supplies, or programs of substitution and improved utilization, there is a comforting probability that raw materials for our civilization can be obtained for a very long period of time in the future. This, however, can be attained only by establishing a suitable economic environment to attract industry participation, and by maintaining a supply of competent and well-trained scientists and engineers.

At the final summing-up session, Mr. Nolan further emphasized the need for fundamental research.

Perhaps my discussion of research in the nonrenewable resources unduly emphasized known techniques, immediate returns, instrumentation, and people.

I did not mean to imply that we must not foster basic research as well. At least equal emphasis should be placed on an intensive study of the fundamental controls that have led to the localization of these resources. Such basic research is going to need not only geologists but chemists, physicists, and biologists.

Several speakers touched on problems of gathering and using basic geologic data.

MR. PEOPLES: As new methods are developed for getting basic data, we are going to become much more aware that we have not made proper use of the methods that have already been developed. For example, people who have used the airborne magnetometer find it of little use unless it is followed up by basic work on the ground.

P. M. HURLEY (Massachusetts Institute of Technology): There is need for research on instrumentation by which we geologists can rather rapidly analyze large numbers of samples without the laborious techniques now required.

MR. PEOPLES: In the search for water, information obtained by drilling is in many cases almost completely wasted. In some states records are obtained and kept, but they are far from adequate, and we are going to have to spend other energy and resources to do the same thing over in the future generations.

JULIAN W. FEISS (Kennecott Copper Corporation): The researcher in geology has been bogged down by the mass of deductive rather than inductive reasoning and only recently has he begun to take a mathematical approach to the distribution of elements in the earth's crust.

Can there be a nonrenewable resource?

MR. MENKE: In looking at nonrenewable resources in the large sense and in the long-distant future, there is no such thing as a nonrenewable resource.

The nonrenewable resource has been moved from the earth, used, and remains somewhere on the earth to be used again. The geologists will have to deal with the scrap dealers, who will be an important resource in the very long-distant future.

The Way Ahead for Research in Sea and Air Resources

FROM THE RECORD

ATHELSTAN F. SPILHAUS (University of Minnesota): The chief resource of the sea is not fish, not salts, not magnesium, nor any of the myriad of valuable things that can be extracted from it—the greatest resource of the sea is water. And it is by the interaction of air and sea plus energy of sunshine that this water is made available to us.

The basic processes of evaporation from the ocean, condensation in the air, and precipitation on the land constitute the essential workings of the earth's solar distillery. The trouble with water is that it is unsuitably distributed in time and space, and consequently one of our major objectives should be towards means of time and space control of all phases of the natural water cycle.

We should lay the groundwork of observation and understanding now, if we expect to utilize properly this resource of sea and air when we need it. The meteorologists-oceanographers-hydrologists who are to attack this problem of total water control will need to be involved in every aspect, not only of that part of the cycle in the oceans and the air but in the way in which controls of water are exercised by the engineers on the land surface.

The basic purpose of the rainfall part of climate control is to take water from places of excess to places of deficit and to even up the times of excess and deficit at the same place.

In space control of rainfall the extreme view is that none of nature's distillate which falls on land should be allowed to flow back into the sea without being used to the maximum extent. If we could change the hydrologic cycle by increasing that portion which returns to sea through transpiration of plants, then we could reduce and perhaps eliminate the need for any flow of fresh water into the sea.

Sand culture in deserts is possible if there is enough water. Artificial canals of the scale of the Nile River could make another part of the Sahara productive by the end of this century. However, such large projects will affect climate, and we should understand how before they are carried too far.

Suitable time distribution of water supply can be accomplished by artificial storage of water above the ground or below in natural underground basins. The use of aboveground or underground storage must be determined by prediction of what the effect of manifold dams will be on climate and also by consideration of the competing demands for the use of land.

I have spoken so far only of the obvious brute force methods of mammoth engineering works. Possibly, with much less energy, both time and space distribution of water and heat can be accomplished by controlling the formation of rainfall before it hits the land.

The control of evaporation is conceivable. Mulches are already used—reforestation is attempted—although the true effects of these on evapo-transpiration are not really known. Deserts occur, not where there is low rainfall necessarily, but wherever evaporation exceeds rainfall and the amount of dew. Some plants absorb dew at night and do not transpire during the day; and they bloom in the desert—a hint perhaps at a mechanism of reducing evaporation in these areas.

So far we have considered the air-ocean water resource in relation to land, but it is well not to forget the effect of the cycle of water and other materials on the sea itself and its products.

Of course, complete land-water conservation would greatly shrink the importance of soil conservation—if all the water returns to the sea by transpiration, no soil can be lost except by wind erosion. On the other hand, the fertility of the sea for the production of fish might be affected by cutting off the supply of nutrients leached from land. Here again, however, if we understood what materials are important to the optimum production of ocean fish it would seem that an artificial and controlled addition of these in the right places would result in an improvement.

Ultimately, breeding, feeding, and harvesting controls must be devised for the farming of the sea. Perhaps the culmination of these is far in the future, but the basic understanding should be laid now.

From work presently under way, there are indications of an intimate relationship between atmospheric processes such as winds, the resultant changes in the oceanic physical environment, and the productivity of the fish—hence, the catch. There are indications, too, that shifts in the major current systems—shifts hardly detectable by present observational programs—may be responsible for migrations of the fish populations. These ocean current shifts depend on atmospheric circulation changes, and a study of the weather map in the future may tell the fisherman where to go for his optimum catch.

For long-range weather forecasting, a study of the deep currents in the sea may provide a factor in prediction. Just as in the atmosphere, periodic pulses or outbreaks of cold bottom water effect the transfer of cold water from higher to lower latitudes. At periods of these outbreaks the bottom currents may be much swifter than our present completely inadequate measurements indicate.

What should we do now to develop the resource of the air and sea?

From the point of view of the water cycle of the atmospheric heat engine and always having *control* as the ultimate objective: (1) We must study evaporation and evapotranspiration of plants; (2) we must understand the mechanism of nuclei, both natural and artificial, in the atmosphere, and the physics of condensation and precipitation, with a view to developing artificial stimulants and inhibitors of precipitation; (3) we should consider the uses of natural polar ice as a possible source of fresh water and consider also the correlated effect any large-scale effort of this kind would have on climate; and (4) we should investigate methods of utilizing fog and dew.

From the point of view of exploring and developing the food resources in the sea, we should also approach the problem from the point of view of control: (1) We should study fish as sensitive indicating instruments of their physical-chemical environment; (2) we should study the actual needs of the particular fish or plants in the ocean with a view to ultimately introducing the materials artificially; (3) we should improve fishing methods so that a controlled number, size, and so forth can be taken; (4) we should study the habits, likes and dislikes of ocean life with the ultimate aim of artificially confining them.

How should we organize to do it? (1) We should build up a global network of *observation* in sea and air; (2) we should assist those institutions where scientists in many different fields may devote their combined efforts to the problem of *understanding* the ocean and the atmosphere; (3) we should add engineers to this group to keep in mind and work out the beginnings of control.

To summarize in one sentence: If the control of the sea and air and the useful things in them is kept clearly as the objective in this search, it will then be an objective large enough and with such a tremendous pay-off that it should attract the best scientific minds.[1]

In the discussion that followed, several participants raised questions concerning weather observation and the effects of industry on climate.

F. W. REICHELDERFER (Weather Bureau, U. S. Department of Commerce): Because of the high cost of maintenance of ocean weather stations and some uncertainty as to aviation requirements, the ocean weather station program is under review. Meantime, the stations in the Atlantic are continuing in operation and we hope that there will be some provision for permanent continuation. Upper air soundings over the oceans are essential to weather forecasting, meteorological research, and air navigation. We need to develop new and less costly techniques for upper air soundings since the cost of the present program prevents it from covering, even at best, more than one-tenth of all ocean regions.

MR. SPILHAUS: The weather ship program was terribly expensive since it used existing vessels. I think it can be done much more cheaply—perhaps by means of bowl-shaped devices that we could use in deep water as observation platforms.

MR. MENKE: Will the large increase in carbon dioxide in the air, due to industrial activity, have any effect on climate?

MR. SPILHAUS: There is fairly good evidence that the higher latitudes of the Northern Hemisphere have warmed up in the past 50 years.

The radiation balance in the atmosphere and ocean is so delicate that this warming up could possibly be due to the increase of industrial activity during that time. In other words, there may be climatic control without the

---

[1] The complete text of Mr. Spilhaus' remarks was published in the July, 1954 issue of *Geographical Review*.

understanding or the prediction of what is going to happen. That is why I emphasized that we must lay the understanding for climatic control right now because actually, in spite of ourselves, we are controlling climate.

MR. OTT: On the other hand, this kind of cycle has existed before. From what I have been reading, I thought there was more or less a repetition of a certain cycle, but I realize if we get enough carbon dioxide in the atmosphere something is going to happen.

Do the fields of meteorology and oceanography offer adequate incentive to qualified students?

COLUMBUS O'D. ISELIN (Woods Hole Oceanographic Institution): I venture to say that there are only about 30 attractive research positions in meteorology in this country. And in oceanography, I doubt that there are more than 10. In other words, there is hardly any opportunity for the student to get to know about these problems or the possibilities that arise from them. We should encourage university administrators to take a chance on this subject.

MR. SPILHAUS: Meteorology and oceanography have had too mediocre objectives. People will go into a field if they see there is somewhere to go, but this business of making a forecast of clear or cloudy tomorrow just doesn't intrigue the type of scientists we would like to see in this field.

Dean Spilhaus was unable to be present at the final summing-up session. Mr. Iselin spoke in his stead.

MR. ISELIN: I thoroughly concur in what Dr. Spilhaus said, but his suggested solution to the problem of attracting better qualified researchers will not come about automatically. It is true enough that if we explained the opportunities and rewards in this general area, people would come forward, but who is likely to do the explaining? Effective public relations for the geophysical sciences—for marine biology—is not easily arranged.

It is generally agreed that between 80 and 90 percent of the photosynthetic activity taking place on the earth occurs in the oceans. Consequently, there is a huge potential reserve of food. The fishing industry can be almost indefinitely expanded, but the research required before this can be made practical is rather staggering.

The fishing industry is unique. Fishermen are still hunters. They remain in the stone age. Although a good American fisherman can earn $10,000 to $15,000 a year, his methods are still extremely primitive.

Off New England today a fisherman can fish at a profit if he gets a price for his catch of 2 cents a pound; and he can land fish at 2 cents a pound in almost unlimited quantities. However, nobody wants fish at 2 cents a pound. We prefer to eat swordfish and shrimp, which are much more difficult to get. The fishing industry is beset by very strange economic and social problems.

Furthermore, there is almost no engineering advice available to it. The fishing industry is not backed up by any facility comparable to the agricultural experiment station.

Fundamental Research as a Resource

FROM THE RECORD

MR. GIBSON: There are two important aspects of the general resources problem. The first concerns the total supply of energy and raw materials with which nature has endowed

our planet, the second concerns man's ability to avail himself of these supplies and use them to best advantage. Whereas there may be some argument as to how large the potential supply of energy and raw materials really is, there is little doubt that it is so large that the second aspect is the one which claims the serious attention of those who wish to do something constructive about resources for the future.

From time immemorial, the exploitation of the resources of nature and the fabrication of the products into beneficial commodities have been the provinces of the "useful arts." During the last century, science has found increasing applications in the field of the useful arts and a modern technology has evolved in which the skill and practical ability of the artist and engineer are suplemented by the understanding generated by scientific research. These applications of science have had far-reaching effects on the availability and utilization of natural resources and even greater effects are to be expected over the next half century. In this session, we shall look at the fountainhead of science, namely fundamental or basic research.

"Science," says C. N. Hinshelwood, "is not the mere collection of facts, which are infinitely numerous and mostly uninteresting, but the attempt of the human mind to order these facts into satisfying patterns. . . ." This statement gives a concise description of the principal objectives of science as the study of human experience, the establishment of the validity of this experience, and the fitting of valid experiences into satisfying patterns or structures, which can be communicated unambiguously to others.

Thus, while the by-products of the scientific research may be items of such importance as new instruments, new materials, new machines, the amassing of data, or even the creation of new sciences, such as electronics or nucleonics, its unique objective is the systematization of valid human experience in satisfying patterns that can be described exactly. This attempt to fit valid experiences or "facts" into satisfying patterns with the help of a system of logic is important from three points of view. In the first place, it facilitates comprehension. An established pattern is an excellent aid to memory, increasing the power of the human mind to comprehend its cumulative experience. In the second place, a pattern gives us a basis for *understanding* by bringing

out relationships among isolated facts or events. We understand new experiences when we can express them in terms of experiences already familiar to us. In the third place, a satisfying pattern always suggests extensions of itself and, thereby, gives a sound and fertile foundation for the *prediction* of new facts or events. In short, a satisfying pattern (or theory) enables us to mobilize knowledge for immediate use, in the domains of pure and applied science.

The methods of fundamental research may be described best in terms of a series of interrelated feed-back loops. One loop involves the interplay of experimental theory and experimental practice in which we recognize three elements (a) observation and accumulation of experience (b) validation of experience (c) tentative hypotheses or theoretical patterns which relate the valid experience. A second loop connects up hypothetic patterns into a broader pattern of theory and relates back to the accumulation and validation of experience. A third loop recognizes the new techniques, materials, etc., which emerge from experimental validation of facts and which provide means for exploring new regions to obtain new facts. A fourth loop involves communications—valid facts and satisfying patterns in science must be capable of exact quantitative communication, so that any other investigator can learn exactly what a fact or theory means and independently verify it.

Facts from all regions accessible to exact observation are the material from which theoretical patterns of science are woven, and the power of these theoretical patterns increases rapidly as they grow. The understanding of nature so generated is the potent catalyst which science has introduced to accelerate the progress of technology. Fundamental research, the source of this understanding is, therefore, a necessity and not a luxury in the effort to increase on an adequate time scale and utilize the national resources available for the support of ever-increasing populations.

The transfer of thoughts among educated minds and the generation and regeneration of ideas that accompanies this transfer are processes of paramount importance in fundamental research. Many types of minds contribute.

If we take a cross section of productive research workers in this country we find represented several kinds of minds which may be classified as (a) the creative, (b) the critical or analytical, (c) the cumulative and inductive, (d) the cumulative and descriptive, (e) the meticulous, (f) the routine industrious. It is evident that more than one of these attributes may be found in any given individual, although one will generally predominate. (a) The creative or Promethean mind tries to inject something radically new into anything it does. It may provide the flash of genius that shows up a new continent of knowledge or gives rise to a new all-embracing theory. It may throw new light on old tough problems. It is a mind that transmutes ideas from one field of experience to another. (b) The critical or analytical mind takes nothing for granted, but examines keenly all statements presented to it, probing deeply into their consequences. It is the questioning mind so needed for clarification of complex situations and for establishing the validity of experience. (c) The cumulative-inductive mind ranges in the literature and in experiment, collecting facts and attempting to put them roughly in order. It is a type of mind which has contributed, for example, largely to physical chemistry. (d) The cumulative and descriptive mind is that of the trained and keen observer who remembers what he sees and describes it clearly for others to read. It is the mind which has laid the foundations of the complex sciences of astronomy, geology, and natural history. (e) The meticulous mind is concerned with the correctness of all details in observation, procedure, and processes in a search for accuracy and precision. (f) The routine-industrious mind follows through relentlessly, especially where many experiments are needed to establish one fact.

All these mental attributes have important roles to play in the sound and steady growth of all branches of science and engineering and we should be guilty of crass intellectual snobbery if we discounted any one of them. Each has his place, and the secret of the efficient use of manpower lies in assigning to each mind a job suited to its attributes and carrying with it recognition of contributions to a worth-while objective.

Throughout the centuries, the progress of science has depended on teamwork. Although each investigator planned and carried out his work in a very private manner, he took care to make his results public as soon as possible through communications to colleagues in various parts of the world or through journals. As a result, the work of any investigator became available to others; all attributes of mind could be brought to bear on a scientific topic once it had been formulated and exposed by an investigator. An unorganized, but nonetheless effective, team made up of men from all nations quarried and polished the stones of which the structure of science is built.

There is ample evidence that improvements in education are required if we are to build up in the public at large an appreciation of research as a resource and if we are to maintain a supply of creative and sound investigators.

The sciences, the humanities, the arts all can give excellent foundations for a sound education. More attention, however, might be paid in the pursuit of any of these disciplines to developing in the mind and personality of the individual five qualities essential to the educated person. The qualities are: (1) The capacity for clear and fluent communications with other people and with the outside world and with himself—powers of observation, description, writing, speech, manners; (2) the capacity for and acquisition of knowledge and experience—building up a well-stocked mental inventory; (3) habits of discipline and continual analysis to distinguish valid from trivial experience—point of view or standard of values; (4) power of building consistent mental patterns of knowledge—the basis of understanding and judgment; (5) cultivation of imagination, the association of ideas and the power of building hypothetical mental patterns, predicting their consequence, and giving a basis for intelligent progress to new experiences.

With such equipment, a man can face any problem or situation in life. In the study of the sciences, he can find training and practice which will develop all these qualities.

Mr. Gibson's remarks on the types of minds that participate in research led to discussion on the potentialities and organization of interdisciplinary teams.

MR. MEIER: Do the six different types of personalities fit into teams or do they tend to differentiate? Perhaps only two or three types would fit together at a time, because there might be some conflict between personality types of these scientists. This is very important in the organization of fundamental research.

MR. GIBSON: Frequently these types of minds do come together, and when they do you get a very powerful although perhaps not harmonious combination. The people, however, should have a common point of view on which they can discuss things, critically, but never to the point where they regard those that differ with them as being crooks.

HARRISON BROWN (California Institute of Technology): Fundamental research, as such, cannot be organized. I think you are talking about developmental research when you speak of organization or integration. I don't think that a person can stand up here and say, "I will get a team and do a fundamental piece of research."

We don't need the single-purpose institute nor the single-purpose department any more. The single-purpose department, in this day and age, actually slows research in very complicated areas, such as biology and ecology.

At the California Institute of Technology we have recently incorporated within the geology department a group of geologists, chemists, physicists, and biologists, working on broad aspects of what happens on the earth. It is not team research, but these men are working together on the same floor. Results thus far have been extremely encouraging.

One of our physicists was stimulated into activity by one of our biologists and by a paleontologist, and the three of them have concocted an analogue computer which I think might be significant in the future.

We need a return to an outlook of science as a whole—the old concept of natural philosophy.

MR. GIBSON: I did not have formal organizations in mind, but the focusing in some way or the other, or the bringing to bear on a topic, of different minds.

ROBERT P. RICH (Johns Hopkins University Applied Physics Laboratory): I would just like to add a word of caution against doing away with specialized departments. What we evidently need is a balance between specialization and generalization.

MR. CAIN: Having mentioned the desirability of team research, I now should add that the great discoveries in science that have been utilized by successful teams in recent years were made by rugged and often ragged individuals. Although there is a great place for teams of specialists coordinated with the generalists, they are not necessarily the primary source of original thought. I think they are extremely successful for the coordination and application and development that can come only from original thought.

There was little attempt to define the precise difference between fundamental and applied research, but several aspects of the relationship were examined. A general feeling of need for more basic research was apparent.

WALTER ISARD (Massachusetts Institute of Technology): It has been said that there is an imbalance between the level of research activities in the basic and applied sciences. If research funds flowing into the applied sciences were diverted to the more basic sciences, would society be better off? Is it not conceivable that, with imagination, applied science can remove some of the limiting resource factors in the world economy and in turn make possible a higher level of research in the basic sciences?

MR. BROWN: Research on resources problems must be backed up with an enormous amount of research that is completely undirected and that is done solely for the purpose of satisfying somebody's curiosity. A case in point is the cure that Professor Huggins at Chicago developed for cancer of the prostate. Here you can analyze the component features that went into that cure. Somebody in Germany was studying the seasonal habits of the hedgehog and somebody else was studying about biochemical effects in castrated bulls. Huggins put this information together and developed a cure, and the question which he can rightfully ask is: What cancer research foundation would have sponsored any of the research that went into that cure? And I think we can all say: None.

RAYMOND H. EWELL (National Science Foundation): We now have under way in the National Science Foundation a comprehensive study of scientific research in the United States, including economic and social effects. The two principal objectives of this report are in answer to the basic questions regarding research: How much research should the United States be doing for its maximum or optimum development? Secondly, what proportion of the total research effort of the nation should be basic research?

Right now we are devoting about 1 percent of the national effort, either measured in money or measured in manpower, to scientific research. The total scientific research budget of the United States last year was $3.5 billion, including military research, as compared with the gross national product, which is about $350 billion.

About 6 to 9 percent of that total research effort is basic research. The ratio of applied to basic research is somewhere between 10:1 and 15:1, and whether that is the optimum ratio or not, we don't know. We are now in the beginning of the fact-finding stage of this problem and we hope in about two years that we will have something concrete to present.

How can research results be evaluated? What are the contributions of industry and of private institutions?

MR. GIBSON: We should try hard to get some index of the results of long-term research, and communicate to the people that have the means to encourage long-range support an index of effectiveness that they can understand.

THEODORE W. SCHULTZ (University of Chicago): May I suggest that the question of investment in research should be: Does it give a higher return to society than the economy gets in other kinds of activity? I think it behooves us to assess the products in their realistic terms, because I share the view that returns to our society in recent decades, measured in terms of factors of input saved, are really tremendous, and this ought to be brought forward in some systematic fashion.

In renewable resources, if we used the same techniques in 1950 that we used in 1910, throughout all American agriculture, it would have taken $46.2 billion of factors instead of $30 billion to produce the same product. The downward trend in the inputs required is strikingly emphasized, because I think most of us who know something about economics would assume rising costs if we had to find the increase in land, labor, and capital—particularly land.

This helps to state the case for more research in this area, in such a way that our business-minded, economy-minded community can see more clearly what is involved.

ALLEN ABRAMS (Marathon Corporation): Some companies continue research because they have carried it on for years and are satisfied that research is an important element in their business.

Other companies want more concrete evidence. They segregate the profits obtained from new research products, and credit to research only the amount in excess of that from other standard products. Then they divide that extra profit by the amount expended for research, and come up with a quotient showing the dollars returned for each dollar spent on research. One large oil company showed returns as high as $12 to $15 for every dollar invested in research; a paper company showed $10 to $12 return.

You may ask: If that is the case, why not spend much more on research? Obviously, there is a point of diminishing return, so that the amount to be spent by any company involves such considerations as expansion through additional capital expenditures.

MR. CAIN: In so-called fast-moving industries, a very much larger percentage of total sales is invested in research than in slow-moving industries, and the money invested in research by industry is primarily on short-range investigation. The people pay for it eventually, anyway; either through taxes or through prices for products and services. The understanding of long-range research is probably clearer on the part of industrial management than it is on the part of Congress. Therefore, it should be easier to get the money for long-range research through industry than through government, and I would like to ask for a reorientation on the part of industry relative to long-range research programs. Parallel to this, industry does not expect to amortize capital investment in plant or machinery in two or three years, so why should it expect to amortize investment in research in two to three years?

MR. SCHULTZ: I think we should stress the capital-saving aspect of research, rather than the capital-absorbing aspect. For example, research on hybrid corn has saved tractors and corn pickers, and consequently, may be called capital-saving.

MR. GIBSON: A notable industrial magnate in Washington once quoted a research director quite literally as saying that "Basic long-range research is that kind of research for which the guy who pays for it never gets any benefit." I am afraid this is often believed seriously.

KARL SAX (Arnold Arboretum, Harvard University): Practically every basic contribution to agriculture—in mineral fertilizers, genetics, antibiotics, and to a large extent in the work of hormone control—has been made by nonagricultural institutions, including industry. There is a strong argument for conducting basic research in private institutions completely free from any political pressure; if they could only get some of the returns from this research, the private institutions would be well off.

MR. ISARD: There is a central problem of how to allocate research resources among the various fields of research and among various persons. We have a limitation of research personnel and funds, and the problem is to establish some criteria whereby we can isolate the more from the less critical areas for research, and set priorities on types of research.

MR. GINZBERG: There may be a point in a dynamic society where research has to be balanced over against the rate of capital accumulation and the ability of the economy to introduce and absorb new products. For example, England cannot afford a very much greater rate of research expenditure at the moment, because it does not have the resources available to put the results into production.

MR. SEARS: I have a very strong impression that the effect of a great deal of research has been to speed up the depletion and exhaustion of resources, because a great deal of our research goes into elaboration of consumer goods, not always with regard to their ultimate real utility.

People and Organization

FROM THE RECORD

PAUL WEISS (University of Chicago): Resources are produced and conserved through science and technology. Science and technology are the most systematic compartments of knowledge. Their growth is tantamount to the growth of knowledge. Unless the way in which knowledge grows is better understood, this whole chain of events cannot become fully effective and productive.

Knowledge grows by research, interpretation, and comprehension. It grows in the manner of an organism. An organism takes in foodstuffs and converts them by a process of assimilation into body substance. Knowledge feeds on data consisting of itemized information and assimilates them by correlation and integration into existing concepts. In this process knowledge not only increases but gradually changes so as to lead to an ever closer likeness of the universe which it tries to help us reproduce, understand, predict, and control.

The process of the growth of knowledge is therefore as intricate and complex as is the growth of an organism. Research, as the gathering of data, is only the beginning. Data in themselves do not make sense. To become properly effective, they must be sorted, ordered, diffused, correlated, rearranged, digested, and rated in their bearing on concepts and theories which they may confirm, contradict, or modify. In this process of digestion, the worth-while data, the foodstuffs, lose their identity—their name tags—and the gatherers may lose their credit lines.

To realize that science is no longer an affair of solitary dreamers, explorers, and inventors, but has become an intricate, almost industrialized, mass endeavor, will give us the correct orientation in arranging our educational and research policies so that they will best serve the advancement of knowledge. While the basic instrument of the scientific process is still the human individual with his brain, we realize that there no longer is such an individual as the complete and perfect and all-around "scientist," and that it takes all kinds of aptitudes to serve in the collective endeavor that is science. It takes the observer, the gatherer of facts, the experimenter, the statistician, the theorist, the classifier, the technical expert, the interpreter, the critic, the teacher, the writer. It needs the help of all hands at all stations, from the research man who conceives a new idea, to the assistants who prepare solutions or tend cultures or animals; from the mechanic who builds a new instrument, to the artist or photographer who prepares indelible records of microscopic specimens or physiological tracings; and last, not least, from the man who willingly gives of his time and effort in order to help obtain and distribute some of the most basic tools of science—fellowships, research grants, materials and jobs—to the one who willingly accepts them to good advantage. They all work for a common cause and should feel above the unjustified and undignified popularity contests that center on such monomaniac questions as: Who is "more important," the "fundamental" or the "applied" scientist? The explorer or the instructor? The technical expert or the philosopher? They are all needed—in their proper stations. And they should be rated not by *what* they are doing but by *how* they are doing it.

Competence, resourcefulness, scholarship, craftsmanship, imagination, self-criticism, discipline, honesty, responsibility, and logical clarity are the only valid criteria of merit; not whether one devotes himself to exploring the vegetation of the jungle or the permeability of a cell membrane. Good work in any line will bring success. Given some luck, discoveries will come abundantly, as Pasteur said, to the "prepared mind." Opportunities are the richer, the wider the field and the more there is yet to be discovered; chances the better, the more freely an individual of good sense can strike out for himself, free from the tyranny of fashion and the lure of popularity.

The realization of this interdependence is a first prerequisite along the road to greater effectiveness of our scientific process. The other is continued emphasis on the role of the *individual mind* in this process. Let us delegate what can be delegated to machines, but reserve for the human mind what it is uniquely fit to form—concepts, thoughts, and ideas. Not every mind is fit for this enterprise, and to impress those less qualified into its services means diluting its efficiency. Yet, not to give full scope and opportunity to those who do have the necessary intellectual endowment is even worse and certainly accounts for the most spectacular waste of our most precious resource —human ability. We indulge in this waste in several ways—educationally, by premature specialization, which narrows the chances of a budding investigator to fit his occupation to his aptitudes, and by overtraining and indoctrination, which limit his vision and power for intelligent self-orientation; administratively, by overloading the born research man with routine teaching or committee duties, or by forcing the effective teacher with no special bent for investigative work to do so-called research of mediocre quality; and economically, by disproportionate support of what happen to be the "hot" and popular trends of the day. Too little encouragement is given to the person willing to risk prospecting in new areas, new ideas, new methods, provided he has the proper imagination and discipline; too little to the crossing of conventional barriers of departmentalization and to adventuring in uncharted territory.

Now, it may seem that we are advocating here conflicting attitudes—first, group collaboration and, then again, assertion of free individual self-determination. However, these are not contradictory, if properly understood; in fact, in their reconciliation lies the secret to scientific progress.

Of course, no single individual has all the necessary techniques and abilities at his command to do a full-sized job in science. Therefore, individuals have to supplement one another. This leads to "team" work. Perhaps the term "team" is bad because it implies the presence of a driver. This is not always necessary. If you just give people of diverse talents and training a common focus, then the situation will take care of itself. Unfortunately, directives of that kind are often missing. We shy away from them because of a certain unjustified stigma attached to the word "planning," misunderstood to be synonymous with "regimenting," that is, enforcement of a given plan. When you go out on a trip to new country, you don't consider anybody is regimenting you by giving you a road map; he is only telling you where the roads are, or where he thinks they are; but whether you use them and where you go is up to you. You still are in the driver's seat.

There seems to be a growing lack among the younger generation of sensitivity to discrepancies and cross-purposes in research. Why? Because they are narrowly indoctrinated by specialist sectarian traditions. There was a time when a student would be exposed to a wide variety of views, but now he is usually under the thumb of one particular institution, one professor, one particular group, one doctrine, and he keeps on grooving himself ever more deeply in that particular rut. This may lead to a rather dangerous development. We foster this narrowness of vision by our research grant procedures, partly, because there is in the minds of the young people a feeling that they are more likely to get fellowships or research grants if they apply for something which is currently "in the headlines," and partly because the grantors likewise may prefer to bet on volume research along popular channels than take the risk of the stab in the dark. More and more people are being sucked into this conformist pattern, and mass research along certain favorite lines thus starves other areas, potentially equally rich, which remain woefully unexplored. It is this present bent for smugness and security, not taking risks on people, and trying to invest only in something which promises reasonably safe returns, which is really herding our young generation into flocks and makes it almost impossible for them to exercise their imagination, initiative, and resourcefulness to best advantage.

The less there is known in an area, the cheaper it will be to find something which pays off. Therefore, we have to do something, and urgently, to spread the young people much more widely over the front of the unexplored, instead of sucking them more and more into the easy channels of that which has already been explored more adequately.

This is, of course, largely a problem of education, but I doubt whether it starts with education. I think it reaches clear back into our present social habits. People expect more or less to be carried. They expect to have a safe road ahead of them as early in life as possible. Whether or not this be a desirable philosophy of life, in science it just won't work. The scientific process is based on the insecurity of adventure, and if we want to revitalize our whole research structure we have to do something about bringing people up in this spirit and with the mental and moral stamina to "take it." Risk-taking must be restored to respectability. However, lest it lead to sheer waste motion in random straying, it must be paired with (a) a clearer exposition of the nature of scientific process, its objectives, rules, and methods, and an honest and true perspective of the problems in each field, particularly the unsolved ones; (b) a heightened sense of responsibility on the part of the investigator so that he will be more conscientious and selective in the self-direction of his efforts; and (c) help to each proven man in finding a type of work for which he is genuinely suited, and giving him the means to concentrate most on what he is uniquely fitted to do.

With this in mind, I venture to predict that our prime efforts toward the furtherance of research will increasingly turn from the clamors for just more money and more workers and more tools, to intelligent ways of getting more for the money we spend, and more out of the workers and tools we have. The amount of unexploited, undigested, stored data, is unbelievably large. Along with digging up new facts, let us not forget to process and extract the old ones; they contain lots of gold. Also, more effective use of our present research money will come about by a slight loosening up of the project system. I would suggest that about 10 percent of all "project" research funds be pooled as a mobile reserve to support scientific adventure. This would be a cheap investment that will give great returns.

To sum up, I would like to make a plea for the indivisibility of the research process. You can't separate practical research results from education or pure research, from the financing and motivation of research, and from the public understanding of what research is all about. A more efficient use of the human resource of research can only come from balanced attention to all of these facets of the "human adventure."

Financial and social incentives for the scientist were recognized to be deficient. Many participants felt that the remedy broadly lies in reappraisal of our social and economic values.

MR. SCHULTZ: In the long run you don't get much more on this deal than what you pay for, and we are not willing to pay very much. We are living now in a period in which the real returns to the scientist and the real returns to the teacher of future scientists are probably only about three-fourths of those in other occupations.

MR. WEISS: Certainly, one of the things we ought to do is give them the proper economic status so that they can do the research. In the eyes of society, their status would be raised if they were given the proper salary structure, and this might produce a chain reaction. But that process has to be paralleled by another process, to extract and exploit talent the better.

MR. GINZBERG: It doesn't follow that the more funds, the more fundamental and good research you get. It is really a more subtle relationship than has been indicated. It has to do with the matter of research institutions, university structures, and career opportunities.

MR. HURLEY: The support of graduate students in any science is a factor that might be considered. It seems to be true that when part-time research positions become available in any department of a graduate school, more qualified students decide to take advanced degree training. Funds for research in educational institutions therefore do affect the supply of scientifically trained manpower.

MR. NOLAN: I would agree we need more money, but I don't think that is the only solution. There is a need to create an atmosphere that will encourage men to follow a research career, rather than to use their talents in other more remunerative fields.

WILLIAM H. STEAD (Resource Management Consultant, Washington, D.C.): We should also begin to utilize the educational institutions as a basis for creating a different set of values in our society, because they reflect the value situation that the society is now setting.

Teacher training and science education at the secondary school level were seen to be major factors in developing research as a resource.

MR. KLOPSTEG: The first thing we must try to get into our students is knowledge or understanding of the things that pertain to science. Then, somehow the students must acquire wisdom or judgment in terms of which to evaluate and utilize that knowledge. They must have skill either in doing research or in the utilization of research. Also, they must be able to get along with others with whom they are working in order to facilitate communication.

RICHARD G. MILLER (Long Beach State College): We aren't searching out the genius and the talent at a level where it can be utilized and brought out and trained. We need the kind of teachers who would be well-trained enough to know whether a youngster has the necessary talents.

MR. SPORN: It seems to me that there is an almost invariable agreement that the basic training of our engineers today isn't broad enough. How much basic training are you going to give them, and how much technological training are you going to give them? If you try to take care of both, you find there just aren't enough years in the average time over which you hold a youngster today in a technical training program.

MR. McINNIS: Is it not reasonable to expect a student at the age of 18 to have the basic background necessary for becoming an educated person—an ability to write literate English, some knowledge of the forces of creation of our present society, and some introduction to the scientific approach?

We would be flattering ourselves to suppose that any of those results are produced by our present system. We are greatly underrating the capacity of the adolescent from 14 to 18. I would hesitate to say what the remedy is. We can't advocate the abolition of all our teachers' colleges for the next generation, although I sometimes feel that it would be a highly constructive step. I am quite sure that there is the point of weakness.

THOMAS A. MARSHALL (Engineers Joint Council): It would be interesting to learn the basic facts about the teaching of science in the secondary schools. Dr. Armsby, the Associate Chief of Education in the United States Office of Education, states that less than 50 percent of the secondary schools in this country provide sufficiently adequate courses in science and mathematics to permit students to go into engineering and science if they want to.

MR. MILLER: I teach in a teachers' college where we have several vacant posts in chemistry and physics because we cannot get the men at the available salaries. Those men can go into industry at much better figures. Teaching jobs in secondary and elementary schools are attracting people who are seeking security. They are conveying the idea to their students and we are not getting an explorative, risk-taking, type of mind as a product.

How can we best use our educational institutions to develop the research talent we need?

HARRY F. LEWIS (Institute of Paper Chemistry): We have neglected to consider as resources the small liberal arts colleges which have been responsible for a fairly sizable percentage of our research people. These should not be overlooked.

Some colleges are highly productive; others are not. And the relationship is not too closely related to the size of the endowments but has something to do with the spirit of the people who teach in the colleges and their sense of mission. I am also concerned with the inadequacy of the funds available for research by the small-college professor. These men are an important research resource not currently being used. I am referring particularly to the many good colleges of low endowment.

MR. OTT: Schools of higher learning are not schools of higher learning entirely any more, in the sense that we used to think of that term. A good many have become, at least in part, schools for vocational training at a higher level.

MR. STEVENSON: We have something like 1,800 educational institutions in the United States. The figure varies as to the number of this 1,800 that are sufficiently competent as research centers or graduate schools to develop to the maximum degree the talent that we depend upon. The minimum is probably 25 centers. In the National Science Foundation we are up against a serious problem in that in awarding fellowships the majority goes to these established centers. One of our directives is to increase the size of this base. Should we have more or should we have larger, or fewer, in view of our limited capacities?

Dr. Weiss asked me to bring up his suggestion that in this area of renewable resources, consideration be given to the organization of three or four research institutes, where the emphasis would be on the over-all study of the processes of growth, in order that men of different disciplines, of different interests, in a region, would have a place where they could gather and work together.

He points out that the difficulty in promoting a thing of that kind with the foundations today is that they will not invest in buildings; there is a shortage of capital funds to provide such working centers. We haven't a dollar, comparatively speaking, invested in any institutions where the biologists can gather and focus their attention collectively, as a team, working with economists, engineers, and others on the process of growth.

MR. SCHULTZ: The evidence is now very strong that our endowed universities ought largely to get out of basic research in the agricultural field. They do not have a comparative advantage, when you look ahead, against the Cornells, the Minnesotas, the Wisconsins, the Iowas, which can command their own resources.

MR. CAIN: I wouldn't like to see a suggestion for focusing attention on renewable resource work in large land-grant colleges go unchallenged. In the first place, they are not in any healthier position than the federal agencies, relative to particular pressures. The other point is that basic truths need to be discovered only once, and they can be discovered in private institutions, small liberal arts colleges, or large private institutions. The large land-grant institutions primarily function in development and extension which needs to be done over every time there is a problem of application.

Better communication is held to be essential to winning public support for education in resources research.

PAUL D. V. MANNING (International Minerals and Chemical Corporation): With the proper type of selling technique we could sell the people who pay the taxes on the idea of paying higher salaries to high school and grammar school teachers, and to university teachers, and thereby build up professional prestige by attracting a higher class of people. I feel sure that there would naturally follow additions to endowments, and additions to grants to universities for carrying on research and other activities of that type.

MR. ABRAMS: Some 30 states have set up foundations, supported by industry, which distribute money to accredited colleges. Industry does not and should not have any part in saying how these funds should be spent.

It is estimated that the non-tax supported colleges and universities of this country need something like $100 million additional this year in order to operate properly. This is a small fraction of 1 percent of the total industrial sales of the country.

It is the job of many of us here to point out to our own management that our most important asset—the people who run our industry—is in jeopardy unless we are willing to spend money on further development. It has been well settled as to the liability of a board of directors in using the funds of the company for support of education. In a friendly suit recently adjudicated the judge ruled that directors were not only entitled to make such expenditures, but that it was a responsibility for them to do so.

MR. STEAD: We can do a much better job than we have done of devising ways of getting the public to recognize some of the resource problems and more immediate limitations. Also, we might challenge the engineer and the technician a little bit more, to recognize that one of the objectives in production may be the conservation of materials and resources. Some special research on these problems of awareness might well be in order.

CHAIRMAN'S SUMMARY

In the deliberations of the Section on Resources Research progress was made toward a common understanding with certain tacit assumptions: that we would continue along the road we now travel; that there will be no disasters incident to war; that we will continue to have access of the present kind to foreign resources, including the interchange of scientific knowledge.

It was stressed that knowledge grows unpredictably and that scientific discoveries cannot be anticipated, nor their long-range effect. There are haphazard elements in the financial and public support of research and in the availability of key personnel. Some guidance can be given in the direction, or directions, that fundamental research may take, and in considering a program for the future it should be noted that, to date, there has been much more backing for the physical sciences than for the biological sciences, including the science of man and human fertility. As a result, there is a greater need for fundamental information in biological fields than in physical; but in the whole area of science and technology there is comparatively little correlation with the social problems which they create.

For the most part, research has exhibited a preoccupation with finite projects, few of which have been studied in the broad context of their physical and human environment. There is, in fact, only a dim appreciation of the infinite possibilities arising from human ingenuity.

The central problem of the renewable resources, as presented by Stanley A. Cain, involves the maintenance of, or increase in, these assets to meet the demands of a growing population. The breadth of the problems involved in the renewable and, specifically, the biological resources makes it difficult to isolate tangible projects that will win financial support. The needs for support range over the entire field.

In the discussion of fundamental research related to the renewable resources, a theme that became recurrent made its first appearance: The future of research depends first of all upon highly qualified personnel; second, upon adequate communications; and, third, upon the integration of the accumulated and new knowledge from different but interrelated areas.

The suggestion that a more conservative view of human needs might limit the problem and thus make it more soluble, was rejected on the assumption that the American people will not accept a recession from current standards of living, and that any research program must accept as its premise a substantial increase in population with a probable rise in the standard of living. In view of the severe limitations of trained personnel and financial support, it was agreed that there must be some determination of priorities, with judicious allocations of research workers and money.

One of the obvious areas of spectacular growth will inevitably be in the need for energy resources. Philip Sporn predicted a fourfold growth in the demand for energy in the next 25 years, and he outlined a number of technological problems for which concentrated research will undoubtedly provide solutions. The major unutilized coal reserves lie in the lignite and sub-bituminous fields of the Missouri Plateau and Rocky Mountains. Utilization will inevitably involve major shifts in population, in the locus of industrial activity, in transportation facilities, and in other economic activities. And to avoid chaos these social factors should be anticipated in any resource research program.

With respect to the supply of nonrenewable resources, consisting principally of metallic and nonmetallic minerals, Thomas B. Nolan sketched the urgent need for fundamental research in the origins of minerals and in the development of tools to detect them; in the distribution of elements in the earth's crust and in the development of techniques to convert lower-grade deposits to economic use; and in the physical and chemical properties of elements and compounds to determine whether substitutes might be found for mineral raw materials in short supply. Once again, the imperative need for research personnel was stressed, as was the need for instrumentation that will enable geologists and geophysicists to locate and to define the potential of mineral deposits well in advance of national need.

Athelstan F. Spilhaus dealt with resources of the sea and air, giving special emphasis to the principal product that both supply—namely, water. He defined the research objective in this area as that of time and space control of precipitation; but before this can be accomplished, there must be a much more exhaustive investigation of scientific principles, specifically in the field of meteorology and oceanography.

Apparently, these fields with all of their potentialities have comparatively little lure for students, and in noting the scarcity of young researchers the homely fact that there are few jobs for graduates in this line of work was emphasized. Yet such fundamental studies as the ocean as a source for food, and as the control of precipitation to assure adequate water supplies for agriculture and in desert lands, while alluring, are of such broad scope that they do not stimulate financial support or provide job opportunities.

From these several discussions it became obvious that fundamental research is in itself a resource to which more emphasis can appropriately be given. Once again, the importance of personnel occupied the attention of the section. The attempt to differentiate fundamental from applied or technological research was only partially successful, but the stimulant that each provided for the other became obvious in the discussion led by R. E. Gibson.

Paul Weiss stressed the fact that scientific research is a collective effort, and that in our institutions of learning there should be more emphasis upon the importance and the rigorous requirements of interdependence. He compared the organization and development of knowledge to the growth and functioning of organisms, making it apparent that knowledge is organic and that it depends to a very high degree not merely upon individual inspiration and ingenuity but upon communication.

Deficiencies in our educational system occupied the attention of the section for some time. The fear was expressed that we may, even at this early date, be too late if we are to give adequate training to the researchers who must provide the answers in resource development a quarter of a century hence. Analysis has shown that many entering the field of public school education are not of the highest intelligence quotients; it is common knowledge that the public accords this group not merely low esteem and inferior status, but inadequate economic support, hence seems to be getting what it pays for.

While no generalizations were attempted at the panel discussion which concluded our sessions this morning, the faith of the Cornucopians in further technological progress for the solution of the resources problems of the next generation appears to be well founded. We have the capabilities. Have we the intelligence to give them free play and support?

EARL P. STEVENSON
December 4, 1953

Section VIII

Chairman

H. CHRISTIAN SONNE
Chairman of the Board
Amsinck, Sonne and Company

Co-Chairman

LUTHER GULICK
President, Institute of
Public Administration

Steering Committee and Advisers

Steering Committee: EDWIN R. COTTON, President, American Watershed Council, Inc. · KARL T. FREDERICK, Vice-President, National Wildlife Federation · JOHN E. IVEY, JR., Director, Southern Regional Education Board · CLYDE S. MARTIN, Forest Counsel, Weyerhaeuser Timber Company · LITHGOW OSBORNE, Vice-President, Auburn Publishing Company · MATT TRIGGS, Assistant Legislative Director, American Farm Bureau Federation · FREDERICK L. ZIMMERMAN, Research Director, New York Joint Legislative Committee on Interstate Cooperation · *Assistant to the Section Chairman:* JOSEPH L. FISHER, Associate Director, Resources for the Future, Inc. · *Section Rapporteur:* LAURIN L. HENRY, Staff Assistant, Public Administration Clearing House

Major Topics

1. COOPERATION AT THE GRASS ROOTS

   Discussion Leader: EDWIN R. COTTON

   Rapporteurs: ROBERT N. HOSKINS, Industrial Forester, Seaboard Air Line Railroad Company; JOHN W. LEHMAN, Clerk, Joint Committee on the Economic Report, U. S. Congress

2. WIDER BASES OF COOPERATION

   Discussion Leader: CHARLES MCKINLEY, Professor of Political Science, Reed College

   Rapporteurs: JAMES C. BRADLEY, Engineering Assistant to the Assistant Secretary for Water and Power, U. S. Department of the Interior; THEODORE GEIGER, Chief of Research, National Planning Association; J. VICTOR SKIFF, Deputy Commissioner, New York State Department of Conservation

3. TAKING FULL ADVANTAGE OF RESEARCH

   Discussion Leader: JOHN E. IVEY, JR.

   Rapporteurs: JOHN C. HONEY, Staff Assistant, Program Analysis Office, National Science Foundation; RAYMOND F. HOWES, Staff Associate, American Council on Education

About 175 people participated in the section's work. The 154 who registered formally are listed on pages 407-10. There was no division into subsections. The three major topics were taken up in order, with the final session given over to a review and summing up. The steering committee working paper for the section was built around actual experiences and in itself represented a considerable job of preliminary research. The paper drew upon information from 71 organizations by way of interviews or answers to a questionnaire, and included 26 brief case studies. These are listed on page 360.

332

PATTERNS OF COOPERATION

DISCUSSION OF RESOURCES leads invariably to questions of cooperation; the record of the other sections of the Conference has time and again made this plain, not only for the different kinds of resources—land, water, or minerals—but also for the broader approaches to all resources from such viewpoints as world relationships or research. In all kinds of difficult situations, present and to come, it has been noted that the practical way out will call for the willingness and ability of different groups to work together.[1]

Here the focus was upon cooperation itself. Section VIII took all resource fields to be its province, and concentrated on how people work together to get things done. How can patterns of cooperation among private and public groups concerned with conserving and developing the nation's resources be improved and extended? The task will not be easy, for the pulls are strong and conflicting. The interplay of many interests and forces will determine how well the country's resources are used and how long some of them will last.

Much has been done already. Over the years business, labor, agriculture, education, and conservation groups, and local, state, federal, and international governmental agencies have worked out a number of cooperative approaches. Increasingly, groups with different interests are modifying extreme positions and working together on specific programs. The bases of cooperation are widening in many instances to cover larger geographic areas or more resources, although joint effort at the grass roots continues to be the core of successful cooperation.

More will need to be done as pressure on the nation's resource base mounts.

The section chairman set the stage in his opening remarks: "Today numerous groups—many of them with widely diverging objectives—have come to realize that they have interests and responsibilities in the resources field. Cooperation is destined to become even more important in the future. The patterns of cooperation—the way in which people and organizations come together, agree on objectives, form new

---

[1] Many of the examples offered of ways by which patterns of cooperation can be worked out point up the discussions in other sections. Problems of forest protection and management, of wildlife and recreation areas, for example, of governmental agency coordination, received considerable attention in Section II; problems of watershed management, similarly, in Sections II and III; and problems of resource education in Section VII. The record of all the other sections provide the background against which the discussions of Section VIII should be read.

groupings, and divide responsibilities between existing organizations—are often well conceived, but also often quite complex.

"This section will concentrate on the paramount importance of human beings working together—as individuals and as groups—to formulate and attain their objectives in the resources field. We will attempt, in a sense, to pull together the portion of the work of other sections that involves organizing to do the resources job.

"We are going to concentrate on how the patterns of cooperation can contribute to intelligent planning. If they have been successful, why? If they have failed, why?"

In the search for principles that apply often enough to serve as general guides, the group concentrated on approaches that promise practical results. This narrowing of the enormous field made discussion more manageable. Questions of resource subject-matter were subordinated; so were the deeper aspects of human motivation. But serious gaps in present understanding of motivation were pointed out. In fact, the need for more basic work in all of the social sciences that can shed light on individual and group behavior was emphasized strongly and from many quarters. This was accompanied by an equally wide emphasis on the improvements in education required to spread new knowledge and put it to work.

Cooperation at the Grass Roots

The fundamentals of cooperation were considered here: How do understanding and willingness to work toward common ends develop among individuals and between groups?

It was recognized from the start that cooperation is not an exact science, but an art in which human relationships are all-important. There was wide agreement, also, that the bare elements of cooperation can best be studied at the grass roots level, where complexities of large-scale organization least obscure the bearing of group action upon concrete problems.

Principal examples offered from the floor were drawn from experiences in forestry, farming, wildlife protection, and stream improvement. These were examined for basic principles and for approaches and techniques that might be adapted to other lines.

In the search for general guidelines a number of common elements appeared. Particular attention was drawn to limited, well-defined aims, clear prospects of gains, and absence of controversial political or economic overtones as factors that tend to make programs flourish.

The importance of education in developing leadership and promoting a broader understanding of resource situations and issues and the need for strengthening the educational system were emphasized.

Among the broader operational problems, two questions aroused particular interest. One concerned the initiative: Are some sources generally preferable to others? The second concerned development and maintenance of cooperation: What incentives usually work best? How often is compliance a serious problem?

FROM THE RECORD

The Human Element

Many observations on the general nature of cooperation came up as sidelights to discussion of principles or examples. The speakers who examined fundamentals somewhat more directly stressed the human element.

MATT TRIGGS (American Farm Bureau Federation): The cooperative approach is fundamentally a product of environment and education; it is an art we learn by experience at the grass roots and not by rules.

There are, of course, such things as irreconcilable conflicts of policy and interest, but more often than not, the obstacle to a cooperative approach involves conflicts of personality that stem from jealousy, stand-pat attitudes, and other human weaknesses.

There are probably no problems of local importance in the resources field that cannot be approached by the cooperative basis to good advantage, even though it is no more than a mutual exchange of reasoned viewpoints on a deep-seated conflict.

Cooperation is the common-sense approach. Any individual or group that wants to find an answer to a problem or accomplish an objective is not being effective unless it seeks allies, tries to explain its views to other interested groups, and at least considers possible modifications of the proposal to obtain broader acceptance and support.

EDWIN R. COTTON (American Watershed Council): Our civilization has become more and more complex until now we are in a position where there is nobody to really sit down and manage our resources. Industries are controlled by management staffs that are so busy with company work they can't carry on obligations which used to be undertaken by the individual businessman, the individual factory owner. Today we are groping for some substitute for the civic cooperation carried on in the past.

The secret of cooperation lies in providing a means for needed understanding and confidence. One of the reasons for controversies between various agencies, individuals, or groups, is that we don't sit down and try to understand the conditions under which the other fellow operates.

HARVEY H. DAVIS (State University of Iowa): Human beings are most easily motivated by their selfish interests. You have to prove to them that their selfish interests will be met or that they should subordinate their private, immediate interests to the long-range interests of their descendents or their fellow man. And then, what do you do with the boys who won't go along? Those seem to be some of the problems we face when dealing with the art of cooperation.

Key Examples: Forestry, Watershed, and General Farm Organizations

Examples of cooperation in three areas were presented in considerable detail and served as springboards for examination of a number of principles and methods.

CLYDE S. MARTIN (Weyerhaeuser Timber Company): In some 46 years of experience with forest resource problems involving multiple uses of the forest, I have become convinced of two things: First, that cooperation among individuals, corporations, towns, and public agencies, both state and federal, is the most effective way of meeting these problems; second, that if we start on the right basis in our communities, with each individual or agency doing the appropriate job, it is easier to solve the big problems.

Cooperative patterns were started in the Pacific Northwest 50 years ago when a few timber owners got together and set up simple forest fire patrols consisting of two or three men with a horse, a bucket, and shovel. Today, the United States has a multimillion-dollar forest protection program involving private, state, and federal participation, and the cooperative approach has become the natural approach to forest problems in our region.

The usual procedure, when a problem arises, is to set up an association or committee composed of industry, school, federal, and state foresters who can pool their knowledge and experience. In almost all cases, including the three I am going to describe, there is little formal organization. Each agency pays the expenses of its representatives, and there are no budgets. The committee members are the foresters and technicians who do the work; the goal is a solution that will benefit everyone in the region.

The Nursery and Planting Committee was originally sponsored by industry and is composed of nursery foresters and those in charge of planting. Federal, state, school, and industry representatives participate. The work of this group has led to the development and manufacture of a more efficient planting tool, the standardization and improvement of both planting techniques and supervision, the careful selection of certified tree seeds, and the improvement of nursery practice. By concentrating the most expert knowledge and skills on one particular group of problems and making the results available to all agencies, the entire region has benefited.

The Second Growth Management Committee is sponsored by the Pacific Northwest Forest Experiment Station, and grew out of the realization that the Douglas Fir region is gradually changing from an old growth forest economy to a second growth economy, which presents new management problems. After a general exploratory meeting, a committee was established, made up of the region's most experienced silviculturists and management foresters from both public and private agencies. The committee initiated a combined study of the past history of the region's second growth stands as a basis for developing sound methods of improved management. It has prepared a manual on the management of small forest ownerships. It is in close touch with experimental work in young growing stands, and will eventually prepare a manual covering the intensive management of growing timber crops.

Work with small timberland owners. The Industrial Forestry Association, which sponsors the tree farm movement in the Pacific Northwest, found that it was impossible to organize the program on a state or regional basis because of the amount of staff required. It is now attempting a new approach on the county level. Public and private foresters are working with small owners on a volunteer basis. They help develop management plans and give technical assistance. When a plan has been approved by a committee from the Industrial Forestry Association, the farmer is provided with a tree farm sign.

MR. TRIGGS: Several years ago the California Farm Bureau, recognizing that little was to be gained by carping and belligerency between farmers and sportsmen, organized a continuing committee, which studied the problem and met with sportsmen's groups and state and federal officials. As a result, the program now being developed is based upon a better understanding and more satisfactory compromises between conflicting interests than would be the case if each group had assumed a stand-pat attitude. Encouraged by this effort, the committee has gone on to other problems, such as the encroachment of brush on public and private grazing land and depredations resulting from excessive deer population. As our urban population grows and the pressure for wildlife and other recreational uses of land increases, cooperative study and consultation can serve a valuable purpose.

Reclamation and watershed projects are other fields where cooperative action can accomplish much. The idea that there should be a larger measure of local participation in the study, financing, construction, and operation of water projects has for many years had substantial and growing public support.

MR. COTTON: The Potomac River Commission was set up with control of pollution in the Potomac River Basin as its prime function. It was given broad powers to undertake studies and it can make recommendations to the states, but it has no police powers. It has to rely on public opinion and cooperative effort.

As a first step, the Commission set up advisory committees consisting of representatives from federal and state agencies, from industry, from wildlife, recreational, and conservation groups of all kinds. You would be amazed at what has been done in obtaining understanding among committee members and in getting coordinated programs under way for the whole area, not only on pollution but on other problems as well.

The Commission then went on to try to carry that same philosophy to the grass roots and encouraged the formation of unofficial associations around the basin. One of these groups, the Monocacy Valley Council (Maryland), consists of citizens of the area—farmers, bankers, representatives of industry. Its prime purpose is to promote conservation. Demonstration areas have been set up, and the six or eight farmers concerned meet and discuss their problems; they get technical advice from the State Department of Forestry, the Extension Service, and the Soil Conservation Service; then they decide what is to be done and do it.

Conditions Favorable to Cooperation

The ultimate goals of a cooperative program furnish the main incentive, but often this is not enough. The steering committee had suggested 11 conditions that, alone or in combination, generally contribute to successful cooperation:

(1) The purpose for which cooperation is being undertaken is limited in scope and clearly defined. (2) The gains from cooperation are obvious and dramatic. (3) The governing policies of the cooperative effort are clear-cut and already agreed on by the cooperating organizations. (4) A tradition of cooperation already exists among the groups concerned before the project is undertaken. (5) The subject matter of cooperation is not highly charged with political or economic issues about which cooperating organizations differ. (6) Even though the subject matter of cooperation is highly charged with political or economic issues, the cooperating parties agree to the results they want. (7) Adequate staff and funds are available for developing and maintaining the cooperative arrangements.

(8) The cooperative pattern is suggested by or required by law or by the nature of governmental agencies or subdivisions involved. (9) The cooperative arrangement accompanies or is an outgrowth of an overriding national emergency. (10) The leadership of the organizations concerned is convinced of the value of cooperation in achieving objectives. (11) The growth of mutual confidence among cooperating groups concerned with small-scale problems provides a basis for broadening the cooperative relationship.

All of these were generally accepted, some were stressed, and a few new ones were added.

R. H. Eckelberry (Ohio State University): In cooperation you have to start where you are. That is the spirit of much that has been said here and of four of the steering committee's points: The purpose for which cooperation is being undertaken is limited in scope and clearly defined; the gains from cooperation are fairly obvious and fairly clear; the subject matter of cooperation is not highly charged with political or economic issues about which cooperating organizations differ; if it is so charged, the cooperating parties agree as to the results they want. You don't want to start out by saying, "First, we have to agree on the basic over-all fundamental theories." Quite the contrary. We may disagree on a lot of things and not want to cooperate in general. But we will have some things we are interested in. Let's cooperate on them. Then we may be able to move on to other things.

Mr. Cotton: You have to have a problem that is sufficiently urgent so that the people of the area are aware of it and want to do something about it. Without that, it is very hard to get cooperation on any program. You may be able to educate them that there is a problem, but they have to realize that the problem is there.

George White (Missouri State Forester): In Missouri our first problem in forestry was forest fire control. Some 20 years ago it was a common practice to burn the forest land so often that the burned area would equal the total forest land area of the state in a 3-year period. We have made considerable progress in fire control largely as a result of our cooperative programs with state, federal, and private agencies and individuals.

ROBERT A. HARRIER (Lehigh University Alumni Association): Real progress will be obtained when we think in broader terms about the over-all conservation problem. There are so many individuals and groups working intensely for certain specific objectives—reclamation projects, flood control, recreation, better farming practices, and so on—that we fail to comprehend or accomplish the over-all objective as rapidly as we might, and we get into conflicts of jurisdiction and planning at all levels of government because each group has not recognized the problems that confront the others.

CLAYTON M. HOFF (Brandywine Valley Association): Much has been said about cooperation between foresters, between farmers, between different agencies. In the Brandywine Valley the cooperation has been between different interests—the farmer, the forester, the fisherman, the hunter, the businessman, industry, the community that wants water supply, the community that needs a sewage disposal plant. The philosophy here is to secure the cooperation of all interests on a common program for the benefit of all. The incentive is downright selfish profit. If certain farm practices will increase a farmer's income as well as improve the water supply of a city fifty miles away, it is easier to sell him on the idea by pointing up the benefits he himself will derive.

This type of cooperation is probably more easily obtained on a watershed basis where people are bound together by interests that may not exist in many political units.

Who Takes the Initiative?

Does the impetus for true grass roots cooperation have to come from the grass roots? The question came up several times and most of those who answered seemed to think not—

that so long as a genuine local end was served, the initiative could come from almost any source, public or private, local, state or national. But it was pointed out that local people should run their own programs.

MR. MARTIN: The source of the initiative varied in the cases I described [pages 335-36]. The Planting Committee was set up following an industry forestry meeting to which foresters of other agencies were invited; the Second Growth Management Committee was probably the result of a general demand through the U.S. Forest Service; and the work with small owners on a county basis developed when problems were encountered in trying to extend the tree farm idea on a state or regional basis.

HAROLD V. MILLER (Tennessee State Planning Commission): A federal agency, TVA, supplied the initiative a few years ago when Tennessee was faced with the problem of finding an economic means for removing weed species left on cutover land or finding a market for it. In this instance there was no large company capable of offering the kind of leadership needed.

EDWARD F. DOLDER (California Department of Natural Resources): Industry was responsible for starting the Redwood Regional Conservation Council to bring to the people of the region an understanding of the economic importance of the redwood and fir forests. The Council then organized a series of Redwood Circles and here the initiative varied. In one town the circle was started by lumber men, in another town by a group of educators, and in another by a civic group. In some instances the interest was in the timber crop; in others it was in the recreational and aesthetic values of the forest.

MR. HARRIER: I agree with the view that cooperative thinking must start at the grass roots. The difficult thing to determine is where the stimulus should come from. People at the local level are not generally conscious of the over-all problems. Unless some particularly urgent problem confronts them, they are not inclined to become interested. Yet there is need for greater public consciousness of our land and water resource problems to effect sound policies. I believe the small watershed organization provides the best medium for both educational and cooperative effort.

MR. COTTON: In the Monocacy Basin the stimulus came partly from the Potomac River Commission and partly from some of the leading citizens who asked for help in getting started. In my experience, it would seem that the stimulus comes from a good many sources.

It is important not to lose sight of the fact that each individual or group has a part in the picture, and that each should do a good job on his own phase and leave other phases to the proper agencies involved. State and federal agencies often seem to forget that they are service agencies. They should advise on a technical plane and leave the policy decisions to the people of the region concerned.

FREDERICK H. LEWIS (Herald Tribune Fresh Air Fund, New York): I should like to suggest five "I's" as identifying some of the difficulties we run into in trying to get cooperation at the grass roots level: *Indifference* of average citizen; *Innocence* of average citizen who does not realize that his well-being is partially unearned; *Inertia* stemming from feeling that someone else has the situation well in hand; *Impatience* that leads to abandoning enthusiastic beginning if results are not immediately forthcoming; *Immaturity*—by which I mean that people often have a rather primitive understanding of the proper relationship between public and private effort, and too many in positions of leadership don't have the enthusiasm and skill to get broad-scale participation and interest in the conservation program.

Maintaining Cooperation

A small minority may not be willing to cooperate: does this constitute a serious obstacle? Are special enforcement provisions necessary?

MR. MARTIN: When people understand the problem the majority usually agree that the "wild" men need control, and then the laws come naturally. As a result of education and

popular support, Washington and Oregon have developed effective forestry laws. If a man is careless with fire, his whole operation can be shut down and he is faced with a fine. If he doesn't leave minimum seed sources as required by the state laws, he has to put up a bond that he will pay the state for reforesting that land. And in the case of the tree farm program, if the farmer does not follow the management practices he has agreed on, his certificate is taken from him.

MR. MILLER: In Tennessee all who contribute to the pollution of streams operate under a conditional permit, with a limited time in the case of those who could theoretically do better. People in communities will usually recognize they must do something about dumping their sewage. But there are instances in which the State Stream Pollution Control Board must set a deadline for the revocation of the permit, and thus force the issue.

Industry is, if anything, more cooperative than the municipalities. In one instance, a $55 million paper mill proposed to locate in the state. The control board set the standard that would have to be met. The engineers of the company went to work on the problem and came up with an announcement that through their design and the arrangement of their processes they could beat the standards by 20 percent and believed they would make money at it.

Education

On many points discussion led back to education as a primary source of wider understanding of resource problems.

FARLEY F. TUBBS (Michigan Department of Conservation): The leadership needed to carry the burden of the grass roots cooperative effort exists in most communities but it may have to be developed. For example, one of our teachers' colleges recently had a request for an adult education class in a small town. What the people wanted was someone to teach them how to talk to each other without getting mad. Secondly, state and federal organizations must have a sympathetic public before they can operate at the grass roots level. If the people have no confidence in these organizations, results are few and far between.

PEARL CHASE (California Conservation Council): If anything is at the grass roots it is the schools. I feel we should study and appreciate the importance of properly trained teachers, not only in the science field but in the social studies and in the vocational fields, agriculture, and so forth. I believe that where industry and state and federal agencies have realized the importance of teacher training in the conservation education field they have profited from the cooperation of the volunteer or civic groups in obtaining a wider field for understanding of the problems.

HARRY W. LAIDLER (League for Industrial Democracy): We should not overlook the great resource for cooperation on natural resources problems that is to be found in the ranks of organized labor, in the young people in the colleges, in women's groups, and in some of the other community groups.

PHILIP G. JOHNSON (Cornell University): If we are to train young people to cooperate and if we are to train them to become scientists, engineers, science teachers, English teachers, and so on, we must not overlook the fact that while the pupil population is increasing, the number of teachers available from our colleges is decreasing.

WAYNE C. SOMMER (American Camping Association): One of the greatest needs in conservation is education. Schools are doing much, but there is another community service that has not been used to anywhere near its potential. This is the camping movement. A 1951 survey reveals between 6,000 and 7,000 children's camps in the United States, with over 4 million participants. Most of these camps are interested in conservation, but few operate with any kind of land management plans, largely because conservationists have been so preoccupied with other matters. Also, in many places there just aren't enough technically trained people to assist.

MR. ECKELBERRY: We need to promote cooperation between the schools and camps on the one hand and local technical personnel such as foresters and soil conservationists on the other if we are to have effective conservation education in the schools and camps.

JOHN RIPLEY FORBES (National Foundation for Junior Museums, Inc.): We should think in terms of grass roots cooperation as early as kindergarten. The National Fund for Junior Museums is setting up nature and conservation centers which start with kindergarten and go right up until college. We would like to see nature study and conservation made a vital part of a child's life, not simply a lesson to be learned in school.

RICHARD L. WEAVER (University of Michigan): As secretary of the Conservation Education Association, I have been asked to make a statement that represents a consensus of 55 conservation people at the Conference.

A program designed to maintain our resources for the future must consider the role of the layman, educators of adults and youth, labor, farmer, capital, industry, business, the professions, and also the schools and colleges. We feel that a strong educational program to reach our adults and youth is perhaps the basic task facing us. Few questions are more important than education on conservation and wise use of resources, carried out in all of our schools and colleges and youth organizations, and through adult education, with every effective means of communication.

Wider Bases of Cooperation

The very nature of our political and social organization—the federal system and the tendency of special interest groups to affiliate on state and national bases—requires at least some degree of large-scale cooperation between individuals, groups, and government agencies on the broader problems of resource management. Discussion, here, centered on ways of improving and extending this cooperation. The emphasis was on organization and administration.

Examples of cooperative relationships that have been developed to deal with resource problems were appraised from a number of angles: What are the factors that contribute to their success? What are the problems? Is the public interest being served? What are the advantages and limitations of some of the organizational devices; especially, how much of the drive and point of local efforts may be sacrificed in broader organization?

It was taken for granted that better organization of the many public agencies— federal and state—concerned with resource problems would solve many of the problems of both public-private and intergovernmental cooperation. Major issues concerned methods. It was suggested that an objective study of existing patterns would make a major contribution to proper resource management.

FROM THE RECORD

Growth of Cooperative Arrangements

Several speakers commented on the political, social, and geographic factors responsible for the growth of cooperative efforts in the resources field.

CHARLES MCKINLEY (Reed College): Science plays a tremendously important role in solving resource problems, but we are not sure that it will either solve all the problems or solve them in time. In our society cooperative arrangements are essential to the proper management of our physical resources. We must recognize the need for private and public cooperation. The success of any public program depends on a tremendous amount of voluntary private cooperative effort. Coercion never is an adequate and full solution, though it is sometimes necessary.

Our particular federal system, which divides power between the nation, the state, and locality, calls for continuing cooperation between agencies. We ought to modify our older concept of federalism as one of competing sovereignties. A large part of the work today is not competing in character; it is collaborative.

Intergovernmental cooperation is unmistakably required by the fact that the nation cannot be neatly divided to encompass within a given area all aspects of the problems of a given resource. Many years ago, when the state system was carved out, rivers were thought of as dividing areas. We know today in connection with our problems of river management that they are linking areas.

And then the interlocking relationship between resources frequently requires inter-resource consideration. Even if you were able to divide an area on the basis of river basins, for example, inter-river basin consideration would still be required.

Another problem results from the organization of our state and national administrative structures. Jurisdictions are divided in such a manner that it is sometimes difficult to get action without interagency cooperation. There would be less need for formal government cooperative arrangements if the administrative structure within the states and the national government were better designed for handling resource problems.

J. VICTOR SKIFF (New York State Department of Conservation): One of the important questions here is why cooperative arrangements have mushroomed in very recent years. Dr. McKinley has given some of the underlying reasons. The professional conservationist feels the answer lies in an increasing recognition of three important facts: First, the welfare of all natural resources is inextricably linked, which means that agencies or programs that started out with a single purpose have had to cooperate to be effective. Second, the people and agencies dealing with these programs have had to get together in ways that weren't provided for in the country's early legislation or early organizational structure. And third, many of today's cooperative arrangements start at the grass roots because it is now more universally realized that you can't carry on conservation from state and federal capitols. It has to be done where the problems actually exist. And much of the land is in private hands.

Conditions that Favor or Hinder Cooperative Efforts

In the search for new or improved approaches to resource problems, the group examined some of the arrangements that have been developed to meet state, regional, and national situations.

Examples of successful efforts at those levels illustrated many of the fundamentals brought out in discussion of cooperation at the grass roots. Here, too, programs are most apt to flourish when the aims are well defined and when either the subject matter is not highly charged with political or economic issues or the cooperating parties agree as to the results they want.

DeWitt Nelson (California Department of Natural Resources): In California, the patterns of cooperation are frequently initiated long before a program has statutory basis. Most agencies have a board that sits as a policy-forming body and provides ample opportunity for individuals and groups to present their points of view. In addition, the state legislature has established interim committees to investigate, study, and make recommendations on most subjects of state-wide importance. The committee hearings again give people the opportunity for self-expression. They also represent one of the major steps in developing the legislative framework within which the boards establish their policies and the functional divisions of government administer their operation.

The patterns I want to discuss relate to cooperation between the state and private landowners and operators. The work deals primarily with private land, and must be carried on cooperatively.

Forest practices program. Following an investigative study by a legislative interim committee, cooperating with forest industries and the State Board of Forestry, a Forest Practice Act was passed in 1945. That Act set the framework for cooperation between the state government and the private timber owner and operator. Briefly, it divided the state into four districts, each with a Forest Practice Committee charged with developing forest practice rules and presenting them to the timber owners and operators in a series of public hearings. After substantial agreement has been reached, the rules are submitted to the State Board of Forestry; if approved, they have the full effect of law, and are administered by the Division of Forestry.

We estimate that 84 percent of our production of approximately 5 billion board feet of lumber a year is harvested in compliance with the minimum forest practice rules and that much is harvested under forest practices considerably in excess of those rules. The major tools of enforcement have been education, persuasion, and cooperation, with a minimum of compulsion.

Throughout this entire program, we have enjoyed the wide support of the timber industry. Many of our most difficult problems lie with the small owners and operators who frequently lack continuity of ownership, management, operation, and policy and have much less interest in the long-term productivity of their lands. But we have a program in its infancy that we hope will touch this particular problem.

The *range problem* is one with which you are all familiar. In California we have developed a cooperative program that is working very effectively. The program involves brush removal, reseeding to forage grasses where natural grasses are nonexistent, and more intensive livestock management on certain brushland areas. Since fire is used as a tool in brush removal, a high degree of cooperation is essential if the program is to succeed and continue to have public support. It is essentially the rancher's program. He constructs the preliminary lines prior to the burn and provides the manpower and the equipment necessary at the time of the burn. The Division of Forestry participates in a consulting capacity on the location of lines, and area to be burned, the manner of reseeding, and so forth. And it provides one or two stand-by crews to assist if the fire gets out of control. This cooperative program has had multiple results. It has reduced the number of brush fires, converted a considerable amount of low-value range lands to relatively high carrying capacities, and stimulated the establishment of good forage grasses on wildland range areas. Here again, the Board of Forestry looks to the users of the program for advice and assistance in establishing operating policies. The Board has an Advisory Range Improvement Committee composed of livestock ranchers, farm and forest organizations, and representatives of the College of Agriculture and public land agencies.

We have a *water pollution control program*, which is rather new and significant. Although the water pollution control boards are endowed with enormous enforcement powers, they have a clear mandate to achieve results through cooperative procedures. The statutes provide for a complete decentralization of the control program and for active local participation. They divided the state into nine water pollution control regions, each governed by a board of five members who represent city and county government, water supply, agriculture, and industrial waste producers. So far as is known, this is the only instance in California where control has been returned from the state level to the local level. On top of those nine regional boards is a state board, which acts as a budgeting organization and directs research. It can also serve as an appeals board, but in the first 3½ years of operation all problems have been settled satisfactorily at the local level.

EUGENE W. WEBER (International Joint Commission): The International Joint Commission between Canada and the United States is a unique pattern of cooperation between nations and one that can be applied in many ways between states and among federal, state, and local interests.

The very origin of the Commission illustrates one of the basic principles we have discussed—that there has to be a need and mutual desire for cooperative action. It was obvious at the turn of the century that many resources problems would arise between Canada and the United States that could not be solved readily through slow diplomatic channels. First, a temporary commission was appointed. It explored the problems of resource development along the border, and concluded that there was a need for a permanent and continuing form of cooperation. Out of that evolved the treaty of 1909 between the two countries.

A noteworthy feature of the treaty is that the purpose was clearly set forth. Briefly, it was to prevent disputes, settle existing problems, and provide the machinery for handling any future problems.

As for principles, the treaty defines how much sovereignty each country would retain and how much it would give up to the Joint Commission. This is important. We must decide, in any cooperative action, to just what extent we are going to retain our individual rights and to what extent we are going to give them up. The treaty also defines what can be done about situations in which the countries neither retained their sovereignty nor gave it up. Here Canada and the United States resolved that, on the request of either country, they would ask the Commission to study the particular problem and make recommendations to the two governments. That seems a rather simple thing, but it is an affirmation of faith and a binding agreement to consider the problems and the possible solutions, and it has proven very effective.

The steering committe had suggested nine conditions that make effective cooperation more difficult.

(1) The cooperative proposal does not command acceptance. (2) The cooperating parties have several loyalties and interests

343

so that cooperation on one objective is made difficult by conflict in others. (3) The cooperative arrangement has been forced upon one or another of the parties, or has been entered into purely as a matter of expediency or temporary gain. (4) The subject matter of cooperation spreads over several resource fields, thereby increasing the complexity of the arrangement. (5) Contact and common understanding between the cooperators lapse while the project is under way, or the goals of one participant shift and an appropriate adjustment of objectives or methods is not made. (6) Overlaps, duplications, and conflicts in the existing organization and structure of the federal government create or aggravate difficulties. (7) Efforts are limited by preconceived notions or "fetishes" which prevent experimentation to achieve new or improved and feasible patterns. (8) The scope of the cooperative arrangement and the jurisdiction of the cooperating parties is not commensurate with the resources problem. (9) Failure to take account of the crucial importance of the human elements in cooperative ventures, of skillful leadership and strongly motivated groups, makes success unlikely, if not impossible.

Many of these problems came up in the discussion. Some of them were regarded as major stumbling blocks.

MR. SKIFF: New York State has had long and comprehensive experience in the development and employment of a wide variety of cooperative arrangements designed to deal with various resource problems. I recently made a tabulation of 28 separate cooperative arrangements in which our state is participating. This tabulation shows some interesting things: first, that cooperative arrangements prevail in all our major fields of conservation (forestry, fish and game, parks, water resources, soil conservation, and so on); and, secondly, that a total of $3 million is annually invested in these cooperative programs—$1.8 million by the state and $1.2 million by our cooperators (largely federal)—and this does not include the additional millions that our cooperating farmers and forest and woodland owners invest as the end result of these programs.

I am sure it is no exaggeration to say that if these cooperative programs suddenly came to an end, a vast amount of progressive work in conservation in our state would come to a sudden and staggering halt.

I am not going to outline the many arrangements in effect, but rather some of the difficulties that have to be overcome if the situation is to be improved. The difficulties that beset the individual, who in many cases is the prime object of the cooperative arrangement, arise in large part from the number of cooperative arrangements that have been built up. In our state, to get the services he is entitled to, a farmer would have to go to eight different agencies in eight different places. It has been said that in this mechanized age, a successful farmer must be a skilled mechanic. To sort out what he has to do to get the services presently available he should also be a Philadelphia lawyer. There is great need, then, to try to streamline and simplify these programs.

Relationships between the state and its local subdivisions are complicated by the diversity of agencies, programs, rules and regulations, and administrative procedures. There is real need for an objective study of the structure and function of state government and local government with a view to coordinating their efforts.

The difficulties in cooperative arrangements between state agencies are largely determined by the way the state government is organized. Where there are a great many separate conservation or resource agencies, the difficulties are almost insuperable.

State and federal cooperative arrangements are beset by fiscal, legislative, and administrative difficulties. Many of our cooperative programs represent partnerships or federal aid programs with the state putting up certain percentages, matching money, and so forth. One of the great difficulties here is that federal programs do not have sufficient continuity to enable a state administrator to plan intelligently. And in our own case, the fiscal years do not match. If a federal agency or the Congress suddenly decides to cut back on a major program, we can do nothing about it if our legislature has adjourned and our fiscal year has started. By the same token, if Congress suddenly increases state aid, we cannot provide the matching funds and must wait a year to qualify. If federal programs could be put on at least a two-year basis, many of these fiscal problems would disappear.

Legislative problems also require better teamwork by Congress and the state legislatures. The Council of State Governments has done a great deal in the way of providing model or uniform legislation and has shown that Congressional and legislative cooperation can be greatly improved.

As for administrative problems, the state administrator, even the experienced one, is often very confused to know how and with whom to do business in Washington. We feel that state cooperation could be enhanced if there were some more centralized federal authority for resource problems.

FREDERICK L. ZIMMERMAN (New York Joint Legislative Committee on Interstate Cooperation): I agree with Mr. Skiff on the need for integration and simplification of the cooperative arrangements. However, we need a variety of types of cooperative management because we must have flexibility in meeting particular situations. It might not be necessary to go to the lengths of drawing up a compact between two states to handle, say, the shad situation in the Hudson River or the New York-Connecticut boundary lakes. Such matters could possibly be handled by a reciprocal statute, a uniform law, an administrative agreement if the administrator has power, or even some very informal pattern. Each method has its particular use. The compact method, for example, has certain real values where you need stability, where you want to incorporate in the laws of the state some formula that will be agreed upon and will remain agreed upon, when you wish to set up joint management or joint facilities. The one real difficulty with this method is that you

must get agreement, and this is sometimes an arduous task.

One of the things that handicaps cooperative efforts is the lack of information, sometimes on the part of the public, sometimes upon the part of state officials, of the values that can be gained through cooperation. Another block to cooperative arrangements is the development of dogma and fetishes with respect to what level of government should do the job, and what method should be used. This makes it difficult to get agreement.

Because of the complexity of our system of government, and the nature, variety, and number of problems that have to be dealt with, we are going to have to depend in part on cooperation. Therefore, we must try to expand and further explore the methods of such cooperation.

IRVING K. FOX (U.S. Department of the Interior, Oklahoma): The Arkansas-White-Red Rivers Survey has pointed up some of the weaknesses we face in planning resource activities. First of all, our studies so far have clearly indicated the need for national leadership in natural resources activities. In my opinion, the Federal Interagency River Basin Committee has failed to provide unification of leadership at the Washington level.

Second, our experience has indicated that the water resources activities of the federal government are not properly organized for unified river basin planning. This has been the most difficult problem faced in our interagency study; we have not resolved it and I do not feel we have achieved a proper approach to meeting it.

Third, the organization of the federal bureaus is not designed to meet the problems of interagency coordination. The bureaus were established to meet the separate functional problems, such as the problems of, say, fish and wildlife, but not the problems of fish and wildlife in relation to other phases of resources work.

Fourth, many of the state governments are not effectively organized to take part in this type of interagency study.

Finally, the AWR survey has pointed up the weak relationships between governmental and nongovernmental agencies and interests on resources work.

Cooperation in the Public Interest

Discussion on how the public interest is best served brought forth a variety of views on division of responsibility between public and private agencies and between the various levels of government, and on the advantages and limitations of specific devices such as the valley authority and the interstate compact.

ARTHUR A. MAASS (Harvard University): I fear we may forget at times that cooperation is not of itself an objective in public policies. As a matter of fact, many types of cooperation run counter to our American heritage— counter to the antitrust tradition, for example. In other words, we should not seek cooperation per se but cooperation in the public interest.

As we get into wider bases of cooperation, the public interest is defined by all manner of interplays between individuals and groups. The public interest is represented, however, by democratic constitutional governments, which, unlike most private industries and groups, are concerned specifically with the public interest. They may become concerned with their own bureaucratic interests—but this is the exception.

Thus, one of the key problems is: How can we insure that governments perform effectively in representing the public interest on wider bases of cooperation for resource development?

One aspect of this problem is organization: Is the government organized adequately to perform effectively? This has been discussed by Mr. Skiff and others.

Another aspect—and one I should like to mention in more detail—is what I call "keeping government agencies subject to popular influence and popular control." Federal and state governments have worked out elaborate and generally adequate means for holding their bureaucracies accountable. A valley authority, for example, since it is an agency of the federal government, is kept subject to popular influence and control, by the same means as the Forest Service. In many ways

it is easier to control than other federal bureaus because it is a decentralized agency located in the area where it functions.

But who controls an interstate compact commission? Here I want to speak to the point raised by Mr. Zimmerman. One type of interstate compact sets up a commission that carries out the functions given to it by the different states. In theory, the commission is responsible to the legislatures of all of the states that participate; they must appropriate money for the commission. Very often, however, the appropriation is a set amount each year, and is scarcely amenable to evaluation and revision by the legislature of any one state; furthermore, the several state legislatures often do not meet in the same year. Thus, it is unlikely that any single state legislature will assume great responsibility for holding the compact commission accountable, and there is no way in which the several of them can do so jointly.

This limitation on the compact device for cooperative action is an important one and must be evaluated, particularly when we are concerned with the type of commission that has been proposed to take over the operation of the federal government's reclamation, flood control, power, and other activities in the Missouri Basin.

You might get the impression from speeches by certain advocates of the compact that the federal government has not cooperated with the people in the Missouri Basin; that the people are fed up and want to insure more active grass roots participation in this development by entering into a compact. This, I would say, is not the case. The federal government has not operated independently in the Missouri Basin. The Bureau of Reclamation undertakes irrigation activities only when it receives assurances that a local irrigation district is prepared to enter into a cooperative contract; and an irrigation district is constitutionally as much a unit of state government as a state land office. The Fish and Wildlife Service operates in each state through a complex of cooperative arrangements with local public organizations.

As I see it, what has happened in recent years in the Missouri Basin states is that the central state executives, the governors, have begun to seek a larger share in representing their states in these cooperative arrangements.

There are any number of reasons for governors coming to the fore. An increased tempo of federal activities and a multipurpose approach to resource problems often affects the entire economy of a state, and the governors may think that, as the central state executives, they are best able to represent the interests of their states. They may feel they should protect state water rights. They may desire to obtain control of units of state government, such as irrigation districts, over which they currently have little or no control.

In some cases, vested interests, particularly private utilities, which are opposed to federal resources development, believe that their purposes can be served best by more active top-level state participation in resources programs.

Participation by state governors may result in better resources programs. But certain questions would have to be answered before one could make an effective case for channeling all federal relations with local people and organizations through the governors' offices.

Are the state governors' offices well equipped to execute the responsibility they seek? The pattern is uneven. For some the answer is probably yes; for others, no.

Does channeling federal relations with states through a single state office lead to more public control, or in certain cases can people participate more effectively if they deal directly with the federal agency? This is hard to answer, but take, for example, the Extension Service. As the years have gone by, control over the county agents has been asserted more and more by a central unit, the state colleges of agriculture—not the governor's office in this case. These colleges have formed the National Association of Land-Grant Colleges. Has this tendency toward centralization meant better popular control over the individual county agent? Maybe so, I wouldn't say no; I am just using this as an illustration of the types of questions that come up when you talk about federal-state-local relations in resources programs.

And finally, will an emphasis on central

state organization insure adequate state financial contributions? I think you will find the greatest local contributions in resources development where the federal government has an active cooperative arrangement with the local district. It is the irrigation district that tries to pay back costs.

MR. ZIMMERMAN: I don't deny the validity of many of the points made by Mr. Maass. But I do say this. First, as to control by the public: The New York Port Authority has been criticized from this angle. However, I think the compact had a provision that enabled the governors of the two states to keep a certain control on what the Authority did. That was a method of control.

And, second, the authority and compact do not have to be alternatives. If you are going to have a completely integrated pattern, you want to get the states into this business. If you do that, you may want to utilize state laws —such things as flood plain zoning, soil conservation district police powers, and so forth. You don't have to have state control of the agency. You could have a weighted representation that would permit both the states and the nation to participate in the agency, and that may be desirable. Some other pattern may achieve this same purpose and we should be willing to consider it, but I do feel that it wouldn't do any harm to try some method by which we could secure more complete integration vertically as well as horizontally.

MR. COTTON: Mr. Maass left the impression that compact agencies are not accountable to anybody, and that is far from the case. The check is very close. Our compact, like most that I know of, specifically says that the commission cannot spend money until it has been appropriated. This means we have to present a budget like any state or federal agency and follow through with hearings before the appropriations committees. We go through this procedure in not one but six jurisdictions. The states have another safeguard in the appointment of their own commissioners or representatives to the body in question. Most compacts provide that the states can pull out at any time.

MR. TUBBS: My concept of resource management is that it must be done by the people of this nation. They can do this individually, in groups, or by creating bureaus and agencies and assisting them in doing the job for them. To my way of thinking, what we are striving for in this Conference is to set up a pattern of grass roots cooperation. Regardless of the scope and the level, we must have the support and understanding of the people if resource management is to be accomplished.

HYMAN H. BOOKBINDER (Congress of Industrial Organizations): Any attempt to establish a dichotomy between governmental responsibility and the need for grass roots cooperation, I think, is completely wrong.

We need to develop grass roots interest, concern, information, and so on, but the whole problem of resources development and conservation is too big to be solved by saying, "Let's teach our people to conserve our natural resources." Our resources are a very serious matter of national concern. And government is our representative of that concern.

We should not minimize the tremendous role that must be played by the federal government, in addition to that of state governments, and multistate combinations. Realization of the seriousness of the problems by all the people throughout the country will be furthered to the extent that all levels of government provide bold leadership in this vital area.

LEON W. DUPUY (Silver Spring, Md.): While the machinery utilized on the Arkansas-White-Red Basin survey and the New England-New York survey is not perfect, a great deal has been accomplished—much more than appears on the surface. Countless decisions and many agreements have been reached. Both committees are accomplishing much in planning resource conservation. They have compiled a large amount of conservation information that will be most useful in the future.

Overcoming the Problems

ERNEST S. GRIFFITH (Library of Congress): I have been struck by the extent to which the present national organization setup in resources is a handicap to the patterns of cooperation locally, regionally, and nationally. Natural resources are now scattered in our national setup among three major departments and four or more minor agencies of our government. No wonder the voices are conflicting at the grass roots.

In the discussion of the larger area, the region, the difficulty in providing effective coordinating mechanisms came up again. A reorganized central authority was advanced as a remedy. The Missouri Valley stands out as perhaps the outstanding example of difficulties and shortcomings.

Difficulties also occur nationally in the absence of an effective pattern of coordination. Professor Maass stated that the government bureaus are responsive to the people. That is true and, in some aspects, all too true. In the present situation nationally, what a bureau is responsive to is a clientele that very often reinforces its splinter approach to resource problems.

I would like to call your attention to three recommendations of the first Hoover Commission Task Force: First, it suggested that a federal department of natural resources be set up to include the Forest Service, for example, the flood control work of the Corps of Engineers, and substantially what is the present Department of the Interior. It further suggested that in the event of such a consolidation, the pattern of cooperation regionally would be better and much more likely to succeed, and that interbureau committees, strengthened and reinforced by representatives of the states and the localities, could provide the kind of regional leadership that is attributed to the central authority. Finally, it suggested a board of review through which the various interests concerned would be certain to have a hearing prior to the adoption of a resource development plan for an area.

I close with two illustrations of problems that have been extremely difficult to resolve and which, in the opinion of the Task Force would be better resolved by a better national organization. The first of these is where the peculiar interest of the locality conflicts with a national interest, as in the case of parks and the wilderness areas; and second, the up-stream-downstream conflict involving flood control, forests, conservation of water resources, and so on.

MR. SKIFF: We have already built a big and powerful machine to deal with resource problems, but it looks like a Rube Goldberg invention. It has extra wheels, and several steering wheels operating independently. It has gears that don't always mesh. It is carrying some dead weight, and it hasn't enough horsepower to do the whole job. It needs a major job of redesign.

The time has arrived for a major intensive and objective study of all types of cooperative arrangements affecting our resources. This would have the triple objective of perfecting existing arrangements, extending them where necessary, and creating new ones where the need is pressing.

Studies should be made of the federal, state, and local structure as it affects natural resource agencies, of interstate arrangements, and of our federal fund relationships. Each of these studies could go forward independently, but for best results there should be a consolidated approach by a team of experts. Our technology on resource conservation is already far ahead of our application of it. If we are ever to catch up, we have to provide a better basic framework for this work to hang on.

In this country, we have the people with the brains, the talent, the experience, the ability—everything it takes—to overhaul our conservation machinery. But some agency has to bring these people together, give them the opportunity to work, and the money for research. Success in this direction could probably do more than anything else to advance resource conservation.

The study suggested by Mr. Skiff received wide support among the group.

STUART C. GIBBONS (Calaveras Grove Association): We should not overlook the need for an organization of some kind to implement what is going to come out of this whole Conference. The idea is so obvious that it seems

that this section was particularly set up to suggest that very thing.

LITHGOW OSBORNE (Auburn Publishing Company): The value of extending the co-operation we now have and the need for further study indeed seem obvious. A study would probably show that some of the states with the greatest need for cooperation of the kind we have been talking about have the least of it. The best way for them to get it would be through some study that would provide information and encouragement. I do hope it is the sense of this group that there should be some continuing study of patterns of cooperation by an objective nongovernmental organization, possibly leading to some sort of federal agency which would encourage cooperation among the states and with local units of government, and between the states and the federal government.

MR. DOLDER: Mr. Skiff, did your paper, in effect, recommend a centralized natural resource agency at the federal level?

MR. SKIFF: We didn't make any specific recommendation. We realize that there are many difficulties in having just one central responsibility in the federal government for resource work, but, so far as the states are concerned, the more that responsibility for resource management can be centralized in the federal government, the more their work with the federal government and others all the way down the line will be facilitated.

ERNEST A. ENGELBERT (University of California): I think that these studies are very much in order, but we should also recognize the need for acting on some of the very fine studies and recommendations that have been made by groups such as the President's Materials Policy Commission, the Hoover Commission, and the Council of State Governments, among others.

MR. LAIDLER: We should not overlook the pattern of cooperation worked out in the Tennessee Valley between the federal government, the state government, the municipalities, the farmers, the workers, the consumers of electricity, those interested in flood control, and so forth. This pattern covers various types of conservation interests such as flood control, navigation, hydroelectric power, reforestation, recreation, and soil conservation. The results have been very interesting. The region has had a greater industrial growth than almost any other part of the country; the use of hydroelectric power by the farmers has increased tremendously; there has been a decrease in tenantry, an increase in farm productivity, and considerable development in reforestation.

One more word: If we simply take the information that comes out of this Conference and put it on the shelf, we will not have done our duty toward conservation. It must lead to the development of a genuine conservation policy. We ought to accumulate the facts and then make them known through local, regional, and national conferences.

The following comment was submitted after the Conference:

Mr. Osborne: Like most American get-togethers our section in its discussions has tended to take far too cheery a view. There has been much emphasis on what has been accomplished through cooperation in a number of particular situations; but not much on how very little has been accomplished in a very much larger number of situations.

As I see it, there are three basic forces working against a wise use of what natural resources are still left to us—increasing population, greater industrial and economic productivity, and human stupidity and selfishness. There is no doubt in my mind that cooperation offers the best chance for salvation in view of our national temperament and our form of government. But I believe also that more government encouragement and regulation are also essential.

Taking Full Advantage of Research

The quality of decisions in a democracy depends largely on how many of the pertinent facts the citizens have before them. No patterns of cooperation can be expected to work well if the people lack sufficient information. In the field of natural resources, as elsewhere, there is need for good communications—education in the broadest sense of the word. This was the focus of discussion at the third session: how best to translate research findings into constructive action.

Many kinds of institutions were looked into, including schools, colleges, adult education systems, youth organizations, and such mass media as newspapers, radio, and television. Techniques of popularization, group discussion, and other lines of endeavor were examined.

John E. Ivey, the discussion leader for this general topic, checked off the main trends and high points of the discussion in his summing-up.

"First, there has been emphasis on the desirability of *closer relationships between research agencies and educational and administrative agencies* all the way through, instead of keeping research and implementation in separate compartments. Second, I gather that many of us feel that no longer can we look at resource conservation and development as a biological and physical science problem alone— that the social sciences have a major role in effectively utilizing the scientific facts on resources. Third, there is wide recognition that we are not doing enough basic and applied research on the communication process itself; that we must do more, in order to break the barriers between the research scientist and the administrative agency on the one hand and the general public on the other."

FROM THE RECORD

Communications Begin Far Back

The nature of research projects and the way they are conducted often bear directly on the problem of communication. Although the discussion here was not aimed at research itself, the group was concerned with more than techniques of disseminating completed findings and often went well behind the finished product. Has the research project itself been selected with a definite goal that calls for reaching certain people in certain ways? Has there been good communication while the research was in progress? Communication is just one link in a much longer chain.

ALAN T. WATERMAN (National Science Foundation): The basic idea may come out of a clear sky from a research worker in an out-of-the-way spot, or it may be the result of a conscious search. But whatever the source, it takes close communication all along the line to get from the basic idea through to production and use.

In industry, the applied research people must keep in contact with the basic research people so as to pick up ideas. The development people have to check with the applied people to see whether something is ready to start in a more practical form. The production people have to keep in touch with the development people to be sure that they can produce the thing and produce it economically. And the sales people must keep in touch all the way to see whether there is demand, whether there will be sales, and so on.

This is a simple, clear-cut case. But suppose we talk about a resources problem of national importance such as water, power, oil. Here the groups are not in one organization, and the communication problem becomes more complex. The basic research people by and large are in universities; the applied research people are in industry and, to some extent, in government; the developmental people are largely in industry; and the production and sales people are almost entirely in industry.

JOSEPH W. BARKER (Research Corporation, Inc.): In the illustration given the flow is perfectly obvious. But while research may be directed toward a particular objective and may succeed, its later development in the pilot plant stages may turn it to something entirely different. You need a process of communication that is not narrowed down so closely that it results only in flow in the desired direction. Otherwise, the idea will never reach those who might see its application to a completely new principle. To show where the carrying forward of a concept may lead, let's take an example in which the time lag between concept of an idea and its practical application in industry is very great. The concept of the gas turbine was well known for many, many years before it came into practical application. This did not happen until correlative research work in another field had moved forward to the point where we had both metal alloys and ceramics, and turbine blades could be made that would stand the temperatures and the erosion.

Then I would like to illustrate what can happen to research directed to a particular objective. In 1931, a young professor at the University of California came to Research Corporation with the idea of the cyclotron. He was trying to crack the atomic nucleus. At the same time a professor at Princeton came to Research Corporation with the same objective but a more conservative approach. We backed both ideas. As you know, the cyclotron was successful. It did what it was intended to do better than the Van de Graaff generator could. But the Van de Graaff generator turned out to have a great many other applications and now is in almost wider use than the cyclotron.

ROSCOE MARTIN (Syracuse University): Unless you get the people interested in taking action involved in the research itself, unless there is a channel between the researcher and those responsible for action, nothing much may happen. All manner of good recommendations come out of studies. The Paley Commission and the Hoover Commission, for example, both had some interesting recommendations on resources administration. But not very many things have been done along these lines.

CHARLES W. ELIOT (Ipswich, Mass.): How do we make research policy or national policy for resource conservation? I think that the answer lies in cooperative action.

We have had many policy proposals that were handed down from on high and got nowhere. We have had others that were undertaken with a cooperative pattern and have had startling success. I see this planning business, or research for policy, as a series of steps. First, there has to be a spark; somewhere there has to be some leadership. Second, there has to be some common interest to stir this spark into a flame. Then, there has to be a statement of the program or problem. From there on it is less an individual undertaking than a group or cooperative job. The next stage is the fact-gathering stage, and, if we are wise, we get large numbers of people and all kinds of interests involved at this stage. There is where the first problem of communication comes to the fore. After the fact gathering, we have to go back to a single mind or small group to get a design or a proposal. Then we have to go back again to the general public, whose understanding, we hope, was increased by their participation in the fact gathering, and try to sell the project or proposal. From there on, our democratic procedures in our governmental setup seem fairly adequate.

MR. WATERMAN: Following one of the recommendations in the Paley Report, the National Science Foundation appointed a panel on minerals research to discover what may be learned from the research stage of the discovery and processing of mineral ores. The committee consists of 15 men who have had a vast amount of experience in the field. Government, universities, and industry are all represented. The point of the policy is that the committee will survey the research situation and report on what is available in research and what additional research might be more profitably done. This is where we in the National Science Foundation would stop. It is then up to industry, universities, or certain government departments, if they choose, to carry on into the applied and developmental phases. This seems to be a sound policy for urgent questions of national concern.

MR. MILLER: The Tennessee State Planning Commission has had very definite problems. But if you use the tactful approach, if you never go into a community until invited (which means you may have to wait until somebody builds a filling station next door to the mayor's house before you talk to a civic club on the value of zoning), then the stage is set for action. It is a matter of making the research product fill a recognized need rather than blowing in and saying, "Our product is good; you ought to use it."

One of the comments received after the Conference related to development of active public interest.

C. W. MATTISON (U.S. Forest Service): Basic to interest is knowledge of the resource inventory and condition. To stimulate active public interest, state and federal agencies dealing with the natural resources should keep the public more fully informed about what is happening to these resources and what is being done with those under their jurisdiction.

The Situation: Problems and Methods

Despite much progress in some lines—notably agriculture—most laymen still are by no means keeping abreast of useful research findings on the conservation and development of resources. Problems and techniques were closely interwoven in this phase of the discussion.

GORDON BLACKWELL (University of North Carolina): Any resource development agency, be it federal, state, public, or private, that develops a program based on the results of scientific research, has the problem of getting the significant findings that should guide the program of the agency across to the people.

The Tennessee Valley Authority had a good deal of research going on, a scientific staff with scientific know-how, and the problem of how to communicate the research results to millions of people in the valley. I suppose the agency used the mass media of communication to some extent, but I rather think they didn't count too much on reaching people through newspapers and radio. They worked through local agencies and organized groups, getting them to participate in resource development activities, and then to learn the necessary facts from science which should guide the research development program. This is another way of bridging the gap between scientific facts and behavior of people which is, after all, the final pay-off in both conservation and resource development.

MR. WEAVER: The North Carolina Resource Use Education Commission was set up as a means of getting research and educational agencies together on this problem of communication. Fifty-two organizations, including government resource agencies, colleges, and professional groups, were represented.

One of the biggest projects undertaken was an adult education program that included a series of radio programs and a movie called "Tar Heel Family."

Workshops were put on at the colleges at the request of the Commission. We helped find the staff members and trained them. Probably the biggest contribution in the education field was made by the summer conferences. The conference publications resulted in a guide to resource use education workshops being published by the American Council on Education and cooperated in by other states interested in workshops.

Probably the biggest by-product was that inclusion of all races in the planning provided an opportunity for the discussion of joint problems. Working together on a common problem was the solution to some of our human relations problems.

JOHN E. IVEY, JR. (Southern Regional Education Board): As I remember that operation, another important by-product was that county agents, soil conservation specialists, foresters, and water experts learned to talk and work with public school teachers, with health experts, and with one another. Some of us were appalled to find out how little these differ-

ent groups knew about one another. Here, you could identify a major problem of pathology in state administration, namely, that a number of public agencies—state, federal, and local—trying to serve the same public, were in many cases competing for the time of that public. Here you learned what other groups were doing and how each could supplement the others' efforts—a little thing, but important in terms of increasing the effectiveness of public and private administration of resources.

MR. DOLDER: We used a somewhat similar medium in California, and at about the same time that the work began in North Carolina. The need to promote teaching of conservation in the public schools and to inform the adult population was brought to the attention of the State Director of Education and the State Director of Natural Resources by civic groups and leaders from several areas. A Chief of Conservation Education was appointed in the Department of Natural Resources to serve as liaison between the educators on the one hand and state and federal resource agencies on the other. The two state departments, utilizing their combined financial and personnel resources and working under the direction of this Chief of Conservation Education, have achieved a great deal in the way of publications, conferences, films, and teacher workshops.

LAUREN K. SOTH (*The Des Moines Register and Tribune*): Agriculture is unique in this business of communicating research, in that most of the research is done by public agencies, principally the state land-grant college experiment stations, and the results are disseminated through the extension services. The tremendous increases in productivity in agriculture in the last 50 years coincide with growth of the experiment stations and the extension services.

In rough terms, two-thirds of American agriculture has accepted the experiment stations and extension services; each new idea is grabbed up as it comes out. But a million to a million and a half farm families still farm about as the better farmers did in 1900. A big reservoir of human resources in this country is not being used effectively. That means that the land and other resources are not used well either.

ROBERT N. HOSKINS (Seaboard Air Line Railroad Company): For two years I had the pleasure of serving as National Chairman of the Conservation Committee of the United States Junior Chamber of Commerce. This group is made up largely of young businessmen from the small and large communities; its membership is lacking to a great extent in persons directly connected with any phase of conservation. The Junior Chamber of Commerce is a most active group, and when projects have been thoroughly explained and understood it has proved to be a strong force in bringing about tangible accomplishments. Most projects in which it has participated have been those where results were achieved in a short period of time. When presenting conservation programs of various types, it has been very reluctant to initiate something new.

When a proposal was made whereby the Junior Chamber of Commerce membership, now totalling more than 200,000, might get behind a tree planting program, a definite lack of interest was shown. But thorough explanation of the tangible benefits resulted in the planting of more than 15 million trees through nation-wide Junior Chamber of Commerce efforts.

I am confident that with sound programs and enlightened leadership, a much better understanding can be had, which will bring about a closer relationship between the farmer and the young businessman to help solve problems which are of mutual interest. Leadership in conservation programs must be kept on a continuing basis if the end results are to produce maximum benefits.

The close tie between research and its communication came up again in examples of how pilot plant testing can be a means of spreading ideas.

MR. BARKER: Pilot plant or large-scale testing may also be used as a means of mass projection of information. Back in 1946 Research Corporation financed a mass study on Bataan peninsula. The peninsula was roughly divided into two groups—a control group that got unenriched white rice, their normal diet; and a test group that had vitamin B₁ and iron-enriched rice furnished to them at the same cost. The experiment went on for a year. I believe the annual death rate from beriberi had been about 180 out of every 100,000 deaths. In the control group, that rate stayed essentially constant; but in the test group it came down practically to zero, and within six months after the test it reached zero. The productivity of the population in the test group went up tremendously, because they weren't debilitated with beriberi. That news spread throughout the Philippines just by word of mouth. We began with an attempt to prove the validity of small amounts of data. We needed mass statistics. We ended up with a combination of a mass experiment and a mass medium of transmission of the idea.

MR. SOTH: That is exactly what the land-grant colleges have done. In fact, they began with demonstration projects. They would set up a project in a community and show how certain corn practices or certain hog-feeding practices work, and the news would spread from there. It amounts, really, to selling the research idea to the people.

MR. GRIFFITH: There is a striking need for a channel between research and legislative policy adoption, whether national or state. The obstacle, historically, has been that the legislator is also a delegate. He brings to his task the interests of the district he represents, while research findings are more likely to bear upon a wider approach. They are more likely to involve multiple benefits, often constituting some threats to local interest. That they are couched in statistical and sometimes rather abstruse terms does not improve their normal chance for adoption. However, a factor on the plus side has been introduced. Legislative staffs now include technicians or specialists who must have two competencies to be successful. One is the professional competence of the research worker; the other, the competence to translate the research into dramatic and understandable terms.

The people on the receiving end present some problems of their own. What might be done to raise the general level of receptivity to useful popularizations? On the other hand, how can research findings be made more intelligible to the people who might use them?

MR. BLACKWELL: We can't just look at this as a problem in communication without looking at the consumers at the other end of the line. Their health, education, and other characteristics all have to be taken into account. A newspaper serving many impoverished farmers was interested in knowing how well it was getting across to its public. It found that most of its material was written at a reading comprehension level of about the eleventh or twelfth grade and that the median educational achievement of the adult population in the area was between the sixth and seventh grade. The newspaper immediately took steps to modify its content.

THOMAS V. DOWNING (Virginia State Department of Education): Many people feel the important thing is to get the results of research over to the farmer. It seems to me the important thing is to develop the individual who is to become a farmer, so that he can more efficiently make use of the results of research. We need better trained individuals to replace the sixth and seventh grade level farmers. Looking to the future, greater emphasis should be placed upon the training of farm boys in high school, as well as young farmers out of school. Unless the young farmer of tomorrow is better trained than the farmer he replaces, the benefits of research cannot become fully effective.

MR. BARKER: In going from research to development you run into a great many road blocks. One road block is the inability of the research man to write up his findings in language that others can understand. The Bell System gets around that by publishing what might be called a layman's edition. The reports of the research workers are rephrased so that others within the system can understand them. But that is too expensive for the small organization. Now the researcher in an educational

institution who publishes his paper in the technical press of his professional society is limited by the number of pages available to him. To boil his report down, he uses scientific jargon that is incomprehensible to the average technician or engineer. Consequently, many a development laboratory fails to pick out the important elements that might lead to a new development for that industry. Then, too, the scientific societies do not have large enough budgets to cover all the research going on. There you have another block.

Research and Training in Resource Communication

Discussion of the major problems of disseminating research findings led several participants very close to home for a careful inward look at how fully research and teaching methods are being employed as tools for improving communication in the resources field. As the discussion leader phrased the question: "Let's direct our attention to the problem of using the scientific method itself more effectively in interpreting information to people."

MR. BLACKWELL: The behavioral sciences have been focusing, especially in the last 15 or 20 years, on research in communication. Certain centers are particularly strong in psychology and sociology, focusing on a scientific understanding of communication processes. We see a good deal about public opinion research, audience research, things of that kind. But we see less research that tries to get at processes in groups in communities, and that is what we need if we are going to understand this communication business.

We need research on the planning process itself: How does a community go about planning? One step would be fact-finding or research. What are the various forces operative in the community, the various groups, the informal leadership patterns of the community? What part does the social stratification of the community play in the success or failure of planning a developmental educational program?

Some research is going on along these lines;

355

we are reaching toward at least a beginning of a science of human relations and social action which will help in improving our efforts at cooperation.

MARGARET HICKEY (National Federation of Business and Professional Women's Clubs): We ought to give recognition and encouragement to the research now going on in community relations. Work is being done by universities through their adult education sections or groups. Michigan, for example, has had some very good community delineation studies. Foundations are supporting work of this kind. A Young Adult Education Study has just been completed, with a grant from the Ford people, on our population group between 18 and 35, who belong to community organizations such as 4-H, Y.M., Y.W., church groups, political groups. The study indicates that those young people are better educated than any other age group, but that their interest in problems of a serious nature is much lower. In fact, it is almost a rejection on their part of identification with what may become a controversial issue with economic and political implications. The great problem today seems to be how they can be reached and given a new personal motivation to come into the field.

MR. WEAVER: Three years ago, when the School of Natural Resources was set up at the University of Michigan, the course structure was reorganized to get social science properly represented in the program. The Department of Conservation has interlocking arrangements with other departments—Economics, Political Science, Architecture, Education, Minerals, Health, Forestry, and so on. A Land Utilization Seminar is participated in by eight departments. The students get credit in their own departments and the projects are approved by their department advisers, but it is a joint operation in planning and execution.

The distribution of emphasis is about one-third social science, one-third natural science, and one-third in communication skills. That distribution is working out effectively. We are not quite ready to place resource generalists or conservationists as rapidly as we can train them. We have to put them in a specialty such

as forestry, economics, education, although they can do a bigger job.

MR. JOHNSON: Cornell has a program in conservation education and one for training science teachers and other public school teachers.

The teaching program includes the basic sciences, a field course in natural history, courses in oral and written expression, including journalism; courses in the use of radio, photography, other audio and visual aids, and an educational TV station is being planned.

MR. ECKELBERRY: The teacher education program at Ohio State University, which involves the cooperation of the State Department of Education, the Division of Wildlife, and four other state universities, has three basic characteristics: First, it is a problem-centered program and not an organized subject-matter program. There are no courses in zoology and botany and geology, and so on. Second, one small team of instructors, five during recent years, works with one group of teacher-students—mostly experienced teachers who know what teaching is all about. This is an entirely different situation from a summer school where a teacher takes one course with one professor and one group of students at 10 o'clock, another course with another teacher and another group of students at 11 o'clock, and so on. Third, it involves field study and first-hand experience rather than complete reliance on lectures, books, or movies. The most distinctive teaching method is to talk about a problem, go out and look at it down on the lake shore or up in the hills, and then come back and talk about it some more. It seems to have been very effective.

HOWARD MENDENHALL (Society for the Protection of New Hampshire Forests): After graduation from forestry school, I talked to a number of foresters about whether I should go on with advanced education. The answers I got were: "Yes, go and take some social science. By all means take some psychology. Take some public relations and journalism." These technical men realized the need for some training in the skills of communication and relations with people. I couldn't take all of their advice, but I did talk with some professors of sociology and psychology, and I was disappointed to find how little they knew of natural resources and conservation. On one occasion I traveled with a sociologist, who couldn't for the life of him see the relationship between land use and the living conditions of the people. The gullies in the hillsides, the denuded lands, and the poverty of the people didn't seem related to this city-bred Ph.D.

MR. SOTH: Rural sociologists have done a good deal of research (though not nearly enough) in finding out how farm people learn about new ideas and what motivates them to put these ideas into operation. We know that the upper-level farmers get most of their information on new methods from mass media —newspapers, farm magazines, radio, and now television. They are good enough man-

agers to put the new practices into effect without much person-to-person teaching on the old Extension Service pattern. The other farmers, the lower third, have to be motivated by person-to-person selling, by demonstrations, and so on. It is important for us to realize that we can't use the same method of communication all the way down the line.

MR. IVEY: It seems to me that the very preservation of democracy depends on the solution of the major problems of communication. If you work and live in a society which bases its whole existence on the assumption that people, given the facts, will make the right decisions, then you must realize that unless they get a chance to get the facts in ways that strengthen local, state, and federal cooperation, and stimulate development of individuals into well-rounded human beings, we can actually lose this democracy in which we exist.

CHAIRMAN'S SUMMARY

Our subject matter was "Patterns of Cooperation." This we took to mean the relations between citizens, organizations of all kinds (business, labor, agriculture, and others), and governments at all levels, through which programs of research, planning, education, and action affecting natural resources are carried on. The discussion was based largely on reports of actual cooperative experiences brought out by the participants. The thought was expressed that Section VIII was especially important to the entire Conference because carrying out solutions proposed in other sec-

tions would depend in large measure on the effectiveness of such cooperative relationships.

In our first session we discussed cooperation at the grass roots. After all, the basic purpose of resource programs is to influence the behavior of individuals and groups as well as the management of the resources. Examples were cited from the fields of forestry, farming, wildlife protection, and stream improvement of successful instances of local initiative and application of good conservation measures.

In the second session we talked about problems of cooperation on wider bases. The resource programs of two states—New York and California—were examined from the viewpoint of the variety of their undertakings, their successful innovations, and the difficult problems encountered. Ways of dealing with river valleys and other resource entities transcending state boundaries were discussed, and a number of aspects of interstate compacts and interstate commissions were explored in some detail. The relevant experience of the United States and Canada with problems along their common boundary was noted.

The third session dealt with the problems of translating knowledge into action by developing effective lines of communication between resource researchers and those who ultimately apply research findings. Instances of the need for better communication were cited, most of them requiring improvements in the processes of planning and application. It was brought out that patterns of social purposes and the necessary competences have to exist before successful cooperative action programs can be achieved.

In our discussions we did not achieve, nor did we seek, agreement on several questions, such as:

The relative emphasis to be placed on local initiative and responsibility as compared to stimulation and support by state, regional, and national agencies and groups (although it was generally agreed that someone must provide the spark of leadership);

What the precise allocation of responsibilities between public and private agencies, and between the various levels of government, should be;

In what instances one or another specific device or organizational form—such as the valley authority, the interstate compact, or the local resources district—should be used, recognizing that each approach has particular advantages.

We can report substantial agreement on several important points:

Problems of resource management should not be left to the inevitable increase of scientific knowledge and technology. Americans, through their government and private bodies, have to take an active interest in resource management if problems are to be dealt with in time.

Our whole political tradition, the character of our people, and the organization of our society are such that resources planning and management can never be completely centralized. There must always be a degree of dependence upon voluntary cooperation between individuals, groups, and government agencies.

Since public agencies contribute much to our effort, it is essential that, regardless of the extent of their powers, they be organized so as to be responsive to the public interest. A clear grouping of functions, coordination of planning, and streamlining of operations in agencies dealing with resources at all levels would facilitate cooperation with private persons as well as intergovernmental cooperation.

The most effective cooperative programs have been those that attacked urgent problems, were definable in scope, had specific objectives, or resulted in easily understood gains. However, there is need to work out better integrated programs to meet complex resource situations.

The will and ability to cooperate—to talk to each other without getting mad, as one participant put it—are essential. The behavioral sciences are providing increasingly useful knowledge about how to organize groups and communicate more effectively; therefore, resources scientists can profit from exchange of knowledge with the social scientists. Cooperation may be an art, but it is not magic.

It was the sense of the meeting that much more needs to be done if the full potentialities of cooperative efforts for resources development and conservation are to be realized.

Specifically, the following proposals were strongly supported:

1. There should be increased emphasis on resource problems in both youth and adult education.

2. We need research on how to utilize the behavioral sciences and communications techniques to carry knowledge of the best resources practices to the people.

3. Finally, and probably most important, building upon the work of this section, there should be continuing study and investigation of patterns of cooperation, either by the organizers of the Conference and/or by some other suitable group. As an example, special study should be given to the administrative arrangements, fiscal and other, which handicap cooperative resource programs as between the states and the national government, as between the states themselves, and as between the states and local agencies and groups.

H. CHRISTIAN SONNE
December 4, 1953

Case Reports of Cooperation[*]

Cooperation at the Grass Roots

1. Brandywine Valley Association
2. Lincoln County Fish and Game Association—State of Maine Atlantic Sea-Run Salmon Commission
3. Michigan United Conservation Clubs—Michigan Department of Conservation
4. Muskingum Watershed Conservancy District
5. Soil Conservation Districts
6. Trees for Tomorrow, Inc.
7. Wisconsin State Department of Conservation—Dell Creek Watershed Association
8. Wisconsin Valley Improvement Company

Wider Bases of Cooperation

9. Cooperative Forest Fire Control Program —U. S. Forest Service
10. International Joint Commission
11. International Pacific Halibut Commission
12. Interstate Commission on the Delaware River (INCODEL)—Corps of Engineers
13. Proposal for Missouri Basin Commission
14. Proposal for Missouri Basin Interstate Compact

---

[*] Summaries of these case reports in limited quantity are available on request to Resources for the Future, Inc.

15. Proposal for Missouri Valley Administration
16. Northeastern Interstate Forest Fire Protection Compact
17. Ohio River Valley Water Sanitation Commission
18. Southern Pulpwood Conservation Association
19. Southern Regional Education Board

Taking Full Advantage of Research

20. American Potash Institute—State Land-Grant Colleges
21. Atomic Energy Commission—first four industrial participation teams
22. Cooperative Weed Control Program of the Bureau of Plant Industry, Soil, and Agricultural Engineering
23. Bureau of Reclamation—Project Development Farms
24. Connecticut Forest and Park Association —Connecticut Agricultural Experiment Station
25. Institute for Research in Social Science— Southern Association of Science and Industry
26. Missouri State Geological Survey, U.S. Geological Survey, and five Missouri mining companies

TWO BROAD
CURRENT ISSUES

TWO ISSUES OF TIMELY INTEREST to all participants were discussed in Conference-wide forum.

The first meeting, presided over by Lewis Webster Jones, Vice-Chairman of the Conference and President of Rutgers University, dealt with the question *The Public Lands—Who Should Control Them?* Judge Robert W. Sawyer, of Bend, Oregon, spoke for retaining federal control of the public lands; Rep. Wesley A. D'Ewart, of Montana, favored greater state and local participation in their management.

The second meeting debated *How Much Should We Depend on Foreign Resources?* Herman W. Steinkraus, Vice-Chairman of the Conference and President of the Bridgeport Brass Company, presided. Speakers were Andrew Fletcher, President of the St. Joseph Lead Company; Charles P. Taft, President of the Committee for a National Trade Policy; and Robert Garner, Vice-President of the International Bank for Reconstruction and Development.

The addresses of these five speakers are summarized below, together with extracts from the record where subsequent discussion supplemented the original statements.

The Public Lands—
Who Should Control Them?

FROM THE RECORD

• MR. SAWYER: In the course of its history the United States has been the owner of nearly three-fourths of the land within its borders. By one route or another, two-thirds of its holdings have gone into other, and for the most part private, ownership. Most of this title change took place more than 40 years ago.

Then there began reacquisition by the federal authority in an amount that now stands at, in round figures, 53 million acres. Roughly half of this acreage has been acquired for national forest purposes. There are, however, several categories of lands in federal ownership that have been reserved for special uses. Among them are the national parks, the national monuments, wildlife refuges, military reservations, Atomic Energy Commission lands, power lines and irrigation project rights-of-way, reservoir floors. Here, ownership and control go hand in hand, and with these lands therefore we are not immediately concerned.

Of the public lands we are here considering, the national forests are the cream, and the so-called unreserved public domain the skimmed remainder of Uncle Sam's land estate. The public domain—some 180 million acres—is virtually all in the 11 western states. So, too, is by far the greater part of the national forests in which are the lands that were first withdrawn to create the watershed and forest reserves. Together these two acreages include approximately 80 percent of the nation's total public land. Ninety percent of all lands in the present federal total have never been in private ownership.

Each of these classes of land—the public domain and the national forests—is an area of multiple uses, five in all. On each there is grazing; from each timber is taken. Grazing is the more important use on the public domain; the tree supply is more important in the forests. Two other uses of these lands are for recreation and wildlife habitat. Finally, there is the use that transcends everything else—maintenance of water supply.

These five uses may be divided into two classes—profit uses and service uses. The profit uses include a rather wide spread of commercial ventures using public domain land, but chiefly they are engaged in by private operators, both big and little, whose use of the public domain is in association with use of their own lands for ranch or mill. They, or some of the more vocal of their number, would like control of these lands. That is why the question before us is posed. Shall they control these public lands or shall the control be in the hands of the people of the nation through their federal government? There is only one possible answer: These public lands should be controlled by their owners—the people of the United States.

The profit motive is the cornerstone of our great American private enterprise system.

With that motive there can be no quarrel. Throughout that system, however, there are restraints and regulations enforced for the common good, and here on the public lands where there are service uses vital to our national well-being the profit uses must be subordinated. That subordination calls for public rather than private control.

At one time there was no control on the public domain lands other than that exercised by the man with the water hole and the Winchester. The profit use only prevailed. No attention was paid to the service uses of the land. Under these conditions, the one-time sea of grass that covered the western range ceased to be. There was overgrazing. There was erosion. There was a quick runoff of precipitation instead of ground storage. Streams dried up. Brush and noxious weeds succeeded grass.

This abuse of range led, finally, in 1934 to the passage of the Taylor Grazing Act. Though a considerable acreage of the public domain was not covered, 140 million acres were reserved for regulation. However, appropriations have never been adequate for effective administration. Just when they had reached a point where the bare essentials of range management could be effectively applied, they were cut back so as to render the administration—the owner, if you please—impotent in control of the land. Today, the users have the upper hand. Private profit use rather than public service use predominates.

In the national forests, public control of the profit use has been far better established and maintained. But efforts have constantly been made—measures are pending even now—to limit the public control of the forest range. What the Forest Service seeks in its management of the profit uses of the forests in its care is sustained yield of the forage on the range and of the timber capital.

In operating these public lands and making them or their products available for profit uses, their federal managers under the authority of Congressional legislation, have set up regulations, uniform throughout all areas. This would not be possible were the control otherwise situated, when the profit motive would, of necessity, dictate the operations. The sum of this is that there *should* be public control of the profit use and since there is no profit in the service uses there *must* be public control.

Concerning these service uses: Recreation and wildlife are unimportant to the profit use, if not actually obnoxious. The managers of the public lands are as aware as are the owners of private lands of the dangers involved in keeping lands open for the free use and enjoyment of the general public. They know it will not pay direct dollars and cents dividends. But they and all the rest of us know that in our country service uses of this kind are something the public has a right to expect—something that in the long run will pay dividends worth much more than dollars. These service uses such as hunting, fishing, hiking, camping, winter sports, unimpaired natural scenery, and the general recreation opportunities which are a part of the multiple use values of the public lands require, for their preservation, control of these lands by the federal authority.

And now I come to the most important use of all—the use of the public lands for the protection, management, development, and maintenance of water supplies. Water is basic to our food supply. It is an essential in industry. Without water we perish. And in wide areas of the United States the water supply comes entirely or largely from the public lands.

There exists in many of our mountains a delicate balance between soil, vegetation, and water. We cannot log, graze, or build roads on some steep hillsides without seriously interfering with this delicate balance. Other areas may tolerate the removal of forest crops if carefully done, while still larger expanses present no difficulties in the harvesting of all forest crops.

Nature, as weather, plays a high part in the annual water drama, but man can have an influence, too, and whether that influence is for the good or for the bad, depends on how he has managed the public lands. Proper management or use of land should be the highest goal to be sought, but it is not a profit use. Its earnings are chiefly for the downstream water users, the local public of that watershed. The control, then, of these public lands where the waters rise should be in the hands of the people

and managed by their federal agencies.

For our public lands as a whole I urge that, since in unregulated profit use there is bound to be disregard of service use values, there must be regulation; and the control of all should be in the hands of the owners—the people of the United States to whom the service uses are next to invaluable in the matter of wildlife and recreation, and supremely invaluable in the matter of water.

● MR. D'EWART: I can agree with Judge Sawyer on his objectives, but I do not altogether agree with him on the road by which we should reach those objectives.

Let us take a look at the present control of these public lands we are discussing which, if we exclude the national parks and monuments, national wildlife refuges, federal water projects, military reservations, wilderness areas, and that part of the national forests that is not primarily used for grazing, comprise some 310 million acres of federal-owned land generally classified as timber and grass land.

First, there are some 5,000 laws, and regulations beyond number, controlling their use and management. Second, the areas are now under the direction of three departments divided into eight or more bureaus and agencies each with its own personnel, each under different law and regulation, each charging different fees for use, and each with its own objectives—often in conflict with another agency or government. To add to the difficulty of management, the areas under different bureaus and agencies are often intermingled. Lastly, the head offices of these agencies in Washington, D.C., are hundreds of miles away from the lands which they administer. All this makes for a complex landlord-manager-tenant relationship in which you and I are the landlords, the bureaus are the managers, and the local users are the tenants. Certainly, no one will argue that such a situation of present control and management is in the best public interest.

What should be our objectives? I think they can be briefly stated: conservation—that is, wise use without waste; development of the great natural resources that are found on and under the surface of these public lands; revitalization of our renewable resources; maintenance of adequate reserves of nonrenewable resources until substitutes are found. In the development and use of these resources, we should encourage private enterprise; solicit the cooperation of local government and institutions; go forward with federal action only when the public interest cannot otherwise be served; maintain at all times the rights of the individuals and the integrity of the states; and avoid monopoly.

Fundamentally, I believe that whenever possible, private responsibility for protection of land is best for this country. It places the burden of protection on the beneficiaries; it allows development without government expense; it brings an economic factor of cost versus benefit into the picture; it gives political stability and soundness to the nation by respecting the rights of individuals as partners in national welfare. Let no one think that I advocate policies contrary to good conservation practice; I feel that self-interest is a conservation force; that policing power can be effective under local governments; and that public ownership should be utilized only when other controls prove to be inadequate or when damage from possible abuse would be too irreparable to risk.

It was no accident that enemies of the American system put the elimination of private property as their first objective. The trends of recent years do not represent what is best for the United States. We must reverse them insofar as they fail to contribute positively to the benefit of this nation.

President Eisenhower, in a message to Congress on July 31, 1953, set forth a program for the control, development, and wise use of these public lands and the resources on and under them. He said: "Our basic problem is to carry forward the tradition of conservation, improvement, and wise use and development of our land and water resources— a policy initiated 50 years ago under the leadership of President Theodore Roosevelt. To do this within the framework of a sound fiscal policy and in the light of defense needs will require the maximum cooperation among the

states and local communities, farmers, businessmen, and other private citizens, and the federal government. . . . It will require the revitalization of renewable resources by users who should be entitled to reasonable assurances in connection with authorized uses. It will require adherence to sound principles for the financing and the sharing of the cost of multipurpose land and water resource development. It will require improved federal organization to accomplish a more logical division of responsibilities among the various federal agencies in order that resource development programs may be carried on with the greatest efficiency and the least duplication. It will require comprehensive river-basin planning with the cooperation of state and local interests . . . public lands should be made available for their best use under conditions that promote stability for communities and individuals and encourage full development of the resources involved."

Here you have a program in our best tradition, one that will require the maximum cooperation of all of us as individuals, state and local communities, and the federal government. It is not planned that the federal government shall carry on alone. Clear guidelines must be enacted setting forth its proper functions. It is hoped that through the new Hoover Commission and through the Commission on Intergovernmental Relations many of the objectives set forth in the President's message can be worked out.

My state of Montana has long recognized its responsibilities in the control of its resources and has set up under state law a Grass Conservation Commission, a Forestry Board, an Oil and Gas Conservation Commission, a Park Service, and a Water Conservation Board. It has provided for irrigation districts, weed control districts, soil conservation districts, state grazing districts, and has taken other steps to assure the wise use, development, and control of our great natural resources. Montana's record in resource management and development completely refutes the belief in some circles that the states are somehow subject to baneful influences and are not competent to manage their own affairs.

In the same circles, there has been a growing belief that the people cannot be trusted. Yet one of the greatest forces for conservation is the self-interest of the individual in protection of his property. I hope that we will use this force to the fullest possible degree.

The people of the 14 western states, where half of the surface is federally controlled, think that there are those among their citizens who are to be trusted to cooperate wisely in the management of these areas in the best public interest. They recognize that the special areas I have already mentioned as being set apart are great national assets and that their benefits reach far beyond the state in which they happen to be located. These should remain in federal control and the responsibilities of the Secretary in charge should not be impaired. However, public-spirited citizens wish for a greater measure of local recognition in the development and use of these areas and they feel they could make a material contribution to their use and development. In addition, there are certain parts of the public domain and the Bankhead-Jones Title III lands whose use and development are primarily local. These areas should be re-examined to see if some of them cannot be better managed by the states and in some instances placed on the tax rolls.

The Uniform Federal Grazing Lands Act (H.R. 4023), which I introduced last year, offered improvement in the system of management of these lands, insofar as livestock use is concerned, without in any way changing control or affecting public and other uses. It would have done this by introducing a uniform system of managing grazing on the national forests, the public domain, and the Soil Conservation Service lands.

Because there were objections to including lands of the Department of Agriculture in the same bill as lands of the Department of the Interior, new legislation, applying only to Forest Service lands (now including Soil Conservation Service lands), has since been introduced by Senator Aiken and Congressman Hope.

However, these two bills attempt a solution of only a small part of these problems. They do not answer the question of future control of public lands. In the control, management, and use of these public lands we must never lose sight of the fact that our greatest asset is a strong, upright, free citizenry. Such a citizenry can be developed, not by bureaucratic control, but by use of its capabilities through encouragement in the wise use of our great natural resources.

The opinions expressed by Judge Sawyer and Representative D'Ewart drew from Conference participants a good deal of varied comment, some by direct statement, others in the form of written questions to which one or other of the speakers replied.

BERNARD DEVOTO (Cambridge, Mass.): In effect, the Congressman says, "Cannot we westerners be trusted to take better care of these lands than the government bureaus?" The answer is, "No, they cannot be trusted."

Among the areas Congressman D'Ewart specifically excepts as being protected forever are the national parks. That is not borne out by the history of the Ellsworth Bill. This bill provides compensation to a timber operator on a sustained-yield basis, if his land should be required by the government, in the form either of money or selection from the national timberlands of an equivalent amount of timber —harking back to the operations of the Timberlake Act, under which some of the most grotesque and indecent of all land frauds were perpetrated.

When that bill went into Congressman D'Ewart's Subcommittee on Public Lands, the national parks were specifically exempted. When it came out, that exemption had been withdrawn. If that bill were to be passed now, a lumberman could go into Yosemite, or into any of the "protected" national parks and get its timber.[1]

In 1946, the Senator from Wyoming introduced a bill which, if passed, would eventually have provided for the sale of grazing lands in the national parks.

No, even in the national parks we cannot trust people to protect them.

---

[1] Two months after the Conference, this bill (H.R. 4646) was reworded to exempt the national parks. (See Part 2, House Report 972).

I wonder if the citizens of southern California are willing to depend for their industrial and domestic water, or the farmers of the Imperial Valley for their irrigation water, on the good citizenship of those who own forested watershed land in Wyoming. I wonder if the citizens of Washington and Oregon are willing to depend on the Congressman's own state to police the headwater streams that provide them with water for their industrial development. I do not think they are.

Incidentally, the Congressman was talking almost exclusively about the Forest Service when he mentioned the great distance dividing the lands from the heads of government bureaus. In his own state, the effective control is exercised from the city of Missoula, which he can reach from his own home in two hours by automobile at an expense of 60 cents, and where he can get a ruling which will not involve Washington at all.

WILLIAM VOIGT (Izaak Walton League of America): Most of the attacks on federal management have come about because management of the national forests has been more concerned with the long-range public interest than with the immediate profit desires of livestock grazers and other profit users. In this respect the Forest Service has been more truly a faithful public servant than some of the other federal agencies involved. In this connection there is a bill, H.R. 6081, which is intended to upgrade the administration of the public domain to the standard we now enjoy in the national forests. If Mr. D'Ewart hopes for the passage of the two bills he mentioned, I believe he should know there is a considerable body of resource conservation thought in this country that also hopes for the enactment of H.R. 6081.

HUGH B. WOODWARD (New Mexico Game Association): Congressman D'Ewart says that we in the West are ready to take over the administration of our own affairs. In the state of New Mexico, we have 12 million acres selected by the Land Commissioner and patented to the state by the federal government for the benefit of our educational institutions.

Since their taking over, those lands—our best grazing lands—have been administered at the will of the lessee, with no supervision and no regulation against misuse and overuse. Under his lease, he may exclude the public from all recreational privileges; and he has paid a uniform rental of 3 cents per acre to the state of New Mexico for the benefit of public institutions, when lands in private ownership side by side with those state lands are commanding a rental of from 15 to 50 cents an acre. I, as one westerner, feel that until such time as the states demonstrate their capacity and willingness to manage those lands for the benefit of all the people, we are not ready to have a change in administration.

MR. D'EWART: I am indeed sorry that the government of New Mexico manages its state lands so poorly. In Montana we have 5 million acres of state-owned land. Last year, those 5 million acres brought into our State Public School Fund something like 10 million dollars. We have in our state 34-odd million acres of federally owned land. Last year, those 34-odd million acres of land brought to our state 1.7 million dollars. Now, which was the better managed? Which returned the most to the schools, the state, and the local governments?

QUESTION: How does the Congressman justify his position when none of the western states, with the exception of Montana, has any effective conservation measures for forest lands owned by them?

MR. D'EWART: I know that some of the states have not gone so far as Montana in passing appropriate legislation. Recently we had in our Committee a bill whereby the federal government would cooperate with states in financing small irrigation projects. We found cases where even the constitution of certain states prohibited their taking part with the federal government in that kind of an enterprise. Some states are aware of this problem and are looking forward to its solution.

QUESTION: Does participation of the owner, namely, the federal government agency and management, imply veto power in proposals put forward by local management?

MR. D'EWART: No. We have been going

through a stage of adjustment. In my state the Forest Service and the Bureau of Land Management now get along very well with the local units. I cannot say that altogether with regard to Indian lands, but Indian lands are not true federal lands.

QUESTION: Would not the question be solved if management standards and land fees under public lands programs were brought up to the standards and fees of the Forest Service? Could economies be effected by combining the two responsible services?

MR. D'EWART: Unquestionably, some shifting of the responsibilities, as recommended by the President, can end in wiser and better use of the public lands. Where the lands are intermingled, as they are for example in Judge Sawyer's state, we have wasted effort and complications of management. In that area there are Forest Service lands; intermingled with these are privately owned lands, lands administered by the Bureau of Land Management, and other lands. The resulting confusion has created difficulty in getting rights-of-way through the differently managed areas so that insect-infested timber might be harvested. That is the kind of thing that needs to be corrected.

QUESTION: Would you limit the amount of federal mineral lands which could be leased to a company if that company had already under lease state-held lands containing the same mineral, but such lands were not being diligently worked due to extremely low-rent costs?

MR. SAWYER: I would say if the federal law permitted an individual or a company to enter on public lands to search for minerals, it would make no difference whether he or the company owned lands elsewhere, and whether or not he or the company were operating them.

QUESTION: Are the public lands to be expanded, particularly by eminent domain and condemnation?

MR. SAWYER: I believe there should be no use of eminent domain for the taking over of private land by federal authority unless there is need for public land for some special federal use.

With regard to the national forests, if it will aid management to straighten boundaries, eliminate privately owned land within the boundaries, take into the forests more land on the borders that is not in the forests, then those things, I think, should be done. Apart from such purposes that have to do with management, I believe there should be no general expansion of federal ownership.

QUESTION: Does Congressman D'Ewart know of any case in which private interests have taken over public domain and successfully revitalized the renewable resources?

MR. D'EWART: Montana's State Grazing Law was set up so that it could lease different intermingled ownerships, put them under one management, and thereby get better grazing practices—practices to benefit the state, the users, and all concerned.

How Much Should We Depend on Foreign Resources?

FROM THE RECORD

● MR. FLETCHER: With the increase in population, this country will, over a period, undoubtedly use more foreign production. But, especially in view of the vagaries of the foreign market, it is difficult to determine how much we should depend on foreign resources. There

can be little argument that domestic production of lead and zinc will decline if our program in relation to mining is along the lines suggested by Mr. Lewis Douglas in his report to the President on British-American trade and currency problems, or by Mr. Henry Ford

II in his very competent address of October 26, 1953, "Expanded Trade and World Peace."

I am going to speak on lead and zinc because I know something about these commodities and because I think they are typical of other world resources.

Granted that the United States produces only two-thirds of its lead and zinc requirements and must import approximately one-third, the unfortunate fact remains that this one-third from abroad is at best an uncertain factor in the supply picture. For example, in 1951, when industrial activity was high and the United States needed lead, total imports were 220,000 tons, or only 22 percent of the required supply. In 1952, with roughly the same consumption requirements, imports amounted to 630,000 tons and accounted for over 55 percent of the supply.

The alternate withholding and flooding of our markets by the foreign suppliers is a major factor in the wide price fluctuations on the metal. In early 1951, for example, the price rose to 19 cents a pound, but dropped within the year to 13 cents. Under similar circumstances in 1948 and 1949, lead dropped from 21.5 cents a pound to 12 cents within a six-month period.

The problem of these fluctuations in price and supply is just as serious for the consumers as for the producers. And to the extent that more and more domestic mines are closed down, the American consumer must place greater dependence on foreign sources, which do not prove reliable.

I have often asked consumers of our product in this country a question similar to the one we are considering tonight: "To what extent do we wish to depend on our domestic mining industry?" The answer usually is that we should not produce less than our yearly average since World War II. But an argument often starts when I ask "How?" And it gets even more heated when I add: "We must find some way to make up the difference between the domestic and the foreign costs of production."

We must not forget that the average cost of producing lead, zinc, and possibly copper in the United States is, and seems destined to continue to be, greater than the average cost outside the United States. This is primarily due to our higher standard of living, with the resultant higher taxes, higher labor rates, higher material and equipment costs. And it is exactly for this same reason that the cost of producing wheat, cotton, wool, petroleum, corn, watches, glass, china, ships, and many other products is higher in this country than in European lands. To date I have not heard it suggested that we should give up farming in the United States, buy our supplies abroad, and save our fields under the slogan, "Trade, not Aid," in the belief that it would be cheaper, our foreign friends would have more dollars to buy our manufactured products, and, when an emergency arose, we could replant. You cannot economically "replant" a shut-down mine. You cannot turn on metal production as you do water from a tap.

Now, the higher United States farm costs are being offset by parity price programs, and the higher cotton, wool, sugar, and other commodity costs by import quotas. Why, then, is it inadvisable to help our domestic mining industry?

I do not share the belief that we are a "have-not" nation and that we must save our few remaining assets by keeping them locked up in the ground. I believe that the United States still has an enormous wealth of natural resources. But, in my opinion, there is no quicker way to drop into the "have-not" class than to let our mines flood, have no younger men coming into the industry, have no incentive or organization to find new ore reserves, no desire to develop and improve mining machinery, and finally to lose all technical know-how.

Many people do not, I think, realize that in reality we "create" raw materials. For example, aluminum cost over $500 per pound in 1861 at the start of the Civil War. There were ample ore reserves, but because of price there was a shortage of metal. Today, because of technical developments, aluminum is ample for our requirements and it is cheap. There is ample titanium ore, but not metal, just because a cheap method has not as yet been found to produce titanium metal. But I am sure that we shall find one. The same applies to other scarce materials.

It is difficult to make a competent statement as to how much we can "create," but I have never been very much impressed with predictions as to supply and consumption in, say, 1975. I have sometimes thought that the depressing predictions were no more than propaganda to justify the "have-not" theory and the necessity to adopt government controls.

Now, production of lead and zinc in the United States and the conversion of ore resources into reserves have been very adversely affected by the reduction in the prewar tariff, that was equivalent to roughly 36 to 42 percent of the value of the metal, to only 6 to 8 percent today. And this reduction was made during a period of very advancing costs. I assure you that we in the United States can create the raw materials if there is sufficient economic need for them and if we are not placed in a position where our means of creation have been shut down. But if you think that I am just crying "Wolf" when I state that the major portion of our lead and zinc industry will be shut down unless some constructive action is taken, and that our great national resources will lie unknown and undeveloped, just take time to read the brief filed with the U. S. Tariff Commission on November 14, 1953, by Mr. Otto Herres, Chairman of the National Lead and Zinc Committee.

We in the United States, I feel, are basically unselfish, and I think that our record supports this conclusion. But sooner or later, I am reasonably sure that our leaders, both inside and outside of government, realizing the absolute necessity of maintaining a strong domestic economy during the cold war, must consider, first, what is the procedure that is for the best interests of a majority of our citizens. And then, if there is anything left over, let's distribute that.

There is no doubt that foreign nations cannot buy from us if we do not buy from them or if we do not give them dollars. But just as they are handicapped without dollars, our own citizens will be handicapped without dollars through curtailment of employment and loss of jobs.

There is no doubt that the world will be better off when currency manipulation can be eliminated and free convertibility reinstated, export and import controls forgotten, tariff barriers lessened, and we hear no more about differential exchange rates or handling unneeded world production by international buffer stocks, no more about multilateral government contracts, quotas, cartels, and other such devices.

But it seems to me that our world program should not be just a one-way United States street; foreign nations themselves should do more to raise their standard of living by adopting their own "Trade, not Aid." For example, France has recently placed duties on metal imports from various countries; Germany earlier this year exported large quantities of zinc, many tons of which found their way to this country, but now Germany has put an embargo on exports. Even our friends to the north are participants in the Empire preference bloc, and they actually have higher tariffs on lead and zinc than ours.

Under existing conditions, I therefore think that we should maintain a practical attitude and develop our own natural resources. We should not jeopardize the safety of our nation, and possibly of the Free World, by shutting down our mines. It is, of course, necessary to have efficient and large-capacity manufacturing plants, but it is even more essential that these plants have raw materials with which to work. They won't have them unless they at least have a stockpile, and in my opinion the best and cheapest stockpile is a prosperous mining industry.

One of my disagreements with the Paley Report is with the underlying suggestion that raw materials should be purchased in the cheapest markets. At the present time the cheapest markets are foreign, but I am not sure that they will be when there is little domestic production. We need a prosperous mining industry as an economic safeguard, just as we need it for national defense.

It is unnecessary for me to detail what, in my opinion, is possibly the best plan for covering the difference between the lower foreign and the higher domestic costs of production.

Many of you have heard me comment on the meaninglessness of tax-saving incentives to an industry that is losing money or is shut down; also, on why import quotas are difficult to administer. The industry opposes a subsidy similar to the Premium Price Plan of World War II, as it leads to inefficiency and in the end will once more demoralize the domestic miners. A flat subsidy is, of course, the easiest solution for our government, or stockpiling, but neither of these methods will curtail the excess world production.

I still think that a sliding-scale, anti-dumping tax—we in the industry use the word "tax" because everyone seems to shudder when anybody mentions tariff—is the best solution, as it gives protection only when needed. It would be reduced as the domestic price increased, and completely eliminated when demand is in balance with supply.

The important matter, it seems to me, is not for us at this conference to decide how much we should depend on foreign resources, but rather whether the best interests of our country will not be served by having a prosperous mining industry. If so, then we should all strive towards that goal.

• MR. TAFT: The fear of what is going to happen from imports—because it obviously hasn't happened yet—is something that is quite characteristic of discussions in this field of raw materials. But the fear is not always justified, and I cannot accept Mr. Fletcher's inference that if imports are allowed to come in, or if the tariff is not increased, the lead and zinc industries are going to fold up.

The best estimate I can make of the low-cost production of both lead and zinc—and the low-cost production of zinc involves certain lead production that would otherwise be high-cost production—is that, without any tariff, there are certainly 300,000 tons a year of lead and 475,000 tons of zinc that would be produced in competition with anybody. Maybe you don't make as much profit on it, but I am talking about living and continuing and running a successful business. The point is that we are not going to lose those industries; part of them, perhaps, and that I want

to discuss, but let's not talk about losing all of both industries.

Now, the main question is, can we supply our essential basic raw materials from within the United States? It seems to me that the answer is perfectly simple: We cannot.

There are three categories of our raw materials. First, we have plenty of coal, plenty of lumber, plenty of sulfur, molybdenum, and short-staple cotton. There are others, but those are the main ones or typical ones in the first category.

Second, we now import 7 percent of our iron ore, 31 percent of our primary copper, 25 percent of our primary lead, 20 percent of our primary zinc, 11 percent of our wood pulp, and 12 percent of our oil.

Then, there is a third category. We have no chrome, no tin, no cobalt, nickel, graphite, quartz crystals, or tantalum. We have only 4 percent of our manganese needs, 1 percent of our mica, and 15 percent of our mercury.

I am not going to argue about whether we are a "have-not" nation, exhausting our reserves—I am assuming that we are not. All I am saying is that we are, in fact, closer to self-sufficiency than any other major power except perhaps Russia; but, in fact also, our production of nearly all the materials in the second and third categories represents progressively less of our total consumption demands. If we went back into war, they would be even less adequate. We wouldn't and we couldn't be self-sufficient.

Now, certainly we should encourage exploration in the United States and on the North American Continent for all items in which we are short; however, even high-cost payment for domestic production, as against low-cost payment for higher-grade foreign production, could not make us self-sufficient. We don't want to race for self-sufficiency. That certainly undermines our standard of living and helps to produce war.

If, on the other hand, the argument is based solely on national defense, then why are not Canada and Mexico just as good war sources as the United States? This kind of economic isolationism is certainly the counsel of despair. We have to rely on foreign resources to some important degree, and we are deeply concerned to make them readily and safely available.

Certainly, we should subsidize by contract the explorations for these minerals that we need the most, just as we did during the war. And I would submit, in spite of what Mr. Fletcher has said, that we should subsidize by contract truly marginal higher-cost mines, where the national interest and security really require it in order to have working mines at once in case of war.

An adequate stockpile gives plenty of time for marginal mines to get into production. And I think I am correct in saying that one of the industry problems, as it is in coal, is that even slight price increases do actually open marginal mines and do add to a surplus that can then accentuate a price swing in the other direction. Mr. Fletcher says you can't turn mines on and off. Some of the marginal mines do exactly that, and that's what gives you some of your trouble in the business.

There is no need, certainly, to keep all the highest-cost mines open either. The sliding-scale tariff, I submit, is a thoroughly bad remedy. What it does is to attempt to produce a stable high price in the United States at the expense of foreign producers, especially in Mexico and Canada, where it would undermine and perhaps destroy by continuously fluctuating prices the very enterprises upon which we must rely in substantial part in time of war.

Not only that, but this tariff would produce immediate reprisals, and justifiably so. It is one more piece of what can only be described as the economic warfare now going on between Canada and the United States.

Any tariff is government intervention, not quite in harmony with a free-enterprise system, although sometimes it has to be used. The tariff is a concealed subsidy, which is no doubt why it is preferred. Only the few direct consumers kick about a tariff. The direct subsidy is out in the open where it has constantly to be justified. In the case of a metal like manganese, of which we import 96 percent, the injustice certainly becomes crystal clear.

Tariffs—and quotas too, for that matter—have as their principal result the raising of the price to protect the high-cost producer. And since St. Joseph Lead in southern Missouri or New Jersey Zinc in the East have well-operated, low-cost mines which can compete, they are not in that category. The effect of the tariff is to increase their profit margins. A discussion of average costs, it seems to me, is quite beside the point, because there is no such thing as an average cost. You have costs that range from the marginal producer down to the very profitable low-cost producer. The statement that our costs are higher here is absolutely incorrect, with the exception of a few areas. In general, our technology puts us way ahead. The outstanding example that I have seen was given in a report of the rice industry in the northern part of California, where rice is produced at a cost of 15 man-hours per acre, whereas the cost in Japan is 900 man-hours. You can afford to pay 60 times the wages in California in producing rice and still compete, assuming that other costs are equal.

The proposed zinc tariff has been estimated to add to our consumer costs something around $200 million, where the subsidy would only be a fraction of that—maybe $10 to $40 million, to give you some sort of comparable figure.

The subsidy method certainly has the highest direct relation to the objective at the lowest cost, and with the least damage to our foreign relations. That is a sound principle to govern intervention in our economic system. It is clearly a case where the national interest should prevail.

The extraordinary thing about all this is that it comes from pressures of people who abhor socialism and object to any slightest criticism of the free-enterprise system. What they are demanding, like the lead and zinc industry, is further intervention for their benefit.

Now, I am certainly not proposing to neglect or ignore the damage that may come from imports. I would endorse government assistance to communities in adjustment to new production—loans perhaps, extension of unemployment compensation, faster depreciation of new machinery and equipment. I would endorse special measures where damages occur in a one-industry community, isolated from other job opportunities, when tariffs are reduced.

I have here a clipping from *The New York Times* of November 1, datelined Park City, Utah, October 31, 1953. It has to do with lead and zinc mining and the effect the ghost towns produced, but it states: "Since other industries in Utah and neighboring states are prosperous, there is little or no visible hardship; the mine workers have been absorbed." That happens in many cases. Where it doesn't, then the local community and the state, and even the federal government, should take appropriate action. But the national interest should control policy.

Now, a second element is needed to protect ourselves, in addition to encouraging the domestic interest when it is found in the national interest. In the case of necessary supplies from abroad, we should encourage foreign investment by tax policy and by appropriate negotiations to improve the climate for investment in other nations.

Foreign nations themselves have to increase their productivity in order to get rid of exchange controls and, in some cases, their tariffs and quotas. The danger to world progress, as a matter of fact, is not so much that excessive imports will damage us—they may to some small degree—as that foreign nations cannot compete in our markets with many of their products, and therefore cannot, by any mutual relaxation of barriers, earn enough more dollars to increase substantially their purchasing power from us. We are now beating Great Britain in Canada on quite a number of products, though they pay less tariff than we do.

In any event, they have no chance to earn those dollars unless we make this U.S. market predictable. We must get rid of the uncertainties in valuations, as proposed in the second Jenkins Bill, and the remaining uncertainties in classifications. We must develop a policy upon which exporters and importers can rely for at least five years in advance. Surely, we cannot raise our tariffs at this time, but sta-

bility is nearly as important as reductions in trade barriers by us or, on the other hand, by other countries. There are some foreign barriers which are extremely serious, I should say —the currency restrictions of the sterling bloc, for instance. The sliding-scale tariff would be certainly a close second.

The stockpile purchasing has not promoted this kind of stability. I am a little doubtful, I am frank to say, about the proposals for various sorts of international buffer stock operations. I wouldn't say that the Commodity Credit Corporation has been exactly an outstanding success in this general area.

There are complicated facts in all of these matters that have been discussed here, and this Conference illustrates, it seems to me, the basic essential for our national progress at home and abroad. That is clearly a broader economic education.

Finally, we cannot forget that the base of all our natural resources is in the men and women who develop and use them. This Conference would be useless unless, for the coming generations, we find and develop from among all boys and girls, without economic distinction, the highest potential of both hand and mind. And that means, too, the cultivation of the leadership of strong personalities who can play on a team, but who will stand as surely as this Conference for requiring that the individual star, no matter how important, play for the interest of the whole team, the people of the United States of America.

● MR. GARNER: I think we will all agree that, to some extent, and at any rate in some commodities, the United States must continue to rely upon foreign resources in meeting its essential raw materials needs. As the Paley Commission has demonstrated, we have become by this mid-century a deficit nation in many vital materials. Although our domestic resources are vast, our needs are still vaster.

The expected growth of our population, the upward trend of our living standards, the increasing complexities of the raw materials required by modern techniques—all these factors indicate greater needs for raw materials in the future. Even if we should decide as a matter of national policy that deliberate steps should be taken to increase our reliance upon domestic supplies, the availability of certain foreign supplies will certainly remain a matter of vital concern to us.

I shall confine my remarks to some of the factors which affect that availability. It is, I think, a matter of plain self-interest for us to try to understand these factors and to take what steps we can to ensure that foreign materials will in fact be offered to us in whatever quantities and qualities we need.

The all-embracing world market which characterized the amazing economic growth of the last century has disappeared. Raw materials can no longer be freely bought by all who can afford to pay. The great political conflict of the modern world now extends with far-reaching effects into the economic field. The resources of the Communist areas no longer flow freely outside. The freedom of major supplying countries to participate in the market system of the Free World is thus seen as an obvious and fundamental condition of United States ability to draw upon foreign supplies.

Apart from the cases in which access to raw materials might be entirely cut off by Communist encroachment, a dramatic change in attitude has taken place in many of the underdeveloped countries. Their peoples are no longer content to see their mineral resources developed and exported without corresponding development of other parts of their economy. They want more of the better things of life for more of themselves. They are pressuring their governments to produce these results.

One of the problems is to get these countries to see the relationship between general economic development and mineral exports, which offer many countries the best means of earning foreign exchange to buy the equipment needed for their balanced development. However, because the development of minerals has necessarily been largely in the hands of foreigners, it is popularly held to be of advantage only to the foreigners, and not to the supplying country. Therefore, many draw the conclusion that foreigners should assist to a greater extent in developments of other fields,

and, if broad development fails to materialize, they are likely to demand that the extractive industries be taken over by their governments, however disastrous this may be to their own best interests.

Another factor which lies at the root of the attitude toward foreign-owned extractive industries has been the wide fluctuation in raw material prices and the consequent ups and downs in the economy of the producing country which relies mainly upon the income drawn from one or two commodities.

In summary, I would say that the continued availability to the United States and other industrial countries of mineral supplies from the underdeveloped areas is in considerable part dependent upon a balanced economic development in those countries and upon direct efforts to bring about a rise in standards of well-being for their people. Therefore, it seems to me quite clear that both the governments and the business people of countries which need these raw materials have a real self-interest in the continued development of the supplying countries.

If so, what are some of the practical things that may be done to assist in this process? In general, I doubt the wisdom of government-to-government loans. That is one of the reasons why I think the contribution of the World Bank can be particularly valuable. We are in a position to supply capital on an objective and nonpolitical basis for many of the needed basic developments in the underdeveloped countries. We have already loaned nearly $500 million for electric power, $250 million for transportation, and $150 million for agriculture and forestry. We have also provided a substantial measure of assistance both in the preparation of development projects and in the formation of long-range development programs. In all our operations we are fully aware of the key position of private enterprise in the role of development, and we lend only where private capital is not available.

In the field of public United States policy, I would suggest that the government can encourage the flow of American capital through its tax policies, and that its tariff and trade policies will obviously have an important influence. It can also provide certain technical and advisory assistance to facilitate progress in these underdeveloped countries. Perhaps most important of all, it can through a firm and consistent attitude give these countries assurance of the continuity of its policy. The economic and financial strength of the United States is so great and its influence so widespread that no friendly government in the world can plan its policies without making assumptions on what the United States foreign economic policies are likely to be in the future. Neither can the American businessman consider investing abroad except as he can make similar assumptions. Consistency in this field is a vital matter. It makes little sense for the United States at one period to make available large financial assistance to other countries and thereafter to impose quotas or raise tariffs against the legitimate exports of those countries.

I do not wish to exaggerate the role of financial assistance in development. Without good management and administration, capital cannot be fully effective. And there must exist the will on the part of the underdeveloped countries to help themselves. There must be willingness to change institutions and to adopt new ways of life. These are things that only a country can do for itself. However, sympathetic and tactful assistance from abroad can encourage this process of change within.

Aside from governmental action, I believe that American business has an important role to play in assisting those forces in the producing countries which will tend towards broad and steady economic growth. Speaking particularly of the American companies in the extractive industries abroad, all of those with which I am familiar are not only doing an excellent technical job but are providing better working and living conditions for their employees than prevail elsewhere in the country.

It is an important fact that this often causes jealousy rather than appreciation. However, I have the impression that most of these companies have failed to recognize fully the importance of their public relations. I believe that they can do more in bringing home to local peoples the benefits to the country as a whole from their operations and in identifying themselves in all practical ways as part of the community rather than merely foreigners in transit. Also, it would seem worth while for the American companies abroad to give all possible practical help in broadening the economic base of the countries in which they are operating.

This statement may appear somewhat removed from the area of main argument tonight—how much the United States should depend on foreign resources. However, that question involves not merely what the United States may desire, but also what other countries want. I have tried to touch on some of the factors which need to be considered if practical and mutually agreeable results are to be achieved.

APPENDIX

THE EDITOR TO THE READER

A Note on How The Conference Record
Has Been Used in This Report

The excerpts from the Conference record that make up the bulk of this book can stand on their own feet as individual opinions and suggestions worth attention. But to see them in true perspective some of the mechanics of the Conference itself and of the editing of this report must be borne in mind.

As Dr. Gustavson has pointed out in his introduction, some important areas of the resources field had to be left out; not all of them could be packed into a three-day agenda. The circumstances under which the remaining issues were discussed—the principal ground rules—also are important. So are the methods of selection by which the fraction of the resource problem that was covered by the Conference has been further compressed into less than one-fifth of the full discussion record.

How the Conference Was Organized

In many respects, the Mid-Century Conference was an integrated group of smaller conferences on important areas in the resource field. Most of the work was done in the eight sections, which were largely autonomous. The Conference as a whole did not pass judgment on the work of sections or attempt to synthesize or interpret their deliberations. These notes concern the working patterns of the sections. The record of the few sessions of the full Conference is self-explanatory.

Each section had an enormous field to work in. Selection of the topics to be discussed and the actual wording of the questions was as important as what was said about them. This half of the job was done in advance by the officers and steering committees of each section; thus it was important that these groups be as representative as possible. Within the limits of the agenda, discussion was free once the section meetings began.

After the issues for each section had been determined by its steering committee, a section working paper was prepared under the committee's direction, giving the main questions and supplying background information.

Each person was asked to select the section in which he wished to take part, and was sent the working paper of his section in advance. Thus nearly everyone who came to the Conference was prepared to discuss the principal issues and to challenge any assumptions of the steering committee or other implications of the paper to which he took exception.

Some of the gaps in the combined section agenda were filled by the Brookings Institution study, *A Mid-Century Look at Resources,* which provided a common economic background for considering the many different resource problems the people of this country will be facing during the next 25 years and beyond. This paper also was circulated in advance to all participants. Many other gaps had to remain. Sections on marine resources, and food problems as such, for example, had been urged at the Council of Sponsors meeting. Since it was not feasible to organize more than eight sections, these broad areas, among others, were touched only indirectly. On the other hand, there were overlaps. The clearest examples, perhaps, were discussion of hydro-electric power in both the Water Resources and the Energy sections, and of some aspects of land utilization in the Water section and the two sections dealing with land. Some duplications of this kind seemed unavoidable, and no effort was made to head them off altogether, but when the same general subjects were discussed in two or more sections, the emphasis and approach were different in each case.

How This Report Was Put Together

The verbatim transcript of the Conference proceedings runs well over 5,000 pages. This report represents less than 1,000 of them.

The source materials are these: (1) the steering committee working papers of the eight sections, (2) the verbatim transcripts of section and subsection meetings and of plenary sessions, (3) the section rapporteurs' digests, (4) the section chairmen's summaries, and (5) the post-Conference comments of participants that bear directly on the section digests or statements made at the Conference.

The section working papers, prepared primarily as discussion guides, have been drawn upon here only for the major questions set before each section and subsection and for occasional background material needed to clarify the issues raised. The rapporteurs' digests were invaluable as guides in selecting and arranging material; they represented the judgment of experts as to the high points of discussion and had been subject to at least quick review by the full membership of each section. Final responsibility for selection, however, rests with the report editors. The digests have been drawn upon heavily in preparing the introductions to section and subsection reports, and

in the running comment in between. The digests themselves have not been quoted extensively; much of the discussion they summarized is given in this report. Several of the post-Conference comments have been used at appropriate places in the text of the report and clearly marked as such.

The section chairmen's summaries, after review by their authors, have been reproduced in full at the end of each section report. Some of them seem to draw conclusions; others do not. Each represents the personal contribution of the section chairman and they are reproduced here on that basis, as important Conference documents.

This report leans most heavily on the verbatim transcript. Many interesting and significant passages have been greatly condensed, and some have been dropped entirely because of space requirements. But the thoughts and language that are presented are those of the speakers.

The integrity of each subsection, or undivided section, as a working unit has been respected. In a few instances, remarks made at the final session of a full section have been placed with the primary discussion in the appropriate subsection. But no material has been moved from one subsection to another; consequently, there are a number of overlaps, most of which are noted by cross references.

Within each subsection, the arrangement of material is generally chronological although some material has been moved with considerable freedom so as to bring together discussion of particular subjects or issues.

The text of that part of the report dealing with each section has been reviewed by the section chairman, with the assistance of his co-chairman and members of his steering committee. The remarks attributed to each individual were sent to him for review, with the understanding that no response after a reasonable period would indicate that the quotation was satisfactory. The great majority of participants have responded with constructive comments; errors have been caught and language clarified.

Section and subsection rapporteurs, assistants to section chairmen, former Conference staff members and others who formally or informally had a hand in the work of the Conference have gone over portions of the manuscript and made many valuable suggestions.

The report was prepared under the general policy supervision of Dr. Gustavson, but selection, condensation, and checking have involved many points of detail for which the editors must stand responsible. We have tried to reflect faithfully the work of the various discussion groups, to choose the passages that will be most useful and to do justice to each individual quoted. The editors are grateful for the helpfulness and patience of the individual participants who are the principal authors of this book.

THE CONFERENCE STAFF

Director
NORVELL W. PAGE

Assistant Director
HENRY JARRETT

Section Assistants

Section I—NORA E. ROOTS; *Section II*—WELDON A. STEIN; *Section III*—RUSSELL LORD; *Section IV*—SAMUEL BOTSFORD; *Section V*—CHARLES SCHWARZ; *Section VI*—MYER RASHISH; *Section VII*—FRANCIS T. CHRISTY, JR.; *Section VIII*—KATHRYN S. ARNOW.

Administrative Staff

Administrative Officer—VERA W. DODDS; *Conference Manager*—MICHAEL A. STAHL; *Assistant Manager*—DOROTHY H. KING; *Press Arrangements*—WILLIAM E. HUGHES, WILLIAM F. FRYE, D. SHANNON ALLEN, JENNIE M. JOHNSON; *Order-of-the-Day*—LLOYD W. THORSEN, ELAINE D. BRONEZ; *Information*—CONSTANCE C. JOHNSON; *Documents Officer*—MARY J. GORDON; *Documents Production*—MARIETTA SCHIRF, ELLEN H. RYAN.

LIST OF REGISTRANTS

Mid-Century Conference on Resources for the Future
December 2, 3, and 4, 1953

GENERAL

ADAMS, ARTHUR S., President, American Council on Education, Washington, D.C.

ALBRIGHT, HORACE M., President, U.S. Potash Company, New York, N.Y.

BOYD, JAMES, Exploration Manager, Kennecott Copper Corporation, New York, N.Y.

BROWN, HARRISON, Professor of Geochemistry, California Institute of Technology, Pasadena, Calif.

BYERRUM, MRS. E. E., Chairman, Conservation Department, General Federation of Women's Clubs, Warrenville, Ill.

CALKINS, ROBERT D., President, The Brookings Institution, Washington, D.C.

CARROLL, THOMAS H., Associate Director, The Ford Foundation, New York, N.Y.

CONDON, EDWARD J., Vice-President, Sears Roebuck and Company, Chicago, Ill.

D'EWART, WESLEY A., Representative from Montana, Washington, D.C.

DOUGLAS, LEWIS W., Chairman of the Board, Mutual Life Insurance Company of New York, N.Y.

EDGERTON, MRS. MALCOLM J., Chairman, Forum Committee, Garden Club of America, New York, N.Y.

ELIOT, CHARLES W., Ipswich, Mass.

FLETCHER, ANDREW, President, St. Joseph Lead Company, New York, N.Y.

FORMAN, JONATHAN, President, Friends of the Land, Worthington, Ohio

GARNER, R. L., Vice-President, International Bank for Reconstruction and Development, Washington, D.C.

GUSTAVSON, R. G., President and Executive Director, Resources for the Future, Inc., Washington, D.C.

HENNIG, ELMER A., Assistant Treasurer, The Ford Foundation, New York, N.Y.

HICKEY, MARGARET, National Federation of Business and Professional Women's Clubs, Inc., and Ladies' Home Journal, Philadelphia, Pa.

JOHNSTON, DON P., President, American Forestry Association, Wake Forest, N.C.

JONES, LEWIS WEBSTER, President, Rutgers University, New Brunswick, N.J.

LIEBERS, OTTO H., Senator, Nebraska State Legislature, Lincoln, Nebr.

MacNAUGHTON, E. B., Chairman of the Board, First National Bank, Portland, Ore.

MADDEN, JAMES L., President, Hollingsworth and Whitney Company, Boston, Mass.

MALLERY, OTTO T., President, National Recreation Association, Philadelphia, Pa.

MARSHALL, NORRIS, A., American University, Washington, D.C.

MILLER, LESLIE A., Cheyenne, Wyo.

MITCHELL, ALBERT, President, T. E. Mitchell and Son Cattle Ranch, Albert, N.Mex.

MITCHELL, JOHN H., Lockwood, Kessler and Bartlett, Inc., New York, N.Y.

ORDWAY, SAMUEL H., JR., Executive Vice-President, The Conservation Foundation, New York, N.Y.

OSBORN, FAIRFIELD, President, The Conservation Foundation, New York, N.Y.

OWEN, WILFRED, The Brookings Institution, Washington, D.C.

PALEY, WILLIAM S., Chairman of the Board, Columbia Broadcasting System, New York, N.Y.

PORTER, FRANK M., President, American Petroleum Institute, New York, N.Y.

SAWYER, ROBERT W., Editor and Publisher, *The Bulletin*, Bend, Ore.

SHISHKIN, BORIS, Director of Research, American Federation of Labor, Washington, D.C.

SPURR, A. C., President, Monongahela Power Company, Fairmont, W.Va.

STEINKRAUS, HERMAN W., President, Bridgeport Brass Company, Bridgeport, Conn.

SUMAN, JOHN R., Vice-President, Standard Oil Company (New Jersey), New York, N.Y.

TAFT, CHARLES P., President, Committee for a National Trade Policy, Washington, D.C.

TOLLEY, HOWARD R., Consultant, The Ford Foundation, Washington, D.C.

VOIGT, WILLIAM, Executive Director, Izaak Walton League of America, Inc., Chicago, Ill.

WEAVER, C. I., Ohio Fuel and Natural Gas Company, Springfield, Ohio.

SECTION 1

ALLEN, SHIRLEY W., Michigan Conservation Commission, Ann Arbor, Mich.

ANDERSON, MRS. LEROY J., California Federation of Women's Clubs, San Fernando Valley, Calif.

ANDREWS, JOHN N., JR., Research Scientist, George Washington University, Washington, D.C.

AUGUR, TRACY B., Director, Urban Targets Division, Office of Defense Mobilization, Washington, D.C.

BAKER, M. L., Associate Director, College of Agriculture, University of Nebraska, Lincoln, Nebr.

BANNER, GILBERT, Department of Conservation, School of Natural Resources, University of Michigan, Ann Arbor, Mich.

BATSCHELET, CLARENCE E., Chief, Geography Division, Bureau of the Census, Suitland, Md.

BEIMFOHR, OLIVER, Southern Illinois University, Carbondale, Ill.

BEUSCHER, JACOB H., Madison, Wis.

BLACK, JOHN D., Professor of Economics, Littauer School of Public Administration, Harvard University, Cambridge, Mass.

BLACKBURN, GEORGE F., President, Potomac Appalachian Trail Club, Washington, D.C.

BLAIR, LACHLAN F., Chief of the Planning Division, Rhode Island Development Council, Providence, R.I.

BLAKEMAN, T. LEDYARD, Executive Director, Detroit Metropolitan Area Regional Planning Commission, Detroit, Mich.

BLUCHER, WALTER H., Executive Director, American Society of Planning Officials, Chicago, Ill.

BROCK, J. ELMER, President, Wyoming Natural Resource Board, Kaycee, Wyo.

BROWN, J. WILLCOX, Assistant Professor of Forestry, School of Natural Resources, University of Michigan, Ann Arbor, Mich.

BUTCHER, DEVEREUX, Field Representative and Editor, National Parks Association, Washington, D.C.

BUTLER, SALLY, General Federation of Women's Clubs, Hammond, Ind.

BUTTENHEIM, HAROLD S., Editor, *The American City*, New York, N.Y.

CAIRNS, GORDON M., University of Maryland, College Park, Md.

CALEF, WESLEY C., Department of Geography, University of Chicago, Chicago, Ill.

CALHOUN, MRS. ERNEST, Pennsylvania Roadside Council, Pittsburgh, Pa.

CARTER, W. D., Fish and Wildlife Service, U.S. Department of the Interior, Washington, D.C.

CAULKINS, E. DANA, Superintendent, Westchester County Recreation Commission, White Plains, N.Y.

CHANDLER, ROBERT F., JR., President, University of New Hampshire, Durham, N.H.

COHEN, JOSEPH H., National Jewish Welfare Board, New York, N.Y.

COLBY, CHARLES C., Professor Emeritus of Geography, University of Chicago, Chicago, Ill.

COLLIER, JANE, Yale University Conservation Program, New Haven, Conn.

COLVARD, D. W., Dean of Agriculture, North Carolina State College, Raleigh, N.C.

CORNICK, PHILIP H., Yonkers, N.Y.

DAVIS, ARTHUR A., Fish and Wildlife Service, U.S. Department of the Interior, Washington, D.C.

DAVIS, THEODORE H., American Forest Products Industries, Inc., Washington, D.C.

DEEG, C. W., Manager, Industrial and Commercial Development Division, Philadelphia Electric Company, Philadelphia, Pa.

DENN, J. HUBER, President, American Industrial Development Council, Chamber of Commerce of Delaware, Wilmington, Del.

DEXTER, WAYNE, Secretary of Outlook and Situation Board, Agricultural Marketing Service, U.S. Department of Agriculture, Washington, D.C.

DRAPER, EARLE S., American Society of Landscape Architects, Bethesda, Md.

DRURY, NEWTON B., Department of Natural Resources, Sacramento, Calif.

DURHAM, JACK, Vienna, Va.

DYCKMAN, JOHN W., Department of Land and City Planning, University of Pennsylvania, Philadelphia, Pa.

EDWARDS, SYDNEY A., Secretary, Natural Resources Council of Connecticut, and Managing Director, Connecticut Development Commission, Hartford, Conn.

EHRHART, EDMUND O., President, Armstrong Forest Company, Johnsonburg, Pa.

FEISS, CARL, U.S. Housing and Home Finance Agency, Washington, D.C.

FELDMAN, EARL R., Assistant Director, Transportation Research, Association of American Railroads, Washington, D.C.

FLEMING, ARKLEY L., State Teachers' College, Salisbury, Md.

FLENNIKEN, WILLIAM W., Rocky Mountain Oil and Gas Association, Denver, Colo.

FOGARTY, EARL R., U.S. Department of the Interior, Washington, D.C.

FOX, MRS. CYRIL G., Pennsylvania Roadside Council, Media, Pa.

FROME, MICHAEL, American Automobile Association, Washington, D.C.

GERSHOVITZ, SAMUEL D., National Jewish Welfare Board, New York, N.Y.

GOLAN, SAMUEL L., International Boundary Commission, United States, Alaska, and Canada, Washington, D.C.

GRAYSON, PAUL E., U.S. Bureau of the Census, Suitland, Md.

GREENSHIELDS, ELCO L., Agricultural Economist, Land Economics Section, Agricultural Research Service, U.S. Department of Agriculture, Washington, D.C.

HAAR, CHARLES, Harvard University Law School, Cambridge, Mass.

HAKES, MRS. JESSE F., National Council of State Garden Clubs, Inc., Glenwood, Md.

HAMPTON, MRS. HARRY L., Larchmont, N.Y.

HARRIS, CHAUNCY D., Department of Geography, University of Chicago, Chicago, Ill.

HAUSER, FRANCIS L., American Institute of Planners, Washington, D.C.

HORTON, DONALD C., U.S. Bureau of the Budget, Washington, D.C.

HOVDE, BRYN J., Executive Director, The Pittsburgh Housing Association, Pittsburgh, Pa.

HOWES, ROBERT M., Tennessee Valley Authority, Knoxville, Tenn.

HOYT, HOMER, Washington, D.C.

HUTCHINS, CURTIS M., Bangor and Aroostook Railroad Company, Bangor, Me.

JAMES, HARRY C., Trailfinders, Banning, Calif.

KANE, EDWARD A., Washington, D.C.

KAUNITZ, RITA D., New York, N.Y.

KENDALL, HENRY M., Department of Geography, Miami University, Oxford, Ohio.

KIENAST, MARGATE S., U.S. Department of Agriculture, Washington, D.C.

KLOVE, ROBERT C., U. S. Bureau of the Census, Suitland, Md.

KUBE, HAROLD D., Broad Run, Va.

LAMB, GEORGE R., Yale University Conservation Program, New Haven, Conn.

LARSON, EDWIN VAN HORN, Editor, Northeastern Forest Experiment Station, Upper Darby, Pa.

LAUSI, ANTHONY T., U.S. Department of the Interior, Washington, D.C.

LINDSAY, GEORGE C., Mechanization, Inc., Washington, D.C.

LOUNSBURY, JOHN F., Antioch College, Yellow Springs, Ohio.

LYNCH, FRANK M., Commissioner, Department of Finance and Control, Hartford, Conn.

MASON, MRS. EDWARD S., Cambridge, Mass.

MATHEWS, WILLIAM R., Editor and Publisher, *Arizona Daily Star*, Tucson, Ariz.

MAYER, HAROLD M., Department of Geography, University of Chicago, Chicago, Ill.

McCLINTOCK, RALPH B., Superintendent of Recreation, Omaha, Nebr.

McGOWIN, JULIAN F., Secretary, W. T. Smith Lumber Company, Chapman, Ala.

McMURRY, K. C., Chairman, Department of Geography, University of Michigan, Ann Arbor, Mich.

MERRILL, ROBERT M., Deere and Company, Moline, Ill.

MEYERSON, MARTIN, Department of Land and City Planning, University of Pennsylvania, Philadelphia, Pa.

MILLER, SLATOR, Hawaiian Sugar Planters Association, Washington, D.C.

MILLER, WILLIS H., Director of Planning, San Diego County Planning Department, San Diego, Calif.

MUNCY, DOROTHY A., Consultant, Industrial Location and Space Requirements, Washington, D.C.

OLSEN, CHESTER J., Regional Forester, Forest Service, U.S. Department of Agriculture, Ogden, Utah

OLSON, SIGURD F., President, National Parks Association, Chicago, Ill.

ORELL, BERNARD L., Vice-President, Weyerhaeuser Sales Company, St. Paul, Minn.

OULTON-CLARK, BERNARD, Yale University, New Haven, Conn.

PAGE, N. McALLISTER, Alexandria, Va.

PARRIOTT, JAMES D., Solicitor's Office, U.S. Department of the Interior, Washington, D.C.

PINCUS, WILLIAM, Assistant Director, Bureau of Land Management, U.S. Department of the Interior, Washington, D.C.

POUGH, RICHARD H., Chairman, Department of Conservation and General Ecology, The American Museum of Natural History, New York, N.Y.

PRENDERGAST, JOSEPH, Executive Director, National Recreation Association, New York, N.Y.

REID, PAUL M., Planning Analyst, Regional Planning Commission, Detroit, Mich.

RETTIE, JAMES G., Forest Service, U.S. Department of Agriculture, Washington, D.C.

RICE, EDWARD K., Department of Engineering, University of California, Los Angeles, Calif.

ROBBINS, CHAUNCEY, Senator, State of Maine, Augusta, Me.

ROSE, JOHN KIRR, Library of Congress, Washington, D.C.

ROSENBLUM, MARCUS, Staff Associate, Office of Chief Sanitary Engineering Officer, U.S. Public Health Service, Washington, D.C.

ROTERUS, VICTOR, Chief, Area Development Division, U.S. Department of Commerce, Washington, D.C.

SAGE, CHARLES H., Vice-President, North Star Timber Company, Neenah, Wis.

SAMPSON, A. W., Professor Emeritus of Forestry, University of California, Berkeley, Calif.

SCHIFFMAN, EDWARD G., Norborne, Mo.

SCHOFIELD, W. R., Secretary-Manager, California Forest Protective Association, San Francisco, Calif.

SHEPARD, PAUL H., Yale University Conservation Program, New Haven, Conn.

SHILLINGER, JACOB E., National Catholic Rural Life Conference, Des Moines, Iowa.

SIEKER, JOHN H., Chief, Division of Recreation and Lands, Forest Service, U.S. Department of Agriculture, Washington, D.C.

SILVEY, TED F., Congress of Industrial Organizations, Washington, D.C.

SMITH, ANTHONY W., Assistant General Counsel and Secretary of the Conservation Committee, Congress of Industrial Organizations, Washington, D.C.

SNIDER, J. NOBLE, Washington, D.C.

SNOWDEN, GEORGE L., The Mead Corporation, Chillicothe, Ohio.

SOLBERG, ERLING D., Agricultural Economist, Land Economics Section, Agricultural Research Service, U.S. Department of Agriculture, Washington, D.C.

STANTON, B. M., Park and Shop, Norfolk, Va.

STEIN, CLARENCE S., President, Regional Development Council of America, Inc., New York, N.Y.

STERN, PETER M., The Conservation Foundation, New York, N.Y.

STEVENSON, LOUIS T., Technical Association of the Pulp and Paper Industry, New York, N.Y.

STOCKWELL, GLENN D., Blue Valley Study Group, Randolph, Kans.

SWIFT, HARLEY L., Harrisburg Railways Company, Harrisburg, Pa.

TAUBIN, HAROLD, Planning Division, Montgomery County, Rockville, Md.

TAYLOR, E. H., The Curtis Publishing Company, Philadelphia, Pa.

THOMPSON, FRED A., Department of Game and Fish, Sante Fe, N.Mex.

TREMBLEY, L. J., Department of Biology, Lehigh University, Bethlehem, Pa.

TYLER, JOHN, Bowaters Southern Paper Corporation, Calhoun, Tenn.

VAN VALKENBURG, SAMUEL, Clark University, Worcester, Mass.

WALTERS, MRS. WILLIAM J., President, National Council of State Garden Clubs, New Brunswick, N.J.

WARREN, GERTRUDE, Woman's National Farm and Garden Association, Washington, D.C.

WATSON, JAMES W., Canadian Department of Mines and Surveys, Ottawa, Canada

WEHRLY, MAX S., Executive Director, The Urban Land Institute, Washington, D.C.

WELLMAN, HARRY R., Vice-President, University of California, Berkeley, Calif.

WESTWOOD, RICHARD W., Editor, *Nature Magazine*, and President, American Nature Association, Washington D.C.

WILLIAMS, D. A., Administrator, Soil Conservation Service, U.S. Department of Agriculture, Washington, D.C.

WILSON, CHESTER S., Director, State Department of Conservation, St. Paul, Minn.

WINHOLTZ, WILFORD G., U.S. Housing and Home Finance Agency, Washington, D.C.

WINSLOW, CARLILE P., Washington, D.C.

WOLFSOHN, JOEL D., Chapman and Wolfsohn, Washington, D.C.

WOOTEN, H. H., Production Economics Research Branch, Agricultural Research Service, U.S. Department of Agriculture, Washington, D.C.

WYCKOFF, STEPHEN N., Director, California Forest and Range Experiment Station, Berkeley, Calif.

SECTION II

AAMODT, OLAF S., Plant Industry Station, U.S. Department of Agriculture, Beltsville, Md.

ALEXANDER, LYLE T., Principal Soil Scientist, Soil Conservation Service, U.S. Department of Agriculture, Beltsville, Md.

ALLAN, PHILIP F., Regional Biologist, Soil Conservation Service, Fort Worth, Tex.

AMBRY, EDWARD, Montclair State Teachers' College, Montclair, N.J.

ANDREWS, RUSSELL P., Chevy Chase, Md.

BAKER, JOHN G., *The Milwaukee Journal*, Milwaukee, Wis.

BAKER, JOHN H., President, National Audubon Society, New York, N.Y.

BAKKEN, ELMAAR H., Boy Scouts of America, New York, N.Y.

BARNES, IRSTON, Audubon Society of the District of Columbia, Washington, D.C.

BARRETT, LEONARD I., Project Leader, Timber Resource Review, Forest Service, U.S. Department of Agriculture, Washington, D.C.

BARSKE, PHILIP, Stratford, Conn.

BARTLEY, ARTHUR M., Executive Director, Ducks Unlimited, Inc., New York, N.Y.

BAYLISS, DUDLEY C., National Parks Service, U.S. Department of the Interior, Washington, D.C.

BAYNE, TERRY F., Tractor Division, Allis-Chalmers Manufacturing Company, Washington, D.C.

BEAL, JAMES A., Division of Forest Insect Investigations, Forest Service, U.S. Department of Agriculture, Washington, D.C.

BEAN, LESLIE L., Arlington, Va.

BEARDSLEY, WILLIAM S., Governor of Iowa, Des Moines, Iowa

BECKER, EDNA E., Children's Museum of Hartford, Hartford, Conn.

BELT, CHARLES B., Treasurer, The International Committee for Bird Preservation, New York, N.Y.

BENEDICT, MURRAY R., Professor of Agricultural Economics, University of California, Berkeley, Calif.

BENNETT, HOWARD D., Forester, Appalachian Hardwood Manufacturers, Inc., Cincinnati, Ohio

BENNETT, HUGH H., President, Soil Conservation Society of America, Des Moines, Iowa

BENNETT, JOHN B., Assistant Director, Technical Review Staff, U.S. Department of the Interior, Washington, D.C.

BERGH, MRS. ROLAND C., Chairman, Conservation Committee, Garden Club of America, Cedarhurst, Long Island, N.Y.

BESLEY, LOWELL, Executive Director-Forester, The American Forestry Association, Washington, D.C.

BIRD, JOHN A., The Curtis Publishing Company, Philadelphia, Pa.

BISSELL, THEODORE L., University of Maryland, College Park, Md.

BIXBY, EVERETT H., Oregon Soil Clinic, Portland, Ore.

BOLES, ASHLEIGH P., Agricultural Development Department, Missouri Pacific Railroad Company, St. Louis, Mo.

BRETT, RICHARD M., Yale University Conservation Program, New Haven, Conn.

BRIEGLEB, PHILIP A., Director, Central States Forest Experiment Station, Columbus, Ohio

BRITT, CLARENCE S., Agricultural Research Center, Beltsville, Md.

BROMLEY, WILLARD S., Executive Secretary, American Pulpwood Association, New York, N.Y.

BROWN, A. G., Deputy Manager in Charge of Agricultural Commission, American Bankers Association, New York, N.Y.

BROWN, CARL B., Assistant Chief, Soil Conservation Service, U.S. Department of Agriculture, Washington, D.C.

BUTLER, OVID, The American Forestry Association, Washington, D.C.

CAHALANE, VICTOR H., U.S. Department of the Interior, Washington, D.C.

CALLISON, CHARLES H., National Wildlife Federation, Washington, D.C.

CANCELL, BENTON R., Vice-President in Charge of Operations, Rhinelander Paper Company, Rhinelander, Wis.

CHESTER, K. STARR, Consultant, Battelle Memorial Institute, Columbus, Ohio

CHRISTENSEN, RAYMOND P., Agricultural Research Service, U.S. Department of Agriculture, Washington, D.C.

CHURCHILL, E. D., Consultant, Washington, D.C.

CLAPPER, LOUIS S., Tennessee Game and Fish Commission, Nashville, Tenn.

CLARK, J. W., Minnesota Department of Business Development, St. Paul, Minn.

CLARK, MRS. LEROY, The Garden Club of America, Englewood, N.J.

CLEPPER, HENRY, Executive Secretary, Society of American Foresters, Washington, D.C.

CLIFF, EDWARD P., Assistant Chief, Forest Service, U.S. Department of Agriculture, Washington, D.C.

COLBY, WILLIAM G., Professor of Agronomy, University of Massachusetts, Amherst, Mass.

COLLINGWOOD, G. HARRIS, Legislative Reference Service, Library of Congress, Washington, D.C.

COLMAN, EDWARD A., In Charge, Division of Watershed Management, California Forest and Range Experiment Station, Berkeley, Calif.

COOK, LARRY, Director, Ohio Reclamation Association, Cleveland, Ohio

COOLEY, PETE E., Conservationist, Decatur Farm Management, Inc., Decatur, Ill.

COTTAM, CLARENCE, Assistant to the Director, Fish and Wildlife Service, U.S. Department of the Interior, Washington, D.C.

COUGILL, K. R., Conservation Department, State of Indiana, Indianapolis, Ind.

CRAFTS, EDWARD C., Assistant Chief, Forest Service, U.S. Department of Agriculture, Washington, D.C.

CRAIG, JAMES B., Editor, *American Forests*, Washington, D.C.

CROFT, A. RUSSELL, Forest Service, U.S. Department of Agriculture, Ogden, Utah.

DAMBACH, CHARLES A., Chief, Division of Wildlife, Ohio Department of Natural Resources, Columbus, Ohio.

D'AMICO, JOHN R., Natural Resources Board, Cheyenne, Wyo.

DANA, SAMUEL T., Dean Emeritus, School of Natural Resources, University of Michigan, Ann Arbor, Mich.

DANA, MRS. SAMUEL T., Ann Arbor, Mich.,

DAVIS, THOMAS J., JR., San Francisco, Calif.

DAVIS, WATERS S., JR., President, National Association of Soil Conservation Districts, League City, Tex.

DAY, ALBERT M., Assistant to the Director, Fish and Wildlife Service, U.S. Department of the Interior, Washington, D.C.

DEAN, GEORGE W., Virginia State Forester, Charlottesville, Va.

DEAS, STANLEY P., Southern Pine Association, New Orleans, La.

DEMMON, ELWOOD L., Director, Southeastern Forest Experiment Station, Asheville, N.C.

DEVALL, WILBUR B., Head, Department of Forestry, Alabama Polytechnic Institute, Auburn, Ala.

DEVOTO, BERNARD, Cambridge, Mass.

DOLBEAR, BERNARD S., Bureau of Land Management, U.S. Department of the Interior, New Orleans, La.

DOWNING, THOMAS V., Assistant State Supervisor of Agricultural Education, Richmond, Va.

DUMONT, PHILIP A., Fish and Wildlife Service, U. S. Department of the Interior, Washington, D.C.

DUTTON, W. L., Chief, Division of Range Management, Forest Service, U.S. Department of Agriculture, Washington, D.C.

DYKSTERHUIS, E. J., Ecological Society of America, Lincoln, Nebr.

EKLUND, CARL R., Fish and Wildlife Service, U.S. Department of the Interior, Washington, D.C.

ENDERSBEE, WILLIAM J., Technical Review Staff, U. S. Department of the Interior, Washington, D.C.

ESCHMEYER, R. W., Executive Vice-President, Sport-Fishing Institute, Washington, D.C.

FAIRBANK, WILLIAM H., JR., Department Secretary, Governor's Office, State of California, Sacramento, Calif.

FARLEY, JOHN L., Director, Fish and Wildlife Service, U.S. Department of the Interior, Washington, D.C.

FELL, GEORGE B., The Nature Conservancy, Washington, D.C.

FERGUSON, JOHN W., Chief, Division of Lands and Soil, Ohio Department of Natural Resources, Columbus, Ohio.

FINDLAY, JOHN D., Fish and Wildlife Service, U.S. Department of the Interior, Washington, D.C.

FLICKINGER, VICTOR W., Chief, Division of Parks, Ohio Department of Natural Resources, Columbus, Ohio

FLORY, CHARLES H., State Forester, South Carolina State Commission of Forestry, Columbia, S.C.

FLORY, EVAN L., Bureau of Indian Affairs, U.S. Department of the Interior, Washington, D.C.

FORSLING, CLARENCE L., Albuquerque, N.Mex.

FOSTER, CHARLES H. W., II, Secretary, Wildlife Conservation Inc., Boston, Mass.

FRANK, BERNARD, Forest Service, U. S. Department of Agriculture, Washington, D.C.

FROST, SHERMAN L., Falls Church, Va.

FULLER, ALBERT M., Milwaukee Public Museum, Milwaukee, Wis.

GARMAN, WILLARD H., U.S. Department of Agriculture, Washington, D.C.

GARRATT, GEORGE A., Connecticut State Park and Forest Commission, New Haven, Conn.

GARVER, WALTER B., Manager, Agricultural Department, Chamber of Commerce of the United States, Washington, D.C.

GETZ, CARL, Eastern Salesmanager, D. B. Smith and Company, Utica, N.Y.

GILES, LESTER A., JR., Director, Wildlife and Conservation Department, The American Humane Education Society, Boston, Mass.

GILL, TOM, Secretary, American Tree Association, Washington, D.C.

GILMAN, VIRGIL D., Extension Service, U.S. Department of Agriculture, Washington, D.C.

GLASS, REBECCA S., Yale University Conservation Program, New Haven, Conn.

GOODLOE, DON B., Maryland Beekeepers, Washington, D.C.

GOTTSCHALK, LOUIS, Geologist, Engineering Division, Soil Conservation Service, U.S. Department of Agriculture, Washington, D.C.

GRAHAM, EDWARD H., Director, Plant Technology Division, Soil Conservation Service, U.S. Department of Agriculture, Washington, D.C.

GRAVES, MRS. EDWIN D., Garden Club of America, Washington, D.C.

GREELEY, W. B., Vice-President, West Coast Lumbermen's Association, Seattle, Wash.

GRIFFITHS, MRS. ALFRED S., Conservation of Natural Resources Committee, General Federation of Women's Clubs, Amityville, N.Y.

GROENVELD, DOUWE R., International Bank for Reconstruction and Development, Washington, D.C.

GUMBEL, WALTER C., Monongahela Power Company, Fairmont, W.Va.

GUNLOGSON, G. B., Racine, Wis.

GUTERMUTH, C. R., Vice-President, Wildlife Management Institute, Washington, D.C.

GUY, DAVID J., Potomac Appalachian Trail Club, Washington, D.C.

GWIN, JAMES M., University of Maryland, College Park, Md.

HAGENSTEIN, W. D., Managing Director, Industrial Forestry Association, Portland, Ore.

HANSON, HERBERT C., Grassland Research Foundation, Washington, D.C.

HARRISON, ROBERT W., Agricultural Economist, Bureau of Land Management, U. S. Department of the Interior, Washington, D.C.

HARROLD, LLOYD L., Soil and Water Conservation Research Branch, Agricultural Research Service, U. S. Department of Agriculture, Coshocton, Ohio

HARTMAN, GEORGE B., Head, Department of Forestry, Iowa State College, Ames, Iowa

HEIDRICH, GEORGE R., Vice-President, National Association of Soil Conservation Districts, Charles Town, W.Va.

HEIMERDINGER, MARY, Yale University Conservation Program, New Haven, Conn.

HEISIG, P. CARL, Agricultural Research Service, U.S. Department of Agriculture, Washington, D.C.

HERBERT, PAUL A., Director, Division of Conservation, Michigan State College, East Lansing, Mich.

HERITAGE, WILLIAM H., Soil Conservation Service, U.S. Department of Agriculture, Haddonfield, N.J.

HERTZLER, R. A., U.S. Department of the Army, Washington, D.C.

HEYWARD, FRANK, JR., Gaylord Container Corporation, Bogalusa, La.

HILARY, BROTHER, M.S.S.S.T., National Catholic Rural Life Conference, Silver Spring, Md.

HILL, RUSSELL G., Extension Soil Conservationist, Michigan State College, East Lansing, Mich.

HITCHCOCK, J. G., Alabama Power Company, Birmingham, Ala.

HOFF, A. B., International Brotherhood of Pulp, Sulphite and Paper Mill Workers, Covington, Va.

HOLM, DUANE, Pennsylvania State College, State College, Pa.

HOLMES, JACK E., Director, Legislative Council Service, New Mexico Legislative Council, Santa Fe, N.Mex.

HOOVER, MARVIN D., Rocky Mountain Forest and Range Experiment Station, Fort Collins, Colo.

HORNADAY, FRED E., Secretary, American Forestry Association, Washington, D.C.

HOWE, SYDNEY, Department of Conservation, University of Michigan, Ann Arbor, Mich.

HOWE, WALTER, Chairman, Natural Resources Council of Connecticut, Litchfield, Conn.

HOYT, EDWARD, II, Director, State Department of Agriculture, Lincoln, Nebr.

HUNT, KENNETH W., Antioch College, Yellow Springs, Colo.

HURSH, CHARLES R., Chief, Division of Water Resource Management, Southeastern Forest Experiment Station, Asheville, N.C.

ILLICK, JOSEPH S., Dean Emeritus, College of Forestry, State University of New York, Syracuse, N.Y.

ISE, HENRY, Chief, Division of Harbors and Rivers, Department of Public Works, Providence, R.I.

JACKSON, KATHERINE, State Senator, Peterborough, N.H.

JACOB, K. D., Chief, Division of Fertilizer and Lime, Bureau of Plant Industry, U.S. Department of Agriculture, Beltsville, Md.

JACOBSON, R. C., Secretary-Treasurer, Minnesota State CIO Council, Minneapolis, Minn.

JAMES, HARLEAN, Executive Secretary, American Planning and Civic Association, Washington, D.C.

JARMAN, MAJ. GEN. SANDERFORD, Consultant, Washington, D.C.

JENKINS, G. R., Professor, Department of Geology, Lehigh University, Bethlehem, Pa.

JOHNSON, SHERMAN E., Director, Farm and Land Management Research, Agricultural Research Service, U.S. Department of Agriculture, Washington, D.C.

JOHNSON, WENDELL, Fish and Wildlife Service, U.S. Department of the Interior, Washington, D.C.

JOSEPHSON, H. R., Chief, Division of Forest Economics, Forest Service, U.S. Department of Agriculture, Washington, D.C.

JOTTER, ERNST V., Consultant Forester, Dayton, Ohio

KAYLOR, JOSEPH F., Director, Maryland Department of Forests and Parks, Annapolis, Md.

KELLEY, OMER J., Agricultural Research Service, Plant Industry Station, Beltsville, Md.

KELLOGG, CHARLES E., Assistant Administrator for Soil Survey, Soil Conservation Service, U.S. Department of Agriculture, Washington, D.C.

KELLY, CHARLES S., President, Quetico Superior Committee, Chicago, Ill.

KENNEDY, SIDNEY S., Chief, State Cooperative Branch, National Park Service, U.S. Department of the Interior, Washington, D.C.

KENYON, RICHARD L., Managing Editor, *Journal of Agricultural and Food Chemistry*, Washington, D.C.

KINNEY, CHARLES W., U.S. Department of the Army, Washington, D.C.

KNEIPP, LEON F., Washington, D.C.

KNOBLAUCH, HAROLD C., Director, State Experiment Stations Division, Agricultural Research Service, U.S. Department of Agriculture, Washington, D.C.

KOLBE, ERNEST L., Chief Forester, Western Pine Association, Portland, Ore.

KUEHN, C. C., American Creosoting Company, Inc., New York, N.Y.

KUTHE, HANS C., Washington, D.C.

LA BUDDE, MRS. EDWARD, Legislative Chairman, Women's Conservation League of America, Milwaukee, Wis.

LAMONT, GORDON, Connecticut State Board of Fisheries and Game, Hartford, Conn.

LANG, FREDERICK, State Forester, Little Rock, Ark.

LARSON, J. DAVID, The J. David Larson Associates, Hinsdale, Ill.

LARSON, MRS. J. DAVID, The J. David Larson Associates, Hinsdale, Ill.

LAYBOURNE, WILLIAM, Executive Secretary, Ohio Forestry Association, Inc., Columbus, Ohio

LEAVITT, RALPH W., International Brotherhood of Pulp, Sulphite and Paper Mill Workers, Bangor, Me.

LEE, RONALD F., Assistant Director, National Park Service, U.S. Department of the Interior, Washington, D.C.

LEEDY, DANIEL L., Fish and Wildlife Service, U.S. Department of the Interior, Washington, D.C.

LEWIS, ORME, Assistant Secretary for Public Land Management, U.S. Department of the Interior, Washington, D.C.

LINCOLN, FREDERICK C., Fish and Wildlife Service, U.S. Department of the Interior, Washington, D.C.

LOKKE, LAURA W., U.S. Bureau of the Budget, Washington, D.C.

LONG, RAYMOND V., Virginia Department of Conservation and Development, Richmond, Va.

LUNDY, MAURICE H., Fish and Wildlife Service, U.S. Department of the Interior, Washington, D.C.

LYLE, S. P., Extension Service, U.S. Department of Agriculture, Washington, D.C.

LYMAN, ARTHUR T., Commissioner of Conservation, Massachusetts Department of Natural Resources, Boston, Mass.

MACDONALD, RONALD G., Technical Association of the Pulp and Paper Industry, New York, N.Y.

MALSBERGER, HENRY J., General Manager and Forester, Southern Pulpwood Conservation Association, Atlanta, Ga.

MARION, A. W., Director, Ohio Department of Natural Resources, Columbus, Ohio

MARSH, RAYMOND E., Washington, D.C.

MARSHALL, CHARLES, President, Nebraska Farm Bureau Federation, Lincoln, Nebr.

MARSHALL, GEORGE, The Wilderness Society, New York, N.Y.

MARTELL, E. R., Head, Department of Forestry and Conservation, Purdue University, Lafayette, Ind.

MCARDLE, R. E., Chief, Forest Service, U.S. Department of Agriculture, Washington, D.C.

MCCANN, Neil F., United Kingdom Scientific Mission, Washington, D.C.

MCCONNELL, RAYMOND A., JR., Editor, *Lincoln Evening Journal*, Lincoln, Nebr.

MELIS, PERCY E., Bureau of Indian Affairs, U.S. Department of the Interior, Washington, D.C.

MERRILL, PERRY H., State Forester, Vermont Forest Service, Montpelier, Vt.

MEYER, ARTHUR B., Society of American Foresters, Washington, D.C.

MILES, RICHARD V., JR., Gulf States Paper Corporation, Tuscaloosa, Ala.

MILNER, GEORGE, Office of Territories, U.S. Department of the Interior, Washington, D.C.

MISKELLY, C. R., Managing Director, Vermont Development Commission, Montpelier, Vt.

MORSE, THOMAS, North Carolina Department of Conservation and Development, Raleigh, N.C.

MOSEBROOK, HARRY S., Forest Resources Assistant, Natural Resources Department, Chamber of Commerce of the United States, Washington, D.C.

MULLANEY, HOWARD J., Board of Engineers for Rivers and Harbors, U.S. Department of the Army, Washington, D.C.

MULLEN, P. H., American Paper and Pulp Association, Washington, D.C.

MURIE, OLAUS J., The Wilderness Society, Moose, Wyo.

MURPHY, ROBERT R., Superintendent of Parks, Oklahoma City, Okla.

NACE, RAYMOND L., Water Resources Division, Geological Survey, U.S. Department of the Interior, Washington, D.C.

NEGAARD, O. A., U.S. Bureau of the Budget, Washington, D.C.

NELSON, DEWITT, Director of Natural Resources, California Department of Natural Resources, Sacramento, Calif.

NELSON, JOHN M., Baltimore, Md.

NETTING, M. GRAHAM, Acting Director, Carnegie Museum, Pittsburgh, Pa.

NIEWENHAUS, MATHIAS, U.S. Department of Commerce, Washington, D.C.

NORTON, ETHAN A., Conservation Needs and Records Branch, Soil Conservation Service, U.S. Department of Agriculture, Washington, D.C.

NORTON, GERALDINE A., National Research Council, Washington, D.C.

NUTTING, A. D., Forest Commissioner, Maine State Forest Service, Augusta, Me.

O'BOYLE, JOHN W., President, Nebo Oil Company, Dallas, Tex.

OGROSKY, HAROLD O., Hydraulic Engineer, Engineering Division, Soil Conservation Service, U.S. Department of Agriculture, Washington, D.C.

ORR, RUSSELL S., Executive Director, League of American Sportsmen, Baltimore, Md.

PACK, RANDOLPH G., Charles Lathrop Pack Forestry Foundation, New York, N.Y.

PACKARD, FRED M., Executive Secretary, National Parks Association, Washington, D.C.

PAGE, CARTER, Corps of Engineers, U.S. Department of the Army, Washington, D.C.

PALEY, HENRY D., Director, Research and Education, United Paperworkers of America, Washington, D.C.

PARKER, KENNETH W., Forest Service, U.S. Department of Agriculture, Washington, D.C.

PARTAIN, LLOYD E., Sales Manager and Farm Market Director, *Country Gentleman Magazine*, The Curtis Publishing Company, Philadelphia, Pa.

PASEK, LEONARD, Kimberly-Clark Corporation, Washington, D.C.

PENFOLD, JOSEPH W., Western Representative, Izaak Walton League of America, Inc., Denver, Colo.

PENN, RAYMOND J., Chairman, Department of Agricultural Economics, University of Wisconsin, Madison, Wis.

PETERSON, ARTHUR G., Office of The Secretary of Defense, Washington, D.C.

PETERSON, H. WEBER, Agriculture Department, Chamber of Commerce of the United States, Washington, D.C.

PETERSON, VAL, Administrator, Federal Civil Defense Administration, Washington, D.C.

PETTIT, TED S., Division of Publications, Boy Scouts of America, New York, N.Y.

PINCHOT, MRS. GIFFORD, Washington, D.C.

POOLE, DANIEL A., Wildlife Management Institute, Washington, D.C.

PORTER, EARL, International Paper Company, Mobile, Ala.

POWELL, CHARLES M., President, American Agricultural Chemical Bank, New York, N.Y.

PRESNALL, CLIFFORD C., Fish and Wildlife Service, U.S. Department of the Interior, Washington, D.C.

QUINN, FRANK D., Chairman, Texas State Parks Board, Austin, Tex.

RADCLIFFE, HARRY E., American Nature Association, Washington, D.C.

RENNER, FREDERIC G., Range Conservation Specialist, Soil Conservation Service, U.S. Department of Agriculture, Washington, D.C.

RIFE, MARVIN, Herald Tribune Fresh Air Fund, New York, N.Y.

RIKER, ALBERT J., Professor of Plant Pathology, University of Wisconsin, Madison, Wis.

ROBINSON, BERT D., Soil Conservation Service, U.S. Department of Agriculture, Washington, D.C.

ROGERS, DORIS D., YWCA, New York, N.Y.

RONALD, MALCOLM B., Associated Missouri Basin Conservationists, Mitchell, S.Dak.

RUHL, HARRY D., Chief, Game Division, Michigan Department of Conservation, Lansing, Mich.

SAFFORD, MRS. TRUMAN S., Yale University Conservation Program, New Haven, Conn.

SALTER, ROBERT M., Agricultural Research Service, Plant Industry Station, Beltsville, Md.

SANDERS, J. T., Legislative Counsel, National Grange, Washington, D.C.

SATER, EDNA N., Division of Information, Fish and Wildlife Service, U.S. Department of the Interior, Washington, D.C.

SCHANTZ, VIOLA S., Fish and Wildlife Service, U.S. Department of the Interior, Washington, D.C.

SEGAL, HENRY, International Brotherhood of Pulp, Sulphite and Paper Mill Workers, Philadelphia, Pa.

SHANKLIN, JOHN F., Technical Review Staff, U.S. Department of the Interior, Washington, D.C.

SHANKS, ROYAL, Professor of Botany, University of Tennessee, Knoxville, Tenn.

SHAW, BYRON T., Administrator, Agricultural Research Service, U.S. Department of Agriculture, Washington, D.C.

SHEPARD, WILLIAM C., Connecticut Forest and Park Association, Berlin, Conn.

SHIRLEY, HARDY L., Dean, College of Forestry, State University of New York, Syracuse, N.Y.

SHOEMAKER, ANNE N., Washington, D.C.

SHOMON, J. J., Chief, Education Division, Virginia Commission of Game and Inland Fisheries, Richmond, Va.

SIMMS, D. HARPER, Director, Division of Information, Soil Conservation Service, U.S. Department of Agriculture, Washington, D.C.

SLOANE, EUGENE H., Director of Publications and Public Relations, American Association for Health, Physical Education and Recreation, National Education Association, Washington, D.C.

SMITH, J. RUSSELL, Professor Emeritus of Geography, Columbia University, Swarthmore, Pa.

SNOW, ALBERT G., JR., Rotary International, College Park, Md.

STAMM, EDWARD P., Industrial Forestry Association, Portland, Ore.

STEPHENSON, JEAN, Editor, *Potomac Appalachian Trailway News*, Washington, D.C.

STERLING, MRS. ROBERT D., Friends of the Land, New York, N.Y.

STEVENS, MURRAY H., Chairman, The Appalachian Trail Conference, New York, N.Y.

STEWART, CHARLES L., Department of Land Economics, University of Illinois, Urbana, Ill.

STEWART, R. D., American Guernsey Cattle Club, Peterborough, N.H.

STINE, O. C., Twentieth Century Fund, Washington, D.C.

STODDARD, CHARLES H., Executive Director, Independent Timber Farmers of America, Minneapolis, Minn.

STROUD, RICHARD H., Sport-Fishing Institute, Washington, D.C.

SWIFT, ERNEST, Conservation Director, State of Wisconsin, Madison, Wis.

TAGGART, J. G., Deputy Minister, Department of Agriculture, Ottawa, Canada

TANI, SULO J., Executive Director, New Hampshire State Planning and Development Commission, Concord, N.H.

TAUB, ELWOOD, International Brotherhood of Pulp, Sulphite and Paper Mill Workers, Washington, D.C.

TAYLOR, MELVIN N., Executive Director, Trees for Tomorrow, Inc., Merrill, Wis.

TEBBE, CHARLES L., Regional Forester, Forest Service, U.S. Department of Agriculture, Philadelphia, Pa.

TERZICK, PETER E., United Brotherhood of Carpenters, Indianapolis, Ind.

THOMPSON, BEN H., Chief, Recreation Planning, National Park Service, U.S. Department of the Interior, Washington, D.C.

THOMPSON, PERRY A., Secretary, Manager, Western Lumber Manufacturers, Inc., San Francisco, Calif.

THORNTON, ARTHUR H., South Dakota Natural Resources Commission, Sioux Falls, S.Dak.

TOLSON, HILLORY A., Assistant Director, National Park Service, U.S. Department of the Interior, Washington, D.C.

TRUITT, PAUL T., American Plant Food Council, Inc., Washington, D.C.

VAN CAMP, J. LLOYD, General Manager, Canadian Forestry Association, Montreal, Canada

VINT, THOMAS C., National Park Service, U.S. Department of the Interior, Washington, D.C.

WANDER, HILDE, Philadelphia, Pa.

WANTRUP, S. V. CIRIACY, Professor of Agricultural Economics, University of California, Berkeley, Calif.

WEAVER, HAROLD, Bureau of Indian Affairs, U.S. Department of the Interior, Washington, D.C.

WEED, JOHN MERRILL, Columbus, Ohio

WELLS, WILLIAM W., Director, State Parks and Recreation Commission, Baton Rouge, La.

WHITNEY, ALVIN G., Nature Conservancy, Delmar, N.Y.

WIEGAND, MARTIN T., Kiwanis International, Chicago, Ill.

WILCOX, WALTER W., Senior Specialist in Agriculture, Legislative Reference Service, Library of Congress, Washington, D.C.

WILLIAMS, ADRIAN, Assistant Chief, Surface Water Branch, Water Resources Division, Geological Survey, U.S. Department of the Interior, Washington, D.C.

WILM, HAROLD, Associate Dean, College of Forestry, State University of New York, Syracuse, N.Y.

WINEBRENER, Philip R., Maryland Board of Natural Resources, Baltimore, Md.

WINTON, DAVID J., National Planning Association, Minneapolis, Minn.

WIRT, FRED A., Advertising Manager, J. I. Case Company, Racine, Wis.

WIRTH, CONRAD L., Director, National Park Service, U.S. Department of the Interior, Washington, D.C.

WOODWARD, HUGH B., President, New Mexico Game Association, Albuquerque, N.Mex.

WOOZLEY, EDWARD, Director, Bureau of Land Management, U.S. Department of the Interior, Washington, D.C.

YOUNGQUIST, C. V., Chief, Division of Water, Department of Natural Resources, Columbus, Ohio.

ZAHNISER, HOWARD, Executive Secretary, The Wilderness Society, Washington, D.C.

ZIMMERMAN, GORDON K., Research Director, National Agricultural Research, Inc., Washington, D.C.

SECTION III

ACKERMAN, EDWARD A., Assistant General Manager, Tennessee Valley Authority, Knoxville, Tenn.

ALDUK, THOMAS J., Commission on the Organization of the Executive Branch of the Government, Washington, D.C.

ALLEN, JAMES H., Secretary, National Water Conservation Conference, Washington, D.C.

ARBINGAST, STANLEY A., Bureau of Business Research, University of Texas, Austin, Tex.

ASSUR, ANDREW, American Meteorological Society, Washington, D.C.

BACK, NATHANIEL A., Office of the Chief of Engineers, U.S. Department of the Army, Washington, D.C.

BALL, HOWARD E., Resources and Civil Works Division, U.S. Bureau of the Budget, Washington, D.C.

BARBER, HARTMAN, Brotherhood of Railway Clerks, Washington, D.C.

BARNES, JACK R., Consulting Ground-Water Engineer, Austin, Tex.

BARNEY, IRVIN, JR., National Legislative Representative, Brotherhood of Railway Carmen of America, Washington, D.C.

BARTON, THOMAS F., Professor of Geography, Indiana University, Bloomington, Ind.

BARUS, MRS. MAXWELL, League of Women Voters, Montclair, N.J.

BAXTER, SAMUEL S., Water Commissioner, Philadelphia, Pa.

BEARD, G. L., Office of the Chief of Engineers, U.S. Department of the Army, Washington, D.C.

BECHERT, CHARLES H., Indiana Department of Conservation, Indianapolis, Ind.

BEHRE, C. EDWARD, Forest Service, U.S. Department of Agriculture, Washington, D.C.

BELL, WILLIAM P., Allis-Chalmers Manufacturing Company, Washington, D.C.

BELLO, FRANCIS C., *Fortune Magazine*, New York, N.Y.

BENSON, ERNEST H., Legal Representative, Brotherhood of Maintenance of Way Employees, Washington, D.C.

BERGEN, STEPHEN W., The Conservation Foundation, New York, N.Y.

BERNSTEIN, MERTON, Legislative Assistant to Senator Morse, Washington, D.C.

BILLINGS, NORMAN, Michigan Water Resources Commission, Lansing, Mich.

BISER, DANIEL B., Pennsylvania State College, State College, Pa.

BLALOCK, HENRY W., Assistant to the Administrator, Southwestern Power Administration, U.S. Department of the Interior, Washington, D.C.

BLEE, C. E., Chief Engineer, Tennessee Valley Authority, Knoxville, Tenn.

BOARDMAN, MARGARET, Garden Club of America, New York, N.Y.

BRAGG, KENDAL B., Commission on Organization of the Executive Branch of the Government, Washington, D.C.

BREIDENTHAL, WILLARD J., The Riverview State Bank, Kansas City, Kans.

BREITENSTEIN, JEAN S., Attorney, Denver, Colo.

BREITKREUTZ, EMIL W., Department of Water Power, Los Angeles, Calif.

BRENNAN, J. R., Office of the Chief of Engineers, U.S. Department of the Army, Washington, D.C.

BROWER, DAVID R., Sierra Club, San Francisco, Calif.

BROWN, ROBERT M., Chief, Bureau of Environmental Hygiene, Maryland Department of Health, Baltimore, Md.

BRUMMEL, B. J., Hi-Plains Underground Water Conservation District, Garnett, Kans.

BRUNGARDT, THERESA S., State Board of Recreation, Montpelier, Vt.

BURKE, WILLIAM J., U.S. Department of the Interior, Washington, D.C.

BURKHOLDER, BOB L., Fish and Wildlife Service, U.S. Department of the Interior, Palmer, Alaska

BURRILL, MEREDITH F., Director, Division of Geography, U.S. Department of the Interior, Washington, D.C.

BURY, RICHARD L., Yale University Conservation Program, New Haven, Conn.

BUTLER, CHARLES, American Farm Bureau Federation, Chicago, Ill.

BUZZELL, D. A., The Associated General Contractors of America, Inc., Washington, D.C.

CAPEN, CHARLES H., New Jersey District Water Supply Commission, Wanaque, N.J.

CAREY, WILLIAM N., American Society of Civil Engineers, Washington, D.C.

CHAPMAN, FRANK R., Yale University Planning Program, Rochester, Mich.

CHINN, O. W., Director, Flood Control and Water Usage, Frankfort, Ky.

CHORPENING, BRIG. GEN. C. H., Assistant Chief of Engineers for Civil Works, U.S. Department of the Army, Washington, D.C.

CHRISTY, HAROLD H., Superintendent, Water and Power Departments, The Colorado Fuel and Iron Corporation, Pueblo, Colo.

CLEARY, EDWARD J., Executive Director and Chief Engineer, Ohio River Valley Water Sanitation Commission, Cincinnati, Ohio

COLLINS, E. H. Washington Water Power Company, Spokane, Wash.

COLLINS, R. D., Treasurer and General Manager, Brazos River Authority, Mineral Wells, Tex.

COOK, HOWARD L., Corps of Engineers, U.S. Department of the Army, Washington, D.C.

COYLE, DAVID CUSHMAN, Washington, D.C.

CRAWFORD, IVAN C., Colorado Water Conservation Board, Denver, Colo.

CRITCHLOW, HOWARD T., New Jersey Division of Water Policy and Supply, Trenton, N.J.

CUNNINGHAM, M. B., American Water Works Association, Oklahoma City, Okla.

CURRAN, CHARLES D., Commission on Organization of the Executive Branch of the Government, Washington, D.C.

DAVIS, BRUCE G., U.S. Department of the Interior, Washington, D.C.

DAVIS, CLARENCE, Solicitor, U.S. Department of the Interior, Washington, D.C.

DAWSON, F. M., State University of Iowa, Iowa City, Iowa

DEAN, ANTHONY P., Chief, Division of Engineering, Forest Service, U.S. Department of Agriculture, Washington, D.C.

DE BREUVERY, IMMANUEL S., United Nations, New York, N.Y.

DICKIE, GEORGE E., Secretary, Federal Interagency Committee on Recreation, Washington, D.C.

DIXON, J. W., U.S. Department of the Interior, Washington, D.C.

DOBBINS, WILLIAM O., Director, State Planning Board, Montgomery, Ala.

DORT, WAKEFIELD, JR., Assistant Professor of Geology, Pennsylvania State College, State College, Pa.

DOWD, M. J., Imperial Irrigation District, El Centro, Calif.

DUNN, ALLISON V., National Park Service, U.S. Department of the Interior, Washington, D.C.

DWORSHAK, HENRY I., American Mining Congress, Washington, D.C.

DYKE, GEORGE E., National Council for Stream Improvement, New York, N.Y.

EDMONSTON, A. D., State Engineer, Chief, California Division of Water Resources, Sacramento, Calif.

ELY, NORTHCUTT, American Public Power Association, Washington, D.C.

ERLANGER, HENRY, Resources and Civil Works Division, U.S. Bureau of the Budget, Washington, D.C.

EVERETT, RICHARD W., McGraw-Hill Publishing Company, New York, N.Y.

FERINGA, GEN. P. A., New Orleans Public Service, Inc., New Orleans, La.

FINK, OLLIE E., Friends of the Land, Columbus, Ohio

FOREMAN, MRS. ORVILLE, League of Women Voters of the United States, Jacksonville, Ill.

FOX, IRVING K., Arkansas-White-Red River Field Staff, U.S. Department of the Interior, Tulsa, Okla.

FREDERICK, MILES L., Director, Delaware State Development Department, Dover, Del.

FRYE, JOHN C., State Geological Survey of Kansas, Lawrence, Kans.

GALE, SAMUEL H., Board of Engineers for Rivers and Harbors, U.S. Department of the Army, Washington, D.C.

GARDNER, CHARLES, Senator Case's Office, Washington, D.C.

GARNSEY, MORRIS E., Professor of Economics, Department of Social Sciences, University of Colorado, Boulder, Colo.

GARRETT, MRS. GEORGE, Garden Club of America, Washington, D.C.

GEHM, HARRY W., Technical Adviser, National Council on Stream Improvement, New York, N.Y.

GIROUX, C. H., Special Assistant to the Chief of Engineers, U.S. Department of the Army, Washington, D.C.

GRAHAM, N. R., Oklahoma Planning and Resources Board, Tulsa, Okla.

GRAMBO, FRANCIS, Bureau of Reclamation, U.S. Department of the Interior, Washington, D.C.

GRANT, GEN. U. S., III, President, American Planning and Civic Association, Washington, D.C.

GRAY, HORACE M., Professor of Economics, University of Illinois, Urbana, Ill.

GREENE, LEE S., Department of Political Science, University of Tennessee, Knoxville, Tenn.

GREGORY, G. ROBINSON, Professor, School of Natural Resources, University of Michigan, Ann Arbor, Mich.

GRIGGS, ROBERT FISKE, Head, Department of Botany, University of Pittsburgh, Pittsburgh, Pa.

GROSART, JOHN W., Board of Engineers for Rivers and Harbors, U.S. Department of the Army, Washington, D.C.

GURNETT-SMITH, ALBAN, Australian Liaison Office, Washington, D.C.

HAAS, FLORALEE, League of Women Voters, Washington, D.C.

HAGIE, FLOYD O., Director, Washington State Development Association, Bellevue, Wash.

HANKIN, GREGORY, Davidsonville, Md.

HANNUM, GEN. WARREN T., Sacramento, Calif.

HANSEN, HARRY, U.S. Public Health Service, Washington, D.C.

HARDING, SIDNEY T., Consulting Civil Engineer, Engineers Joint Council, Berkeley, Calif.

HARE, FRED P., JR., Administrative Assistant, Governor's Office, Harrisburg, Pa.

HARRISON, JOHN J., Washington, D.C.

HARTLEY, ROBERT W., The Brookings Institution, Washington, D.C.

HATHAWAY, G. A., Corps of Engineers, U.S. Department of the Army, Washington, D.C.

HAYDEN, JOSEPH E., Federal Power Commission, Washington, D.C.

HAYDEN, PAUL V., Vice-President, Connecticut River Watershed Council, Inc., Hartford, Conn.

HAZEN, RICHARD, Consulting Engineer, Hazen and Sawyer, Inc., New York, N.Y.

HEBLEY, HENRY F., Research Consultant, Pittsburgh Consolidation Coal Company, Pittsburgh, Pa.

HENDERSON, GEORGE, Kern County Land Company, Bakersfield, Calif.

HERSHEY, H. GARLAND, Iowa Geological Survey, Iowa City, Iowa

HIATT, WILLIAM, Chief, Hydrologic Services Division, U.S. Weather Bureau, Washington, D.C.

HILL, RAYMOND A., Leeds, Hill and Jewett, Los Angeles, Calif.

HOAK, RICHARD D., Senior Fellow, Mellon Institute of Industrial Research, University of Pittsburgh, Pittsburgh, Pa.

HOFF, CLAYTON M., Executive Vice-President, Brandywine Valley Association, Wilmington, Del.

HOLLIS, MARK D., Assistant Surgeon General, U.S. Public Health Service, Washington, D.C.

HORNE, FRED F., Carmel Valley, Calif.

HORNER, W. W., Consulting Engineer to the City of St. Louis, St. Louis, Mo.

HOULIHAN, DANIEL J., Knappen-Tippetts-Abbett-McCarthy, Engineers, New York, N.Y.

HOUSTON, HOLLAND H., Technical Consultant to the Governor of Washington, Olympia, Wash.

HUBLEY, GEORGE W., Jr., Ohio Valley Improvement Association, Louisville, Ky.

HUFSCHMIDT, MAYNARD M., Technical Review Staff, U.S. Department of the Interior, Washington, D.C.

HULL, WILLIAM J., Executive Assistant, Ashland Oil and Refining Company, Ashland, Ky.

ITSCHNER, BRIG. GEN. E. C., Corps of Engineers, U.S. Department of the Army, Washington, D.C.

JACK, MARJORIE, *Fortune Magazine*, New York, N.Y.

JACKSON, CHARLES E., National Fisheries Institute, Washington, D.C.

JACKSON, STANLEY, Corps of Engineers, U.S. Department of the Army, Washington, D.C.

JEFFERS, GEORGE, Longwood College, Farmville, Va.

JENS, STIFEL W., Consulting Engineer, St. Louis, Mo.

JENSEN, J. GRANVILLE, Chairman, Department of Natural Resources, Oregon State College, Corvallis, Ore.

JOHNSON, ALBERT R., Technical Review Staff, U.S. Department of the Interior, Washington, D.C.

JONES, MALCOLM H., Foreign Operations Administration, Washington, D.C.

JORDAN, HARRY E., Secretary, American Water Works Association, Inc., New York, N.Y.

KEEGAN, GEORGE R., Connecticut River Watershed Council, Westfield, Mass.

KELLEY, CLAUDE D., President, National Wildlife Federation, Atmore, Ala.

KELLY, RAYMOND C., Executive Manager, Cooling Tower Institute, Palo Alto, Calif.

KELSO, M. M., Dean of Agriculture, Montana State College, Bozeman, Mont.

KERR, MRS. CHARLES E., Wichita, Kans.

KIEFFER, JERRY, Commission on the Organization of the Executive Branch of the Government, Washington, D.C.

LANE, RICHARD A., Philadelphia Electric Company, Philadelphia, Pa.

LANGBEIN, WALTER B., Geological Survey, U.S. Department of the Interior, Washington, D.C.

LAWRENCE, WILLIAM MASON, New York State Conservation Department, Albany, N.Y.

LE BOSQUET, MAURICE, U.S. Public Health Service, Washington, D.C.

LINDEMER, LAWRENCE, Commission on the Organization of the Executive Branch of the Government, Washington, D.C.

LING, PERRY M., State of Arizona, Phoenix, Ariz.

LOGAN, CHARLES A., U.S. Department of Agriculture, Beltsville, Md.

LOGAN, EDWARD B., Budget Secretary, Governor's Office, Harrisburg, Pa.

LORD, RUSSELL, Editor, *The Land*, Bel Air, Md.

LUDDEN, ROBERT W., National Park Service, U.S. Department of the Interior, Washington, D.C.

LUDWIG, JOHN H., U.S. Public Health Service, Washington, D.C.

MARKS, HERBERT S., Washington, D.C.

MARSH, FRANCIS B., Associate Editor, *Water Works Engineering*, New York, N.Y.

MARTIN, S. C., Bureau of State Services, U.S. Public Health Service, Washington, D.C.

MCCARTHY, DANIEL V., Bureau of Reclamation, U.S. Department of the Interior, Washington, D.C.

MCCARTY, ROBERT L., American Public Power Association, Washington, D.C.

MCCLAMROCH, MRS. ROLAND, Conservation Chairman, North Carolina Federation of Garden Clubs, Chapel Hill, N.C.

MCFARLAND, T. J., Manager, High Plains Underground Water Conservation District No. 1, Lubbock, Tex.

MCGREGOR, LOUIS D., Michigan United Conservation Clubs, Flint, Mich.

MCPHERSON, M. B., Professor, Department of Geology, Lehigh University, Bethlehem, Pa.

MELCHORN, FRANK, Izaak Walton League of America, Inc., Washington, D.C.

MEYER, ADOLPH F., Consulting Hydraulic Engineer, Minneapolis, Minn.

MILLER, HOWARD A., Executive Secretary, Southern California Conservation Association, Los Angeles, Calif.

MOEUR, J. H., Phoenix, Ariz.

MONAT, ANNA H., Commission on the Organization of the Executive Branch of the Government, Washington, D.C.

MORRIS, SAMUEL B., General Manager and Chief Engineer, Department of Water and Power, Los Angeles, Calif.

MORRIS, T., Manager, Water Service, The Pennsylvania Railroad, Philadelphia, Pa.

MUFFLY, MRS. JAMES, General Federation of Women's Clubs, Lewisburg, Pa.

MULKERN, MRS. FRANK J., Washington, D.C.

MURPHY, WARREN T., Division of Flood Prevention and River Basin Programs, Forest Service, U.S. Department of Agriculture, Washington, D.C.

NEILSON, MRS. EDWARD S., Chairman, National Parks Committee, Garden Club of America, New York, N.Y.

NORMAN, OLIVER L., National Water Conservation Conference, Kensington, Md.

NORTHROP, VERNON, Vice-President, Lester B. Knight and Associates, Inc., Consulting Engineers, Washington, D.C.

ORVILLE, HOWARD T., Bendix Aviation Corporation, Baltimore, Md.

PATRICK, RUTH, Curator of Limnology, Academy of Natural Sciences, Philadelphia, Pa.

PAULSEN, C. G., Chief, Water Resources Division, Geological Survey, U.S. Department of the Interior, Washington, D.C.

PETERSON, RONALD B., Director, Bureau of Business Promotion, New York State Department of Commerce, Albany, N.Y.

PHILLIPS, GEORGE R., U.S. Department of Agriculture, Washington, D.C.

PICKEN, ISABEL, U.S. Department of the Interior, Tulsa, Okla.

PITKIN, F. A., Executive Director, State Planning Board, Department of Commerce, Harrisburg, Pa.

POHL, PEARL L., Isaak Walton Conservation League, Milwaukee, Wis.

PORTER, IRA L., President, Peoples Banking Company, Oberlin, Ohio

PRICE, REGINALD C., General Engineer, Project Review Coordinator, U.S. Department of the Interior, Washington, D.C.

RAINSFORD, DOROTHY A., Yale University Conservation Program, New Haven, Conn.

RECK, CHARLES W., Geological Survey, U.S. Department of the Interior, Washington, D.C.

REDMAN, ALBERT E., Chamber of Commerce for Ohio State, Columbus, Ohio

REGAN, MARK, Agricultural Economist, Land Economics Section, U.S. Department of Agriculture, Washington, D.C.

REICHELDERFER, F. W., Chief, U.S. Weather Bureau, Washington, D.C.

REYNOLDS, GEORGE M., Publisher, Little Rock, Ark.

RISING, E. W., National Water Conservation Conference, Washington, D.C.

ROBBINS, PAUL H., National Society of Professional Engineers, Washington, D.C.

ROSECRANS, W. S., Chairman, California State Board of Forestry, Los Angeles, Calif.

ROWE, JAMES H., JR., Washington, D.C.

RUSSELL, RICHARD J., Louisiana State University, Baton Rouge, La.

SABOL, LEONARD P., Westinghouse Electric International Company, Washington, D.C.

SALKIND, VICTOR A., Scientific Attaché, Embassy of Israel, Washington, D.C.

SALMOND, GORDON R., Division of Watershed Management, Forest Service, U.S. Department of Agriculture, Washington, D.C.

SAVILLE, THORNDIKE, Dean of the College of Engineering, New York University, New York, N.Y.

SAY, HAROLD B., Washington Representative, Portland Chamber of Commerce, Washington, D.C.

SCHEIDENHELM, F. W., Consulting Engineer, New York, N.Y.

SCHEIDT, MELVIN E., Resources and Civil Works Division, U.S. Bureau of the Budget, Washington, D.C.

SCHIFF, PHILIP, National Jewish Welfare Board, Washington, D.C.

SCHMITT, EDWIN A., Interstate Commission of the Potomac River Basin, Washington, D.C.

SCHWARTZ, CARL H., JR., Chief, Resources and Civil Works Division, U.S. Bureau of the Budget, Washington, D.C.

SCHWOB, CARL E., Chief, Division of Water Pollution Control, U.S. Public Health Service, Washington, D.C.

SCOTT, HOWARD E., Office of Rep. Wayne N. Aspinall, Washington, D.C.

SEIB, CHARLES C., Pennsylvania Power and Light Company, Allentown, Pa.

SHEPHARD, E. FENTON, U.S. Bureau of the Budget, Washington, D.C.

SHINE, HENRY M., Commission for the Organization of the Executive Branch of the Government, Washington, D.C.

SHOEMAKER, CARL D., National Wildlife Federation, Washington, D.C.

SHORT, JOHN, U.S. Department of Agriculture, Tulsa, Okla.

SMITH, BERT L., Irrigation Districts Association of California, San Francisco, Calif.

SMITH, WALDO E., Executive Secretary, American Geophysical Union, Washington, D.C.

SPENCE, H. W., U.S. Public Health Service, Washington, D.C.

SPRAGUE, CHARLES A., Editor and Publisher, *The Oregon Statesman*, Salem, Ore.

STEELE, HARRY A., U.S. Department of Agriculture, Lincoln, Nebr.

STEIDINGER, DEAN K., Allis-Chalmers Manufacturing Company, Washington, D.C.

STEVENS, ROBERT T., Friends of the Land, Leesburg, Va.

STRAUS, MICHAEL W., Washington, D.C.

STRONG, ARTHUR D., Secretary, Upper Mississippi Water Association, Minneapolis, Minn.

STURROCK, J. E., General Manager, Texas Water Conservation Association, Austin, Tex.

SUGGITT, FRANK W., Head, Department of Land and Water Conservation, Michigan State College, East Lansing, Mich.

TAYLOR, PERRY R., Assistant to the Chief, Division of Water Pollution Control, U.S. Public Health Service, Washington, D.C.

TERRELL, JOHN U., Colorado River Association, Washington, D.C.

THORNTHWAITE, C. WARREN, Laboratory of Climatology of Johns Hopkins University, Seabrook, N.J.

TIPTON, ROYCE J., R. J. Tipton and Associates, Inc., Denver, Colo.

TRINKA, HENRY, International Brotherhood of Pulp, Sulphite and Paper Mill Workers, New York, N.Y.

TROSSEVIN, C. V., Association of American Railroads, Washington, D.C.

TUPPER, STANLEY R., State Sea and Shore Fisheries Commission, Augusta, Me.

TURRENTINE, JOHN W., American Potash Institute, Washington, D.C.

VAN TUYL, DONALD W., Chamber of Commerce of the United States, Washington, D.C.

VAN VLIET, R., Pennsylvania Power and Light Company, Allentown, Pa.

VOGEL, BRIG. GEN. HERBERT D., Corps of Engineers, U.S. Department of the Army; Chairman, Arkansas-White-Red Basins Interagency Commission, Dallas, Tex.

VOORHEES, HERBERT W., New Jersey Farm Bureau, Trenton, N.J.

WALKER, ROSS H., Virginia State Water Control Board, Richmond, Va.

WALLACE, TOM, Editor Emeritus, *Louisville Times,* Louisville, Ky.

WARNER, DAVID C., Water Conservation Engineer, Ohio Department of Natural Resources, Columbus, Ohio

WATERMAN, ALAN T., Director, National Science Foundation, Washington, D.C.

WATSON, IRA A., Bureau of Reclamation, U.S. Department of the Interior, Washington, D.C.

WEAVER, FRANK L., Special Adviser on Power, Commission on Organization of the Executive Branch of the Government, Washington, D.C.

WEAVER, PAUL, Texas A. and M. College, College Station, Tex.

WEAVER, BRIG. GEN. THERON D., Office of the Chief of Engineers, U.S. Department of the Army, Washington, D.C.

WEBB, WILLIAM H., National Rivers and Harbors Congress, Washington, D.C.

WEBER, RAE S., U.S. Department of the Interior, Washington, D.C.

WEINKAUFF, HENRY C. C., Board of Engineers for Rivers and Harbors, U.S. Department of the Army, Washington, D.C.

WELSH, WILLIAM E., National Reclamation Association, Washington, D.C.

WEST, HERBERT G., Inland Empire Waterways Association, Walla Walla, Wash.

WETMORE, LOUIS E., Massachusetts Institute of Technology, Cambridge, Mass.

WHITE, GILBERT F., President, Haverford College, Haverford, Pa.

WHITE, WALTER G., New Hampshire Water Resources Board, Concord, N.H.

WHITE, WILLIAM M., U.S. Department of the Interior, Washington, D.C.

WIESLEY, O. A., Chairman, Industrial Commission of Utah, Salt Lake City, Utah

WIETERS, ALFRED H., U.S. Public Health Service, Washington, D.C.

WILL, JOHN GEOFFREY, Secretary, Upper Colorado River Commission, Grand Junction, Colo.

WILLIAMS, WILLIAM M., Colorado State Planning Commission, Denver, Colo.

WILSON, A. C., Baltimore, Md.

WINGET, RUSSELL L., Executive Secretary, National Council for Stream Improvement, New York, N.Y.

WISE, WILLIAM S., State Water Commission, Hartford, Conn.

WOLF, ALFRED C., American Political Science Association, Cambridge, Mass.

WOLLNER, HERBERT J., American Conditioning House, Inc., Boston, Mass.

WOLMAN, ABEL, Professor of Sanitary Engineering, Johns Hopkins University, Baltimore, Md.

WRIGHT, MRS. ROBERT C., Director, Garden Club of America, Haverford, Pa.

XANTEN, WILLIAM A., American Public Works Association, Washington, D.C.

YOUNG, GLADWIN E., Deputy Administrator, Soil Conservation Service, U.S. Department of Agriculture, Washington, D.C.

SECTION IV

ADKERSON, J. CARSON, American Manganese Producers Association, Washington, D.C.

AMES, JOHN A., The Baltimore and Ohio Railroad Company, Baltimore, Md.

ANDREWS, MILDRED, The Tungsten Institute, Washington, D.C.

BACON, JAMES E., JR., Jefferson Lake Sulphur Company, Washington, D.C.

BACON, JAMES EVERETT, Mining Consultant, Washington, D.C.

BARLOW, WALLACE D., Office of Naval Material, U.S. Department of the Navy, Washington, D.C.

BARRINGER, EDWIN C., Institute of Scrap Iron and Steel, Inc., Washington, D.C.

BAUMAN, EDWARD W., National Slag Association, Washington, D.C.

BENNETT, ELMER, Legislative Counsel, U.S. Department of the Interior, Washington, D.C.

BORCINA, DAVID M., Lead Industries Association, Brooklyn, N.Y.

BRADLEY, P. R., JR., Chairman, California State Mining Board, San Francisco, Calif.

BROADGATE, WILLIAM C., Arizona State Department of Mineral Resources, Phoenix, Ariz.

CALLAGHAN, EUGENE, Director, New Mexico Bureau of Mines and Mineral Resources, Socorro, N.Mex.

CAMPBELL, MAJOR MARION L., Office of the Assistant Chief of Staff, G-4, Logistics, U.S. Department of the Army, Washington, D.C.

CARLSON, HUGO A., Executive Secretary, South Dakota Natural Resources Commission, Pierre, S.Dak.

CAZELL, GABRIEL F., Arlington, Va.

CLARK, EDWARD L., State Geologist, Division of Geological Survey and Water Resources, Rolla, Mo.

CONOVER, JULIAN D., Executive Vice-President, American Mining Congress, Washington, D.C.

COOLEY, CHARLES M., Acting Editor, *Mining Engineering*, New York, N.Y.

COVEL, THOMAS E., Aluminum Import Corporation, Washington, D.C.

CSERVENYAK, F. J., U.S. Department of the Interior, Washington, D.C.

DAVIDSON, DONALD M., Vice-President, E. J. Longyear Company, Minneapolis, Minn.

DAVIS, ROBERT H., U.S. Air Force Reserve, Washington, D.C.

DE BRUL, STEPHEN, General Motors Corporation, Detroit, Mich.

DEUTCH, MICHAEL J., Consulting Engineer, Washington, D.C.

DIETRICH, WALDEMAR F., Bureau of Mines, U.S. Department of the Interior, Washington, D.C.

DUNBECK, NORMAN J., Vice-President, Industrial Minerals Division, International Minerals and Chemical Corporation, Chicago, Ill.

EVANS, CHARLES, JR., Columbia-Southern Chemical Corporation, Pittsburgh, Pa.

FOX, JOHN C., American Mining Congress, Washington, D.C.

FRENCH, JOHN, Wyoming Natural Resource Board, Cheyenne, Wyo.

GARDNER, E. D., Chief Mining Engineer, Bureau of Mines, U.S. Department of the Interior, Washington, D.C.

GENT, ERNEST V., American Zinc Institute, Inc., New York, N.Y.

GENTRY, R. W. H., E. I. du Pont de Nemours and Company, Wilmington, Del.

GILBERT, ARTHUR D., E. I. du Pont de Nemours and Company, Wilmington, Del.

GRANGER, CHRISTOPHER M., Bethesda, Md.

GREENE, COL. R. W., Chief, Materials and Components Division, Industrial Resources, U.S. Department of the Air Force, Washington, D.C.

GREENLEE, R. E., Battelle Memorial Institute, Columbus, Ohio

GROGAN, ROBERT M., E. I. du Pont de Nemours and Company, Wilmington, Del.

HAFFNER, JULIUS B., Vice-President, Bunker Hill and Sullivan Mining and Concentrating Company, Kellogg, Idaho

HEAD, JAMES L., Mining and Metallurgical Society of America, New York, N.Y.

HEARST, ALLEN L., Private Mine Operator, Philadelphia, Pa.

HERFINDAHL, O. C., Committee for Economic Development, Washington, D.C.

HOFFMAN, LEWIS E., Chief, Division of Minerals, Bureau of Land Management, U.S. Department of the Interior, Washington, D.C.

HOLBROOK, RAYMOND B., Attorney with U.S. Smelting, Refining and Mining Company, Salt Lake City, Utah

IMHOFF, LAWRENCE E., U.S. Department of the Interior, Washington, D.C.

INGERSON, EARL, Geological Survey, U.S. Department of the Interior, Washington, D.C.

INSLEY, HERBERT, Chief, Division of Mineral Products, National Bureau of Standards, Washington, D.C.

ISERN, ELMER, Eagle Picher Company, Miami, Okla.

JACKSON, W. F., E. I. du Pont de Nemours and Company, Wilmington, Del.

JOHNSON, C. H., U.S. Department of the Interior, Washington, D.C.

JOSEPHSON, G. W., Bureau of Mines, U.S. Department of the Interior, Washington, D.C.

JULIAN, COMDR. H. W., Office of Naval Material, U.S. Department of the Navy, Washington, D.C.

JUST, EVAN, Vice-President, Cyprus Mines Corporation, New York, N.Y.

KEENAN, PEGGY, Keenan Properties, Spearfish, S.Dak.

KIRKPATRICK, JAMES S., Magnesium Association, Detroit, Mich.

KLINE, MITCHELL H., U.S. Department of the Interior, Washington, D.C.

KLOPSTEG, PAUL E., Associate Director, National Science Foundation, Washington, D.C.

KOENIG, ROBERT, President, Cerro de Pasco Corporation, New York, N.Y.

LASKY, S. G., Technical Review Staff, U.S. Department of the Interior, Washington, D.C.

LEITH, CHARLES K., Washington, D.C.

LEROY, PAUL G., Bear Creek Mining Company, Arlington, Va.

LOCKWOOD, BENONI, JR., Foreign Operations Administration, Washington, D.C.

LONG, W. LUNSFORD, Vice-President, Tungsten Mining Corporation, Warrenton, N.C.

MACDONALD, GILMOUR B., Professor, Forestry Department, Iowa State College, Ames, Iowa

MARTIN, JAMES S., U.S. Steel Corporation, Pittsburgh, Pa.

MAURY, JESSE L., Friendship Heights, Md.

MAXWELL, WELLWOOD H., Calumet and Hecla, Inc., Washington, D.C.

MCCASKILL, JOSEPH C., Indian Arts and Crafts Board, U.S. Department of the Interior, Washington, D.C.

MCCORMICK, ROBERT B., Materials Branch, Production and Schedules, Office of the Assistant Secretary of Defense, Washington, D.C.

MELCHER, NORWOOD B., Bureau of Mines, U.S. Department of the Interior, Washington, D.C.

MELVIN, JOHN H., Chief, Division of Geological Survey, Ohio Geological Survey, Columbus, Ohio

MILES, PHIL M., Kentucky Agricultural and Industrial Development Board, Frankfort, Ky.

MILLER, ROY F., Aluminum Company of America, Pittsburgh, Pa.

MILLER, THOMAS H., Assistant Director, Bureau of Mines, U.S. Department of the Interior, Washington, D.C.

MILLS, HAROLD F., Manager, Iron King Branch of Shattuck Denn Mining Corporation, Humboldt, Ariz.

MIXTER, GEORGE, Executive Vice-President, United States Smelting, Refining and Mining Company, Boston, Mass.

MOFFETT, HARRY L., American Mining Congress, Washington, D.C.

MOORE, PERRY N., Emergency Procurement Service, General Services Administration, Washington, D.C.

MORGAN, JOHN D., JR., Materials Office, Office of Defense Mobilization, Washington, D.C.

MUMFORD, RUSSELL W., American Potash and Chemical Corporation, Los Angeles, Calif.

NETSCHERT, BRUCE C., Materials Office, Office of Defense Mobilization, Washington, D.C.

NOTMAN, ARTHUR, Magma Copper Company, New York, N.Y.

O'LEARY, JOHN F., U.S. Department of the Interior, Washington, D.C.

O'NEIL, COL. THOMAS A., Industrial College of the Armed Forces, Washington, D.C.

PAINTER, ROBERT J., Executive Secretary, American Society for Testing Materials, Philadelphia, Pa.

PALMER, R. S., Colorado Mineral Resources Board, Denver, Colo.

PAYNE, JOHN, JR., Manager of Mining Operations, American Metal Company Limited, New York, N.Y.

PEIRCE, W. M., Technical Assistant, New Jersey Zinc Company, New York, N.Y.

POLLARA, FRANK, United Steel Workers of America, Pittsburgh, Pa.

POWELL, WILLIAM I., American Mining Congress, Washington, D.C.

PRICE, GALEN B., Ford Motor Company, Dearborn, Mich.

RAMSEY, ROBERT H., Editor, *Engineering and Mining Journal*, New York, N.Y.

RICHARDSON, A. C., Technical Director, Battelle Memorial Institute, Columbus, Ohio

ROBIE, EDWARD H., Secretary, American Institute of Mining and Metallurgical Engineers, New York, N.Y.

ROGERS, CLYDE L., Vice-President, National Industrial Conference Board, New York, N.Y.

SCOTT, WARREN W., Library of Congress, Washington, D.C.

SHAFFER, L. E., Professor of Mining, Department of Engineering, University of California, Berkeley, Calif.

SHENON, PHILIP J., Consulting Geologist, Salt Lake City, Utah

SHERMAN, ALLAN, Chief, Office of Minerals Reports, Bureau of Mines, U.S. Department of the Interior, Washington, D.C.

SKAVANG, NILS B., U.S. Department of the Air Force, Washington, D.C.

SMITH, RICHARD W., Chamber of Commerce of the United States, Washington, D.C.

SPINGARN, EDWIN E., General Counsel's Office, Atomic Energy Commission, Washington, D.C.

STEPHENSON, H. KIRK, National Science Foundation, Washington, D.C.

TAYLOR, WILLIAM E., Raw Materials Department, British Embassy, Washington, D.C.

THAYER, T. P., Geologist, Mineral Deposits Branch, Geological Survey, U.S. Department of the Interior, Washington, D.C.

TINDULA, ROY W., Chief, Office of Technical Services, U.S. Department of Commerce, Washington, D.C.

TRAMMELL, C. M., Washington, D.C.

VANDERWILT, JOHN, President, Colorado School of Mines, Golden, Colo.

WALDRON, HOWARD L., *Mining World*, New York, N.Y.

WEAVER, ELMER H., Assistant Director for Materials, Office of Defense Mobilization, Washington, D.C.

WHITE, JAMES A., The Tungsten Institute, Washington, D.C.

WHITE, JOHN W., Executive Director, U.S. Inter-American Council, Washington, D.C.

WILES, GLOYD M., Manager, National Lead Company, Port Washington, N.Y.

WILLISTON, SAMUEL H., Chairman, Strategic Materials Committee, American Mining Congress, Palo Alto, Calif.

WINSTON, A. W., Assistant Manager, Magnesium Department, The Dow Chemical Company, Midland, Mich.

WORMSER, FELIX E., Assistant Secretary, U.S. Department of the Interior, Washington, D.C.

WRIGHT, CHARLES WILL, Washington, D.C.

YOUNG, HOWARD I., President, American Zinc, Lead and Smelting Company, St. Louis, Mo.

ZIEGFELD, ROBERT L., Secretary, Lead Industries Association, New York, N.Y.

ZINNER, PAUL, Chief, Minerals Division, Bureau of Mines, U.S. Department of the Interior, Washington, D.C.

SECTION V

ADAMS, FRANCIS L., Chief, Bureau of Power, Federal Power Commission, Washington, D.C.

ADAMS, L. H., Geophysical Laboratory, Carnegie Institution of Washington, Washington, D.C.

AGGER, DONALD G., Materials Division, General Services Administration, Washington, D.C.

AMES, NORMAN B., Professor, George Washington University, Washington, D.C.

AYRES, EUGENE, Consultant, Gulf Research and Development Company, Pittsburgh, Pa.

BABBITT, JOHN D., Canadian Scientific Liaison Office, Washington, D.C.

BAKER, CARY F., JR., McGraw-Hill Book Company, Inc., New York, N.Y.

BAKER, RAYMOND C., National Association of Electric Companies, Crestwood, N.Y.

BARNEA, JOSEPH, Department of Economic Affairs, United Nations, New York, N.Y.

BARNES, RAYMOND M., Bozell and Jacobs, Inc., Washington, D.C.

BARNETT, HAROLD, The Rand Corporation, Washington, D.C.

BAUER, JOHN, League for Industrial Democracy, New York, N.Y.

BAYFIELD, W. W., Executive Vice-President, American Coal Sales Association, Washington, D.C.

BENNETT, CLAUDIUS E., Chief, Electrical Division, Federal Power Commission, Washington, D.C.

BENNION, H. S., Managing Director, Edison Electric Institute, New York, N.Y.

BIEMILLER, ANDREW J., Legislative Representative, American Federation of Labor, Washington, D.C.

BOGGS, MAYWOOD, International Representative, International Brotherhood of Boilermakers, Iron Shipbuilders, Blacksmiths, Forgers and Helpers, Washington, D.C.

BROWNE, E. WAYLES, JR., Bethesda, Md.

CADLE, AUSTIN, Economist, Standard Oil Company of California, San Francisco, Calif.

CAINE, WALTER E., Texas Eastern Transportation Corporation, Shreveport, La.

CAMPBELL, F. DOUGLAS, Detroit Edison Company, Detroit, Mich.

CAMPBELL, ROLLA D., Island Creek Coal Company, Huntington, W.Va.

CARMODY, JOHN M., Washington, D.C.

CHRISTIANSEN, A. J., Secretary-Treasurer, Illinois Coal Strippers Association, Chicago, Ill.

COCKE, COMDR. THOMAS P., Manager, Power and Utilities Branch, Bureau of Yards and Docks, U.S. Department of the Navy, Washington, D.C.

COE, ROGER J., New England Electric System, Boston, Mass.

COHN, DAVID E., U.S. Bureau of the Budget, Washington, D.C.

COLE, W. STERLING, Joint Congressional Committee on Atomic Energy, Washington, D.C.

COOK, MELVIN A., Department of Metallurgical Engineering, University of Utah, Salt Lake City, Utah

COOMBS, PHILIP H., Fund for the Advancement of Education, New York, N.Y.

COOPER, W. R., Tennessee Valley Authority, Chattanooga, Tenn.

COPPOC, WILLIAM J., Director of Research, The Texas Company, New York, N.Y.

COZZENS, BRADLEY, Assistant Chief Electrical Engineer, Department of Water and Power, Los Angeles, Calif.

CROOK, LEONARD T., Board of Engineers for Rivers and Harbors, U.S. Department of the Army, Washington, D.C.

CUNNINGHAM, JAMES H., National Coal Association, Washington, D.C.

DAILEY, T. M., JR., Humble Oil and Refining Company, Houston, Tex.

DANIELS, FARRINGTON, Chairman, Department of Chemistry, University of Wisconsin, Madison, Wis.

DAVIDSON, T. E., II, Iowa Development Commission, Des Moines, Iowa

DE LA FLEUR, LOUIS E., Federal Communications Commission, Washington, D.C.

DELZELL, THOMAS W., Chairman of the Board, Portland General Electric Company, Portland, Ore.

DE POLO, TABER, Ball Associates, Washington, D.C.

DOTY, DALE E., Federal Power Commission, Washington, D.C.

DRAKE, E. J., Officer-in-Charge, Australian Scientific Liaison Office, Washington, D.C.

DWYER, CORNELIUS J., Industrial Specialists Division, Foreign Operations Administration, Washington, D.C.

EDWARDS, FORD K., National Coal Association, Washington, D.C.

ELLIS, C. B., Walter B. Kidde Nuclear Laboratories, Garden City, Long Island, N.Y.

ERTL, TELL, Department of Mining and Petroleum Engineering, Ohio State University, Columbus, Ohio.

FAIRLAMB, WILBUR F., Regional Engineer, Federal Power Commission, Fort Worth, Tex.

FALCK, EDWARD, Washington, D.C.

FASSETT, F. G., JR., Director of the Technology Press, Massachusetts Institute of Technology, Cambridge, Mass.

FERGUSON, HARRY, Pennsylvania Power and Light Company, Allentown, Pa.

FIELDNER, A. C., Chief Fuels Technologist, Bureau of Mines, U.S. Department of the Interior, Washington, D.C.

FINLEY, S. R., General Superintendent, Electric Power Board of Chattanooga, Chattanooga, Tenn.

FIRFER, ALEX, Economics Division, Federal Communications Commission, Washington, D.C.

FIRST, ROBERT S., Celanese Corporation of America, New York, N.Y.

FITCH, H. S., West Penn Power Company, Pittsburgh, Pa.

FOLEY, J. W., The Texas Company, New York, N.Y.

FOLK, ROBERT E., Washington, D.C.

FRICK, CLIFFORD H., Manager, Coal Bureau, Pennsylvania Power and Light Company, Allentown, Pa.

FRITZ, WILBERT G., Office of Defense Mobilization, Washington, D.C.

FROST, LAURANCE E., Consolidated Edison Company, New York, N.Y.

FURNAS, C. C., Cornell Aeronautical Laboratory, Buffalo, N.Y.

GALL, LAWRENCE H., Independent Natural Gas Association of America, Washington, D.C.

GALLAGHER, JOSEPH J., Bureau of Mines, U.S. Department of the Interior, Washington, D.C.

GARY, HOWARD C., The Texas Company, New York, N.Y.

GERBER, ABRAHAM, American Gas and Electric Company, New York, N.Y.

GLANTZ, HERBERT H., U.S. Department of State, Washington, D.C.

GODAIRE, J. G., Falls Church, Va.

GOSS, GEORGE H., Consumers Union of U.S., Inc., Washington, D.C.

GRIMM, GEORGE A., Office of Assistant Secretary of Defense, Washington, D.C.

HALL, CAMERON P., Executive Director, National Council of Churches, New York, N.Y.

HAMILTON, WALTER A., Joint Congressional Committee on Atomic Energy, Washington, D.C.

HARBOTTLE, R. B., Economic Development Department, Shell Oil Company, New York, N.Y.

HEDGES, MARION H., Washington, D.C.

HILL, WILHELMINA, American Federation of Soroptimist Clubs, Washington, D.C.

HITCHCOCK, DAL, Clark, Hitchcock and Associates, Washington, D.C.

HITTLE, O. G., Public Utility District No. 1 of Cowlitz County, Longview, Wash.

HOLLAR, PHILIP A., Vice-President, Association of American Railroads, Washington, D.C.

HOPKINS, GEORGE R., Office of Defense Mobilization, Washington, D.C.

HORWITZ, SOLIS, Washington, D.C.

HOTTEL, H. C., Department of Chemical Engineering, Massachusetts Institute of Technology, Cambridge, Mass.

HUNTER, THOMAS W., Bureau of Mines, U.S. Department of the Interior, Washington, D.C.

IRELAND, R. L., Chairman of the Executive Committee, Pittsburgh Consolidation Coal Company, Cleveland, Ohio

IRWIN, FRANK, Pittsburg and Midway Coal Mining Company, Pittsburg, Kans.

JACKSON, GARDNER, Legislative Department, Congress of Industrial Organizations, Washington, D.C.

JEFFRIES, DONALD W., Arthur D. Little, Inc., Cambridge, Mass.

JONES, E. O., Ethyl Corporation, New York, N.Y.

JONES, HERSCHEL F., Power Manager, Bonneville Power Administration, U.S. Department of the Interior, Portland, Ore.

JONES, JOHN H., Monongahela Power Company, Fairmont, W.Va.

JUDD, ORVILLE D., Sinclair Refining Company, Washington, D.C.

JURENEV, SERGE B., Assistant to the Chairman of the Board, Continental Oil Company, New York, N.Y.

KAHN, HARRY, JR., Washington, D.C.

KAMPMEIER, ROLAND A., Assistant Manager of Power and Director of Power Supply, Tennessee Valley Authority, Chattanooga, Tenn.

KELLY, HARRY C., Assistant Director, National Science Foundation, Washington, D.C.

KERR, C. PHILLIPS, Office of Defense Mobilization, Washington, D.C.

KESTER, WILLIAM H., Research Department, Federal Reserve Bank of St. Louis, St. Louis, Mo.

KNAPP, EDWARD M., Franklin P. Wood Association, Inc., Washington, D.C.

KREAGER, H. DEWAYNE, Industrial Consultant, Washington, D.C.

LAING, R. T., Central Pennsylvania Coal Producers Association, Altoona, Pa.

LAMB, GEORGE A., Pittsburgh Consolidation Coal Company, Pittsburgh, Pa.

LANDRY, BERTRAND A., Battelle Memorial Institute, Columbus, Ohio

LANE, R. K., Public Service Company of Oklahoma, Tulsa, Okla.

LAVIERS, HARRY, President, South-East Coal Company, Paintsville, Ky.

LAWRENCE, GROVE, American Gas Association, Los Angeles, Calif.

LEPAWSKY, ALBERT, Professor of Political Science, University of California, Berkeley, Calif.

LEVIN, JACK, Legislative Reference Service, Library of Congress, Washington, D.C.

LÖF, GEORGE O. G., Chemical Engineer, Denver, Colo.

LYONS, W. A., Vice-President, New York Gas and Electric Company, Binghamton, N.Y.

MATHER, KIRTLEY F., Professor, Geological Museum, Harvard University, Cambridge, Mass.

MAYOTT, CLARENCE W., Consultant, retired from The Hartford Electric Light Company, Hartford, Conn.

McCABE, LOUIS C., Chief, Fuels and Explosives Division, Bureau of Mines, U.S. Department of the Interior, Washington, D.C.

McDERMOTT, MARY E., Research Economist, Atlantic Refining Company, Philadelphia, Pa.

McGANN, PAUL W., Chief Economist, Bureau of Mines, U.S. Department of the Interior, Washington, D.C.

McLAUGHLIN, GLEN E., Economist, Export-Import Bank of Washington, Washington, D.C.

McLAUGHLIN, J. WARREN, Office of Defense Mobilization, Washington, D.C.

MELAMID, ALEXANDER, New School for Social Research, New York, N.Y.

MENKE, JOHN R., President, Nuclear Development Associates, Inc., White Plains, N.Y.

MORGAN, J. W., Ayrshire Collieries Corporation, Indianapolis, Ind.

MORGEN, R. A., Program Director for Engineering Sciences, National Science Foundation, Washington, D.C.

MORRIS, CURTIS, American Gas Association, Washington, D.C.

MORRIS, R. E., Allis-Chalmers Manufacturing Company, Washington, D.C.

NEWMAN, RALPH, Foundation for Equity, Washington, D.C.

NORMAN, LT. COL. WILLIAM R., Industrial College of the Armed Forces, Washington, D.C.

NOYES, HOWARD B., Vice-President, Washington Gas Light Company, Washington, D.C.

OLIVER, CARROLL A., President, American Public Power Association, Taunton, Mass.

O'NEAL, SAM A., Tennessee Valley Public Power Association, Washington, D.C.

OTTE, HERMAN F., Professor of Economic Geography, Columbia University, New York, N.Y.

PARSON, DANIEL, Director, Bureau of Statistics, American Gas Association, New York, N.Y.

PATTON, M. L., National Coal Association, Washington, D.C.

PEARY, ANTHONY J., Bureau of Reclamation, U.S. Department of the Interior, Washington, D.C.

PETERSON, C. PETRUS, President, National Reclamation Association, Lincoln, Nebr.

PETTYJOHN, ELMORE S., Vice-President, Institute of Gas Technology, Chicago, Ill.

PILCHER, MILTON A., U.S. Bureau of the Budget, Washington, D.C.

POWELL, ALFRED R., Koppers Company, Inc., Pittsburgh, Pa.

PRICE, PAUL H., State Geologist and Director of Geological and Economic Survey, Morgantown, W.Va.

RADIN, ALEX, General Manager, American Public Power Association, Washington, D.C.

READ, DONALD E., Bureau of Mines, U.S. Department of the Interior, Washington, D.C.

REEVES, E. D., Executive Vice-President, Standard Oil Development Company, New York, N.Y.

RENFREW, MARTHA JANE, Stanford Research Institute, Washington, D.C.

ROBBINS, CHARLES E., Atomic Industrial Forum, Inc., New York, N.Y.

ROBINSON, J FRENCH, President, Consolidated Natural Gas Company, New York, N.Y.

RODMAN, ROLAND V., Anderson-Prichard Oil Corporation, Oklahoma City, Okla.

RUBEL, A. C., Union Oil Company of California, Los Angeles, Calif.

SALL, GEORGE W., American Mining Congress, Washington, D.C.

SARGENT, HENRY B., President, Arizona Public Service Company, Phoenix, Ariz.

SAUTTER, LT. COMDR. FREDERICK R., Office of Navy Material, U.S. Department of the Navy, Washington, D.C.

SCHACHT, R. L., General Manager, Consumers Public Power District, Columbus, Nebr.

SCHANZ, JOHN J., JR., Division of Mineral Economics, Pennsylvania State College, State College, Pa.

SCHMIDT, NORMAN G., Eastern Coal Corporation, Washington, D.C.

SCHROEDER, W. C., Chemical Engineer, Department of Chemical Engineering, University of Maryland, College Park, Md.

SCHURR, SAM H., The Rand Corporation, Washington, D.C.

SHANNON, SPENCER S., Bedford, Pa.

SHERWIN, JAMES N., American Coal Sales Association, Cleveland, Ohio

SHOCH, CLARENCE T., Vice-President, National Society of Professional Engineers, Allentown, Pa.

SMITH, P. L., President, National Association of Electric Companies, Washington, D.C.

SMITH, WILLIAM G., Washington, D.C.

SNYDER, WILLIAM H., U.S. Bureau of the Budget, Washington, D.C.

SOUTHWARD, GLENN B., American Mining Congress, Washington, D.C.

SPARKS, W. J., Standard Oil Development Company, Linden, N.J.

SPENCER, K. W., H. Zinder and Associates, Inc., Washington, D.C.

SPENCER, VIVIAN EBERLE, U.S. Bureau of the Census, Suitland, Md.

STONE, EDWARD, Institute of Life Insurance, New York, N.Y.

STORCH, H. H., Bureau of Mines, U.S. Department of the Interior, Washington, D.C.

STRAUB, HAROLD J., Utility Workers Union of America, Washington, D.C.

STRINER, HERBERT E., Bureau of Mines, U.S. Department of the Interior, Washington, D.C.

SULLIVAN, G. DON, National Coal Association, Washington, D.C.

SWEARINGEN, J. E., Vice-President (Production), Standard Oil Company (Indiana), Chicago, Ill.

TALBOT, FRANK, Chemical Engineer, Washington, D.C.

TEARE, B. R., JR., Dean, College of Engineering and Science, Carnegie Institute of Technology, Pittsburgh, Pa.

TELKES, MARIA, New York University, New York, N.Y.

THOMAS, ALMON D., Federal Power Commission, Washington, D.C.

THOMPSON, SHELBY, Chief, Public Information Service, Atomic Energy Commission, Washington, D.C.

TOBIAS, GEORGE, U.S. Department of Labor, Washington, D.C.

TUCKER, LAWRENCE, American University, Washington, D.C.

TUFTY, HAROLD G., Franklin P. Wood Associates, Inc., Washington, D.C.

TURNER, HAROLD, Vice-President and General Manager, The Ohio Power Company, Canton, Ohio

VADEN, T. HUNT, The Southern Company, Atlanta, Ga.

VAN ROYEN, WILLIAM, University of Maryland, College Park, Md.

VAN SCOYOC, MELWOOD W., Assistant Chief, Bureau of Accounts, Finance, and Rates, Federal Power Commission, Washington, D.C.

WALKER, MRS. EGBERT H., Potomac Appalachian Trail Club, Takoma Park, Md.

WALL, GLEN B., Assistant Director of Research, International Brotherhood of Electrical Workers, Washington, D.C.

WARDEN, WILLIAM FRANKLIN, JR., American University, Washington, D.C.

WARING, JOHN A., JR., New York, N.Y.

WARREN, FREDERICK H., Consulting Engineer, Washington, D.C.

WATSON, J. P., University of Pittsburgh, Pittsburgh, Pa.

WATTS, PHILIP E., Ministry of Fuel and Power, London, England

WAYLAND, RUSSELL G., Geological Survey, U.S. Department of the Interior, Washington, D.C.

WEIDENHAMMER, ROBERT M., Washington, D.C.

WEIL, GEORGE L., Consultant, Washington, D.C.

WHIPPLE, COL. WILLIAM, Corps of Engineers, U.S. Department of the Army, Washington, D.C.

WHITCOMB, LAWRENCE, Professor, Department of Geology, Lehigh University, Bethlehem, Pa.

WILD, CLAUDE C., JR., Mid-Continent Oil and Gas Association, Washington, D.C.

WILHOITE, L. J., Chairman, Electric Power Board of Chattanooga, Chattanooga, Tenn.

WILLIAMS, JAMES E., Washington, D.C.

WILSON, GEORGE, California Farm Bureau Federation, Berkeley, Calif.

WINDFOHR, ROBERT F., President, Mid-Continent Oil and Gas Association, Fort Worth, Tex.

WISE, WILLIAM C., Wise and Potamkin, Washington, D.C.

WOOD, RAMSAY, Federal Reserve Board, Washington, D.C.

WOODWARD, DONALD B., New York, N.Y.

WRATHER, WILLIAM E., Director, Geological Survey, U.S. Department of the Interior, Washington, D.C.

YOHALEM, MORTON E., Reconstruction Finance Corporation, Washington, D.C.

YOUNG, W. H., Bureau of Mines, U.S. Department of the Interior, Washington, D.C.

SECTION VI

AKI, KOICHI, Resources Council, Prime Minister's Office, Japanese Government, Tokyo, Japan

ANDERSON, SAMUEL W., Assistant Secretary of Commerce, Washington, D.C.

ANDREWS, JOHN N., JR., George Washington University, Washington, D.C.

ARANT, JACK, American Mining Congress, Washington, D.C.

ARMSTRONG, WILLIS C., Deputy Director, Office of International Materials Policy, U.S. Department of State, Washington, D.C.

AUERBACH, BEATRICE FOX, Service Bureau for Women's Organizations, Hartford, Conn.

BATEMAN, ALAN M., Department of Geology, Yale University, New Haven, Conn.

BELCHER, MARJORIE S., Washington, D.C.

BELL, GEORGE L., Industrial Consultant, Washington, D.C.

BENNETT, JACK, Chevy Chase, Md.

BERGUE, JEAN-PIERRE, Commercial Counselor's Office, French Embassy, Washington, D.C.

BERNSTEIN, EDWARD M., Director, Research Division, International Monetary Fund, Washington, D.C.

BERQUIST, FRED E., Economist, Joint Economic Commission of Congress, Washington, D.C.

BIDWELL, PERCY W., Council on Foreign Relations, New York, N.Y.

BISSELL, RICHARD M., JR., Washington, D.C.

BLACK, LLOYD D., U.S. Department of Agriculture, Washington, D.C.

BLACK, ROBERT, Foreign Operations Administration, Washington, D.C.

BURGESS, ROBERT W., Director, U.S. Bureau of the Census, Suitland, Md.

CAMERON, FRANCIS, Vice-President, St. Joseph Lead Company, New York, N.Y.

CAROTHERS, NEIL, Special Assistant to the Director, National Science Foundation, Washington, D.C.

CAVALCANTI, CELSO BARBOZA, Brazilian Embassy, Washington, D.C.

CHAPMAN, A. W., Washington, D.C.

CLARK, ROBERT L., Clark, Hitchcock and Associates, Washington, D.C.

CLEM, HAROLD J., Industrial College of the Armed Forces, Washington, D.C.

CLEVELAND, H. VAN BUREN, Committee for Economic Development, Washington, D.C.

CLIFFE, L. E., Acting Foreign Activities Officer, Bureau of Reclamation, U.S. Department of the Interior, Washington, D.C.

CLINE, ALBERT C., Forest Service, U.S. Department of Agriculture, Washington, D.C.

COLLADO, E. G., Assistant Treasurer, Standard Oil Company (New Jersey), New York, N.Y.

COLONNA, C. B., Italian Embassy, Washington, D.C.

CONCANNON, CHARLES C., International Consultant, Business and Defense Administration, U.S. Department of Commerce, Washington, D.C.

CORBASSON, FRANCOIS P., Head of Mission, Organisation for European Economic Co-operation, Washington, D.C.

COTHERN, L. I., National Coal Association, Tazewell, Va.

CRAIG, GLENN, Foreign Operations Administration, Washington, D.C.

CRESSEY, GEORGE BABCOCK, Department of Geography, Syracuse University, N.Y.

CRONIN, REV. JOHN F., National Catholic Welfare Conference, Washington, D.C.

CROSTON, JOHN, General Services Administration, Washington, D.C.

CURRAN, HUGH N., Caracas, Venezuela

DARBYSHIRE, B. N., Graduate Institute of International Studies, Geneva, Switzerland

DEDRICK, CALVERT L., Coordinator, International Statistics, U.S. Bureau of the Census, Washington, D.C.

DeSHAZO, MRS. CHARLES N., Country Women's Council, Tappahannock, Va.

DE STACKELBERG, C., Washington, D.C.

DOWNING, WARWICK, Chairman, Oil and Gas Conservation Commission of the State of Colorado, Denver, Colo.

DRECHSLER, GEORGE D., Bureau of Mines, U.S. Department of the Interior, Washington, D.C.

DUNN, READ P., JR., Director, Foreign Trade, National Cotton Council of America, Washington, D.C.

EASSON, MRS. LELIA M., U.S. Department of Commerce, Washington, D.C.

EATON, EDGAR I., U.S. Department of Labor, Washington, D.C.

EHLERS, JOSEPH H., American Society of Civil Engineers, Washington, D.C.

ENGLISH, ROBERT, State Senator, Hancock, N.H.

EVANS, JACK, Asiatic Petroleum Corporation, Washington, D.C.

EVANS, JOHN W., Director, Office of International Materials Policy, U.S. Department of State, Washington, D.C.

FANE, H. F. B., First Secretary, British Embassy, Washington, D.C.

FICK, NATHANIEL C., U.S. Department of Defense, Washington, D.C.

FIELD, THOROLD F., Consulting Mining Engineer, Duluth, Minn.

FIELDS, MORRIS J., U.S. Department of the Treasury, Washington, D.C.

FITZGERALD, DENNIS A., Deputy Director for Operations, Foreign Operations Administration, Washington, D.C.

FRANK, ISAIAH, U.S. Department of State, Washington, D.C.

FREED, JEANETTE, Curriculum Supervisor, Montgomery County Schools, Dayton, Ohio

FRIEDRICH, WILLIAM GEORGE, Association for International Development, Washington, D.C.

FRITZLE, C., Food and Agriculture Organization of the United Nations, North American Regional Office, Washington, D.C.

FULLINWIDER, REAR ADM. EDWIN G., National Research Council, Washington, D.C.

GAMBLE, EDWARD W., JR., Manufacturing Chemists Association, Washington, D.C.

GATES, WILLIAM B., JR., Economist, Export-Import Bank, Washington, D.C.

GAUTHIER, J. P. C., Materials Division, Canadian Department of Defense Production, Ottawa, Canada

GIDEONSE, MAX, Chairman, Department of Economics, Rutgers University, New Brunswick, N.J.

GOLD, RUTH S., U.S. Department of State, Washington, D.C.

GOLDSMITH, ROBERT, Raw Materials Department, British Embassy, Washington, D.C.

GOOCH, WINSLOW L., Forestry Consultant, West Point, Va.

GORLITZ, SAMUEL J., Chief, Economic Development Branch, U.S. Department of State, Washington, D.C.

GRAHAM, EARL A., Federal Trade Commission, Washington, D.C.

GREENSPAN, BENJAMIN, New School for Social Research, New York, N.Y.

GREGG, KENNETH P., SR., Consulting Engineer, Mineral Resource Industries, Washington, D.C.

GRIEFEN, JOHN R., Massachusetts Department of Commerce, Boston, Mass.

GRIFFITH, RICHARD A., General Electric Company, Schenectady, N.Y.

GRUBER, GUENTHER R., Austrian Embassy, Washington, D.C.

HAYES, DAVID J., U.S. Department of the Army, Washington, D.C.

HEDLUND, CHARLES J., Standard Oil Company (New Jersey) New York, N.Y.

HEIKES, GEORGE CONRAD, Consulting Mining Geologist, Los Altos, Calif.

HENKEL, LOWELL L., Industrial College of the Armed Forces, Washington, D.C.

HEYL, MARY JANE, Office of Industrial Resources, Foreign Operations Administration, Washington, D.C.

HICKS, WILLIAM T., School of Commerce and Business Administration, University of Mississippi, University, Miss.

HINRICHS, A. F., Committee for a National Trade Policy, Washington, D.C.

HITCHENS, P. T., Director of Research, National Foreign Trade Council, Inc., New York, N.Y.

HUDDLE, FRANKLIN P., U.S. Department of Defense, Washington, D.C.

HUDNELL, BRIG. GEN. W. T., Assistant for Logistic Plans, U.S. Department of the Air Force, Washington, D.C.

INCE, CHARLES, Vice-President, St. Joseph Lead Company, New York, N.Y.

ISENBERGH, MAX, Atomic Energy Commission, Washington, D.C.

ISHIMITSU, TOHRU, Yale University Conservation Program, New Haven, Conn.

JENSEN, F. B., Professor, Lehigh University, Bethlehem, Pa.

JOHNSON, F. ERNEST, National Council of the Churches of Christ in the United States, New York, N.Y.

JOHNSTON, WILLIAM D., JR., Chief, Foreign Geology Branch, Geological Survey, U.S. Department of the Interior, Washington, D.C.

KALIJARVI, THORSTEN V., U.S. Department of State, Washington, D.C.

KAMARCK, ANDREW M., International Bank for Reconstruction and Development, Washington, D.C.

KELLER, HAROLD, New York State Department of Commerce, Albany, N.Y.

LEVY, WALTER J., New York, N.Y.

LINDEMAN, JOHN, Economist, Washington, D.C.

LOVE, L. W., U.S. Department of the Navy, Washington, D.C.

LOWDERMILK, WALTER C., Berkeley, Calif.

LUND, R. J., Battelle Memorial Institute, Columbus, Ohio

MALENBAUM, WILFRED, Visiting Professor, Massachusetts Institute of Technology, Cambridge, Mass.

MASON, EDWARD S., Dean, Graduate School of Public Administration, Harvard University, Cambridge, Mass.

MATHER, WILLIAM B., Chairman, Mineral Technology, Southwest Research Institute, San Antonio, Tex.

MATTHEWS, ALLAN F., Johns Hopkins University, Operations Research Office, Chevy Chase, Md.

MAY, STACY, Economist, International Basic Economy Corporation, New York, N.Y.

MAYER, CHARLES T., Société-Général de Belgique, Washington, D.C.

McCLELLAND, W. RAY, Canadian Department of Mines and Technical Surveys, Ottawa, Canada

McMAHON, ALBERT D., U.S. Department of Commerce, Washington, D.C.

MERIE, LOUIS, French Embassy, Washington, D.C.

MICHANOWSKY, GEORGE, President, Amazonia Foundation, Inc., New York, N.Y.

MILLER, E. WILLARD, Chief, Division of Geography, Pennsylvania State College, State College, Pa.

MILLS, A. L., JR., Board of Governors of the Federal Reserve System, Washington, D.C.

MOEREL, M. H., Netherlands Embassy, Washington, D.C.

NYSTROM, J. WARREN, Chamber of Commerce of the United States, Washington, D.C.

OATES, N. STANLEY, Ford Motor Company, Washington, D.C.

O'BRIEN, MAJ. GEN. JOHN W., Australian Embassy, Washington, D.C.

O'KEEFE, THOMAS D., Washington, D.C.

PAGE, ROBERT G., President, Phelps Dodge Corporation, New York, N.Y.

PARKS, ROLAND D., Massachusetts Institute of Technology, Cambridge, Mass.

PEARSON, PAUL B., Atomic Energy Commission, Washington, D.C.

PEHRSON, ELMER W., Regional Director, Foreign Minerals, Bureau of Mines, U.S. Department of the Interior, Washington, D.C.

PHELPS, D. M., Professor, School of Business Administration, University of Michigan, Ann Arbor, Mich.

PHILLIPS, WILLIAM T., Professor of International Economics, School of Advanced International Studies of the Johns Hopkins University, Washington, D.C.

PILAND, COL. JULIUS L., Office of Chief of Engineers, U.S. Department of the Army, Washington, D.C.

PINCUS, JOSEPH, Arlington, Va.

PLEVA, EDWARD G., Professor, Department of Geography, University of Western Ontario, London, Ontario, Canada

POOL, ITHIEL D. S., Center of International Studies, Massachusetts Institute of Technology, Cambridge, Mass.

POWERS, PHILIP N., Monsanto Chemical Company, St. Louis, Mo.

RAUSHENBUSH, STEPHEN, American Academy of Political and Social Science, Washington, D.C.

REUFELS, JOSEF G., German Mission to Foreign Operations Administration, Washington, D.C.

REYSSET, BERNARD, Commercial Counselor's Office, French Embassy, Washington, D.C.

RICE, ANDREW E., American Veteran's Committee, Washington, D.C.

RICHARDS, EARL M., Vice-President in Charge of Planning and Development, Republic Steel Corporation, Cleveland, Ohio

RICHTER, JOHN H., Foreign Agricultural Service, U.S. Department of Agriculture, Washington, D.C.

RIDDELL, GUY C., Senior Consultants, Inc., New York, N.Y.

ROSNER, MICHAEL, Director, Industrial Development Department, Ministry of Industry, Government of Israel, Jerusalem, Israel

ROSS, EMERSON A., Chief, Investment and Economic Development Staff, Office of Financial and Development Policy, U.S. Department of State, Washington, D.C.

ROSS, GEORGE T., Washington, D.C.

ROSSANT, M. J., McGraw-Hill Book Company, New York, N.Y.

ROTHSCHILD, GEORGE W., Foreign Operations Administration, Washington, D.C.

ROTIVAL, MAURICE E. H., New York, N.Y.

ROVE, OLAF N., Geological Survey, U.S. Department of the Interior, Washington, D.C.

RUDOLPH, WALTER M., U.S. Department of State, Washington, D.C.

RUTTENBERG, STANLEY H., Director, Department of Education and Research, Congress of Industrial Organizations, Washington, D.C.

SANDERSON, FRED H., U.S. Department of State, Washington, D.C.

SCHEIBE, ELIZABETH CH, Chairman, German Diplomatic Mission, Washington, D.C.

SCHULTZ, W. W., Office of Defense Mobilization, Washington, D.C.

SCHWENGER, ROBERT B., Chief, Regional Investigations Branch, Foreign Agricultural Service, U.S. Department of Agriculture, Washington, D.C.

SCOLL, E. EDWARD, Investment and Economic Development Staff, U.S. Department of State, Washington, D.C.

SESSIONS, GORDON M., Sessions and Caminita, Washington, D.C.

SHELDON, KENNETH P., American Institute for Economic Research, Lenox, Mass.

SHEPARD, DAVID A., Standard Oil Company (New Jersey), New York, N.Y.

SHOR, JUDITH J., Washington, D.C.

SMITH, GUY-HAROLD, Chairman, Department of Geography, Ohio State University, Columbus, Ohio

SMITH, H. DEWITT, Consulting Engineer, New York, N.Y.

SOWDER, R. D., Sinclair Refining Company, Washington, D.C.

SPIRO, BENJAMIN P., International Bank for Reconstruction and Development, Washington, D.C.

STATLER, FRANK L., Allis-Chalmers Manufacturing Company, Washington, D.C.

STEPHENS, WALDO, Oklahoma City, Okla.

STRAUSS, SIMON D., Vice-President, American Smelting and Refining Company, New York, N.Y.

STRICKER, ADAM K., JR., U.S. Inter-American Council, Detroit, Mich.

SYMONDS, EDWARD, Assistant Director, Office of Public Relations, International Bank for Reconstruction and Development, Washington, D.C.

TAYLOR, WAYNE C., Foreign Operations Administration, Washington, D.C.

TERREL, C. L., President, International Consultants, Inc., Washington, D.C.

THOM, WILLIAM T., JR., Princeton, N.J.

TOUTAY, JEAN, Commercial Counselor's Office, French Embassy, Washington, D.C.

TURNER, EARL, Texas Independent Producers and Royalty Owners Association, Austin, Tex.

UPHAM, THOMPSON E., *Journal of Agriculture and Food Chemistry*, Washington, D.C.

VOSKUIL, WALTER H., State Geological Survey, Urbana, Ill.

VUILLEQUEZ, JEAN, Vice-President, The American Metal Company, Ltd., New York, N.Y.

WARREN, F. G., U.S. Department of Commerce, Washington, D.C.

WARREN, J. ED, National City Bank, New York, N.Y.

WAYNE, JULES H., U.S. Department of State, Washington, D.C.

WEBER, RICHARD, Foreign Operations Administration, Washington, D.C.

WHEELER, LESLIE A., International Federation of Agricultural Producers, Washington, D.C.

WICKES, WM. W., Harnischfeger Corporation, Milwaukee, Wis.

WILSON, EVAN F., Arlington, Va.

WILSON, PHILIP D., Lehman Brothers, New York, N.Y.

WOLF, CHARLES, JR., The Ford Foundation, Washington, D.C.

WORTHING, MARION W., Chief of the Commodity Staff, Division of Functional Intelligence, Office of Intelligence Research, U.S. Department of State, Washington, D.C.

WYNNE, WILLIAM H., U.S. Department of the Treasury, Washington, D.C.

YOUNG, RICHARD A., Vice-President, American Zinc, Lead and Smelting Company, St. Louis, Mo.

SECTION VII

ABRAMS, ALLEN, Vice-President, Marathon Corporation, Rothschild, Wis.

ALEXANDER, MARY, United Kingdom Scientific Mission, Washington, D.C.

ALLEN, DURWARD L., Fish and Wildlife Service, U.S. Department of the Interior, Washington, D.C.

ALT, RICHARD M., Arthur D. Little, Inc., Cambridge, Mass.

BAIRD, FREDERICK T., JR., Maine Department of Sea and Shore Fisheries, Edgecombe, Me.

BARNES, CARLETON P., U.S. Department of Agriculture, Washington, D.C.

BECK, NIELS C., Armour Research Foundation, Chicago, Ill.

BECKLER, DAVID Z., Office of Defense Mobilization, Washington, D.C.

BEER, LOUISE, American University, Washington, D.C.

BENEDICT, LT. COL. HAROLD B., Industrial College of the Armed Forces, Washington, D.C.

BERGER, J. J., U.S. Department of the Interior, Washington, D.C.

BOWMAN, DEAN O., Chairman of Planning Staff, Crown Zellerbach Corporation, San Francisco, Calif.

BRADLEY, WILMOT H., Chief, Geologic Division, Geological Survey, U.S. Department of the Interior, Washington, D.C.

BRINSER, AYERS, Harvard University, Cambridge, Mass.

BUELL, MURRAY F., Rutgers University, New Brunswick, N.J.

BULGER, JOHN D., National Wildlife Federation, Washington, D.C.

BUTLER, GEORGE D., Director of Research, National Recreation Association, New York, N.Y.

CAIN, STANLEY A., Chairman, Department of Conservation, School of Natural Resources, University of Michigan, Ann Arbor, Mich.

CALE, EDWARD G., Director, Office of Regional American Affairs, Bureau of Inter-American Affairs, U.S. Department of State, Washington, D.C.

CARLETON, ROBERT H., National Education Association, Washington, D.C.

CARLSON, FRANK T., Yale University Conservation Program, New Haven, Conn.

CHRISTENSEN, GLENN J., Department of Geology, Lehigh University, Bethlehem, Pa.

COOK, ROBERT CARTER, Population Reference Bureau, Washington, D.C.

CRAINE, LYLE E., University of Michigan, Ann Arbor, Mich.

CRARY, RALPH W., California Research Corporation, Standard Oil Company of California, Washington, D.C.

CURTIS, HARRY A., Director, Tennessee Valley Authority, Knoxville, Tenn.

DAUPHINÉE, WILFRED T., Minister of Trade and Industry, Halifax, N.S., Canada

DAVIDSON, W. L., Atomic Energy Commission, Washington, D.C.

DAVIS, JAMES O., JR., General Counsel and Assistant to Director, Auburn Research Foundation, Auburn, Ala.

DAVIS, KINGSLEY, Columbia University, New York, N.Y.

DAY, ERNEST H., Patent Attorney, Washington, D.C.

DE LUXEMBOURG, Col. A. M. I., Washington, D.C.

DESMOND, ANNABELLE, Population Reference Bureau, Washington, D.C.

DOERING, WILLIAM V., Professor of Organic Chemistry, Yale University, New Haven, Conn.

DORICK, ISADORE L., Department of Geography, Johns Hopkins University, Baltimore, Md.

DOW, ROBERT L., Maine Department of Sea and Shore Fisheries, Augusta, Me.

ECKLER, A. ROSS, Deputy Director, U.S. Bureau of the Census, Washington, D.C.

ELIAS, NATHANIEL M., Chemical Consultant, New York, N.Y.

EMBREY, LEE ANNA, National Science Foundation, Washington, D.C.

ENDLER, OSCAR L., Office of Defense Mobilization, Washington, D.C.

EWELL, RAYMOND H., Assistant Director for Program Analysis, National Science Foundation, Washington, D.C.

FEISS, JULIAN W., Kennecott Copper Corporation, New York, N.Y.

FISHER, FRANK L., Silver Spring, Md.

FOOTE, PAUL D., Executive Vice-President, Gulf Research and Development Company, Gulf Oil Corporation, Pittsburgh, Pa.

FREDERICK, JOHN H., Head, Department of Business Organization, College of Business and Public Administration, University of Maryland, College Park, Md.

FRENCH, ROBERT W., Dean, School of Business Administration, Tulane University, New Orleans, La.

GARRETT, JOHN H., Office of the Secretary of Defense, Washington, D.C.

GIBBS, R. C., National Research Council, Washington, D.C.

GIBSON, R. E., Director, Johns Hopkins University Applied Physics Laboratory, Silver Spring, Md.

GINZBERG, ELI, Professor of Economics, Graduate School of Business, Columbia University, New York, N.Y.

GOODRIDGE, EDWIN T., Horizons, Inc., Princeton, N.J.

GOODWIN, RICHARD H., Connecticut College, New London, Conn.

GRAY, D. M., Vice-President, Stoner-Mudge, Inc., Pittsburgh, Pa.

GREENSFELDER, ALBERT P., Trustee, St. Louis Regional Conservation Foundation, St. Louis, Mo.

GRINTER, L. E., Dean of Graduate Studies and Director of Research, University of Florida, Gainesville, Fla.

HAGOOD, MARGARET JARMAN, Vice-President, Population Association of America, Washington, D.C.

HAMMER, PHILIP, Executive Officer, Committee of the South, Atlanta, Ga.

HARRELL, WILLIAM B., Vice-President, Business Affairs, University of Chicago, Chicago, Ill.

HENLE, PETER, American Federation of Labor, Washington, D.C.

HEROY, W. B., Beers and Heroy, Dallas, Tex.

HITCHCOCK, CHARLES B., Director, American Geographical Society, New York, N.Y.

HOYT, W. T., Executive Secretary, Scrap Conservation Committee of the Steel Industry, New York, N.Y.

HUCK, SUSAN, Instructor in Geography, Washington College, Chestertown, Md.

HURLEY, P. M., Professor of Geology, Massachusetts Institute of Technology, Cambridge, Mass.

ISARD, WALTER, Massachusetts Institute of Technology, Cambridge, Mass.

ISELIN, COLUMBUS O'D., Senior Physical Oceanographer, Woods Hole Oceanographic Institution, Woods Hole, Mass.

KAUFERT, FRANK H., Professor, School of Forestry, Institute of Agriculture, University of Minnesota, St. Paul, Minn.

KEIRSTEAD, RALPH E., School Department, Hartford, Conn.

KNIGHT, PAUL, Washington, D.C.

LAKE, BARBARA, Managing Editor, *The Journal of Heredity*, Washington, D.C.

LARNER, BERNARD, U.S. Bureau of the Budget, Washington, D.C.

LEWIS, HARRY F., Institute of Paper Chemistry, Appleton, Wis.

LI, C. C., School of Public Health, University of Pittsburgh, Pittsburgh, Pa.

LIVELY, CHARLES E., College of Agriculture, University of Missouri, Columbia, Mo.

LOEB, WILLIAM A., Nuclear Development Associates, Inc., White Plains, N.Y.

LOFTNESS, ROBERT L., Project Engineer, Atomic Energy Research Department, North American Aviation, Inc., Downey, Calif.

LOWRY, HOMER H., Coal Research Laboratory, Carnegie Institute of Technology, Pittsburgh, Pa.

MANNING, P. D. V., International Minerals and Chemical Corporation, Chicago, Ill.

MARSHALL, THOMAS A., JR., Engineers Joint Council, New York, N.Y.

McADOO, RICHARD B., Harper and Brothers, New York, N.Y.

McCORMACK, MAJ. GEN. JAMES, Vice-Commander, Air Research and Development Command, U.S. Department of the Air Force, Baltimore, Md.

McCOY, GEORGIA F., Assistant to the Secretary, U.S. Department of Health, Education and Welfare, Washington, D.C.

McDANIEL, PAUL W., Deputy Director, Division of Research, Atomic Energy Commission, Washington, D.C.

McGLOTHLIN, WILLIAM J., Southern Regional Education Board, Atlanta, Ga.

McINNIS, EDGAR, President, Canadian Institute of International Affairs, Toronto, Canada

McKNIGHT, HENRY T., Forest Farmers Association Cooperative, Vienna, Va.

MEIER, RICHARD L., Assistant Professor, University of Chicago, Chicago, Ill.

MERCK, GEORGE W., Vermont Forest and Farmland Foundation, New York, N.Y.

MEYERHOFF, HOWARD A., Executive Director, Scientific Manpower Commission, Washington, D.C.

MILLER, RICHARD GORDON, Assistant Professor of Biology, Long Beach State College, Long Beach, Calif.

MILLS, G. A., Director of Research, Houdry Process Corporation, Philadelphia, Pa.

MOSEMAN, ALBERT H., Chief, Bureau of Plant Industry, U.S. Department of Agriculture, Beltsville, Md.

MURCH, WILFRED M., Dow Chemical Company, Midland, Mich.

NEFF, PHILIP, Research Associate, Institute of Industrial Relations, University of California, Los Angeles, Calif.

NOLAN, THOMAS B., Assistant Director, Geological Survey, U.S. Department of the Interior, Washington, D.C.

ORENDORFF, JOSEPH H., Director, Division of Housing Research, U.S. Housing and Home Finance Agency, Washington, D.C.

OTT, EMIL, Director of Research, Hercules Powder Company, Wilmington, Del.

OUTTEN, BURNET, JR., Western Metal Products Company, St. Louis, Mo.

PAULEY, SCOTT S., Cabot Foundation, Harvard University, Petersham, Mass.

PEOPLES, JOE WEBB, Professor, Department of Geology, Wesleyan University, Middletown, Conn.

PRUITT, EVELYN L., Office of Naval Research, U.S. Department of the Navy, Washington, D.C.

QUISENBERRY, KARL S., Assistant Director, Crops Research, Agricultural Research Service, U.S. Department of Agriculture, Washington, D.C.

RAUP, HUGH M., Director, Harvard Forest, Petersham, Mass.

REED, STANLEY F., Reed Research Incorporated, Washington, D.C.

REIFEL, BEULAH B., Bristol, Va.

RICH, ROBERT P., Johns Hopkins University Applied Physics Laboratory, Silver Spring, Md.

RILEY, RODERICK H., Washington, D.C.

ROBERTS, HOWARD RADCLYFFE, Director, The Academy of Natural Sciences, Philadelphia, Pa.

ROBOCK, STEFAN H., Chief, Industrial Economic Branch, Division of Regional Studies, Tennessee Valley Authority, Knoxville, Tenn.

RODWIN, LLOYD, Department of City and Regional Planning, Massachusetts Institute of Technology, Cambridge, Mass.

ROWE, HAROLD B., The Brookings Institution, Washington, D.C.

SAUCHELLI, VINCENT, Director of Agricultural Research, The Davison Chemical Corporation, Baltimore, Md.

SAX, KARL, Arnold Arboretum, Harvard University, Cambridge, Mass.

SCHNEE, VERNE H., National Research Council, Washington, D.C.

SCHULTZ, THEODORE W., Chairman, Department of Economics, University of Chicago, Chicago, Ill.

SEARS, PAUL B., Chairman, Yale University Conservation Program, New Haven, Conn.

SMITH, ADM. EDWARD H., Director, Woods Hole Oceanographic Institution, Woods Hole, Mass.

SNIDER, ROBERT G., Vice-President-Director of Research, The Conservation Foundation, New York, N.Y.

SNOW, GLENN E., National Education Association, Washington, D.C.

SPECHT, VIRGINIA G., Brookeville, Md.

SPENGLER, KENNETH C., American Meteorological Society, Boston, Mass.

SPILHAUS, ATHELSTAN, Dean of the Institute of Technology, University of Minnesota, Minneapolis, Minn.

SPORN, PHILIP, President, American Gas and Electric Service Corporation, New York, N.Y.

STAFF, C. E., Bakelite Company, New York, N.Y.

STALEY, EUGENE, Professor, Division of Economics Research, Stanford Research Institute, Palo Alto, Calif.

STEAD, WILLIAM H., Resource Management Consultant, Washington, D.C.

STEVENSON, EARL P., President, Arthur D. Little, Inc., Cambridge, Mass.

STEWART, ILEEN E., American Institute of Biological Sciences, Washington, D.C.

TAYLOR, JOSEPH H., Agricultural and Industrial Development Board of Kentucky, Frankfort, Ky.

THOMSON, CHARLES A. H., The Brookings Institution, Washington, D.C.

TRAYER, GEORGE W., Division of Forest Research, Forest Service, U.S. Department of Agriculture, Washington, D.C.

TRUITT, R. V., Director, Department of Research and Education, Solomons, Md.

TYLER, CHAPLIN, Development Department, E. I. du Pont de Nemours and Company, Wilmington, Del.

VAN ANTWERPEN, F. J., Editor, *Chemical Engineering Progress*, New York, N.Y.

VAN PELT, J. R., Montana School of Mines, Butte, Mont.

VAN STRAELEN, ELIZABETH, Yale University Conservation Program, New Haven, Conn.

VOGT, WILLIAM, National Director, Planned Parenthood Federation of America, New York, N.Y.

WALFORD, LIONEL A., Chief Marine Biologist, Fish and Wildlife Service, U.S. Department of the Interior, Washington, D.C.

WALKER, ERIC A., Pennsylvania State College, State College, Pa.

WARNE, COLSTON E., President, Consumers Union of U. S., Inc., New York, N.Y.

WEEKS, DON C., Director, Michigan Department of Economic Development, Lansing, Mich.

WEIDLEIN, EDWARD R., President, Mellon Institute of Industrial Research, University of Pittsburgh, Pittsburgh, Pa.

WEISS, PAUL, Professor of Zoology, University of Chicago, Chicago, Ill.

WEISS, SAMUEL, Executive Director, American Statistical Association, Washington, D.C.

WENGERT, NORMAN I., Chairman, Social Science Department, North Dakota Agricultural College, Fargo, N.Dak.

WIECKING, ERNST H., U.S. Department of Agriculture, Washington, D.C.

WILLIAMS, BEN M., Washington, D.C.

WILLIAMS, FAITH M., Chief, Office of Labor Economics, Bureau of Labor Statistics, U.S. Department of Labor, Washington, D.C.

WORK, HAROLD K., College of Engineering, Research Division, New York University, New York, N.Y.

WOYTINSKY, E. S., Twentieth Century Fund, Washington, D.C.

WOYTINSKY, W. S., Twentieth Century Fund, Washington, D.C.

SECTION VIII

ABRAHAMSEN, MARTIN A., Farmer Cooperative Service, U.S. Department of Agriculture, Washington, D.C.

ACKERMAN, WILLIAM C., Columbia Broadcasting System, New York, N.Y.

ADAMS, CLIFFORD H., Public Relations Staff, National Coal Association, Washington, D.C.

ANDREWS, COL. JOHN N., Veterans Administration, Washington, D.C.

ANTHONY, DOROTHY D., Washington, D.C.

BARKER, JOSEPH W., President, Research Corporation, Inc., New York, N.Y.

BARTLETT, WILLIAM H., American Camping Association, Chicago, Ill.

BEACH, GRACE O., Izaak Walton League of America, Inc., Chicago, Ill.

BELL, LAIRD, Bell, Boyd, Marshall and Lloyd, Chicago, Ill.

BELSLEY, G. LYLE, Associate Director, Public Administration Clearing House, Washington, D.C.

BESSEY, ROY F., Resources Consultant, Washington, D.C.

BETHEA, J. W., National Committee for Traffic Safety, Chicago, Ill.

BLACK, RICHARD B., Office of Naval Research, U.S. Department of the Navy, Washington, D.C.

BLACKWELL, GORDON, Institute for Research in Social Science, University of North Carolina, Chapel Hill, N.C.

BOOKBINDER, HYMAN H., Chief of Congressional Research, Congress of Industrial Organizations, Washington, D.C.

BRADLEY, JAMES C., Engineering Assistant to the Assistant Secretary for Water and Power, U.S. Department of the Interior, Washington, D.C.

BRALY, EARL B., Office of the Governor, Austin, Tex.

BREWER, GEORGE E., Vice-President, The Conservation Foundation, New York, N.Y.

BREWER, MICHAEL F., School of Natural Resources, University of Michigan, Ann Arbor, Mich.

BROADY, K. O., Dean, Extension Division, University of Nebraska, Lincoln, Nebr.

BRUERE, HENRY, Bowery Savings Bank, New York, N.Y.

BURR, M. VASHTI, Deputy Attorney General of the Commonwealth of Pennsylvania, Washington, D.C.

BURR, SAMUEL ENGLE, JR., Director of the Institute on the United States in World Affairs, American University, Washington, D.C.

CAPPS, F. OLIN, Conservation Commission, Jefferson City, Mo.

CARLETON, ROBERT H., National Science Teachers Association, Washington, D.C.

CASE, CLARENCE C., Washington, D.C.

CHASE, PEARL, Executive Vice-President, California Conservation Council, Santa Barbara, Calif.

CHRISTIANSEN, MILO F., The Athletic Institute, Chicago, Ill.

CLARK, J. W., Department of Business Development, State Capitol, St. Paul, Minn.

CLEAVELAND, FREDERIC N., Institute for Research in Social Science, University of North Carolina, Chapel Hill, N.C.

COHEN, HYMEN EZRA, Washington, D.C.

COLM, GERHARD, Chief Economist, National Planning Association, Washington, D.C.

CONE, JAMES W., Chemical Corps, U.S. Department of the Army, Washington, D.C.

COOPER, SHIRLEY, Assistant Secretary, National Education Association, Washington, D.C.

COTTON, EDWIN R., President, American Watershed Council, Inc., Washington, D.C.

CRAWFORD, ROBERT W., Deputy Commissioner and Superintendent of Recreation, Philadelphia, Pa.

DANIEL, ROBERT P., President, Virginia State College, Petersburg, Va.

DAVIS, HARVEY H., Provost, State University of Iowa, Iowa City, Iowa

DEAN, ALAN L., U. S. Bureau of the Budget, Washington, D.C.

D'HAUCOURT, GENEVIEVE M., Washington, D.C.

DICKEY, FRANK E., JR., American University, Washington, D.C.

DIEHL, JAMES N., Chief, Division of Cooperative Forest Protection, Forest Service, U.S. Department of Agriculture, Washington, D.C.

DOLDER, EDWARD F., Chief, Conservation Education, State Department of Natural Resources, Sacramento, Calif.

DUCKWORTH, WILLIAM C., Tennessee Corporation, College Park, Ga.

DUPUY, LEON W., Silver Spring, Md.

DWORSKY, LEONARD, U.S. Public Health Service, Washington, D.C.

EATON, EUGENE D., Chevy Chase, Md.

ECKELBERRY, R. H., Editor and Professor, Bureau of Educational Research, College of Education, Ohio State University, Columbus, Ohio

EDDY, GERALD E., Director, Department of Conservation, Lansing, Mich.

EDSON, MAJ. GEN. M. A., Executive Director, National Rifle Association, Washington, D.C.

ELSBREE, HUGH L., Legislative Reference Service, Library of Congress, Washington, D.C.

ENGELBERT, ERNEST A., Professor, Department of Political Science, University of California, Los Angeles, Calif.

FISHER, JOSEPH L., Associate Director, Resources for the Future, Inc., Washington, D.C.

FLUGGER, ANNETTE L., Pan American Union, Washington, D.C.

FORBES, JOHN RIPLEY, Director, National Foundation for Junior Museums, Inc., Sacramento, Calif.

FOSTER, EARL, Executive Secretary, Interstate Oil Compact Commission, Oklahoma City, Okla.

FRANC, MILOS, Austrian Embassy, ERP Office, Washington, D.C.

FREDERICK, KARL T., Vice-President, National Wildlife Federation, New York, N.Y.

GEIGER, THEODORE, Chief of Research, National Planning Association, Washington, D.C.

GIBBONS, STUART C., Calaveras Grove Association, Stockton, Calif.

GIBBS, FRED, American University, Washington, D.C.

GIBBS, JOHN C., The Conservation Foundation, New York, N.Y.

GIBBS, JOHN T., Washington, D.C.

GREY, HUGH M., University of Michigan, Ann Arbor, Mich.

GRIFFITH, ERNEST S., Director, Legislative Reference Service, Library of Congress, Washington, D.C.

HADSALL, LEO F., President, Fresno State College, Fresno, Calif.

HAGUE, BART, Department of Conservation, School of Natural Resources, University of Michigan, Ann Arbor, Mich.

HALLER, CAPT. FRANKLIN M., Bethesda, Md.

HARNEY, SYLVIA, Lincoln Public Schools, Lincoln, Nebr.

HARRIER, ROBERT A., Executive Secretary, Alumni Association of Lehigh University, Bethlehem, Pa.

HARRISON, FLORENCE L., Director, Service Bureau for Women's Organizations, Hartford, Conn.

HAYDON, STUART, The Citizens' Foundation, Washington, D.C.

HENRY, LAURIN L., Staff Assistant, Public Administration Clearing House, Washington, D.C.

HERTZIER, RICHARD A., U.S. Department of the Army, Washington, D.C.

HEYDECKER, WAYNE D., Secretary-Treasurer, Atlantic States Marine Fisheries Commission, Mount Vernon, N.Y.

HOLMES, LUCILE M., Rural Electrification Administration, Washington, D.C.

HONEY, JOHN C., Staff Assistant, Program Analysis Office, National Science Foundation, Washington, D.C.

HOPKINS, ARTHUR S., Executive Secretary, Northeastern Forest Fire Protection Commission, Chatham, N.Y.

HOSKINS, ROBERT N., Industrial Forester, Seaboard Air Line Railroad Company, Norfolk, Va.

HOWES, RAYMOND F., Staff Associate, American Council on Education, Washington, D.C.

HUDOBA, MICHAEL, Washington Editor, *Sports Afield*, Washington, D.C.

HUEBNER, JAMES, Pennsylvania Power and Light Company, Allentown, Pa.

IVEY, JOHN E., JR., Director, Southern Regional Education Board, Atlanta, Ga.

JACOBI, HERBERT J., American Legion, Washington, D.C.

JEBENS, ARTHUR B., Director, Division of Management Research, U.S. Department of the Interior, Washington, D.C.

JOHNSON, PHILIP G., Cornell University, Ithaca, N.Y.

KELLEHER, GRACE J., U.S. Department of the Air Force, Washington, D.C.

KEY, NORMAN, Secretary, National Committee on Safety Education, National Education Association, Washington, D.C.

KIMMEL, LEWIS H., The Brookings Institution, Washington, D.C.

KIRK, DUDLEY, U.S. Department of State, Washington, D.C.

KNOX, JOSEPH C., Secretary, New England Interstate Water Pollution Control Committee, Boston, Mass.

LAIDLER, HARRY W., Executive Director, League for Industrial Democracy, New York, N.Y.

LEHMAN, JOHN W., Clerk, Joint Committee on the Economic Report, U. S. Congress, Washington, D.C.

LENT, MRS. DAVID, Reed College, Portland, Ore.

LEWIS, FREDERICK H., Herald Tribune Fresh Air Fund, New York, N.Y.

LLOYD, GRENVILLE B., University of Michigan, Ann Arbor, Mich.

LOVERIDGE, EARL W., Assistant Chief, Administrative Management and Information Divisions, Forest Service, U.S. Department of Agriculture, Washington, D.C.

MAASS, ARTHUR A., Associate Professor of Government, Harvard University, Cambridge, Mass.

MANTHEY, CARL W., Science Department, Lincoln High School, Lincoln, Nebr.

MARTIN, CLYDE S., Forest Counsel, Weyerhaeuser Timber Company, Tacoma, Wash.

MARTIN, ROSCOE, Maxwell Graduate School of Public Affairs, Syracuse University, Syracuse, N.Y.

MATTISON, C. W., Forest Service, U.S. Department of Agriculture, Washington, D.C.

MCCARTY, RHEA, Executive Director, Ohio Development and Publicity Commission, Columbus, Ohio

MCKINLEY, CHARLES, Professor of Political Science, Reed College, Portland, Ore.

MCQUATTERS, GENEVA G., National Federation of Business and Professional Women's Clubs, New York, N.Y.

MENDENHALL, HOWARD, Society for the Protection of New Hampshire Forests, Concord, N.H.

MERRILL, HAROLD A., U.S. Housing and Home Finance Agency, Washington, D.C.

MILLER, HAROLD V., Executive Director, Tennessee State Planning Commission, Nashville, Tenn.

MILLER, JOHN F., Executive Secretary, National Planning Association, Washington, D.C.

MONAHAN, THOMAS A., Executive Director, Rhode Island Development Council, Providence, R.I.

MONROE, J. ELMER, Vice-President, Bureau of Railway Economics, Washington, D.C.

MUNGER, ROBERT L., Lincoln High School Publication Department, Lincoln, Nebr.

NATHAN, LOUIS, Organisation for European Economic Co-operation, Washington, D.C.

NAVASKY, VICTOR, American University, Washington, D.C.

NELSEN, ANCHER, Administrator, Rural Electrification Administration, Washington, D.C.

NICHOLS, R. WHITE, Lincoln County Fish and Game Association, Wiscasset, Me.

OGBURN, CHARLTON, Southern Law Center, Macon, Ga.

OSBORNE, LITHGOW, Vice-President, Auburn Publishing Company, Auburn, N.Y.

OVERBY, KERMIT O., Chief, Information Services Division, Rural Electrification Administration, Washington, D.C.

PALMER, EPHRAIM L., National Wildlife Federation, Ithaca, N.Y.

PETSHEK, KIRK R., Washington, D.C.

POST, ALBERT R., New Jersey Department of Conservation and Economic Development, Trenton, N.J.

PRINCE, LESLIE HILL, Secretary-Treasurer, Association of State Planning and Development Agencies, Washington, D.C.

RABINOWITZ, ALAN, Washington, D.C.

RANDALL, ROBERT H., U.S. Bureau of the Budget, Washington, D.C.

RAWALT, MARGUERITE, First Vice-President, National Federation of Business and Professional Women's Clubs, Inc., Washington, D.C.

RICHARD, OSCAR E., U.S. Weather Bureau, Extended Forecast Section, Hyattsville, Md.

SANDERS, JENNINGS B., Office of Education, U.S. Department of Health, Education, and Welfare, Washington, D.C.

SARGISSON, GEORGE T., Executive Director, Recreation Promotion Service, Wilmington, Del.

SAYRE, A. NELSON, Geological Survey, U.S. Department of the Interior, Washington, D.C.

SCALES, O. L., Vice-President, The Enos Coal Mining Company, Indianapolis, Ind.

SCHMEECKLE, FRED J., Director, Department of Conservation Education, Wisconsin State College, Stevens Point, Wis.

SELLS, A. M., Vice-President, Wisconsin Electric Power Company, Milwaukee, Wis.

SKIFF, J. VICTOR, Deputy Commissioner, New York State Department of Conservation, Albany, N.Y.

SMITH, KERRY, Association for Higher Education, Washington, D.C.

SOMMER, WAYNE C., American Camping Association, Hyattsville, Md.

SONNE, H. CHRISTIAN, Chairman of the Board of the National Planning Association and of Amsinck, Sonne and Company, New York, N.Y.

SOTH, LAUREN K., Editor of the Editorial Pages, *The Des Moines Register and Tribune*, Des Moines, Iowa

SPRECHER, GEORGE E., Wisconsin Department of Conservation, Madison, Wis.

STARK, PAUL C., National Council for Community Improvement, St. Louis, Mo.

STROMSEN, KARL E., Chief of Training, U.S. Department of the Interior, Washington, D.C.

SWINGLER, W. S., State and Private Forestry Divisions, Forest Service, U.S. Department of Agriculture, Washington, D.C.

TALLEY, COL. BENJAMIN B., Division Engineer, North Atlantic Division, Corps of Engineers, U.S. Department of the Army, and Chairman, New England-New York Inter-Agency Committee, New York, N.Y.

TOEPFER, MRS. ALBERT F., Founder, Woman's Conservation League of America, Inc., Milwaukee, Wis.

TOMLINSON, G. E., Bureau of Reclamation, U.S. Department of the Interior, Washington, D.C.

TRIGGS, MATT, Assistant Legislative Director, American Farm Bureau Federation, Washington, D.C.

TUBBS, FARLEY F., Michigan Department of Conservation, Lansing, Mich.

VAN ATTA, F. F., Special Assistant, American Society for Testing Materials, Philadelphia, Pa.

WARRICK, L. F., Bureau of State Service, U.S. Public Health Service, Washington, D.C.

WEAVER, RICHARD L., Secretary, Conservation Education Association, Ann Arbor, Mich.

WEBER, EUGENE W., Commissioner, United States Section, International Joint Commission—United States and Canada, Washington, D.C.

WENGERT, EGBERT S., University of Oregon, Eugene, Ore.

WHITE, GEORGE, State Forester, Missouri Conservation Commission, and President, Association of State Foresters, Jefferson City, Mo.

ZIMMERMAN, FREDERICK L., Research Director, New York Joint Legislative Committee on Interstate Cooperation, New York, N.Y.

INDEX TO SPEAKERS*

* Remarks of the speakers who have contributed to this report will be found on the pages indicated. Roman numerals refer to the Conference sections in which the speakers registered. (See List of Registrants, p. 380.)

GUIDE TO
PRINCIPAL SUBJECTS

The table of contents, page ix, indicates in general where the main discussion of broad topics may be found. The selective list below has been prepared in a further effort to help the reader find his way around in the report. Topics that received more than passing notice, especially those that were discussed in more than one section, are grouped under subject headings. No detailed index has been attempted.